ASPECTS OF SCIENTIFIC EXPLANATION

AND OTHER ESSAYS

IN THE PHILOSOPHY OF SCIENCE

ASPECTS of

And Other

Carl G. Hempel

SCIENTIFIC EXPLANATION

Essays in the Philosophy of Science

THE FREE PRESS
A Division of Macmillan Publishing Co., Inc.
New York

Collier Macmillan Publishers
London

TO *Diane*

The Free Press
A Division of Macmillan Publishing Co., Inc.
866 Third Avenue, New York, New York 10022

Collier Macmillan Canada,Ltd.
First Free Press Paperback Edition 1970

Library of Congress Catalog Card Number: 65-15441

PRINTING NUMBER   2   3   4   5   6   7   8   9   10

PREFACE

THE ESSAYS gathered in this volume address themselves to one or another of four major topics in the philosophy of science, and have accordingly been grouped under the headings "Confirmation, Induction, and Rational Belief," "Conceptions of Cognitive Significance," "Structure and Function of Scientific Concepts and Theories," and "Scientific Explanation."

All but one of the pieces are revised versions of articles that have previously appeared in print, as indicated in the footnotes on their origins. The longest of the essays, from which this collection takes its title, was specifically written for this volume. It presents a self-contained study of scientific explanation, including a reexamination of the concept of explanation by covering laws as it had been partially developed in two earlier essays, which are here reprinted as items 9 and 10. The title essay also deals in some detail with explanation by statistical laws, a subject that had received only brief consideration in those earlier articles. The analysis of statistical explanation here presented differs in important respects from a previous study of the subject, published in 1962, which is listed in the bibliography but not included in this volume.

Though articles 9 and 10 slightly overlap the title essay, they have been reprinted here because they have been widely discussed in the recent literature on explanation, so that it seemed worthwhile to make them available for reference; and because most of the substance of those articles is not included in the title essay.

While I still regard the central ideas of the reprinted essays as basically sound, I have naturally changed my views on various points of detail. Where it seemed appropriate, such changes have been indicated in footnotes marked

"Added in 1964" or in the Postscripts by which I have supplemented three of the articles. Stylistic changes, deletions of passages that did not advance the argument, and corrections of minor errors have been effected without special notice.

In the Postscripts just mentioned, I have also commented on some recent developments in the philosophical analysis of the central problems, and I have added some afterthoughts of my own. But I have not attempted to bring the bibliographies of all the reprinted articles up to date, since merely to list more recent publications without discussing their contents would have been pointless.

As I have tried to make clear at appropriate places in these essays and in the added notes and Postscripts, I have greatly benefitted from the work of others, from discussions and criticisms of my writings that have appeared in print, and from personal exchanges of ideas with friends, colleagues, and students: to all these intellectual benefactors I am grateful.

Several of these essays were written during summer months in air-conditioned seclusion at the house of my old friends Paul and Gabrielle Oppenheim in Princeton. To Paul Oppenheim, with whom I have discussed philosophical questions for many a year, I am grateful also for letting me reprint here one of the articles we wrote jointly. Work on some of the other essays was done during a year as Fulbright Research Fellow in Oxford, 1959-60. Finally, a sabbatical leave from Princeton University in conjunction with a Fellowship for 1963-64 at that scholarly haven, the Center for Advanced Study in the Behavioral Sciences, enabled me to write the title essay and to revise the earlier articles for republication.

I am much indebted to the editors and publishers who permitted me to reprint the articles and excerpts reproduced in this volume.

I gratefully dedicate this book to my wife; her sympathetic encouragement and unfaltering support would have deserved a better offering.

C. G. H.

Stanford, California,

June, 1964

CONTENTS

I.

CONFIRMATION, INDUCTION,

AND RATIONAL BELIEF

1. STUDIES IN THE LOGIC

OF CONFIRMATION

1. OBJECTIVE OF THE STUDY[1]

THE DEFINING characteristic of an empirical statement is its capability of being tested by a confrontation with experiential findings, *i.e.* with the results of suitable experiments or focused observations. This feature distinguishes statements which have empirical content both from the statements of the formal sciences, logic and mathematics, which require no experiential test for their validation, and from the formulations of transempirical metaphysics, which admit of none.

The testability here referred to has to be understood in the comprehensive sense of "testability in principle" or "theoretical testability"; many empirical statements, for practical reasons, cannot actually be tested now. To call a statement of this kind testable in principle means that it is possible to state just what experiential findings, if they were actually obtained, would constitute favorable evidence

1. The present analysis of confirmation was to a large extent suggested and stimulated by a cooperative study of certain more general problems which were raised by Dr. Paul Oppenheim, and which I have been investigating with him for several years. These problems concern the form and the function of scientific laws and the comparative methodology of the different branches of empirical science.

In my study of the logical aspects of confirmation, I have benefited greatly by discussions with Professor R. Carnap, Professor A. Tarski, and particularly Dr. Nelson Goodman, to whom I am indebted for several valuable suggestions which will be indicated subsequently.

A detailed exposition of the more technical aspects of the analysis of confirmation presented in this essay is included in my article 'A Purely Syntactical Definition of Confirmation,' *The Journal of Symbolic Logic*, vol. 8 (1943).

This article is reprinted, with some changes, by kind permission of the editor of *Mind*, where it appeared in volume 54, pp. 1-26 and 97-121 (1945).

for it, and what findings or "data," as we shall say for brevity, would constitute unfavorable evidence; in other words, a statement is called testable in principle if it is possible to describe the kind of data which would confirm or disconfirm it.

The concepts of confirmation and of disconfirmation as here understood are clearly more comprehensive than those of conclusive verification and falsification. Thus, e.g., no finite amount of experiential evidence can conclusively verify a hypothesis expressing a general law such as the law of gravitation, which covers an infinity of potential instances, many of which belong either to the as yet inaccessible future or to the irretrievable past; but a finite set of relevant data may well be "in accord with" the hypothesis and thus constitute confirming evidence for it. Similarly, an existential hypothesis, asserting, say, the existence of an as yet unknown chemical element with certain specified characteristics, cannot be conclusively proved false by a finite amount of evidence which fails to "bear out" the hypothesis; but such unfavorable data may, under certain conditions, be considered as weakening the hypothesis in question, or as constituting disconfirming evidence for it.[2]

While, in the practice of scientific research, judgments as to the confirming or disconfirming character of experiential data obtained in the test of a hypothesis are often made without hesitation and with a wide consensus of opinion, it can hardly be said that these judgments are based on an explicit theory providing general criteria of confirmation and of disconfirmation. In this respect, the situation is comparable to the manner in which deductive inferences are carried out in the practice of scientific research: this, too, is often done without reference to an explicitly stated system of rules of logical inference. But while criteria of valid deduction can be and have been supplied by formal logic, no satisfactory theory providing general criteria of confirmation and disconfirmation appears to be available so far.

In the present essay, an attempt will be made to provide the elements of a theory of this kind. After a brief survey of the significance and the present status of the problem, I propose to present a detailed critical analysis of some common conceptions of confirmation and disconfirmation and then to construct explicit definitions for these concepts and to formulate some basic principles of what might be called the logic of confirmation.

2. SIGNIFICANCE AND PRESENT STATUS OF THE PROBLEM

The establishment of a general theory of confirmation may well be regarded as one of the most urgent desiderata of the present methodology of empirical science. Indeed, it seems that a precise analysis of the concept of confirmation is

2. This point as well as the possibility of conclusive verification and conclusive falsification will be discussed in some detail in section 10 of the present paper.

a necessary condition for an adequate solution of various fundamental problems concerning the logical structure of scientific procedure. Let us briefly survey the most outstanding of these problems.

(a) In the discussion of scientific method, the concept of relevant evidence plays an important part. And while certain inductivist accounts of scientific procedure seem to assume that relevant evidence, or relevant data, can be collected in the context of an inquiry prior to the formulation of any hypothesis, it should be clear upon brief reflection that relevance is a relative concept; experiential data can be said to be relevant or irrelevant only with respect to a given hypothesis; and it is the hypothesis which determines what kind of data or evidence are relevant for it. Indeed, an empirical finding is relevant for a hypothesis if and only if it constitutes either favorable or unfavorable evidence for it; in other words, if it either confirms or disconfirms the hypothesis. Thus, a precise definition of relevance presupposes an analysis of confirmation and disconfirmation.

(b) A closely related concept is that of instance of a hypothesis. The so-called method of inductive inference is usually presented as proceeding from specific cases to a general hypothesis of which each of the special cases is an "instance" in the sense that it conforms to the general hypothesis in question, and thus constitutes confirming evidence for it.

Thus, any discussion of induction which refers to the establishment of general hypotheses on the strength of particular instances is fraught with all those logical difficulties—soon to be expounded—which beset the concept of confirmation. A precise analysis of this concept is, therefore, a necessary condition for a clear statement of the issues involved in the problem complex of induction and of the ideas suggested for their solution—no matter what their theoretical merits or demerits may be.

(c) Another issue customarily connected with the study of scientific method is the quest for "rules of induction." Generally speaking, such rules would enable us to infer, from a given set of data, that hypothesis or generalization which accounts best for all the particular data in the given set. But this construal of the problem involves a misconception: While the process of invention by which scientific discoveries are made is as a rule *psychologically guided and stimulated* by antecedent knowledge of specific facts, its results are *not logically determined* by them; the way in which scientific hypotheses or theories are discovered cannot be mirrored in a set of general rules of inductive inference.[3] One of the crucial

3. See the lucid presentation of this point in Karl Popper's *Logik der Forschung* (Wien, 1935), esp. sections 1, 2, 3, and 25, 26, 27; *cf.* also Albert Einstein's remarks in his lecture *On the Method of Theoretical Physics* (Oxford, 1933), 11, 12. Also of interest in this context is the critical discussion of induction by H. Feigl in "The Logical Character of the Principle of Induction," *Philosophy of Science*, vol. 1 (1934).

considerations which lead to this conclusion is the following: Take a scientific theory such as the atomic theory of matter. The evidence on which it rests may be described in terms referring to directly observable phenomena, namely to certain macroscopic aspects of the various experimental and observational data which are relevant to the theory. On the other hand, the theory itself contains a large number of highly abstract, nonobservational terms such as 'atom', 'electron', 'nucleus', 'dissociation', 'valence' and others, none of which figures in the description of the observational data. An adequate rule of induction would therefore have to provide, for this and for every other conceivable case, mechanically applicable criteria determining unambiguously, and without any reliance on the inventiveness or additional scientific knowledge of its user, all those new abstract concepts which need to be created for the formulation of the theory that will account for the given evidence. Clearly, this requirement cannot be satisfied by any set of rules, however ingeniously devised; there can be no general rules of induction in the above sense; the demand for them rests on a confusion of logical and psychological issues. What determines the soundness of a hypothesis is not the way it is arrived at (it may even have been suggested by a dream or a hallucination), but the way it stands up when tested, *i.e.* when confronted with relevant observational data. Accordingly, the quest for rules of induction in the original sense of canons of scientific discovery has to be replaced, in the logic of science, by the quest for general objective criteria determining (A) whether, and—if possible—even (B) to what degree, a hypothesis H may be said to be corroborated by a given body of evidence E. This approach differs essentially from the inductivist conception of the problem in that it presupposes not only E, but also H as given, and then seeks to determine a certain logical relationship between them. The two parts of this latter problem can be related in somewhat more precise terms as follows:

(A) To give precise definitions of the two nonquantitative relational concepts of confirmation and of disconfirmation; *i.e.* to define the meaning of the phrases 'E confirms H' and 'E disconfirms H'. (When E neither confirms nor disconfirms H, we shall say that E is neutral, or irrelevant, with respect to H.)

(B) (1) To lay down criteria defining a metrical concept "degree of confirmation of H with respect to E," whose values are real numbers; or, failing this,

(2) To lay down criteria defining two relational concepts, "more highly confirmed than" and "equally well confirmed as," which make possible a nonmetrical comparison of hypotheses (each with a body of evidence assigned to it) with respect to the extent of their confirmation.

Interestingly, problem B has received much more attention in methodological research than problem A; in particular, the various theories of the so-called probability of hypotheses may be regarded as concerning this problem complex;

we have here adopted[4] the more neutral term' degree of confirmation' instead of 'probability' because the latter is used in science in a definite technical sense involving reference to the relative frequency of the occurrence of a given event in a sequence, and it is at least an open question whether the degree of confirmation of a hypothesis can generally be defined as a probability in this statistical sense.

The theories dealing with the probability of hypotheses fall into two main groups: the "logical" theories construe probability as a logical relation between sentences (or propositions; it is not always clear which is meant);[5] the "statistical" theories interpret the probability of a hypothesis in substance as the limit of the relative frequency of its confirming instances among all relevant cases.[6] Now it is a remarkable fact that none of the theories of the first type which have been developed so far provides an explicit general definition of the probability (or degree of confirmation) of a hypothesis *H* with respect to a body of evidence *E*; they all limit themselves essentially to the construction of an uninterpreted postulational system of logical probability.[7] For this reason, these theories fail to provide a complete solution of problem B. The statistical approach, on the other hand, would, if successful, provide an explicit numerical definition of the degree of confirmation of a hypothesis; this definition would be formulated in terms of the numbers of confirming and disconfirming instances for *H* which constitute the body of evidence *E*. Thus, a necessary condition for an adequate interpretation of degrees of confirmation as statistical probabilities is the establishment of precise criteria of confirmation and disconfirmation; in other words, the solution of problem A.

4. Following R. Carnap's use in "Testability and Meaning," *Philosophy of Science*, Vols. 3 (1936) and 4 (1937); esp. section 3 (in Vol. 3).

5. This group includes the work of such writers as Janina Hosiasson-Lindenbaum [*cf.* for instance, her article "Induction et analogie: Comparaison de leur fondement,", *Mind*, Vol. 50 (1941)], H.Jeffreys, J. M. Keynes, B.O. Koopman, J. Nicod, St. Mazurkiewicz, and F.Waismann. For a brief discussion of this conception of probability, see Ernest Nagel, *Principles of the Theory of Probability* (International Encyclopedia of United Science, Vol. I, no. 6, Chicago, 1939), esp. sections 6 and 8.

6. The chief proponent of this view is Hans Reichenbach; *cf.* especially "UeberInduktion und Wahrscheinlichkeit," *Erkenntnis*, vol. 5 (1935), and *Experience and Prediction* (Chicago, 1938), Chap. V.

7. (Added in 1964.) Since this article was written, R. Carnap has developed a theory of inductive logic which, for formalized languages of certain types, makes it possible explicitly to define—without use of the qualitative notion of confirming instance—a quantitative concept of degree of confirmation which has the formal characteristics of a probability; Carnap refers to it as inductive, or logical, probability. For details, see especially R. Carnap, "On Inductive Logic," *Philosophy of Science*, vol. 12 (1945); *Logical Foundations of Probability* (Chicago, 1950; 2nd ed., 1962); *The Continuum of Inductive Methods* (Chicago, 1952); "The Aim of Inductive Logic" *in* E. Nagel, P. Suppes, and A. Tarski, eds., *Logic, Methodology, and Philosophy of Science. Proceedings of the 1960 International Congress* (Stanford, 1962).

However, despite their great ingenuity and suggestiveness, the attempts which have been made so far to formulate a precise statistical definition of the degree of confirmation of a hypothesis seem open to certain objections,[8] and several authors[9] have expressed doubts as to the possibility of defining the degree of confirmation of a hypothesis as a metrical magnitude, though some of them consider it as possible, under certain conditions, to solve at least the less exacting problem B (2), *i.e.* to establish standards of nonmetrical comparison between hypotheses with respect to the extent of their confirmation. An adequate comparison of this kind might have to take into account a variety of different factors;[10] but again the numbers of the confirming and of the disconfirming instances which the given evidence includes will be among the most important of those factors.

Thus, of the two problems, A and B, the former appears to be the more basic one, first, because it does not presuppose the possibility of defining numerical degrees of confirmation or of comparing different hypotheses as to the extent of their confirmation; and second because our considerations indicate that any attempt to solve problem B—unless it is to remain in the stage of an axiomatized system without interpretation—is likely to require a precise definition of the concepts of confirming and disconfirming instance of a hypothesis before it can proceed to define numerical degrees of confirmation, or to lay down nonmetrical standards of comparison.

(*d*) It is now clear that an analysis of confirmation is of fundamental importance also for the study of a central problem of epistemology, namely, the elaboration of standards of rational belief or of criteria of warranted assertibility. In the methodology of empirical science this problem is usually phrased as concerning the rules governing the test and the subsequent acceptance or rejection of empirical hypotheses on the basis of experimental or observational findings, while in its epistemological version the issue is often formulated as concerning the validation of beliefs by reference to perceptions, sense data, or the like. But no matter how the final empirical evidence is construed and in what terms it is accordingly expressed, the theoretical problem remains the same: to

---

8. *Cf.* Karl Popper, *Logik der Forschung* (Wien, 1935), section 80; Ernest Nagel, *l.c.*, section 8, and "Probability and the Theory of Knowledge," *Philosophy of Science*, vol. 6 (1939); C. G. Hempel, "Le problème de la vérité," *Theoria* (Göteborg), vol. 3 (1937), section 5, and "On the Logical Form of Probability Statements," *Erkenntnis*, Vol. 7 (1937-38), esp. section 5. *Cf.* also Morton White, "Probability and Confirmation," *The Journal of Philosophy*, Vol. 36 (1939).

9. See, for example, J. M. Keynes, *A Treatise on Probability* (London, 1929), esp. Chap. III; Ernest Nagel, *Principles of the Theory of Probability*, esp. p. 70; compare also the somewhat less definitely skeptical statement by Carnap, *l.c.* (note 4) section 3, p. 427.

10. See especially the survey of such factors given by Ernest Nagel in *Principles of the Theory of Probability*, pp. 66-73.

characterize, in precise and general terms, the conditions under which a body of evidence can be said to confirm, or to disconfirm, a hypothesis of empirical character; and that is again our problem A.

(e) The same problem arises when one attempts to give a precise statement of the empiricist and operationalist criteria for the empirical meaningfulness of a sentence; these criteria, as is well known, are formulated by reference to the theoretical testability of the sentence by means of experiential evidence,[11] and the concept of theoretical testability, as was pointed out earlier, is closely related to the concepts of confirmation and disconfirmation.[12]

Considering the great importance of the concept of confirmation, it is surprising that no systematic theory of the nonquantitative relation of confirmation seems to have been developed so far. Perhaps this fact reflects the tacit assumption that the concepts of confirmation and of disconfirmation have a sufficiently clear meaning to make explicit definitions unnecessary or at least comparatively trivial. And indeed, as will be shown below, there are certain features which are rather generally associated with the intuitive notion of confirming evidence, and which, at first, seem well suited to serve as defining characteristics of confirmation. Closer examination will reveal the definitions thus obtainable to be seriously deficient and will make it clear that an adequate definition of confirmation involves considerable difficulties.

Now the very existence of such difficulties suggests the question whether the problem we are considering does not rest on a false assumption: Perhaps there are no objective criteria of confirmation; perhaps the decision as to whether a given hypothesis is acceptable in the light of a given body of evidence is no more subject to rational, objective rules than is the process of inventing a scientific hypothesis or theory; perhaps, in the last analysis, it is a "sense of evidence," or a feeling of plausibility in view of the relevant data, which ultimately decides whether a hypothesis is scientifically acceptable.[13] This view is comparable to the opinion that the validity of a mathematical proof or of a logical argument has to be judged ultimately by reference to a feeling of soundness or convincingness; and both theses have to be rejected on analogous grounds: they involve a con-

11. *Cf.*, for example, A. J. Ayer, *Language, Truth and Logic* (London and New York, 1936), Ch. I; R. Carnap, "Testability and Meaning," sections 1, 2, 3; H. Feigl, "Logical Empiricism" (in *Twentieth Century Philosophy*, ed. by Dagobert D. Runes, New York, 1943); P. W. Bridgman, *The Logic of Modern Physics* (New York, 1928).

12. It should be noted, however, that in his essay "Testability and Meaning," R. Carnap has constructed definitions of testability and confirmability which avoid reference to the concept of confirming and of disconfirming evidence; in fact, no proposal for the definition of these latter concepts is made in that study.

13. A view of this kind has been expressed, for example, by M. Mandelbaum in "Causal Analyses in History," *Journal of the History of Ideas*, Vol. 3 (1942); *cf.* esp. pp. 46–47.

fusion of logical and psychological considerations. Clearly, the occurrence or non-occurrence of a feeling of conviction upon the presentation of grounds for an assertion is a subjective matter which varies from person to person, and with the same person in the course of time; it is often deceptive and can certainly serve neither as a necessary nor as a sufficient condition for the soundness of the given assertion.[14] A rational reconstruction of the standards of scientific validation cannot, therefore, involve reference to a sense of evidence; it has to be based on objective criteria. In fact, it seems reasonable to require that the criteria of empirical confirmation, besides being objective in character, should contain no reference to the specific subject matter of the hypothesis or of the evidence in question; it ought to be possible, one feels, to set up purely formal criteria of confirmation in a manner similar to that in which deductive logic provides purely formal criteria for the validity of deductive inference.

With this goal in mind, we now turn to a study of the nonquantitative concept of confirmation. We shall begin by examining some current conceptions of confirmation and exhibiting their logical and methodological inadequacies; in the course of this analysis, we shall develop a set of conditions for the adequacy of any proposed definition of confirmation; and finally, we shall construct a definition of confirmation which satisfies those general standards of adequacy.

3. NICOD'S CRITERION OF CONFIRMATION AND ITS SHORT-COMINGS

We consider first a conception of confirmation which underlies many recent studies of induction and of scientific method. A very explicit statement of this conception has been given by Jean Nicod in the following passage: "Consider the formula or the law: *A entails B*. How can a particular proposition, or more briefly, a fact, affect its probability? If this fact consists of the presence of B in a case of A, it is favorable to the law '*A entails B*'; on the contrary, if it consists of the absence of B in a case of A, it is unfavorable to this law. It is conceivable that we have here the only two direct modes in which a fact can influence the probability of a law. . . . Thus, the entire influence of particular truths or facts on the probability of universal propositions or laws would operate by means of these two elementary relations which we shall call *confirmation* and *invalidation*."[15] Note that the applicability of this criterion is restricted to hypotheses of the form '*A entails B*'. Any hypothesis *H* of this kind may be expressed in the notation

---

14. See Popper's statement, *l.c.*, section 8.

15. Jean Nicod, *Foundations of Geometry and Induction* (transl. by P. P. Wiener), London, 1930; 219; *cf.* also R. M. Eaton's discussion of "Confirmation and Infirmation," which is based on Nicod's views; it is included in Chap. III of his *General Logic* (New York, 1931).

of symbolic logic[16] by means of a universal conditional sentence, such as, in the simplest case,

$$(x)[P(x) \supset Q(x)]$$

i.e. 'For any object x: if x is a P, then x is a Q,' or also 'Occurrence of the quality P entails occurrence of the quality Q.' According to the above criterion this hypothesis is confirmed by an object a if a is P and Q; and the hypothesis is disconfirmed by a if a is P, but not Q.[17] In other words, an object confirms a universal conditional hypothesis if and only if it satisfies both the antecedent (here: '$P(x)$') and the consequent (here: '$Q(x)$') of the conditional; it disconfirms the hypothesis if and only if it satisfies the antecedent, but not the consequent of the conditional; and (we add this to Nicod's statement) it is neutral, or irrelevant, with respect to the hypothesis if it does not satisfy the antecedent.

This criterion can readily be extended so as to be applicable also to universal conditionals containing more than one quantifier, such as 'Twins always resemble each other', or, in symbolic notation, '$(x)(y)(\text{Twins}(x, y) \supset \text{Rsbl}(x, y))$'. In these cases, a confirming instance consists of an ordered couple, or triple, etc., of objects satisfying the antecedent and the consequent of the conditional. (In the case of the last illustration, any two persons who are twins and resemble each other would confirm the hypothesis; twins who do not resemble each other would disconfirm it; and any two persons not twins—no matter whether they resemble each other or not—would constitute irrelevant evidence.)

We shall refer to this criterion as Nicod's criterion.[18] It states explicitly what is perhaps the most common tacit interpretation of the concept of confirmation. While seemingly quite adequate, it suffers from serious shortcomings, as will now be shown.

(*a*) First, the applicability of this criterion is restricted to hypotheses of universal conditional form; it provides no standards of confirmation for existential hypotheses (such as 'There exists organic life on other stars', or 'Poliomyelitis is caused by some virus') or for hypotheses whose explicit formulation calls for the use of both universal and existential quantifiers (such as 'Every human

16. In this essay, only the most elementary devices of this notation are used; the symbolism is essentially that of *Principia Mathematica*, except that parentheses are used instead of dots, and that existential quantification is symbolized by '(E)' instead of by the inverted 'E.'

17. (Added in 1964). More precisely we would say, in Nicod's parlance, that the hypothesis is confirmed by the *proposition* that a is both P and Q, and is disconfirmed by the *proposition* that a is P but not Q.

18. This term is chosen for convenience, and in view of the above explicit formulation given by Nicod; it is not, of course, intended to imply that this conception of confirmation originated with Nicod.

being dies some finite number of years after his birth', or the psychological hypothesis, ' You can fool all of the people some of the time and some of the people all of the time, but you cannot fool all of the people all of the time', which may be symbolized by '$(x)(Et)\text{Fl}(x, t) \cdot (Ex)(t)\text{Fl}(x, t) \cdot \sim (x)(t)\text{Fl}(x, t)$', (where 'Fl$(x, t)$' stands for 'You can fool person x at time t'). We note, therefore, the desideratum of establishing a criterion of confirmation which is applicable to hypotheses of *any* form.[19]

(*b*) We now turn to a second shortcoming of Nicod's criterion. Consider the two sentences

$$S_1: \text{'}(x)[\text{Raven}(x) \supset \text{Black}(x)]\text{'};$$

$$S_2: \text{'}(x)[\sim\text{Black}(x) \supset \sim \text{Raven}(x)]\text{'}$$

(*i.e.* 'All ravens are black' and 'Whatever is not black is not a raven'), and let *a*, *b*, *c*, *d* be four objects such that *a* is a raven and black, *b* a raven but not black, *c* not a raven but black, and *d* neither a raven nor black. Then according to Nicod's criterion, *a* would confirm S_1, but be neutral with respect to S_2; *b* would disconfirm both S_1 and S_2; *c* would be neutral with respect to both S_1 and S_2, and *d* would confirm S_2, but be neutral with respect to S_1.

But S_1 and S_2 are logically equivalent; they have the same content, they are different formulations of the same hypothesis. And yet, by Nicod's criterion, either of the objects *a* and *d* would be confirming for one of the two sentences, but neutral with respect to the other. This means that Nicod's criterion makes confirmation depend not only on the content of the hypothesis, but also on its formulation.[20]

One remarkable consequence of this situation is that every hypothesis to which the criterion is applicable—*i.e.* every universal conditional—can be stated in a form for which there cannot possibly exist any confirming instances. Thus, *e.g.* the sentence

$$(x)[(\text{Raven}(x) \cdot \sim \text{Black}(x)) \supset (\text{Raven}(x) \cdot \sim \text{Raven}(x)]$$

is readily recognized as equivalent to both S_1 and S_2 above; yet no object whatever can confirm this sentence, *i.e.* satisfy both its antecedent and its consequent;

19. For a rigorous formulation of the problem, it is necessary first to lay down assumptions as to the means of expression and the logical structure of the language in which the hypotheses are supposed to be formulated; the desideratum then calls for a definition of confirmation applicable to any hypothesis which can be expressed in the given language. Generally speaking, the problem becomes increasingly difficult with increasing richness and complexity of the assumed language of science.

20. This difficulty was pointed out, in substance, in my article "Le problème de la vérité," *Theoria* (Göteborg), vol. 3 (1937), esp. p. 222.

for the consequent is contradictory. An analogous transformation is, of course, applicable to any other sentence of universal conditional form.

4. THE EQUIVALENCE CONDITION

The results just obtained call attention to the following condition which an adequately defined concept of confirmation should satisfy, and in the light of which Nicod's criterion has to be rejected as inadequate:

Equivalence condition: Whatever confirms (disconfirms) one of two equivalent sentences, also confirms (disconfirms) the other.

Fulfillment of this condition makes the confirmation of a hypothesis independent of the way in which it is formulated; and no doubt it will be conceded that this is a necessary condition for the adequacy of any proposed criterion of confirmation. Otherwise, the question as to whether certain data confirm a given hypothesis would have to be answered by saying: "That depends on which of the different equivalent formulations of the hypothesis is considered"—which appears absurd. Furthermore—and this is a more important point than an appeal to a feeling of absurdity—an adequate definition of confirmation will have to do justice to the way in which empirical hypotheses function in theoretical scientific contexts such as explanations and predictions; but when hypotheses are used for purposes of explanation or prediction,[21] they serve as premises in a deductive argument whose conclusion is a description of the event to be explained or predicted. The deduction is governed by the principles of formal logic, and according to the latter, a deduction which is valid will remain so if some or all of the premises are replaced by different but equivalent statements; and indeed, a scientist will feel free, in any theoretical reasoning involving certain hypotheses, to use the latter in whichever of their equivalent formulations are most convenient for the development of his conclusions. But if we adopted a concept of confirmation which did not satisfy the equivalence condition, then it would be possible, and indeed necessary, to argue in certain cases that it was sound scientific procedure to base a prediction on a given hypothesis if formulated in a sentence S_1, because a good deal of confirming evidence had been found for S_1; but that it was altogether inadmissible to base the prediction (say, for convenience of deduction) on an equivalent formulation S_2, because no confirming evidence for S_2 was

---

21. For a more detailed account of the logical structure of scientific explanation and prediction, *cf.* C. G. Hempel, "The Function of General Laws in History," *The Journal of Philosophy*, vol. 39 (1942), esp. sections 2, 3, 4. The characterization, given in that paper as well as in the above text, of explanations and predictions as arguments of a deductive logical structure, embodies an oversimplification: as will be shown in section 7 of the present essay, explanations and predictions often involve "quasi-inductive" steps besides deductive ones. This point, however, does not affect the validity of the above argument.

available. Thus, the equivalence condition has to be regarded as a necessary condition for the adequacy of any definition of confirmation.

5. THE PARADOXES OF CONFIRMATION

Perhaps we seem to have been laboring the obvious in stressing the necessity of satisfying the equivalence condition. This impression is likely to vanish upon consideration of certain consequences which derive from a combination of the equivalence condition with a most natural and plausible assumption concerning a sufficient condition of confirmation.

The essence of the criticism we have leveled so far against Nicod's criterion is that it certainly cannot serve as a necessary condition of confirmation; thus, in the illustration given in the beginning of section 3, object a confirms S_1 and should therefore also be considered as confirming S_2, while according to Nicod's criterion it is not. Satisfaction of the latter is therefore not a necessary condition for confirming evidence.

On the other hand, Nicod's criterion might still be considered as stating a particularly obvious and important sufficient condition of confirmation. And indeed, if we restrict ourselves to universal conditional hypotheses in one variable[22] —such as S_1 and S_2 in the above illustration—then it seems perfectly reasonable to qualify an object as confirming such a hypothesis if it satisfies both its antecedent and its consequent. The plausibility of this view will be further corroborated in the course of our subsequent analyses.

Thus, we shall agree that if a is both a raven and black, then a certainly confirms

22. This restriction is essential: In its general form which applies to universal conditionals in any number of variables, Nicod's criterion cannot even be construed as expressing a sufficient condition of confirmation. This is shown by the following rather surprising example: Consider the hypothesis:

$$S_1 : (x)(y)[\sim(R(x,y) \cdot R(y,x)) \supset (R(x,y) \cdot \sim R(y,x))].$$

Let a, b be two objects such that $R(a,b)$ and $\sim R(b, a)$. Then clearly, the couple (a, b) satisfies both the antecedent and the consequent of the universal conditional S_1; hence, if Nicod's criterion in its general form is accepted as stating a sufficient condition of confirmation, (a, b) constitutes confirming evidence for S_1. But S_1 can be shown to be equivalent to

$$S_2: (x)(y)R(x, y)$$

Now, by hypothesis, we have $\sim R(b, a)$; and this flatly contradicts S_2 and thus S_1. Thus, the couple (a, b), although satisfying both the antecedent and the consequent of the universal conditional S_1, actually constitutes disconfirming evidence of the strongest kind (conclusively disconfirming evidence, as we shall say later) for that sentence. This illustration reveals a striking and—as far as I am aware—hitherto unnoticed weakness of that conception of confirmation which underlies Nicod's criterion. In order to realize the bearing of our illustration upon Nicod's original formulation, let A and B be $\sim (R(x, y) \cdot R(y, x))$ and $R(x, y) \cdot \sim (R(y, x)$, respectively. Then S_1 asserts that A entails B, and the couple (a, b) is a case of the presence of B in the presence of A; this should, according to Nicod, be favorable to S_1.

S_1: '(x) (Raven$(x) \supset$ Black(x)))', and if d is neither black nor a raven, d certainly confirms S_2: '(x) [$\sim$ Black$(x) \supset \sim$ Raven(x))]'.

Let us now combine this simple stipulation with the equivalence condition. Since S_1 and S_2 are equivalent, d is confirming also for S_1; and thus, we have to recognize as confirming for S_1 any object which is neither black nor a raven. Consequently, any red pencil, any green leaf, any yellow cow, etc., becomes confirming evidence for the hypothesis that all ravens are black. This surprising consequence of two very adequate assumptions (the equivalence condition and the above sufficient condition of confirmation) can be further expanded: The sentence S_1 can readily be shown to be equivalent to S_3: '(x) [(Raven(x) v $\sim$ Raven(x)) $\supset$ ($\sim$ Raven(x) v Black(x)))]', *i.e.* 'Anything which is or is not a raven is either no raven or black'. According to the above sufficient condition, S_3 is certainly confirmed by any object, say e, such that (1) e is or is not a raven and, in addition (2) e is not a raven or is also black. Since (1) is analytic, these conditions reduce to (2). By virtue of the equivalence condition, we have therefore to consider as confirming for S_1 any object which is either no raven or also black (in other words: any object which is no raven at all, or a black raven).

Of the four objects characterized in section 3, a, c and d would therefore constitute confirming evidence for S_1, while b would be disconforming for S_1. This implies that any nonraven represents confirming evidence for the hypothesis that all ravens are black.[23]

We shall refer to these implications of the equivalence condition and of the above sufficient condition of confirmation as the *paradoxes of confirmation*.

How are these paradoxes to be dealt with? Renouncing the equivalence condition would not represent an acceptable solution, as it is shown by the considerations presented in section 4. Nor does it seem possible to dispense with the stipulation that an object satisfying two conditions, C_1 and C_2, should be considered as confirming a general hypothesis to the effect that any object which satisfies C_1 also satisfies C_2.

But the deduction of the above paradoxical results rests on one other assumption which is usually taken for granted, namely, that the meaning of general empirical hypotheses, such as that all ravens are black, or that all sodium salts burn yellow, can be adequately expressed by means of sentences of universal

---

23. (Added in 1964). The following further "paradoxial" consequence of our two conditions might be noted: Any hypothesis of universal conditional form can be equivalently rewritten as another hypothesis of the same form which, even if true, can have no confirming instances in Nicod's sense at all, since the proposition that a given object satisfies the antecedent and the consequent of the second hypothesis is self-contradictory. For example, '(x) [$P(x) \supset Q(x)$]' is equivalent to the sentence '(x) [$(P(x) \cdot \sim Q(x)) \supset (P(x) \cdot \sim P(x))$]', whose consequent is true of nothing.

conditional form, such as '(x) [Raven(x) ⊃ Black(x)]' and '(x) (Sod. Salt(x) ⊃ Burn Yellow (x))', etc. Perhaps this customary mode of presentation has to be modified; and perhaps such a modification would automatically remove the paradoxes of confirmation? If this is not so, there seems to be only one alternative left, namely to show that the impression of the paradoxical character of those consequences is due to misunderstanding and can be dispelled, so that no theoretical difficulty remains. We shall now consider these two possibilities in turn: Subsections 5.11 and 5.12 are devoted to a discussion of two different proposals for a modified representation of general hypotheses; in subsection 5.2, we shall discuss the second alternative, *i.e.* the possibility of tracing the impression of paradoxicality back to a misunderstanding.

5.11. It has often been pointed out that while Aristotelian logic, in agreement with prevalent everyday usage, confers existential import upon sentences of the form 'All P's are Q's', a universal conditional sentence, in the sense of modern logic, has no existential import; thus, the sentence

$$'(x) \text{ [Mermaid}(x) \supset \text{Green}(x)]'$$

does not imply the existence of mermaids; it merely asserts that any object either is not a mermaid at all, or a green mermaid; and it is true simply because of the fact that there are no mermaids. General laws and hypotheses in science, however —so it might be argued— are meant to have existential import; and one might attempt to express the latter by supplementing the customary universal conditional by an existential clause. Thus, the hypothesis that all ravens are black would be expressed by means of the sentence S_1: '[(x) (Raven(x) ⊃ Black(x)]· (Ex)Raven(x)'; and the hypothesis that no nonblack things are ravens by S_2: '(x)[∼Black(x) ⊃ ∼ Raven(x)] · (Ex) ∼ Black(x)'. Clearly, these sentences are not equivalent, and of the four objects a, b, c, d characterized in section 3, part (b), only a might reasonably be said to confirm S_1, and only d to confirm S_2. Yet this method of avoiding the paradoxes of confirmation is open to serious objections:

(a) First of all, the representation of every general hypothesis by a conjunction of a universal conditional and an existential sentence would invalidate many logical inferences which are generally accepted as permissible in a theoretical argument. Thus, for example, the assertions that all sodium salts burn yellow, and that whatever does not burn yellow is no sodium salt are logically equivalent according to customary understanding and usage, and their representation by universal conditionals preserves this equivalence; but if existential clauses are added, the two assertions are no longer equivalent, as is illustrated above by the analogous case of S_1 and S_2.

(b) Second, the customary formulation of general hypotheses in empirical science clearly does not contain an existential clause, nor does it, as a rule, even indirectly determine such a clause unambiguously. Thus, consider the hypothesis that if a person after receiving an injection of a certain test substance has a positive skin reaction, he has diphtheria. Should we construe the existential clause here as referring to persons, to persons receiving the injection, or to persons who, upon receiving the injection, show a positive skin reaction? A more or less arbitrary decision has to be made; each of the possible decisions gives a different interpretation to the hypothesis, and none of them seems to be really implied by the latter.

(c) Finally, many universal hypotheses cannot be said to imply an existential clause at all. Thus, it may happen that from a certain astrophysical theory a universal hypothesis is deduced concerning the character of the phenomena which would take place under certain specified extreme conditions. A hypothesis of this kind need not (and, as a rule, does not) imply that such extreme conditions ever were or will be realized; it has no existential import. Or consider a biological hypothesis to the effect that whenever man and ape are crossed, the offspring will have such and such characteristics. This is a general hypothesis; it might be contemplated as a mere conjecture, or as a consequence of a broader genetic theory, other implications of which may already have been tested with positive results; but unquestionably the hypothesis does not imply an existential clause asserting that the contemplated kind of cross-breeding referred to will, at some time, actually take place.

5.12. Perhaps the impression of the paradoxical character of the cases discussed in the beginning of section 5 may be said to grow out of the feeling that the hypothesis that all ravens are black is about ravens, and not about nonblack things, nor about all things. The use of an existential clause was one attempt at exhibiting this presumed peculiarity of the hypothesis. The attempt has failed, and if we wish to express the point in question, we shall have to look for a stronger device. The idea suggests itself of representing a general hypothesis by the customary universal conditional, supplemented by the indication of the specific "field of application" of the hypothesis; thus, we might represent the hypothesis that all ravens are black by the sentence '$(x) [\text{Raven}(x) \supset \text{Black}(x)]$' or any one of its equivalents, plus the indication 'Class of ravens', characterizing the field of application; and we might then require that every confirming instance should belong to the field of application. This procedure would exclude the objects c and d from those constituting confirming evidence and would thus avoid those undesirable consequences of the existential-clause device which were pointed out in 5.11 (c). But apart from this advantage, the second method is open to objections similar to those which apply to the first: (a) The way in which general hypotheses are used in science never involves the statement of a field of application; and the choice of the latter in a symbolic formulation of a given hypothesis thus introduces again a considerable measure of arbitrariness. In particular, for a scientific hypothesis to the effect that all *P*'s are *Q*'s, the field of application cannot simply be said to be the class of all *P*'s; for a hypothesis such as that all sodium salts burn yellow finds important application in tests with negative results; *e.g.*, it may be applied to a substance of which it is not known whether it contains sodium salts, nor whether it burns yellow; and if the flame does not turn yellow, the hypothesis serves to establish the absence of sodium salts. The same is true of all other hypotheses used for tests of this type. (*b*) Again, the consistent use of a field of application in the formulation of general hypotheses would involve considerable logical complications, and yet would have no counterpart in the theoretical procedure of science, where hypotheses are subjected to various kinds of logical transformation and inference without any consideration that might be regarded as referring to changes in the fields of application. This method of meeting the paradoxes would therefore amount to dodging the problem by means of an *ad hoc* device which cannot be justified by reference to actual scientific procedure.

5.2 We have examined two alternatives to the customary method of representing general hypotheses by means of universal conditionals; neither of them proved an adequate means of precluding the paradoxes of confirmation. We shall now try to show that what is wrong does not lie in the customary way of construing and representing general hypotheses, but rather in our reliance on a misleading intuition in the matter: The impression of a paradoxical situation is not objectively founded; it is a psychological illusion.

(*a*) One source of misunderstanding is the view, referred to before, that a hypothesis of the simple form 'Every *P* is a *Q*', such as 'All sodium salts burn yellow', asserts something about a certain limited class of objects only, namely, the class of all *P*'s. This idea involves a confusion of logical and practical considerations: Our interest in the hypothesis may be focussed upon its applicability to that particular class of objects, but the hypothesis nevertheless asserts something about, and indeed imposes restrictions upon, *all* objects (within the logical type of the variable occurring in the hypothesis, which in the case of our last illustration might be the class of all physical objects). Indeed, a hypothesis of the form 'Every *P* is a *Q*' forbids the occurrence of any objects having the property *P* but lacking the property *Q*; *i.e.* it restricts all objects whatsoever to the class of those which either lack the property *P* or also have the property *Q*. Now, every object either belongs to this class or falls outside it, and thus, every object— and not only the *P*'s—either conforms to the hypothesis or violates it; there is no object which is not implicitly referred to by a hypothesis of this type. In particular, every object which either is no sodium salt or burns yellow conforms to, and thus bears out, the hypothesis that all sodium salts burn yellow; every other object violates that hypothesis.

The weakness of the idea under consideration is evidenced also by the observation that the class of objects about which a hypothesis is supposed to assert something is in no way clearly determined, and that it changes with the context, as was shown in 5.12 (*a*).

(*b*) A second important source of the appearance of paradoxicality in certain cases of confirmation is exhibited by the following consideration.

Suppose that in support of the assertion 'All sodium salts burn yellow' somebody were to adduce an experiment in which a piece of pure ice was held into a colorless flame and did not turn the flame yellow. This result would confirm the assertion, 'Whatever does not burn yellow is no sodium salt' and consequently, by virtue of the equivalence condition, it would confirm the original formulation. Why does this impress us as paradoxical? The reason becomes clear when we compare the previous situation with the case where an object whose chemical constitution is as yet unknown to us is held into a flame and fails to turn it yellow, and where subsequent analysis reveals it to contain no sodium salt. This outcome, we should no doubt agree, is what was to be expected on the basis of the hypothesis that all sodium salts burn yellow—no matter in which of its various equivalent formulations it may be expressed; thus, the data here obtained constitute confirming evidence for the hypothesis. Now the only difference between the two situations here considered is that in the first case we are told beforehand the test substance is ice, and we happen to "know anyhow" that ice contains no sodium salt; this has the consequence that the outcome of the flame-color test becomes entirely irrelevant for the confirmation of the hypothesis and thus can yield no new evidence for us. Indeed, if the flame should not turn yellow, the hypothesis requires that the substance contain no sodium salt — and we know beforehand that ice does not; and if the flame should turn yellow, the hypothesis would impose no further restrictions on the substance: hence, either of the possible outcomes of the experiment would be in accord with the hypothesis.

The analysis of this example illustrates a general point: In the seemingly paradoxical cases of confirmation, we are often not actually judging the relation of the given evidence *E* alone to the hypothesis *H* (we fail to observe the methodological fiction, characteristic of every case of confirmation, that we have no relevant evidence for *H* other than that included in *E*); instead, we tacitly introduce a comparison of *H* with a body of evidence which consists of *E* in conjunction with additional information that we happen to have at our disposal; in our illustration, this information includes the knowledge (1) that the substance used in the experiment is ice, and (2) that ice contains no sodium salt. If we assume this additional information as given, then, of course, the outcome of the experiment can add no strength to the hypothesis under consideration. But if we are careful to avoid this tacit reference to additional knowledge (which entirely changes the character of the problem), and if we formulate the question as to the confirming character of the evidence in a manner adequate to the concept of confirmation as used in this paper, we have to ask: Given some object *a* (it happens to be a piece of ice, but this fact is not included in the evidence), and given the fact that *a* does not turn the flame yellow and is no sodium salt: does *a* then constitute confirming evidence for the hypothesis? And now—no matter whether *a* is ice or some other substance—it is clear that the answer has to be in the affirmative; and the paradoxes vanish.

So far, in section (*b*), we have considered mainly that type of paradoxical case which is illustrated by the assertion that any nonblack nonraven constitutes confirming evidence for the hypothesis, 'All ravens are black.' However, the general idea just outlined applies as well to the even more extreme cases exemplified by the assertion that any nonraven as well as any black object confirms the hypothesis in question. Let us illustrate this by reference to the latter case. If the given evidence *E*—*i.e.* in the sense of the required methodological fiction, all data relevant for the hypothesis—consists only of one object which, in addition, is black, then *E* may reasonably be said to support even the hypothesis that all objects are black, and *a fortiori E* supports the weaker assertion that all ravens are black. In this case, again, our factual knowledge that not all objects are black tends to create an impression of paradoxicality which is not justified on logical grounds. Other paradoxical cases of confirmation may be dealt with analogously. Thus it turns out that the paradoxes of confirmation, as formulated above, are due to a misguided intuition in the matter rather than to a logical flaw in the two stipulations from which they were derived.[24,25]

24. The basic idea of section (*b*) in the above analysis is due to Dr. Nelson Goodman, to whom I wish to reiterate my thanks for the help he rendered me, through many discussions, in clarifying my ideas on this point.

25. The considerations presented in section (*b*) above are also influenced by, though not identical in content with, the very illuminating discussion of the paradoxes by the Polish methodologist and logician Janina Hosiasson-Lindenbaum; *cf.* her article "On Confirmation," *The Journal of Symbolic Logic*, vol. 5 (1940), especially section 4. Dr. Hosiasson's attention had been called to the paradoxes by my article "Le problème de la vérité" (*cf.* note 20) and by discussions with me. To my knowledge, hers has so far been the only publication which presents an explicit attempt to solve the problem. Her solution is based on a theory of degrees of confirmation, which is developed in the form of an uninterpreted axiomtaic system, and most of her arguments presuppose that theoretical framework. I have profited, however, by some of Miss Hosiasson's more general observations which proved relevant for the analysis of the paradoxes of the nongraduated or qualitative concept of confirmation which forms the object of the present study.

One point in those of Miss Hosiasson's comments which rest on her theory of degrees of confirmation is of particular interest, and I should like to discuss it briefly. Stated in reference to the raven hypothesis, it consists in the suggestion that the finding of one nonblack object which is no raven, while constituting confirming evidence for the hypothesis, would increase

6. CONFIRMATION CONSTRUED AS A RELATION BETWEEN SENTENCES

Our analysis of Nicod's criterion has so far led to two main results: The rejection of that criterion in view of several deficiencies, and the emergence of the equivalence condition as a necessary condition of adequacy for any proposed definition of confirmation. Another aspect of Nicod's criterion requires consideration now. In our formulation of the criterion, confirmation was construed as a dyadic relation between an object or an ordered set of objects, representing the evidence, and a sentence, representing the hypothesis. This means that confirmation was conceived of as a semantical relation[26] obtaining between certain extra-linguistic objects[27] on one hand and certain sentences on the other. It is possible, however, to construe confirmation in an alternative fashion as a relation between two sentences, one describing the given evidence, the other expressing the hypothesis. Thus, instead of saying that an object *a* which is both a raven and black (or the fact of *a* being both a raven and black) confirms the hypothesis that all ravens are black, we may say that the evidence sentence,

26. For a detailed account of this concept, see C. W. Morris, *Foundations of the Theory of Signs* (Internat. Encyclopedia of Unified Science, vol. I, No. 2, Chicago, 1938) and R. Carnap *Introduction to Semantics* (Cambridge, Mass., 1962), esp. sections 4 and 37.

27. Instead of making the first term of the relation an object or a sequence of objects we might construe it as a state of affairs (or perhaps as a fact, or a proposition, as Nicod puts it), such as that state of affairs which consists in *a* being a black raven, etc.

---

the degree of confirmation of the hypothesis by a smaller amount than the finding of one raven which is black. This is said to be so because the class of all ravens is much less numerous than that of all nonblack objects, so that—to put the idea in suggestive though somewhat misleading terms—the finding of one black raven confirms a larger portion of the total content of the hypothesis than the finding of one nonblack nonraven. In fact, from the basic assumptions of her theory, Miss Hosiasson is able to derive a theorem according to which the above statement about the relative increase in degree of confirmation will hold provided that actually the number of all ravens is small compared with the number of all nonblack objects. But is this last numerical assumption actually warranted in the present case and analogously in all other "paradoxical" cases? The answer depends in part upon the logical structure of the language of science. If a "coordinate language" is used, in which, say, finite space-time regions figure as individuals, then the raven hypothesis assumes some such form as 'Every space-time region which contains a raven contains something black'; and even if the total number of ravens ever to exist is finite, the class of space-time regions containing a raven has the power of the continum, and so does the class of space-time regions containing something nonblack; thus, for a coordinate language of the type under consideration, the above numerical assumption is not warranted. Now the use of a coordinate language may appear quite artificial in this particular illustration; but it will seem very appropriate in many other contexts, such as, *e.g.*, that of physical field theories. On the other hand, Miss Hosiasson's numerical assumption may well be justified on the basis of a "thing language," in which physical objects of finite size function as individuals. Of course, even on this basis, it remains an empirical question, for every hypothesis of the form 'All *P*'s are *Q*'s', whether actually the class of non-*Q*'s is much more numerous than the class of *P*'s; and in many cases this question will be very difficult to decide.

'*a* is a raven and *a* is black', confirms the hypothesis-sentence (briefly, the hypothesis), 'All ravens are black'. We shall adopt this conception of confirmation as a relation between sentences here for the following reasons: First, the evidence adduced in support or criticism of a scientific hypothesis is always expressed in sentences, which frequently have the character of observation reports; and second, it will prove very fruitful to pursue the parallel, alluded to in section 2 above, between the concepts of confirmation and of logical consequence. And just as in the theory of the consequence relation, *i.e.* in deductive logic, the premises of which a given conclusion is a consequence are construed as sentences rather than as "facts," so we propose to construe the data which confirm a given hypothesis as given in the form of sentences.

The preceding reference to observation reports suggests a certain restriction which might be imposed on evidence sentences. Indeed, the evidence adduced in support of a scientific hypothesis or theory consists, in the last analysis, in data accessible to what is loosely called direct observation, and such data are expressible in the form of "observation reports." In view of this consideration, we shall restrict the evidence sentences which form the domain of the relation of confirmation to sentences of the character of observation reports. In order to give a precise meaning to the concept of observation report, we shall assume that we are given a well-determined "language of science," in terms of which all sentences under consideration, hypotheses as well as evidence sentences, are formulated. We shall further assume that this language contains, among other terms, a clearly delimited "observational vocabulary" which consists of terms designating more or less directly observable attributes of things or events, such as, say, 'black,' 'taller than', 'burning with a yellow light', etc., but no theoretical constructs such as 'aliphatic compound', 'circularly polarized light', 'heavy hydrogen', etc.

We shall now understand by a *hypothesis* any sentence which can be expressed in the assumed language of science, no matter whether it is a generalized sentence, containing quantifiers, or a particular sentence referring only to a finite number of particular objects. An *observation report* will be construed as a finite class (or a conjunction of a finite number) of observation sentences; and an observation sentence as a sentence which either asserts or denies that a given object has a certain observable property (*e.g.* '*a* is a raven', '*d* is not black'), or that a given sequence of objects stand in a certain observable relation (*e.g.* '*a* is between *b* and *c*').

Now the concept of observability itself obviously is relative to the techniques of observation used. What is unobservable to the unaided senses may well be observable by means of suitable devices such as telescopes, microscopes, polariscopes, lie detectors, Gallup polls, etc. If by direct observation we mean such observational procedures as do not make use of auxiliary devices, then such property terms as 'black', 'hard', 'liquid', 'cool', and such relation terms as 'above', 'between', 'spatially coincident', etc., might be said to refer to directly observable attributes; if observability is construed in a broader sense, so as to allow for the use of certain specified instruments or other devices, the concept of observable attribute becomes more comprehensive. If, in our study of confirmation, we wanted to analyze the manner in which the hypotheses and theories of empirical science are ultimately supported by "evidence of the senses," then we should have to require that observation reports refer exclusively to directly observable attributes. This view was taken, for simplicity and concreteness, in the preceding parts of this section. Actually, however, the general logical characteristics of that relation which obtains between a hypothesis and a group of empirical statements which support it, can be studied in isolation from this restriction to direct observability. All we will assume here is that in the context of the scientific test of a given hypothesis or theory, certain specified techniques of observation have been agreed upon; these determine an observational vocabulary, namely, a set of terms designating properties and relations observable by means of the accepted techniques. For our purposes it is entirely sufficient that these terms, constituting the observational vocabulary, be given. An observation sentence is then defined simply as a sentence affirming or denying that a given object, or sequence of objects, possesses one of those observable attributes.[28]

Let it be noted that we do not require an observation sentence to be true, nor to be accepted on the basis of actual observations; rather, an observation sentence expresses something that is decidable by means of the accepted techniques of

28. The concept of observation sentence has, in the context of our study, a status and a logical function closely akin to that of the concepts of protocol statement or basis sentence, etc., as used in many recent studies of empiricism. However, the conception of observation sentence which is being proposed in the present study is more liberal in that it renders the discussion of the logical problems of testing and confirmation independent of various highly controversial epistemological issues; thus, *e.g.*, we do not stipulate that observation reports must be about psychic events, or about sense perceptions (*i.e.* that they have to be expressed in terms of a vocabulary of phenomenology, or of introspective psychology). According to the conception of observation sentence adopted in the present study, the "objects" referred to in an observation sentence may be construed in any one of the senses just referred to, or in various other ways; for example, they might be space-time regions, or again physical objects such as stones, trees, etc. (most of the illustrations given throughout this article represent observation sentences belonging to this kind of "thing language"); all that we require is that the few very general conditions stated above be satisfied.

These conditions impose on observation sentences and on observation reports certain restrictions with respect to their form; in particular, neither kind of sentence may contain any quantifiers. This stipulation recommends itself for the purposes of the logical analysis here to be undertaken; but we do not wish to claim that this formal restriction is indispensable. On the contrary, it is quite possible and perhaps desirable also to allow for observation sentences containing quantifiers: our simplifying assumption is introduced mainly in order to avoid considerable logical complications in the definition of confirmation.

observation. In other words, an observation sentence describes a possible outcome of the accepted observational techniques; it asserts something that might conceivably be established by means of those techniques. Possibly, the term "observation-type sentence" would be more suggestive; but for convenience we give preference to the shorter term. An analogous comment applies, of course, to our definition of an observation report as a class or a conjunction of observation sentences. The need for this broad conception of observation sentences and observation reports is readily recognized: Confirmation as here conceived is a logical relationship between sentences, just as logical consequence is. Now whether a sentence S_2 is a consequence of a sentence S_1 does not depend on whether or not S_1 is true (or known to be true); and analogously, the criteria of whether a given statement, expressed in terms of the observational vocabulary, confirms a certain hypothesis cannot depend on whether the statements in the report are true, or based on actual experience, or the like. Our definition of confirmation must enable us to indicate what kind of evidence *would* confirm a given hypothesis *if* it were available; and clearly the sentence characterizing such evidence can be required only to express something that *might* be observed, but not necessarily something that has actually been established by observation.

It may be helpful to carry the analogy between confirmation and consequence one step further. The truth or falsity of S_1 is irrelevant for the question of whether S_2 is a consequence of S_1 (whether S_2 can be validly inferred from S_1); but in a logical inference which justifies a sentence S_2 by showing that it is a logical consequence of a conjunction of premises, S_1, we can be certain of the truth of S_2 only if we know S_1 to be true. Analogously, the question of whether an observation report stands in the relation of confirmation to a given hypothesis does not depend on whether the report states actual or fictitious observational findings; but for a decision as to the soundness or acceptability of a hypothesis which is confirmed by a certain report, it is of course necessary to know whether the report is based on actual experience or not. Just as a conclusion of a logical inference, shown to be true, must be (a1) validly inferred from (a2) a set of true premises, so a hypothesis, to be scientifically acceptable, must be (b1) formally confirmed by (b2) reliable reports on observational findings.

The central problem of this essay is to establish general criteria for the formal relation of confirmation as referred to in (b1); the analysis of the concept of a reliable observation report, which belongs largely to the field of pragmatics,[29] falls outside the scope of the present study. One point, however, deserves mention here. A statement in the form of an observation report (for example, about the position of the pointer of a certain thermograph at 3 A.M.) may be accepted or

29. An account of the concept of pragmatics may be found in the publications listed in note 26.

rejected in science either on the basis of direct observation, or because it is indirectly confirmed or disconfirmed by other accepted observation sentences (in the example, these might be sentences describing the curve traced by the pointer during the night); and because of this possibility of indirect confirmation, our study has a bearing also on the question of the acceptance of hypotheses which have themselves the form of observation reports.

The conception of confirmation as a relation between sentences analogous to that of logical consequence suggests yet another requirement for the attempted definition of confirmation: While logical consequence has to be conceived of as a basically semantical relation between sentences, it has been possible, for certain languages, to establish criteria of logical consequence in purely syntactical terms. Analogously, confirmation may be conceived of as a semantical relation between an observation report and a hypothesis; but the parallel with the consequence relation suggests that it should be possible, for certain languages, to establish purely syntactical criteria of confirmation. The subsequent considerations will indeed eventuate in a definition of confirmation based on the concept of logical consequence and other purely syntactical concepts.

The interpretation of confirmation as a logical relation between sentences involves no essential change in the central problem of the present study. In particular, all the points made in the preceding sections can readily be rephrased in accordance with this interpretation. Thus, for example, the assertion that an object a which is a swan and white confirms the hypothesis '(x) [Swan(x) $\supset$ White(x)]' can be expressed by saying that the observation report 'Swan(a)· White(a)' confirms that hypothesis. Similarly, the equivalence condition can be reformulated as follows: If an observation report confirms a certain sentence, then it also confirms every sentence which is logically equivalent with the latter. Nicod's criterion as well as our grounds for rejecting it can be reformulated along the same lines. We presented Nicod's concept of confirmation as referring to a relation between nonlinguistic objects on one hand and sentences on the other because this approach seemed to approximate most closely Nicod's own formulations,[30] and because it enabled us to avoid certain technicalities which are actually unnecessary in that context.

7. THE PREDICTION-CRITERION OF CONFIRMATION AND ITS SHORTCOMINGS

We are now in a position to analyze a second conception of confirmation,

---

30. (Added in 1964.) Actually this is not correct; *cf.* note 17 above. But, as is readily seen, the objections raised in this article against Nicod's criterion remain in force also when that criterion is understood as taking general hypotheses to be confirmed or disconfirmed by propositions **rather than** by objects.

which is reflected in many methodological discussions and which can claim a great deal of plausibility. Its basic idea is very simple: General hypotheses in science as well as in everyday use are intended to enable us to anticipate future events; hence, it seems reasonable to count any prediction that is borne out by subsequent observation as confirming evidence for the hypothesis on which it is based, and any prediction that fails as disconfirming evidence. To illustrate: Let H_1 be the hypothesis that all metals, when heated, expand; symbolically: '(x) [(Metal (x) · Heated (x)) $\supset$ Exp(x))]'. If we have an observation report to the effect that a certain object a is metallic and is heated, then by means of H_1 we can derive the prediction that a expands. Suppose that this is borne out by observation and described in an additional observation statement. We should then have the total observation report: {Metal(a), Heated(a), Exp(a)}.[31] This report would be qualified as confirming evidence for H_1 because its last sentence bears out what could be predicted, or derived, from the first two by means of H_1; more explicitly, because the last sentence can be derived from the first two in conjunction with H_1. Now let H_2 be the hypothesis that all swans are white; symbolically: '(x) [Swan (x) $\supset$ White(x))]'; and consider the observation report {Swan(a), $\sim$ White(a)}. This report would constitute disconfirming evidence for H_2 because the second of its sentences contradicts (and thus fails to bear out) the prediction 'White(a)' which can be deduced from the first sentence in conjunction with H_2; or, symmetrically, because the first sentence contradicts the consequence '$\sim$Swan(a)' which can be derived from the second in conjunction with H_2. Obviously, either of these formulations implies that H_2 is incompatible with the given observation report. These illustrations suggest the following general definition of confirmation:

PREDICTION CRITERION OF CONFIRMATION: Let H be a hypothesis, B an observation report, *i.e.* a class of observation sentences. Then

(a) B is said to confirm H if B can be divided into two mutually exclusive subclasses B_1 and B_2 such that B_2 is not empty, and every sentence of B_2 can be logically deduced from B_1 in conjunction with H, but not from B_1 alone;

(b) B is said to disconfirm H if H logically contradicts B;[32]

---

31. An (observation) report, it will be recalled, may be represented by a conjunction or by a class of observation sentences: in the latter case, we characterize it by writing the sentences between braces; the single quotes which normally would be used to mention the sentences are, for convenience, assumed to be absorbed by the braces.

32. It might seem more natural to stipulate that B disconfirms H if it can be divided into two mutually exclusive classes B_1 and B_2 such that the denial of at least one sentence in B_2 can be deduced from B_1 in conjunction with H; but this condition can be shown to be equivalent to (b) above.

(*c*) *B* is said to be neutral with respect to *H* if it neither confirms nor disconfirms *H*.[33]

But while this criterion is quite sound as a statement of sufficient conditions of confirmation for hypotheses of the type illustrated above, it is considerably too narrow to serve as a general definition of confirmation. Generally speaking, this criterion would serve its purpose if all scientific hypotheses could be construed as asserting regular connections between observable features of the subject matter under investigation; *i.e.* if they all were of the form "Whenever the observable characteristic *P* is present in an object or a situation, then the observable characteristic *Q* is present as well." But actually, most scientific hypotheses and laws are not of this simple type; as a rule, they express regular connections of characteristics which are not observable in the sense of direct observability, nor even in a much more liberal sense. Consider, for example, the following hypothesis: 'Whenever plane-polarized light of wave length λ traverses a layer of quartz of thickness *d*, then its plane of polarization is rotated through an angle α which is proportional to *d*/λ'. Let us assume that the observational vocabulary, by means of which our observation reports have to be formulated, contains exclusively terms referring to directly observable attributes. Then, since the question of whether a given ray of light is plane-polarized and has the wave length λ cannot be decided by means of direct observation, no observation report of the kind here admitted could afford information of this type. This in itself would not be crucial if at least we could assume that the fact that a given ray of light is plane-polarized, etc., could be logically inferred from some possible observation report; for then, from a suitable report of this kind, in conjunction with the given hypothesis, one would be able to predict a rotation of the plane of polarization; and from this prediction, which itself is not yet expressed in exclusively observational terms, one might expect to derive further predictions in the form of genuine observation sentences. But actually, a hypothesis to the effect that a given ray of light is plane-polarized has to be considered as a general hypothesis which entails an unlimited number of observation sentences; thus it cannot be logically inferred from, but at best be confirmed by, a suitable set of observational findings. The logically essential point can best be exhibited by

---

33. The following quotations from A. J. Ayer's book *Language, Truth and Logic* (London, 1936) formulate in a particularly clear fashion the conception of confirmation as successful prediction (although the two are not explicitly identified by definition): ". . . the function of an empirical hypothesis is to enable us to anticipate experience. Accordingly, if an observation to which a given proposition is relevant conforms to our expectations, . . . that proposition is confirmed" (*loc. cit.* pp. 142–43); ". . . it is the mark of a genuine factual proposition . . . that some experiential propositions can be deduced from it in conjunction with certain premises without being deducible from those other premises alone." (*loc. cit.* p. 26).

reference to a very simple abstract case: Let us assume that R_1 and R_2 are two relations of a kind accessible to direct observation, and that the field of scientific investigation contains infinitely many objects. Consider now the hypothesis

(H) $$(x)[(y)R_1(x, y) \supset (Ez)R_2(x, z)]$$

i.e.: Whenever an object x stands in R_1 to every object y, then it stands in R_2 to at least one object z. This simple hypothesis has the following property: However many observation sentences may be given, H does not enable us to derive any new observation sentences from them. Indeed—to state the reason in suggestive though not formally rigorous terms— in order to make a prediction concerning some specific object a, we should first have to know that a stands in R_1 to every object; and this necessary information clearly cannot be contained in any finite number, however large, of observation sentences, because a finite set of observation sentences can tell us at best for a finite number of objects that a stands in R_1 to them. Thus an observation report, which always involves only a finite number of observation sentences, can never provide a sufficiently broad basis for a prediction by means of H.[34] Besides, even if we did know that a stood in R_1 to every object, the prediction derivable by means of H would not be an observation sentence; it would assert that a stands in R_2 to *some* object, without specifying which, and where to find it. Thus, H is an empirical hypothesis that contains, besides purely logical terms, only expressions belonging to the observational vocabulary, and yet the predictions which it renders possible neither start from nor lead to observation reports.

It is therefore a considerable oversimplification to say that scientific hypotheses and theories enable us to derive predictions of future experiences from descriptions of past ones. Unquestionably, scientific hypotheses do have a predictive function; but the way in which they perform this function, the manner in which they establish logical connections between observation reports, is logically more complex than a deductive inference. Thus, in the last illustration, the predictive use of H may assume the following form: On the basis of a number of individual tests, which show that a does stand in R_1 to three objects b, c, and d, we might accept the hypothesis that a stands in R_1 to all objects; or in terms of our formal mode of speech: In view of the observation report $\{R_1(a, b),\ R_1(a, c),\ R_1(a, d)\}$, the hypothesis that $(y)R_1(a, y)$ might be accepted as confirmed by,

---

34. To illustrate: a might be an iron object which possibly is a magnet; R_1 might be the relation of attracting; the objects under investigation might be iron objects. Then a finite number of observation reports to the effect that a did attract a particular piece of iron is insufficient to *infer* that a will attract every piece of iron.

though not logically inferable from, that report.[35] This process might be referred to as quasi-induction.[36] From the hypothesis thus established we can then proceed to derive, by means of H, the prediction that a stands in R_2 to at least one object. This again, as was pointed out above, is not an observation sentence; and indeed no observation sentence can be derived from it; but it can, in turn, be confirmed by a suitable observation sentence, such as '$R_2(a, b)$'. In other cases, the prediction of actual observation sentences may be possible; thus if the given hypothesis asserts that $(x)((y)R_1(x, y) \supset (z)R_2(x, z))$, then after quasi-inductively accepting, as above, that $(y)R_1(a, y)$, we can derive, by means of the given hypothesis, the sentence that a stands in R_2 to every object, and thence, we can deduce particular predictions such as '$R_2(a, b)$', which do have the form of observation sentences.

Thus, the chain of reasoning which leads from given observational findings to the "prediction" of new ones actually involves, besides deductive inferences, certain quasi-inductive steps each of which consists in the acceptance of an intermediate statement on the basis of confirming, but usually not logically conclusive, evidence. In most scientific predictions, this general pattern occurs in multiple reiteration; an analysis of the predictive use of the hypothesis mentioned above, concerning plane-polarized light, could serve as an illustration. In the present context, however, this general account of the structure of scientific prediction is sufficient. It shows that a general definition of confirmation by reference to successful prediction becomes circular; indeed, in order to make the original formulation of the prediction-criterion of confirmation sufficiently comprehensive, we should have to replace the phrase "can be logically deduced" by "can be obtained by a series of steps of deduction and quasi-induction"; and the definition of "quasi-induction" in the above sense presupposes the concept of confirmation.

Let us note, as a by-product of the preceding consideration, that an adequate analysis of scientific prediction (and analogously, of scientific explanation, and of the testing of empirical hypotheses) requires an analysis of the concept of confirmation. The reason may be restated in general terms as follows: Scientific

---

35. Thus, in the illustration given in the preceding footnote, the hypothesis that the object a will attract every piece of iron might be accepted as sufficiently well substantiated by, though by no means derivable from, an observation report to the effect that in tests a did attract the iron objects b, c, and d.

36. The prefix "quasi" is to contradistinguish the procedure in question from so-called induction, which is usually supposed to be a method of discovering, or inferring, general regularities on the basis of a finite number of instances. In quasi-induction, the hypothesis is not "discovered" but has to be *given* in addition to the observation report; the process consists in the acceptance of the hypothesis if it is deemed sufficiently confirmed by the observation report. *Cf.* also the discussion in section 1*c*, above.

laws and theories, as a rule, connect terms which lie on the level of abstract theoretical constructs rather than on that of direct observation; and from observation sentences, no merely deductive logical inference leads to statements about theoretical constructs, which can serve as starting points for scientific predictions; statements about theoretical constructs, such as 'This piece of iron is magnetic' or 'Here, a plane-polarized ray of light traverses a quartz crystal' can be confirmed, but not entailed, by observation reports. Thus, even though based on general scientific laws, the prediction of new observational findings by means of given ones is a process involving confirmation in addition to logical deduction.[37]

8. CONDITIONS OF ADEQUACY FOR ANY DEFINITION OF CONFIRMATION

The two most customary conceptions of confirmation, which were rendered explicit in Nicod's criterion and in the prediction criterion, have thus been found unsuitable for a general definition of confirmation. Besides this negative result, the preceding analysis has also exhibited certain logical characteristics of scientific prediction, explanation, and testing, and it has led to the establishment of certain standards which an adequate definition of confirmation has to satisfy. These standards include the equivalence condition and the requirement that the definition of confirmation be applicable to hypotheses of any degree of logical complexity, rather than to the simplest type of universal conditional only. An adequate definition of confirmation, however, has to satisfy several further logical requirements, to which we now turn.

First of all, it will be agreed that any sentence which is logically entailed by a given observation report has to be considered as confirmed by that report: entailment is a special case of confirmation. Thus, e.g., we want to say that the observation report 'a is black' confirms the sentence (hypothesis) 'a is black or grey'; and—to refer to one of the illustrations given in the preceding section—the observation sentence '$R_2(a, b)$' should certainly be confirming evidence for the sentence '$(Ez)R_2(a, z)$'. We are therefore led to the stipulation that any adequate definition of confirmation must insure the fulfilment of the

37. In the above sketch of the structure of scientific prediction, we have disregarded the fact that in practically every case where a prediction is said to be obtained by means of a certain hypothesis or theory, a considerable body of auxiliary theories is used in addition. Thus, the prediction of observable effects of the deflection of light in the gravitational field of the sun on the basis of the general theory of relativity requires such auxiliary theories as mechanics and optics. But an explicit consideration of this fact would not affect our result that scientific predictions, even when based on hypotheses or theories of universal form, still are not purely deductive in character, but involve quasi-inductive steps as well.

(8.1) ENTAILMENT CONDITION. Any sentence which is entailed by an observation report is confirmed by it.[38]

This condition is suggested by the preceding consideration, but of course not proved by it. To make it a standard of adequacy for the definition of confirmation means to lay down the stipulation that a proposed definition of confirmation will be rejected as logically inadequate if it is not constructed in such a way that (8.1) is unconditionally satisfied. An analogous remark applies to the subsequently proposed further standards of adequacy.

Second, an observation report which confirms certain hypotheses would invariably be qualified as confirming any consequence of those hypotheses. Indeed: any such consequence is but an assertion of all or part of the combined content of the original hypotheses and has therefore to be regarded as confirmed by any evidence which confirms all of the latter. This suggests the following condition of adequacy:

(8.2) CONSEQUENCE CONDITION. If an observation report confirms every one of a class K of sentences, then it also confirms any sentence which is a logical consequence of K.

If (8.2) is satisfied, then the same is true of the following two more special conditions:

(8.21) SPECIAL CONSEQUENCE CONDITION. If an observation report confirms a hypothesis H, then it also confirms every consequence of H.

(8.22) EQUIVALENCE CONDITION. If an observation report confirms a hypothesis H, then it also confirms every hypothesis which is logically equivalent with H.

(8.22) follows from (8.21) in view of the fact that equivalent hypotheses are mutual consequences of each other. Thus, the satisfaction of the consequence condition entails that of our earlier equivalence condition, and the latter loses its status of an independent requirement.

In view of the apparent obviousness of these conditions, it is interesting to note that the definition of confirmation in terms of successful prediction, while satisfying the equivalence condition, would violate the consequence condition. Consider, for example, the formulation of the prediction criterion given in the

---

38. As a consequence of this stipulation, a contradictory observation report, such as [Black(a), $\sim$ Black(a)] confirms every sentence, because it has every sentence as a consequence. Of course, it is possible to exclude contradictory observation reports altogether by a slight restriction of the definition of 'observation report'. There is, however, no important reason to do so.

earlier part of the preceding section. Clearly, if the observational findings B_2 can be predicted on the basis of the findings B_1 by means of the hypothesis H, the same prediction is obtainable by means of any equivalent hypothesis, but not generally by means of a weaker one.

On the other hand, any prediction obtainable by means of H can obviously also be established by means of any hypothesis which is stronger than H, i.e. which logically entails H. Thus while the consequence condition stipulates in effect that whatever confirms a given hypothesis also confirms any weaker hypothesis, the relation of confirmation defined in terms of successful prediction would satisfy the condition that whatever confirms a given hypothesis also confirms every stronger one.

But is this "converse consequence condition," as it might be called, not reasonable enough, indeed should it not be included among our standards of adequacy for the definition of confirmation? The second of these two suggestions can be readily disposed of: The adoption of the new condition, in addition to (8.1) and (8.2), would have the consequence that any observation report B would confirm any hypothesis H whatsoever. Thus, e.g., if B is the report 'a is a raven' and H is Hooke's law, then, according to (8.1), B confirms the sentence 'a is a raven'; hence B would, according to the converse consequence condition, confirm the stronger sentence 'a is a raven, and Hooke's law holds'; and finally, by virtue of (8.2), B would confirm H, which is a consequence of the last sentence. Obviously, the same type of argument can be applied in all other cases.

But is it not true, after all, that very often observational data which confirm a hypothesis H are considered also as confirming a stronger hypothesis? Is it not true, for example, that those experimental findings which confirm Galileo's law, or Kepler's laws, are considered also as confirming Newton's law of gravitation?[39] This is indeed the case, but it does not justify the acceptance of the converse consequence condition as a general rule of the logic of confirmation; for in the cases just mentioned, the weaker hypothesis is connected with the stronger one by a logical bond of a particular kind: it is essentially a substitution instance of the stronger one; thus, e.g., while the law of gravitation refers to the force obtaining between any two bodies, Galileo's law is a specialization referring to the case where one of the bodies is the earth, the other an object near its surface. In the preceding case, however, where Hooke's law was shown to be confirmed by the observation report that a is a raven, this situation does not prevail; and here, the rule that whatever confirms a given hypothesis also confirms any stronger

---

39. Strictly speaking, Galileo's law and Kepler's laws can be deduced from the law of gravitation only if certain additional hypotheses—including the laws of motion—are presupposed; but this does not affect the point under discussion.

one becomes an entirely absurd principle. Thus, the converse consequence condition does not provide a sound general condition of adequacy.[40]

A third condition remains to be stated:[41]

(8.3) CONSISTENCY CONDITION. Every logically consistent observation report is logically compatible with the class of all the hypotheses which it confirms.

The two most important implications of this requirement are the following:

(8.31) Unless an observation report is self-contradictory,[42] it does not confirm any hypothesis with which it is not logically compatible.

(8.32) Unless an observation report is self-contradictory, it does not confirm any hypotheses which contradict each other.

The first of these corollaries will readily be accepted; the second, however,—and consequently (8.3) itself—will perhaps be felt to embody a too severe restriction. It might be pointed out, for example, that a finite set of measurements concerning the changes of one physical magnitude, x, associated with those of another, y, may conform to, and thus be said to confirm, several different hypotheses as to the particular mathematical function in terms of which the relationship of x and y can be expressed; but such hypotheses are incompatible because to at least one value of x, they will assign different values of y.

No doubt it is possible to liberalize the formal standards of adequacy in line with these considerations. This would amount to dropping (8.3) and (8.32) and retaining only (8.31). One of the effects of this measure would be that when a logically consistent observation report B confirms each of two hypotheses, it

---

40. William Barrett, in a paper entitled "Discussion on Dewey's Logic" (*The Philosophical Review*, vol. 50, 1941, pp. 305 ff., esp. p. 312) raises some questions closely related to what we have called above the consequence condition and the converse consequence condition. In fact, he invokes the latter (without stating it explicitly) in an argument which is designed to show that "not every observation which confirms a sentence need also confirm all its consequences," in other words, that the special consequence condition (8.21) need not always be satisfied. He supports his point by reference to "the simplest case: the sentence 'C' is an abbreviation of 'A·B', and the observation O confirms 'A', *and so* 'C', but is irrelevant to 'B', which is a consequence of 'C'." (Italics mine).

For reasons contained in the above discussion of the consequence condition and the converse consequence condition, the application of the latter in the case under consideration seems to me unjustifiable, so that the illustration does not prove the author's point; and indeed, there seems to be every reason to preserve the unrestricted validity of the consequence condition. As a matter of fact, Barrett himself argues that "the degree of confirmation for the consequence of a sentence cannot be less than that of the sentence itself"; this is indeed quite sound; but it is hard to see how the recognition of this principle can be reconciled with a renunciation of the special consequence condition, which may be considered simply as its correlate for the nongraduated relation of confirmation.

41. For a fourth condition, see note 46.

42. A contradictory observation report confirms every hypothesis (*cf.* note 38) and is, of course, incompatible with every one of the hypotheses it confirms.

does not necessarily confirm their conjunction; for the hypotheses might be mutually incompatible, hence their conjunction self-contradictory; consequently, by (8.31), B could not confirm it. This consequence is intuitively rather awkward, and one might therefore feel inclined to suggest that while (8.3) should be dropped and (8.31) retained, (8.32) should be replaced by the requirement (8.33): If an observation sentence confirms each of two hypotheses, then it also confirms their conjunction. But it can readily be shown that by virtue of (8.2) this set of conditions entails the fulfilment of (8.32).

If, therefore, the condition (8.3) appears to be too rigorous, the most obvious alternative would seem to lie in replacing (8.3) and its corollaries by the much weaker condition (8.31) alone. [Added in 1970: But as G. L. Massey has pointed out to me, satisfaction of (8.1), (8.2), and (8.31) logically implies satisfaction of (8.3); hence, that alternative fails.] One of the advantages of a definition which satisfies (8.3) is that it sets a limit, so to speak, to the strength of the hypotheses which can be confirmed by given evidence.[43]

The remainder of the present study, therefore, will be concerned exclusively with the problem of establishing a definition of confirmation which satisfies the more severe formal conditions represented by (8.1), (8.2), and (8.3) together.

The fulfilment of these requirements, which may be regarded as general laws of the logic of confirmation, is of course only a necessary, not a sufficient, condition for the adequacy of any proposed definition of confirmation. Thus, e.g., if 'B confirms H' were defined as meaning 'B logically entails H', then the above three conditions would clearly be satisfied; but the definition would not be adequate because confirmation has to be a more comprehensive relation than entailment (the latter might be referred to as the special case of *conclusive* confirmation). Thus, a definition of confirmation, to be acceptable, also has to be materially adequate: it has to provide a reasonably close approximation to that conception of confirmation which is implicit in scientific procedure and methodological discussion. That conception is vague and to some extent quite unclear, as I have tried to show in earlier parts of this paper; therefore, it would be too much to expect full agreement as to whether a proposed definition of confirmation is materially adequate. On the other hand, there will be rather general agreement on certain points; thus, e.g., the identification of confirmation with entailment, or the Nicod criterion of confirmation as analyzed above, or any definition of confirmation by reference to a "sense of evidence," will probably now be admitted not to be adequate approximations to that concept of confirmation which is relevant for the logic of science.

---

43. This was pointed out to me by Dr. Nelson Goodman. The definition later to be outlined in this essay, which satisfies conditions (8.1), (8.2) and (8.3), lends itself, however, to certain generalizations which satisfy only the more liberal conditions of adequacy just considered.

On the other hand, the soundness of the logical analysis (which, in a clear sense, always involves a logical reconstruction) of a theoretical concept cannot be gauged simply by our feelings of satisfaction at a certain proposed analysis; and if there are, say, two alternative proposals for defining a term on the basis of a logical analysis, and if both appear to come fairly close to the intended meaning, then the choice has to be made largely by reference to such features as the logical properties of the two reconstructions, and the comprehensiveness and simplicity of the theories to which they lead.

9. THE SATISFACTION CRITERION OF CONFIRMATION

As has been mentioned before, a precise definition of confirmation requires reference to some definite "language of science," in which all observation reports and all hypotheses under consideration are assumed to be formulated, and whose logical structure is supposed to be precisely determined. The more complex this language, and the richer its logical means of expression, the more difficult it will be, as a rule, to establish an adequate definition of confirmation for it. However, the problem has been solved at least for certain cases: With respect to languages of a comparatively simple logical structure, it has been possible to construct an explicit definition of confirmation which satisfies all of the above logical requirements, and which appears to be intuitively rather adequate. An exposition of the technical details of this definition has been published elsewhere;[44] in the present study, which is concerned with the general logical and methodological aspects of the problem of confirmation rather than with technical details, it will be

44. In my article referred to in note 1. The logical structure of the languages to which the definition in question is applicable is that of the lower functional calculus with individual constants, and with predicate constants of any degree. All sentences of the language are assumed to be formed exclusively by means of predicate constants, individual constants, individual variables, universal and existential quantifiers for individual variables, and the connective symbols of denial, conjunction, alternation, and implication. The use of predicate variables or of the identity sign is not permitted.

As to the predicate constants, they are all assumed to belong to the observational vocabulary, *i.e.* to denote properties or relations observable by means of the accepted techniques. ("Abstract" predicate terms are supposed to be defined by means of those of the observational vocabulary and then actually to be replaced by their definientia, so that they never occur explicitly.)

As a consequence of these stipulations, an observation report can be characterized simply as a conjunction of sentences of the kind illustrated by '$P(a)$', '$\sim P(b)$', '$R(c, d)$', '$\sim R(e, f)$', etc., where 'P', 'R', etc., belong to the observational vocabulary, and 'a', 'b', 'c', 'd', 'e', 'f', etc., are individual names, denoting specific objects. It is also possible to define an observation report more liberally as any sentence containing no quantifiers, which means that besides conjunctions also alternations and implication sentences formed out of the above kind of components are included among the observation reports.

attempted to characterize the definition of confirmation thus obtained as clearly as possible with a minimum of technicalities.

Consider the simple case of the hypothesis H: '$(x)(\text{Raven}(x) \supset \text{Black}(x))$', where 'Raven' and 'Black' are supposed to be terms of our observational vocabulary. Let B be an observation report to the effect that $\text{Raven}(a) \cdot \text{Black}(a) \cdot \sim \text{Raven}(c) \cdot \text{Black}(c) \cdot \sim \text{Raven}(d) \cdot \sim \text{Black}(d)$. Then B may be said to confirm H in the following sense: There are three objects mentioned in B, namely a, c, and d; and as far as these are concerned, B informs us that all those which are ravens (*i.e.* just the object a) are also black.[45] In other words, from the information contained in B we can infer that the hypothesis H does hold true within the finite class of those objects which are mentioned in B.

Let us apply the same consideration to a hypothesis of a logically more complex structure. Let H be the hypothesis 'Everybody likes somebody'; in symbols: '$(x)(Ey)\text{Likes}(x, y)$', *i.e.* 'For every (person) x, there exists at least one (not necessarily different person) y such that x likes y'. (Here again, 'Likes' is supposed to be a relation term which occurs in our observational vocabulary.) Suppose now that we are given an observation report B in which the names of two persons, say 'e' and 'f', occur. Under what conditions shall we say that B confirms H? The previous illustration suggests the answer: If from B we can infer that H is satisfied within the finite class $\{e, f\}$; *i.e.*, that within $\{e, f\}$ everybody likes somebody. This in turn means that e likes e or f, and f likes e or f. Thus, B would be said to confirm H if B entailed the statement 'e likes e or f, and f likes e or f'. This latter statement will be called the development of H for the finite class $\{e, f\}$.

The concept of *development of a hypothesis, H, for a finite class of individuals, C*, can be defined precisely by recursion; here it will suffice to say that the development of H for C states what H would assert if there existed exclusively those objects which are elements of C. Thus, *e.g.*, the development of the hypothesis $H_1 =$'$[(x)(P(x) \mathbf{v} Q(x)]$' (*i.e.* 'Every object has the property P or the property Q') for the class $\{a, b\}$ is '$[P(a) \mathbf{v} Q(a)] \cdot [P(b) \mathbf{v} Q(b)]$' (*i.e.* '$a$ has the property P or the property Q, and b has the property P or the property Q'); the development of the existential hypothesis H_2 that at least one object has the property P, *i.e.* '$(Ex)P(x)$', for $\{a, b\}$ is '$P(a) \mathbf{v} P(b)$'; the development of a hypothesis which contains no quantifiers, such as H_3: '$P(c) \mathbf{v} K(c)$' is defined as that hypothesis itself, no matter what the reference class of individuals is.

A more detailed formal analysis based on considerations of this type leads to the introduction of a general relation of confirmation in two steps; the first

45. I am indebted to Dr. Nelson Goodman for having suggested this idea; it initiated all those considerations which finally led to the definition to be outlined below.

consists in defining a special relation of direct confirmation along the lines just indicated; the second step then defines the general relation of confirmation by reference to direct confirmation.

Omitting minor details, we may summarize the two definitions as follows:

(9.1 Df). An observation report B directly confirms a hypothesis H if B entails the development of H for the class of those objects which are mentioned in B.

(9.2 Df.) An observation report B confirms a hypothesis H if H is entailed by a class of sentences each of which is directly confirmed by B.

The criterion expressed in these definitions might be called the *satisfaction criterion of confirmation* because its basic idea consists in construing a hypothesis as confirmed by a given observation report if the hypothesis is satisfied in the finite class of those individuals which are mentioned in the report.

Let us now apply the two definitions to our last examples: The observation report B_1: '$P(a) . Q(b)$' directly confirms (and therefore also confirms) the hypothesis H_1, because it entails the development of H_1 for the class $\{a, b\}$, which was given above. The hypothesis H_3 is not directly confirmed by B, because its development, *i.e.* H_3 itself, obviously is not entailed by B_1. However, H_3 is entailed by H_1, which is directly confirmed by B_1; hence, by virtue of (9.2), B_1 confirms H_3. Similarly, it can readily be seen that B_1 directly confirms H_2.

Finally, to refer to the first illustration in this section: The observation report 'Raven$(a) \cdot$ Black$(a) \cdot \sim$ Raven$(c) \cdot$ Black$(c) \cdot \sim$ Raven$(d) \cdot \sim$ Black(d)' confirms (even directly) the hypothesis '(x)[Raven$(x) \supset$ Black(x)]', for it entails the development of the latter for the class $\{a, c, d\}$, which can be written as follows: '[Raven$(a) \supset$ Black(a)] $\cdot$ [Raven$(c) \supset$ Black(c)] $\cdot$ [Raven$(d) \supset$ Black(d)]'.

It is now easy to define disconfirmation and neutrality:

(9.3 Df.) An observation report B disconfirms a hypothesis H if it confirms the denial of H.

(9.4 Df.) An observation report B is neutral with respect to a hypothesis H if B neither confirms nor disconfirms H.

By virtue of the criteria laid down in (9.2), (9.3), (9.4), every consistent observation report B divides all possible hypotheses into three mutually exclusive classes: those confirmed by B, those disconfirmed by B, and those with respect to which B is neutral.

The definition of confirmation here proposed can be shown to satisfy all the formal conditions of adequacy embodied in (8.1), (8.2), and (8.3) and their consequences. For the condition (8.2) this is easy to see; for the other conditions the proof is more complicated.[46]

---

46. For these proofs, see the article referred to in note 1. I should like to take this opportunity to point out and to remedy a certain defect of the definition of confirmation which was

(continued overleaf)

Furthermore, the application of the above definition of confirmation is not restricted to hypotheses of universal conditional form (as Nicod's criterion is, for example), nor to universal hypotheses in general; it applies, in fact, to any hypothesis which can be expressed by means of property and relation terms of the observational vocabulary of the given language, individual names, the customary connective symbols for 'not', 'and', 'or', 'if-then', and any number of universal and existential quantifiers.

Finally, as is suggested by the preceding illustrations as well as by the general considerations which underlie the establishment of the above definition, it seems that we have obtained a definition of confirmation which is also materially

developed in that article, and which has been outlined above: this defect was brought to my attention by a discussion with Dr. Olaf Helmer.

It will be agreed that an acceptable definition of confirmation should satisfy the following further condition which might well have been included among the logical standards of adequacy set up in section 8 above: (8.4) If B_1 and B_2 are logically equivalent observation reports and B_1 confirms (disconfirms, is neutral with respect to) a hypothesis H, then B_2, too, confirms (disconfirms, is neutral with respect to) H. This condition is indeed satisfied if observation reports are construed, as they have been in this article, as classes or conjunctions of observation sentences. As was indicated at the end of note 44, however, this restriction of observation reports to a conjunctive form is not essential; in fact, it has been adopted here only for greater convenience of exposition, and all the preceding results, including especially the definitions and theorems of the present section, remain applicable without change if observation reports are defined as sentences containing no quantifiers. (In this case, if 'P' and 'Q' belong to the observational vocabulary, such sentences as '$P(a) \lor Q(a)$', '$P(a) \lor \sim Q(b)$', etc., would qualify as observation reports.) This broader conception of observation reports was therefore adopted in the article referred to in note 1; but it has turned out that in this case, the definition of confirmation summarized above does not generally satisfy the requirement (8.4). Thus, e.g., the observation reports, $B_1 = $ '$P(a)$' and $B_2 = $ '$P(a) \cdot [Q(b) \lor \sim Q(b)]$' are logically equivalent, but while B_1 confirms (and even directly confirms) the hypothesis $H_1 = $ '$(x)P(x)$', the second report does not do so, essentially because it does not entail '$P(a) \cdot P(b)$', which is the development of H_1 for the class of those objects mentioned in B_2. This deficiency can be remedied as follows: The fact that B_2 fails to confirm H_1 is obviously due to the circumstance that B_2 contains the individual constant 'b', without asserting anything about b: The object b is mentioned only in an analytic component of B_2. The atomic constituent '$Q(b)$' will therefore be said to occur (twice) *inessentially* in B_2. Generally, an atomic constituent A of a molecular sentence S will be said to occur inessentially in S if by virtue of the rules of the sentential calculus S is equivalent to a molecular sentence in which A does not occur at all. Now an object will be said to be mentioned inessentially in an observation report if it is mentioned only in such components of that report as occur inessentially in it. The sentential calculus provides mechanical procedures for deciding whether a given observation report mentions any object inessentially, and for establishing equivalent formulations of the same report in which no object is mentioned inessentially. Finally, let us say that an object is mentioned essentially in an observation report if it is mentioned, but not only mentioned inessentially, in that report. Now we replace 9.1 by the following definition:

(9.1*a*) An observation report B directly confirms a hypothesis H if B entails the development of H for the class of those objects which are mentioned essentially in B.

The concept of confirmation as defined by (9.1*a*) and (9.2) now satisfies (8.4 in addition to (8.1, (8.2), (8.3) even if observation reports are construed in the broader fashion characterized earlier in this footnote.

adequate in the sense of being a reasonable approximation to the intended meaning of confirmation.

A brief discussion of certain special cases of confirmation might serve to shed further light on this latter aspect of our analysis.

10. THE RELATIVE AND THE ABSOLUTE CONCEPTS OF VERIFI-CATION AND FALSIFICATION

If an observation report entails a hypothesis *H*, then, by virtue of (8.1), it confirms *H*. This is in good agreement with the customary conception of confirming evidence; in fact, we have here an extreme case of confirmation, the case where *B conclusively confirms H*; this case is realized if, and only if, *B* entails *H*. We shall then also say that *B verifies H*. Thus, verification is a special case of confirmation; it is a logical relation between sentences; more specifically, it is simply the relation of entailment with its domain restricted to observation sentences.

Analogously, we shall say that *B conclusively disconfirms H*, or *B falsifies H*, if and only if *B* is incompatible with *H*; in this case, *B* entails the denial of *H* and therefore, by virtue of (8.1) and (9.3), confirms the denial of *H* and disconfirms *H*. Hence, falsification is a special case of disconfirmation; it is the logical relation of incompatibility between sentences, with its domain restricted to observation sentences.

Clearly, the concepts of *verification and falsification* as here defined are *relative;* a hypothesis can be said to be verified or falsified only with respect to some observation report; and a hypothesis may be verified by one observation report and may not be verified by another. There are, however, hypotheses which cannot be verified and others which cannot be falsified by any observation report. This will be shown presently. We shall say that a given *hypothesis is verifiable (falsifiable)* if it is possible to construct an observation report which verifies (falsifies) the hypothesis. Whether a hypothesis is verifiable, or falsifiable, in this sense depends exclusively on its logical form. Briefly, the following cases may be distinguished:

(*a*) If a hypothesis does not contain the quantifier terms 'all' and 'some' or their symbolic equivalents, then it is both verifiable and falsifiable. Thus, *e.g.*, the hypothesis 'Object *a* turns blue or green' is entailed and thus verified by the report 'Object *a* turns blue'; and the same hypothesis is incompatible with, and thus falsified by, the report 'Object *a* turns neither blue nor green'.

(*b*) A purely existential hypothesis (*i.e.* one which can be symbolized by a formula consisting of one or more existential quantifiers followed by a sentential function containing no quantifiers) is verifiable, but not falsifiable, if—as is usually assumed—the universe of discourse contains an infinite number of objects. Thus, *e.g.*, the hypothesis 'There are blue roses' is verified by the observation report 'Object a is a blue rose', but no finite observation report can ever contradict and thus falsify the hypothesis.

(*c*) Conversely, a purely universal hypothesis (symbolized by a formula consisting of one or more universal quantifiers followed by a sentential function containing no quantifiers) is falsifiable but not verifiable for an infinite universe of discourse. Thus, *e.g.*, the hypothesis '(x)[Swan(x) ⊃ White(x)]' is completely falsified by the observation report {Swan(a), $\sim$ White(a)} ; but no finite observation report can entail and thus verify the hypothesis in question.

(*d*) Hypotheses which cannot be expressed by sentences of one of the three types mentioned so far, and which in this sense require both universal and existential quantifiers for their formulation, are as a rule neither verifiable nor falsifiable.[47] Thus, *e.g.*, the hypothesis 'Every substance is soluble in some solvent' —symbolically '$(x)(Ey)$Soluble(x, y)'—is neither entailed by nor incompatible with any observation report, no matter how many cases of solubility or nonsolubility of particular substances in particular solvents the report may list. An analogous remark applies to the hypothesis 'You can fool some of the people all of the time', whose symbolic formulation '$(Ex)(t)$Fl(x,t)' contains one existential and one universal quantifier. But of course, all of the hypotheses belonging to this fourth class are capable of being confirmed or disconfirmed by suitable observation reports; this was illustrated early in section 9 by reference to the hypothesis '$(x)(Ey)$Likes(x, y)'.

This rather detailed account of verification and falsification has been presented not only in the hope of further elucidating the meaning of confirmation and disconfirmation as defined above, but also in order to provide a basis for a sharp differentiation of two meanings of verification (and similarly of falsification) which have not always been clearly separated in recent discussions of the character of empirical knowledge. One of the two meanings of verification which we wish to distinguish here is the relative concept just explained; for greater clarity we shall sometimes refer to it as *relative verification*. The other meaning is what may be called *absolute or definitive verification*. This latter concept of verification does not belong to formal logic, but rather to pragmatics: it refers to the acceptance of hypotheses by observers or scientists, etc., on the basis of relevant evidence. Generally speaking, we may distinguish three phases in the scientific test of a given hypothesis (which do not necessarily occur in the order in which they are listed here). The first phase consists in the performance of suitable

---

47. A more precise study of the conditions of nonverifiability and nonfalsifiability would involve technicalities which are unnecessary for the purposes of the present study. Not all hypotheses of the type described in (*d*) are neither verifiable nor falsifiable; thus, *e.g.*, the hypothesis '$(x)(Ey)[P(x) \vee Q(y)]$' is verified by the report '$Q(a)$', and the hypothesis '$(x)(Ey)[(P(x) \cdot Q(y)]$' is falsified by '$\sim P(a)$'.

experiments or observations and the ensuing acceptance of observation reports stating the results obtained; the next phase consists in confronting the given hypothesis with the accepted observation reports, *i.e.* in ascertaining whether the latter constitute confirming, disconfirming or irrelevant evidence with respect to the hypothesis; the final phase consists either in accepting or rejecting the hypothesis on the strength of the confirming or disconfirming evidence constituted by the accepted observation reports, or in suspending judgment, awaiting the establishment of further relevant evidence.

The present study has been concerned almost exclusively with the second phase. As we have seen, this phase is of a purely logical character; the standards of evaluation here invoked—namely the criteria of confirmation, disconfirmation and neutrality—can be completely formulated in terms of concepts belonging to pure logic.

The first phase, on the other hand, is of a pragmatic character; it involves no logical confrontation of sentences with other sentences. It consists in performing certain experiments or systematic observations and noting the results. The latter are expressed in sentences which have the form of observation reports, and their acceptance by the scientist is connected (by causal, not by logical relations) with experiences occurring in those tests. Of course, a sentence which has the form of an observation report may in certain cases be accepted, not on the basis of direct observation, but because it is confirmed by other observation reports which were previously established; but this process is illustrative of the second phase, which was discussed before. Here we are considering the case where a sentence is accepted directly "on the basis of experiential findings" rather than because it is supported by previously established statements.

The third phase, too, can be construed as pragmatic, namely as consisting in a decision on the part of a scientist or a group of scientists to accept (or reject, or leave in suspense, as the case may be) a given hypothesis after ascertaining what amount of confirming or of disconfirming evidence for the hypothesis is contained in the totality of the accepted observation sentences. However, it may well be attempted to give a reconstruction of this phase in purely logical terms. This would require the establishment of general "rules of acceptance". Roughly speaking, these rules would state how well a given hypothesis has to be confirmed by the accepted observation reports to be scientifically acceptable itself;[48] *i.e.* the rules would formulate criteria for the acceptance or rejection of a hypothesis by reference to the kind and amount of confirming or disconfirming evidence for it embodied in the totality of accepted observation reports. Possibly, these

---

48. A stimulating discussion of some aspects of what we have called rules of acceptance is contained in an article by Felix Kaufmann, "The Logical Rules of Scientific Procedure", *Philosophy and Phenomenological Research*, June, 1942.

criteria would also refer to such additional factors as the simplicity of the hypothesis in question, the manner in which it fits into the system of previously accepted theories, etc. It is at present an open question to what extent a satisfactory system of such rules can be formulated in purely logical terms.[49]

At any rate, the acceptance of a hypothesis on the basis of a sufficient body of confirming evidence will as a rule be tentative, and will hold only "until further notice," *i.e.* with the proviso that if new and unfavorable evidence should turn up (in other words, if new observation reports should be accepted which disconfirm the hypothesis in question) the hypothesis will be abandoned again.

Are there any exceptions to this rule? Are there any empirical hypotheses which are capable of being established definitively, hypotheses such that we can

---

49. The preceding division of the test of an empirical hypothesis into three phases may prove useful for the clarification of the question whether or to what extent an empiricist conception of confirmation implies a "coherence theory of truth." This issue has recently been raised by Bertrand Russell, who, in chap. x of his *Inquiry into Meaning and Truth*, has levelled a number of objections against the views of Otto Neurath on this subject (*cf.* the articles mentioned in the next footnote), and against statements made by myself in articles published in *Analysis* in 1935 and 1936. I should like to add here a few, necessarily brief, comments on this issue.

(1) While, in the articles in *Analysis*, I argued in effect that the only possible interpretation of the phrase 'Sentence S is true' is 'S is highly confirmed by accepted observation reports', I should now reject this view. As the work of A. Tarski, R. Carnap, and others has shown, it is possible to define a semantical concept of truth which is not synonymous with that of strong confirmation, and which corresponds much more closely to what has customarily been referred to as truth, especially in logic, but also in other contexts. Thus, *e.g.*, if S is any empirical sentence, then either S or its denial is true in the semantical sense, but clearly it is possible that neither S nor its denial is highly confirmed by available evidence. To assert that a hypothesis is true is equivalent to asserting the hypothesis itself; therefore the truth of an empirical hypothesis can be ascertained only in the sense in which the hypothesis itself can be established: *i.e.* the hypothesis—and thereby *ipso facto* its truth—can be more or less well confirmed by empirical evidence; there is no other access to the question of the truth of a hypothesis.

In the light of these considerations, it seems advisable to me to reserve the term 'truth' for the semantical concept ; I should now phrase the statements in the *Analysis* articles as dealing with confirmation. (For a brief and illuminating survey of the distinctive characteristics of truth and confirmation, see R. Carnap, "Wahrheit und Bewährung," *Actes I*^{er} *Congrès Internat. de Philosophie Scientifique* 1935, vol. 4; Paris, 1936).

(2) It is now clear also in what sense the test of a hypothesis is a matter of confronting sentences with sentences rather than with "facts", or a matter of the "coherence" of the hypothesis and the accepted basic sentences: All the logical aspects of scientific testing, *i.e.* all the criteria governing the second and third of the three phases distinguished above, are indeed concerned only with certain relationships between the hypotheses under test and certain other sentences (namely the accepted observation reports); no reference to extra-linguistic "facts" is needed. On the other hand, the first phase, the acceptance of certain basic sentences in connection with certain experiments or observations, involves, of course, extra-linguistic procedures; but this had been explicitly stated by the author in the articles referred to before. The claim that the views concerning truth and confirmation which are held by contemporary logical empiricism involve a coherence theory of truth is therefore mistaken.

be sure that once accepted on the basis of experiential evidence, they will never have to be revoked? Hypotheses of this kind will be called absolutely or definitively verifiable; and the concept of absolute or definitive falsifiability will be construed analogously.

While the existence of hypotheses which are relatively verifiable or relatively falsifiable is a simple logical fact, which was illustrated in the beginning of this section, the question of the existence of absolutely verifiable, or absolutely falsifiable, hypotheses is a highly controversial issue which has received a great deal of attention in recent empiricist writings.[50] As the problem is only loosely connected with the subject of this essay, I shall restrict myself here to a few general observations.

Let it be assumed that the language of science has the general structure characterized and presupposed in the previous discussions, especially in section 9. Then it is reasonable to expect that only such hypotheses can possibly be absolutely verifiable as are relatively verifiable by suitable observation reports; hypotheses of universal form, for example, which are not even capable of relative verification, certainly cannot be expected to be absolutely verifiable. In however many instances such a hypothesis may have been borne out by experiential findings, it is always possible that new evidence will be obtained which disconfirms the hypothesis. Let us, therefore, restrict our search for absolutely verifiable hypotheses to the class of those hypotheses which are relatively verifiable.

Suppose now that *H* is a hypothesis of this latter type, and that it is relatively verified, *i.e.* logically entailed, by an observation report *B*, and that the latter is accepted in science as an account of the outcome of some experiment or observation. Can we then say that *H* is absolutely verified; that it will never be revoked? Clearly, that depends on whether the report *B* has been accepted irrevocably, or whether it may conceivably suffer the fate of being disavowed later. Thus the question as to the existence of absolutely verifiable hypotheses leads back to the question of whether all, or at least some, observation reports become irrevocable parts of the system of science once they have been accepted in connection with certain observations or experiments. This question is not

---

50. *Cf.* especially A. Ayer, *The Foundations of Empirical Knowledge* (New York, 1940); see also the same author's article, "Verification and Experience," *Proceedings of the Aristotelian Society* for 1937. R. Carnap, "Ueber Protokollsätze," *Erkenntnis*, vol. 3 (1932), and § 82 of the same author's *The Logical Syntax of Language* (New York and London, 1937). O. Neurath, "Protokollsätze," *Erkenntnis*, vol. 3 (1932); "Radikaler Physikalismus und "wirkliche Welt,"" *Erkenntnis*, vol. 4 (1934); "Pseudorationalismus der Falsifikation," *Erkenntnis*, vol. 5 (1935). K. Popper, *Logik der Forschung* (see note 3). H. Reichenbach, *Experience and Prediction* (Chicago, 1938), chap. iii. Bertrand Russell, *An Inquiry into Meaning and Truth* (New York, 1940), especially chaps. x and xi. M. Schlick, "Ueber das Fundament der Erkenntnis," *Erkenntnis*, vol. 4 (1934).

simply one of fact; it cannot adequately be answered by a descriptive account of the research behavior of scientists. Here, as in all other cases of logical analysis of science, the problem calls for a rational reconstruction of scientific procedure, *i.e.* for the construction of a consistent and comprehensive theoretical model of scientific inquiry, which is then to serve as a system of reference, or a standard, in the examination of any particular scientific research. The construction of the theoretical model has, of course, to take account of the characteristics of actual scientific procedure, but it is not determined by the latter in the sense in which a descriptive account of some scientific study would be. Indeed, it is generally agreed that scientists sometimes infringe the standards of sound scientific procedure; besides, for the sake of theoretical comprehensiveness and systematization, the abstract model will have to contain certain idealized elements which cannot possibly be determined in detail by a study of how scientists actually work. This is true especially of observation reports. A study of the way in which laboratory reports, or descriptions of other types of observational findings, are formulated in the practice of scientific research is of interest for the choice of assumptions concerning the form and the status of observation sentences in the model of a language of science; but clearly, such a study cannot completely determine what form observation sentences are to have in the theoretical model, nor whether they are to be considered as irrevocable once they are accepted.

Perhaps an analogy may further elucidate this view concerning the character of logical analysis: Suppose that we observe two persons whose language we do not understand playing a game on some kind of chess board; and suppose that we want to "reconstruct" the rules of the game. A mere descriptive account of the playing behavior of the individuals will not suffice to do this; indeed, we should not even necessarily reject a theoretical reconstruction of the game which did not always characterize accurately the actual moves of the players: we should allow for the possibility of occasional violations of the rules. Our reconstruction would rather be guided by the objective of obtaining a consistent and comprehensive system of rules which are as simple as possible, and to which the observed playing behavior conforms at least to a large extent. In terms of the standard thus obtained, we may then describe and critically analyze any concrete performance of the game.

The parallel is obvious; and it appears to be clear, too, that in both cases the decision about various features of the theoretical model will have the character of a convention, which is influenced by considerations of simplicity, consistency, and comprehensiveness, and not only by a study of the actual procedure of scientists at work.[51]

---

51. A clear account of the sense in which the results of logical analysis represent conventions can be found in §§ 9–11 and 25–30 of K. Popper's *Logik der Forschung*.

This remark applies in particular to the question here under consideration, namely whether "there are" in science any irrevocably accepted observation reports (all of whose consequences would then be absolutely verified empirical hypotheses). The situation becomes clearer when we put the question into this form: Shall we allow, in our rational reconstruction of science, for the possibility that certain observation reports may be accepted as irrevocable, or shall the acceptance of all observation reports be subject to the "until further notice" clause? In comparing the merits of the alternative stipulations, we would have to investigate the extent to which each of them is capable of elucidating the structure of scientific inquiry in terms of a simple, consistent theory. We do not propose to enter into a discussion of this question here except for mentioning that various considerations militate in favor of the convention that no observation report is to be accepted definitively and irrevocably.[52] If this alternative is chosen, then not even those hypotheses which are entailed by accepted observation reports are absolutely verified, nor are those hypotheses which are found incompatible with accepted observation reports thereby absolutely falsified: in fact, in this case, no hypothesis whatsoever would be absolutely verifiable or absolutely falsifiable. If, on the other hand, some—or even all—observation sentences are declared irrevocable once they have been accepted, then those hypotheses entailed by or incompatible with irrevocable observation sentences will be absolutely verified, or absolutely falsified, respectively.

It should now be clear that the concepts of absolute and of relative verifiability (and falsifiability) differ fundamentally from each other. Failure to distinguish them has caused considerable misunderstanding in recent discussions on the nature of scientific knowledge. Thus, *e.g.*, K. Popper's proposal to admit as scientific hypotheses exclusively sentences which are (relatively) falsifiable by suitable observation reports has been criticized by means of arguments which, in effect, support the claim that scientific hypotheses should not be construed as being absolutely falsifiable—a point that Popper had not denied. As can be seen from our earlier discussion of relative falsifiability, however, Popper's proposal to limit scientific hypotheses to the form of (relatively) falsifiable sentences involves a very severe restriction of the possible forms of scientific hypotheses.[53] In particular, it rules out all purely existential hypotheses as well as most hypotheses whose formulation requires both universal and existential quantification; and

52. *Cf.* especially the publications by Carnap, Neurath, and Popper mentioned in note 50; also Reichenbach, *loc. cit.*, section 9.

53. This was pointed out by R. Carnap; *cf.* his review of Popper's book in *Erkenntnis*, vol. 5 (1935), and "Testability and Meaning," §§ 25, 26. For a discussion of Popper's falsifiability criterion, see for example H. Reichenbach, "Ueber Induktion und Wahrscheinlichkeit," *Erkenntnis*, vol. 5 (1935); O. Neurath, "Pseudorationalismus der Falsifikation," *Erkenntnis*, vol. 5 (1935).

it may be criticized on this account, for in terms of this theoretical reconstruction of science it seems difficult or altogether impossible to give an adequate account of the status and function of the more complex scientific hypotheses and theories.

What has been said above about the nature of the logical analysis of science in general, applies to the present analysis of confirmation in particular: It is a specific proposal for a systematic and comprehensive logical reconstruction of a concept which is basic for the methodology of empirical science as well as for epistemology. The need for a theoretical clarification of that concept was evidenced by the fact that no general theoretical account of confirmation has been available so far, and that certain widely accepted conceptions of confirmation involve difficulties so serious that it might be doubted whether a satisfactory theory of the concept is at all attainable.

It was found, however, that the problem can be solved: A general definition of confirmation, couched in purely logical terms, was developed for scientific languages of a specified, relatively simple, logical character. The logical model thus obtained appeared to be satisfactory in the sense of the formal and material standards of adequacy that had been set up previously.

I have tried to state the essential features of the proposed analysis and reconstruction of confirmation as explicitly as possible in the hope of stimulating a critical discussion and of facilitating further inquiries into the various issues pertinent to this problem area. Among the open questions which seem to deserve careful consideration, I should like to mention the exploration of concepts of confirmation which fail to satisfy the general consistency condition; the extension of the definition of confirmation to the case where even observation sentences containing quantifiers are permitted; and finally the development of a definition of confirmation for languages of a more complex logical structure than that incorporated in our model.[54] Languages of this kind would provide a greater variety of means of expression and would thus come closer to the high logical complexity of the language of empirical science.

---

54. The languages to which our definition is applicable have the structure of the lower functional calculus without identity sign; it would be highly desirable so to broaden the general theory of confirmation as to make it applicable to the lower functional calculus with identity, or even to higher functional calculi; for it seems hardly possible to give a precise formulation of more complex scientific theories without the logical means of expression provided by the higher functional calculi.

CONFIRMATION

1. ON THE PARADOXES

The views expressed in my essay in regard to the paradoxes still seem sound to me: the "paradoxical" cases have to be counted as confirmatory, or positive, instances; impressions to the contrary may be attributable to factors such as those suggested in section 5.2 Several writers[1] have concurred with this estimate either fully or to a large extent.

A number of commentators[2] have argued, in a manner more or less akin to that of Mrs. Hosiasson-Lindenbaum[3], that on certain assumptions, objective logical differences can be established between paradoxical and nonparadoxical

1. Among them, H. G. Alexander, "The Paradoxes of Confirmation," *The British Journal for the Philosophy of Science*, vol. 9 (1958–59), 227–33; R. Carnap. *Logical Foundations of Probability* (Chicago, 1950), 469; I. J. Good,"The Paradox of Confirmation,"Parts I and II,*The British Journal for the Philosophy of Science*, vol. 11 (1960), 145–48; vol. 12 (1961), 63–64; N. Goodman, *Fact, Fiction, and Forecast* (Cambridge, Mass., 1955), pp. 69–73; J. L. Mackie, "The Paradoxes of Confirmation," *The British Journal for the Philosophy of Science*, vol. 13 (1963), 265–77; I. Scheffler, *The Anatomy of Inquiry* (New York, 1963), Part III. Critical questions have been raised, in the name of Popper's anti-inductivism, for example by J. W. N. Watkins, "Between Analytic and Empirical," *Philosophy*, vol. 32 (1957), 112–31, and "A rejoinder to Professor Hempel's Reply," *Philosophy*, vol. 33 (1958), 349–55; J. Agassi, "Corroboration versus Induction," *The British Journal for the Philosophy of Science*, vol. 9 (1959), 311–17. For a discussion of these and other strictures see Alexander, *loc. cit.*; Hempel, "A Note on the Paradoxes of Confirmation," *Mind*, vol. 55 (1946), 79–82 and "Empirical Statements and Falsifiability," *Philosophy*, vol. 33 (1958), 342–48; Mackie, *loc. cit.*; Scheffler, *loc. cit.*; R. H. Vincent, "The Paradoxes of Confirmation," *Mind*, vol. 73 (1964), 273–79.

2. Among them, Alexander, *loc. cit.*; Good, *loc. cit.*; D. Pears, "Hypotheticals," *Analysis*, vol. 10 (1950), 49–63; G. H. von Wright, *The Logical Problem of Induction* (Oxford, 1957), pp. 122–27.

3. See note 25 of the preceding essay.

instances of generalizations of the form 'All P's are Q's'. The principal requisite assumption is to the effect that there are many more non–Q's than P's (or alternatively, that the probability of an object being a non–Q is much greater than that of its being a P). Several writers presuppose in addition a suitable theory of degrees of confirmation or inductive probabilities, and some also assume that the generalization has a positive initial probability. On such assumptions it is then argued that, for example, examining a nonblack thing for nonravenhood involves much less risk of refuting the generalization 'All ravens are black' than does examining a raven for blackness, and that a positive outcome of the former kind of test has therefore much less importance or weight than a positive outcome of the latter (thus Pears, who does not invoke a theory of degrees of confirmation); or that an instance of a paradoxical kind will increase the prior probability of the generalization by much less than a nonparadoxical one.

Some of these arguments seem to me open to questions such as those suggested in note 25 of my essay. But—and this is the essential point—even if satisfactorily established, such differences in degree between paradoxical and nonparadoxical instances clearly do not refute my diagnosis of the paradoxical cases as confirmatory. My essay is concerned exclusively with the classificatory or qualitative concept of confirmation, and it does not claim that the different kinds of positive instance are all confirmatory to the same degree or that they carry the same weight in testing a generalization.

As for the pragmatic question of why paradoxical cases appear to be nonconfirmatory, Pears[4] may well be right in suggesting that those descriptive words (e.g. 'raven', 'black') which we normally use to formulate our generalizations pick out classes that satisfy (perhaps, better, that are commonly believed to satisfy) the crucial assumption about relative size, and that this in turn explains, in virtue of the kind of argument mentioned before, why paradoxical instances "are thought to provide less confirmation" than nonparadoxical ones. Indeed, as Mackie[5] suggests, it might even explain why to some persons the finding of a nonblack thing that is not a raven seems not to be evidentially relevant at all. This may well constitute a further factor, different from those suggested in section 5.2 of my article, that partly contributes to the impression of paradoxicality.[6]

2. ON THE GENERAL DEFINITION OF CONFIRMATION

My general formal definition of qualitative confirmation now seems to me

---

4. Pears, *loc. cit.*, pp. 51-52.—This was suggested also by Miss Hosiasson-Lindenbaum in footnote 11 of her article.

5. Mackie, *loc. cit.*, pp. 266–67.

6. *Cf.* also the lucid discussion of these issues by Scheffler, *loc. cit.*

rather too restrictive. Here are some of the reasons for this appraisal, in order of increasing importance:

(a) Some hypotheses of the kind covered by my definition, though logically consistent, are not capable of confirmation by any logically consistent observation report. For example, a hypothesis of the form

$$(x) (\exists y) Sxy \cdot (x)(y)(z) [(Sxy \cdot Syz) \supset Sxz] \cdot (x) \sim Sxx$$

can be satisfied only in an infinite domain; its development for any finite class of objects is self-contradictory. Generally, no scientific hypothesis that implies the existence of infinitely many objects can, on my definition, be confirmed by any observation report. This seems worth noting, but it surely constitutes no serious shortcoming of the definition.

(b) My definition qualifies as neutral certain kinds of evidence that would normally be regarded as confirmatory. Thus, as Canfield[7] has pointed out, no finite set of sentences of the type

$$Rab, \ Rbc, \ Rcd, \ Rde, \dots$$

qualifies as confirming the hypothesis

$$H_1: (x)(y)Rxy$$

A report that mentions just the individuals a and b, for example, confirms H_1 only if it implies the development of H_1 for the class $\{a,b\}$, *i.e.*, the sentence

$$Raa \cdot Rab \cdot Rba \cdot Rbb$$

And as the number of individuals mentioned in an observation report increases, the condition the report has to meet if it is to confirm H_1 becomes increasingly stringent. Analogous remarks apply to the case of disconfirmation.

(c) Some writers[8] have argued that the consistency condition for confirmation is too strong, for a reason I had considered, but then set aside, in my comments on that condition in section 8: One and the same observable phenomenon may well be accounted for by each of two incompatible hypotheses, and the observation report describing its occurrence would then normally be regarded as confirmatory for either hypothesis. This point does seem to me to carry considerable weight; but if it is granted, then the consequence condition has to be given up along with the consistency condition. Otherwise, a report confirming each of two incompatible hypotheses would count as confirming any consequence of the two, and thus any hypothesis whatsoever.

---

7. J. Canfield, "On the Paradox of Confirmation," *Metrika*, vol. 5 (1962), 105–18.

8. Particularly Carnap in his detailed exposition and critical analysis of my essay, in sections 87, 88 of *Logical Foundations of Probability* (*cf.* especially pp. 476–78). See also the comment in K. Popper, *The Logic of Scientific Discovery* (London, 1959), p. 374.

For the reasons here briefly surveyed, I believe Carnap is right in his estimate that the concept of confirmation defined in my essay "is not clearly too wide but is clearly too narrow."[9] Accordingly, I think that the criteria specified in my definition may be sufficient, but are not necessary for the confirmation of a hypothesis H by an observation report B.

Perhaps the problem of formulating adequate criteria of qualitative confirmation had best be tackled, after all, by means of the quantitative concept of confirmation. This has been suggested especially by Carnap, who holds that "any adequate explicatum for the classificatory concept of confirmation must be in accord with at least one adequate explicatum for the quantititive concept of confirmation"; i.e., there must be at least one function c that is a suitable explicatum for the concept of logical probability such that whenever B qualitatively confirms H, then $c(H,B) > c(H,t)$, where t is the tautological, or null, evidence.[10] In other words: on some suitable definition of logical probability, the probability of H on B should exceed the *a priori* probability of H whenever B qualitatively confirms H.[11] This general principle leads Carnap also to reject the consequence condition for qualitative confirmation and to restrict the entailment condition to the case where H is not a logical truth.

Finally, I shall discuss quite a different aspect of the problem. In accordance with the objective stated toward the end of section 6, my definition of confirmation is purely syntactical, since for the formalized languages in question the concept of logical consequence, which occurs in the definiens, is characterizable in purely syntactical terms, as are all other concepts used in the definition. But confirmation—whether in its qualitative or in its quantitative form—cannot be adequately defined by syntactical means alone. That has been made clear especially by Goodman,[12] who has shown that some hypotheses of the form '$(x)(Px \supset Qx)$' can obtain no confirmation at all even from evidence sentences of the form '$Pa \cdot Qa$'. To illustrate this, I will adapt Goodman's example to my ornithological paradigm. Let 'x is P' stand for 'x is a raven' and 'x is Q' for 'x is blite', where an object is said to be blite if it has been examined before a certain time t and is black or has not been examined before t and is white. Then any raven observed before t and found to be black affords a formally confirming instance, in the sense of Nicod's criterion, of the hypothesis 'All ravens are blite'.

9. Carnap, *loc. cit.*, p. 479.

10. Carnap, *loc. cit.*, p. 472.

11. As noted by Mackie, several other writers construe confirmation rather in accordance with "the *Inverse Principle*, that a hypothesis h is confirmed by an observation-report b in relation to background knowledge if and only if the observation-report is made more probable by the adding of the hypothesis to the background knowledge" (*loc. cit.*, p. 267; author's italics).

12. Goodman, *loc. cit.*, chapters III and IV.

Yet no matter how many such instances may have been collected, they lend no support or confirmation to the hypothesis; for the latter implies that all ravens not examined before *t*—hence in particular all those that might be examined after *t*—are white, and this consequence must surely count as disconfirmed rather than as confirmed. Whether a universal conditional hypothesis is capable of being confirmed by its positive instances, whether it can be "projected," as Goodman says, from examined cases to unexamined ones, will depend on the character of its constituent predicates; use of the predicate 'blite', for example, precludes projectibility. Goodman traces the difference between predicates that can occur in projectible hypotheses and those that cannot to their "entrenchment," *i.e.*, the extent to which they (or predicates coextensive with them) have been used in previously projected generalizations; 'blite,' for example, never having been so used, is much less well entrenched than such terms as 'black', 'white', and 'raven'. By reference to the comparative entrenchment of the constituent predicates, Goodmen formulates criteria for the comparative projectibility of universal conditional hypotheses, and thus also for their susceptibility to confirmation by formally positive instances.

Thus the search for purely syntactical criteria of qualitative or quantitative confirmation presupposes that the hypotheses in question are formulated in terms that permit projection; and such terms cannot be singled out by syntactical means alone. Indeed, the notion of entrenchment that Goodman uses for this purpose is clearly pragmatic in character.

2. INDUCTIVE

INCONSISTENCIES[1]

1. INTRODUCTION

IN the philosophical study of induction, no task is of greater importance than that of giving a clear characterization of inductive procedures: only when this has been done can the problem of justification significantly be raised. If induction is conceived as a peculiar type of inferential reasoning, its precise characterization will naturally call for the formulation of distinctive rules of inductive inference. A variety of such rules have indeed been set forth in the philosophical literature. But certain quite familiar types of such rules, though widely countenanced even in recent writings on the subject, can be shown to lead into logical inconsistencies. This is the more serious because the defective rules include some which have been held to represent the most basic types of sound inductive reasoning. In this article, I propose to exhibit this defect in two familiar types of induction rules and to examine the sources of the "inductive inconsistencies" they generate. The ideas here set forth are based to a large extent on the work of others, and especially on Carnap's conception of inductive logic and its applications.

2. INCONSISTENCIES GENERATED BY STATISTICAL SYLLOGISMS

One type of inductive inference that leads into inconsistencies is represented by the so-called statistical syllogism and its variants.

1. Written during my tenure, on a United States Government Fellowship, as a Fulbright Research Fellow at the University of Oxford, 1959-60.

This article is reprinted, with slight changes, by kind permission of the General Editorial Committee, from *Synthese* 12, pp. 439-69 (1960).

A statistical syllogism[2] is an argument of the form:

(2.1)
a is F
The proportion of F's that are G is q
Hence, with probability q, a is G

In some variants of this mode of reasoning, the conclusion or also the second premise is expressed in non-numerical terms. Thus, e.g. Toulmin[3] puts forward as valid certain types of argument which he calls quasi-syllogisms, and which take forms such as the following:

(2.2)
a is F
The proportion of F's that are G is less than 2 per cent
So, almost certainly (or: probably) a is not G.

(2.3)
a is F
The proportion of F's that are G is minute
So, almost certainly (or probably,) a is not G.

The inference patterns here listed are applicable only when the reference class F is finite; for only then has the phrase 'the proportion of F's that are G's' a clear meaning. Analogous types of argument which are not subject to this restriction are suggested, however, by the frequency interpretation of statistical probability. In current mathematical theory, statistical probabilities are construed as set-measures governed by certain axioms; and a formula of the form '$p(G, F) = r$', which specifies the statistical probability of set G with respect to set F, asserts, roughly, that the measure of the intersection of G and F, divided by the measure of F, equals r. The application of the mathematical theory to empirical subject matter is effected by the frequency interpretation of statistical probability, which construes '$p(G, F) = r$' as stating the long-run relative frequency, r, with which a "random experiment" of some specified kind F—performed by man or by nature—tends to yield an outcome of kind G. For the case where r is close to 1, this frequency interpretation is usually expressed in in the following form: If $p(G, F)$ is very close to 1, then if an experiment of kind F is performed just once, it is practically certain that a result of kind G will occur.[4]

2. See for, example, D. C. Williams, *The Ground of Induction* (Harvard University Press, 1947); and the discussion of the idea in chap. IV of S. Barker, *Induction and Hypothesis* (Cornell University Press, 1957.)

3. S. Toulmin, *The Uses of Argument* (Cambridge University Press, 1958), pp. 109ff. (For the conclusion-form 'almost certainly, or probably, a is not G', see p. 139).

4. This formulation follows closely those given in H. Cramér, *Mathematical Methods of Statistics* (Princeton University Press, 1946), p. 150, and in A. Wald, *On the Principles of Statistical Inference* (University of Notre Dame, Indiana, 1942), p. 2.

This principle might be thought to authorize the following inference schema, in which the second premise no longer requires the reference class F to be finite:

> *a* is F
>
> (2.4) The statistical probability for an F to be a G is nearly 1
>
> So, it is almost certain that *a* is G.

For convenience, I shall henceforth refer to all the different types of inference just listed, and to certain analogous ones, as *broadly statistical syllogisms*, or briefly as *statistical syllogisms*. Now it is readily seen that all broadly statistical syllogisms lead into inconsistencies because the individual case *a* which the conclusion assigns to the class G (or: to which the conclusion attributes the characteristic, or property, G) will in fact belong to different reference classes, F_1, F_2, ... whose members exhibit G with different relative frequencies or statistical probabilities. For arguments of form (2.1), an example given by Barker[5] illustrates this neatly: Suppose that Jones is a Texan, and that 99 per cent of Texans are millionaires; but that Jones is also a philosopher, and that only 1 per cent of these are millionaires. Then rule (2.1) permits the construction of two statistical syllogisms, both with true premises, which yield the incompatible conclusions that, with probability .99, Jones is a millionaire, and that, with probability .01, Jones is a millionaire.

Consider next Toulmin's example of a quasi-syllogism of form (2.2):[6]

> Petersen is a Swede
>
> (2.5) The proportion of Roman Catholic Swedes is less than 2 per cent
>
> So, almost certainly, Petersen is not a Roman Catholic.

Suppose that the premises of this argument are true. Then, as Cooley[7] has pointed out, the premises of the following quasi-syllogism may well be equally true:

> Petersen made a pilgrimage to Lourdes
>
> (2.6) Less than 2 per cent of those making a pilgrimage to Lourdes are not Roman Catholics
>
> So, almost certainly, Petersen is a Roman Catholic.

5. Barker, *loc. cit.*, p. 76.

6. Toulmin, *loc. cit.*, p. 109.

7. J. Cooley, "On Mr. Toulmin's Revolution in Logic," *The Journal of Philosophy* 56: 297-319 (1959), p. 305. The phrasing of Cooley's example has been slightly modified to make it fit the pattern (2.2) more closely.

Thus, the quasi-syllogistic inference schema can lead from true premises to incompatible conclusions.[8]

To construct an analogous example for the schema (2.4), consider a set of 10,000 balls of which 9,000 are made of glass and are white, while the remaining 1,000 are made of ivory, one of them being white, the other 999, black. Let D be a certain procedure of selecting one of the 10,000 balls. Let us assume that this is a random procedure, so that the statistical probability of obtaining a white ball as a result of D will be $p(W, D) = .9001$. Let the event b be one particular performance of the experiment D. Then (2.4) yields the following argument with true premises:

b is D

(2.7) $p(W, D) = .9001$

Hence, it is almost certain that b is W (i.e. that b yields a white ball).

Suppose now that b yields an ivory ball. Then b may also be regarded as an instance of another experiment, D^*, which consists in selecting at random one of the ivory balls in the given set. But for this experiment, the probability of selecting a nonwhite ball is $p(-W, D^*) = .999$; and schema (2.4) now authorizes the argument:

b is D^*

(2.8) $p(-W, D^*) = .999$

Hence, it is almost certain that b is $-W$ (i.e. that b does not yield a white ball).

Again, we have a pair of rival arguments conforming to the same rule and starting with true premises, and yet leading to incompatible conclusions. Despite its apparent plausibility, then, the construal of certain types of statistical argument as having the form of broadly statistical syllogisms is untenable; for those syllogisms generate *inductive inconsistencies*[9] in the following sense: For an argument with true premises that has the form of a statistical syllogism, there exists

8. While Toulmin repeatedly emphasizes that quasi-syllogisms are *valid*, he later adds the remark: "It must of course be conceded that quasi-syllogisms can properly be advanced only if the initial data from which we argue state all that we know of relevance to the question at issue" (*loc. cit.*, p. 140). This remark, which implies that the argument (2.5) 'can be properly advanced' only if the premises of Cooley's quasi-syllogism are not known to be true, will be considered in section 4 below.

9. In an essay dealing with the explanatory and predictive use of statistical probability statements, I have referred to this peculiarity as the *ambiguity* of statistical explanation and prediction; cf. "Deductive-Nomological *vs.* Statistical Explanation," in H. Feigl and G. Maxwell (eds.) *Minnesota Studies in the Philosophy of Science*, vol. III (Minneapolis: University of Minnesota Press, 1962), pp. 98–169. See also section 3.4 of the essay "Aspects of Scientific Explanation" in the present volume.

in general a rival argument of the same form, again with true premises, whose conclusion is logically incompatible with that of the first argument.

This is true also of an inductive rule of a slightly different kind, which is among those listed by Black in essays dealing with the justifiability of induction. Black formulates it as follows:

R: To argue from *Most instances of A's examined in a wide variety of conditions have been B* to (probably) *The next A to be encountered will be B*.[10]

Black adds that inductive arguments governed by R vary in "strength" according to the number and variety of the favorable instances reported in the premise; so that "although R permits us to *assert a certain conclusion categorically*, . . . the strength of the assertion fluctuates with the character of the evidence."[11] In contrast to broadly statistical syllogisms, then, rule R leads to a conclusion which does not contain a modal qualifier like 'probably' or 'certainly'; yet, the conclusion is supposed to be asserted with more or less 'strength'. Our earlier illustrations show readily that an argument which, in accordance with R, leads from true premises to a very strong assertion of a given conclusion can generally be matched by a rival one, governed by the same rule, which from equally true premises leads to the strong assertion of the contradictory of that conclusion. In this sense, rule R generates inconsistencies.

Deductive forms of inference never generate inconsistencies, of course. In particular, for an argument of the syllogistic form

$$a \text{ is } F$$
(2.9) $$\text{All } F \text{ are } G$$
$$a \text{ is } G$$

whose premises are true, there exists no rival argument of the same form whose premises are true as well, and whose conclusion is logically incompatible with that of the given argument: incompatible conclusions can be deduced only from incompatible premise-sets, and sets of true premises are not incompatible.

3. PROBABILITY: MODAL QUALIFIER OR RELATION?

The inconsistencies just noted do not show, of course, that all nondeductive arguments based on statistical information are unsound, but only that the construal

10. M. Black, "Self-Supporting Inductive Arguments," *The Journal of Philosophy* 55: 718-25 (1958), p. 720 (italics in the originals); see also the same author's "The Inductive Support of Inductive Rules," in M. Black, *Problems of Analysis* (Cornell University Press, 1954), p. 196.

11. Black, "Self-Supporting Inductive Arguments," p. 720 (Italics supplied). Black notes that the rule "as it stands" is not "a wholly acceptable rule for inductive inference" (*ibid.*); but he holds that the rule R can be used in a legitimate inductive argument supporting R itself, and it seems fair, therefore, to assume that the faults he finds with this rule do not include so decisive a defect as that of generating inconsistencies.

of such arguments as quasi-syllogistic is untenable. That construal seems to aim at too close a formal assimilation of nondeductive statistical arguments to deductive inference. Thus, e.g., given that the premises of the deductive syllogism (2.9) are true, the conclusion 'a is G' will "necessarily"—i.e., as a logical consequence—be true as well and can therefore be categorically asserted. In the corresponding statistical arguments, however, the truth of the premises does not thus guarantee the truth of 'a is G'; and if, in analogy to the deductive case, one insists on formulating a sentence which the truth of the premises would entitle us to assert, it may seem tempting to do so by prefixing to 'a is G' a qualifying phrase such as 'it is practically certain that', 'very probably', or 'with probability r'. And this is precisely what is done when statistical arguments are construed as quasi-syllogistic.

That this is a misconstrual becomes clear when we reflect that by the same token we should be able to schematize the deductive syllogism (2.9) in the form

     a is F
(3.1) All F are G
     Hence, certainly (or, necessarily) a is G.

In fact, Toulmin does just this when he puts the syllogistic counterpart of one of his quasi-syllogistic arguments into the form

     Petersen is a Swede
(3.2) No Swedes are Roman Catholics
     So, certainly, Petersen is not a Roman Catholic.[12]

But the certainty here in question is clearly a logical relation between the premises and the conclusion of a deductive argument: the statement 'a is G' is *certain*, or *necessary, relative to the given premises*, i.e., it is logically implied by them. To treat the term 'certainly' in the manner of (3.1) and (3.2), as a qualifier applicable to a single statement, is incorrect: If the logical force of the argument (2.9) is to be expressed with the help of the term 'certain' or its cognates, then it has to be done in an explicitly relativized form, such as this:

(3.3) 'a is G' is certain relative to (i.e., is logically implied by) 'a is F' and 'All F are G'.

To say this is not to deny that the word 'certain' and its cognates can also be used as qualifiers of single statements, in contexts of the form 'it is certain that p', 'certainly p', etc. Let me distinguish three major purposes for which phrases of this kind are used: (i) to claim that the particular statement standing at the place of 'p', or briefly the p-statement, is a logico-mathematical truth or perhaps

12. Toulmin, *loc. cit.*, p. 131.

a nomological one (i.e., a consequence of certain laws of nature), so that we are entitled to assert it categorically and without qualifications; (ii) to claim that the *p*-statement is categorically and unqualifiedly assertable in some more inclusive, and more elusive, sense which is conceived as being governed by objective standards (some would make this claim, for example, for a class of presumptive *a priori* truths thought to include the truths of logic and of mathematics as a proper subclass); (iii) to show—rather than to state—that the utterer of the phrase means to assert the *p*-statement without qualification, and perhaps with special emphasis. But if 'certainly' is understood in the first of these senses, then arguments such as (3.1) and (3.2) are simply fallacious. The same holds true for the second sense of 'certainly'. If, for example, that qualifier is taken to apply to all and only those sentences which are *a priori* truths in some specified sense, then it may well happen that in an argument of the form (3.1) which has true premises, the conclusion, though true, is not an *a priori* truth: hence, in arguments of the form (3.1) the premises then by no means warrant the conclusion. The schema (3.1) could be turned into a sound form of argument by adding the prefix 'certainly' to both of the premises; but the resulting schema would no longer represent the syllogistic argument whose logical structure (3.1) was intended to exhibit. Finally, if the word 'certainly' is taken in the third sense, then its presence is as irrelevant to the logic of the argument as would be the occurrence of such words as 'emphatically', 'fortunately', or 'unexpectedly' in its place.

In sum, then, it is simply incorrect to represent the logical force of a syllogistic argument in the manner of (3.1) or (3.2), where the word 'certainly' plays the role of a modal qualifier of the conclusion: certainty must be construed here as a logical relation, in the manner of (3.3). The fact that the phrasing 'certain relative to . . .', which is used in (3.3), does not occur in ordinary English is not, of course, a flaw of the proposed construal: in fact, it is precisely a too close adherence to phrasings used in everyday discourse which has obscured the logic of the inferences here under consideration.

Analogous remarks apply to statistical arguments of the kind which the notions of statistical syllogism and of quasi-syllogism are intended to illuminate. In the context of such arguments, phrases such as 'it is practically certain that', etc., as well as Black's expression 'strength of assertion', must be construed, not as qualifying the conclusion, but as representing a logical relationship between the premises and the conclusion: they indicate the extent to which the premises support or confirm the (unqualified) conclusion. Thus, e.g., the arguments whose structure the schema (2.2) was meant to exhibit are not to the effect that from the given premises we may validly infer 'Almost certainly, *a* is not *G*', but rather to the effect that those premises lend very strong support to the statement '*a* is not *G*', or that the premises confer upon this statement a very high probability.

Thus, in analogy to (3.3), the arguments which (2.2) was meant to represent might be schematized as follows:

(3.4) 'a is not G' is almost certain (or: is highly probable) relative to the two statements 'a is F' and 'Less than 2 per cent of F's are G'.

The concept of probability here invoked is not, of course, the statistical one, which, as we noted, represents a quantitative relation between two kinds or classes of events, F and G; rather, it is what Carnap has called logical or inductive probability, or degree of confirmation—a concept representing a logical relation between statements. This inductive probability is the central concept of the theories of probability developed by Keynes, Mazurkiewicz, Jeffreys, von Wright, and other writers. It is still a controversial question to what extent the inductive support conferred by an evidence statement e upon a hypothesis h can be represented by a precise quantitative concept $c(h, e)$ with the formal characteristics of a probability. At any rate, Carnap has developed a rigorous general method of defining such a concept which is applicable to formalized languages having the structure of a first-order functional calculus.[13]

But the main point here at issue is independent of the prospects for the development of a precise quantitative theory of inductive logic: If terms such as 'almost certainly', probably", and 'with probability r' are to express the force of the inductive statistical arguments we have been considering then they must be understood, not as qualifiers of single statements, but as representing relations between statements. These relations might be expressed in the manner of (3.4); or, in the framework of a quantitative inductive logic such as Carnap's, in formulas of the form

(3.5) $c(h, e_1 e_2 \ldots e_n) = r$

which indicate that the statements (inductive "premises") $e_1, e_2, \ldots, e_n$ jointly confer the logical probability r upon the statement (inductive "conclusion") h.

In conclusion of this brief comparison of deductive and inductive inference, one further point should be noted: The schematizations (3.3), (3.4), (3.5) are concerned only with the logical connections between the premises and the conclusion and not at all with their truth or falsehood. But since in a deductive argument the conclusion cannot fail to be true if the premises are true, deductive inference rules can be used to effect a transition from given statements which are known or considered to be true to another statement which has the same status; thus, as Carnap puts it,[14] deductive inference rules permit, as it were, the acquisition

---

13. See especially his *Logical Foundations of Probability* (The University of Chicago Press, 1950), section 100; and the generalization in *The Continuum of Inductive Methods* (The University of Chicago Press, 1952).

14. Carnap, *Logical Foundations of Probability*, p. 206.

of new statements on the basis of statements already possessed. In an inductive inference, on the other hand, the "premises" lend only partial support to the "conclusion," and truth is not, therefore, automatically transferred from the former to the latter. Hence even if the premises all belong to the class of statements previously accepted or possessed, the conclusion cannot be added to that class; it can only be qualified by a number representing its probability relative to the premises. In reference to inductive "inferences" or "arguments," therefore, one can speak of a "conclusion" only *cum grano salis*: the conclusion cannot be detached from the premises and asserted on its own when the premises are true. The question whether the detachability of the conclusion of a deductive inference with true premises has at least some weaker analogue in the case of inductive inference will be considered in the final section of this essay.

The idea that in the context of inductive arguments probability has to be construed as a relation has recently been criticized at length by Toulmin, who takes especially Carnap and Kneale to task for holding this view, and who insists, on the contrary, "that 'probably' and its cognates are, characteristically, modal qualifiers of our assertions;" more specifically: "To say 'Probably p' is to assert guardedly, and/or with reservations, that p: it is *not* to assert that you are tentatively prepared to assert that p."[15] Now surely, in ordinary discourse, the word 'probably' and its cognates are often used in this way. We may distinguish here, more precisely, between two purposes which the qualifier in phrases such as 'probably p' may serve: (i) It may show—rather than state—to what extent the speaker is willing to commit himself to p. (If the qualifier has the form 'With probability r', then the quotient $r/(1 - r)$ may indicate the odds at which—for whatever reasons—the speaker is prepared to bet on p); or else (ii) the qualifier may indicate the extent to which it is rationally assertable or credible that p, where rational assertability or credibility is thought of as governed by objective standards. Toulmin does not seem to opt quite unequivocally for one of these two meanings in which 'probably' and its cognates may be used. The following statement of his, for example, suggests the first meaning: "When I say 'S is probably P', I commit myself guardedly, tentatively or with reservations to the view that S is P and (likewise guardedly) lend my authority to that view."[16] However, the second meaning appears to be closer to what Toulmin has in mind; as is suggested, for example by his remark: "Actually, statements about the probability of p are concerned, in practice, with the extent to which we are *entitled* to bank on, take it that, subscribe to, put our weight and our shirts on p ..."[17]

15. Toulmin, *loc. cit.*, pp. 84 and 85. (Author's italics)
16. Toulmin, *loc. cit.*, p. 53.
17. Toulmin, *loc. cit.*, p. 83 (Italics supplied).

But when used in the first sense, qualifiers such as 'probably' clearly cannot serve to exhibit the logic of a statistical argument; and if they are understood in the second sense, then they have to be construed as relative to given grounds. For the credibility of an empirical assertion—in sharp contrast to its truth or falsity—depends on the available evidence; the phlogiston theory of combustion, for example, was much more highly credible on the evidence available before Lavoisier's researches than afterwards. Hence, a phrase of the form 'It is highly credible that p' (or 'probably p', in the sense here under discussion) is not a self-contained statement any more than a phrase of the form 'x is a larger number'. Frequently, expressions of the form 'almost certainly, p','probably p', etc., as used in ordinary discourse, can be regarded as elliptical statements referring to the total evidence available at the time of utterance or at some other time suggested by the context. When we say, for example, 'Probably, there is no life on the moon', the tacit reference is presumably to the evidence available at present. But if the qualifier in the conclusion of a statistical syllogism is thus understood as relative to the total evidence available at the time when the syllogism is presented, the argument is of course invalid: The premises of (2.2), for example, do not warrant the conclusion that on the *total* evidence available, it is very probable that a is not G. The only reasonable construal left is that suggested in (3.4).

Toulmin emphatically rejects this relativization of probability and insists that reference to the total evidence is required only for estimating or measuring the probability of a hypothesis, which itself is a nonrelational characteristic, just as reference to evidence is required to estimate the truth value of a hypothesis.[18] But this analogy is misleading. The truth values, truth and falsity, are nonrelational characteristics of hypotheses; i.e., a phrase of the form 'hypothesis h is true' is a self-contained statement which need not be supplemented by specifying some body of evidence. To estimate whether a given hypothesis h is true or false, we have to refer to the available evidence, say e, which will confer on h a more or less high confirmation, $c(h, e)$: the latter represents the probability of h—or, what comes to the same, the probability that h is true—on the evidence e. This probability will normally change with the evidence, whereas the truth value of h is completely independent of it. Thus, as we noted before, phrases of the form 'h is probable', or 'h has the probability r', are not self-contained statements at all, and it makes no sense therefore to speak of measuring or estimating the probability of h, any more than it makes sense to speak of estimating whether the number 7 is larger. And though Toulmin has interesting things to say about the ordinary use of words like 'probably', his remarks give no clear meaning at all

18. Toulmin, *loc. cit.*, pp. 80–81.

to the notion of probability as a nonrelational concept.[19] In this case, ordinary usage has surely proved to be an unreliable guide.[20]

As soon as, in the schematization of statistical inferences, the concepts of probability, near-certainty, etc., are recognized as relational and the various types of broadly statistical syllogism are accordingly replaced by schemata of the kind suggested in (3.4) and (3.5), one perplexing aspect of statistical arguments vanishes; namely, the impression that statistical arguments make it possible to establish, on the basis of true premises, pairs of incompatible conclusions of such forms as 'Almost certainly (very probably) *a* is *G*' and 'Almost certainly (very probably) *a* is not *G*'. For example, the two apparently conflicting arguments (2.5) and (2.6) do not, as their quasi-syllogistic construal incorrectly suggests, establish the conclusions that Petersen almost certainly is a Roman Catholic, and that he almost certainly is not: rather, the arguments show that relative to *one* set of premises, the statement 'Petersen is a Roman Catholic' is highly probable, whereas its contradictory is highly probable relative to *another* set of premises: and this does not involve a logical inconsistency any more than does the observation that certain sets of premises deductively imply the statement 'Petersen is a Roman Catholic', whereas other sets deductively imply its contradictory.

4. THE REQUIREMENT OF TOTAL EVIDENCE

But while construal in the manner of (3.4) thus removes one puzzling aspect of statistical arguments, it does not fully dispose of the problem raised by the inconsistencies encountered in section 2. The unresolved residual problem is this: If two sets of statements deductively imply contradictory consequences then the statements in the two sets cannot all be true: hence at least one of the arguments is based on some false premises. But, as we noted, if two sets of statements confer very high probabilities upon contradictory conclusions, the statements in the two sets may be all true. Thus, we face the question: Given two valid induc-

---

19. He does say (*loc. cit.*, p. 55): "surely, if I say 'It is probably raining' and it turns out not to be, then. . . I was mistaken;" and later he again qualifies as "paradoxical and inconsistent with our common ways of thinking" the idea that "if I say, 'it is probably raining', the discovery that no rain was falling would not refute my statement." (*loc. cit.*, p. 84). These remarks suggest strongly that in Toulmin's view the statement 'it is probably raining' implies 'it is not the case that it is probably raining'. But then, by contraposition, 'it is probably raining' would imply 'it is raining'. And while this construal would give a strong empirical content to sentences of the form 'probably *p*', it is of course quite unacceptable; and it also conflicts with Toulmin's general observation that "one cannot specify any happening which would conclusively verify or falsify a prediction held out as having only a certain probability" (*loc. cit.*, p.82): thus, his views on the content and on the refutability of non-relativized probability statements remain unclear.

20. For further discussion of the relations between truth, probability, and verification, see Carnap, R. "Truth and Confirmation," and "The Two Concepts of Probability," sec. VI; both in H. Feigl and W. Sellars, (eds.) *Readings in Philosophical Analysis* (New York: Appleton-Century-Crofts, 1949).

tive arguments whose premises have been tested and accepted as presumably true, but whose conclusions—pertaining perhaps to some future event—are logically incompatible: on which, if any, of them are we to base our expectations and decisions? Or, more generally: On the basis of different sets of statements that we consider as true, a given hypothesis h—e.g., a prediction—can be assigned quite different probabilities; which of these, if any, is to count as a guide in forming our beliefs concerning the truth of h and in making decisions whose outcomes depend on whether h is true?

An answer is suggested by a principle to which we have alluded before, and which has in fact been tacitly or explicitly accepted by many writers on inductive reasoning. Carnap calls it *the requirement of total evidence* and formulates it as follows: "In the application of inductive logic to a given knowledge situation, the total evidence available must be taken as a basis for determining the degree of confirmation."[21] Broadly speaking, we might say that according to this requirement, the credence which it is rational to give to a statement at a given time must be determined by the degree of confirmation, or the logical probability, which the statement possesses on the total evidence available at the time. Alternatively, that credence may be determined by reference to any part of the total evidence which gives to the statement the same support or probability as the total evidence: In this case, the omitted portion of the total evidence is said to be *inductively irrelevant* to the statement, relative to the evidence actually used.

For our residual problem, this principle implies the maxim that the support which the premises of a statistical argument confer upon its conclusion can serve to determine the credence rationally to be given to that conclusion or the decisions rationally to be based on it only if the premises constitute either the total evidence e available at the time or else a part of e which supports the conclusion to the same extent as does e.

Compliance with the requirement of total evidence disposes of our residual problem. For suppose we are confronted with two statistical arguments of which one attributes near-certainty to 'a is G', the other to 'a is not G'. Then these arguments cannot both meet the requirement of total evidence. For if they did, the probabilities which their premises confer upon 'a is G' and 'a is not G', respectively, would equal the probabilities which the total evidence confers upon those statements: but one and the same body of evidence, e.g. the total evidence—provided only that it is logically consistent—cannot confer high probabilities on each of two contradictory statements; for the two probabilities add up to 1.

21. Carnap, *Logical Foundations of Probability*, p. 211; cf. also R. Carnap, "On the Application of Inductive Logic," *Philosophy and Phenomenological Research* 8: 133–48 (1947–48), esp. 138–39.

Incidentally, the requirement of total evidence is trivially satisfied by any *deductive* argument whose premises are part of the total evidence. For here, the premises confer certainty, and thus the logical probability 1, upon the conclusion; but so does the total evidence available since, by hypothesis, it includes the premises of the given argument.[22]

At this point, let us consider briefly a criticism which Ayer[23] has levelled against the principle of total evidence and indeed against the conception of inductive probability as a logical relation between statements. Ayer notes that according to Keynes, Kneale, Carnap, and certain other authors, probability statements are nonempirical: if they are true, they are necessarily true; if false, necessarily false. This feature is especially clear in Carnap's theory of inductive probability, according to which any statement of the form '$c(h, e) = r$', which is the basic form of an inductive probability statement, is either analytic or self-contradictory. Now, if for h we choose some fixed hypothesis, such as that our favorite horse will win tomorrow's race, then, Ayer points out, we can assign to it many different probabilities simply by taking into account more and more of the relevant evidence. But since each of these probability statements would constitute a necessary truth, none of them can be regarded as superior to the others. "The addition of more evidence may, indeed, yield a higher or lower probability for the statement in which we are interested. But . . . this probability cannot be said to be more, or less, correct than the one which was yielded by the evidence with which we started."[24] The difficulty here adumbrated is closely related to the residual problem mentioned at the beginning of this section; and Ayer notes Carnap's proposal to meet it by means of the principle of total evidence. But while granting that this principle seems to accord, to some extent, with common sense, Ayer questions the possibility of justifying it "on Carnap's principles," precisely because a true probability statement concerning h which is not based on the total evidence is no less analytic than is one that does meet the requirement of total evidence.

But this demand for a justification of the total-evidence requirement in terms of the principles of inductive logic is beside the point; for, as Carnap notes, the principle of total evidence "is not a rule of inductive logic, but of the methodology of induction."[25] More explicitly, we might say that the principle specifies a necessary, though not sufficient, condition for the rationality of inductive

---

22. On this point, see also Carnap, *Logical Foundations of Probability*, p. 211.

23. A. J. Ayer, "The conception of probability as a logical relation." S. Körner, (ed.) *Observation and Interpretation. Proceedings of the Ninth Symposium of the Colston Research Society* (New York and London, 1957), pp. 12-17.

24. Ayer, *loc. cit.*, p. 14.

25. Carnap, *Logical Foundations of Probability*, p. 211. On Carnap's conception of the methodology of induction, see also pp. 202-205 of the same work.

beliefs and decisions. Certain conditions of rationality can be formulated also for the application of deductive reasoning (though, as we noted, the requirement of total evidence is trivially satisfied in this case); for example, rationality of belief requires that if a set of statements is accepted as presumably true, or as expressing presumably true beliefs, then any logical consequence of that set must be accepted as well. This is not a principle of formal logic, however. Formal logic tells us that if a given set of statements is true then such and such other statements are true as well; but it does not tell us what statements to believe or to act on. Indeed, the notion of accepting certain statements, like the notion of total evidence, is pragmatic in character and cannot be defined in terms of the concepts of formal deductive or inductive logic.

But if the requirement of total evidence cannot be justified by the principles of formal inductive logic, on what grounds can it be advocated? One might well say that it is simply a partial explication of conditions governing rational belief and rational choice. Thus, Carnap constructs an example in which the requirement is violated and rightly points out that everybody would regard this violation as a serious mistake in inductive reasoning.[26] It might be added, in the same vein, that if we allowed ourselves to depart from this requirement, we would sometimes be led to give high credence to statements which the available evidence told us were false. For example, we might give high credence to the generalization 'Any egg that hatches yields a chicken' as a result of limiting our evidence to that subset of our total evidence e pertaining to hens' eggs only, and thus disregarding further information, also included in e, about birds hatched from other kinds of eggs, which would show our generalization to be false. And while, of course, it is to be expected that inductive arguments from available evidence will sometimes lead us to give high credence to statements which, unbeknownst to us, are in fact false, rationality surely demands that high credibility must not be assigned to a statement that is known to be false, or, more precisely, to a statement that is logically incompatible with accepted evidence statements.

The practical application of the requirement of total evidence faces considerable difficulties, for our total information is always so comprehensive and complex that it cannot be expressed in two statements having the simple form of the premises in schemata such as (3.4); indeed, it is vastly more complex than the kind of evidence contemplated in any of the theorems of inductive logic that are now available. But as Carnap notes, a theorem of inductive logic—and any such theorem provides a schema for valid inductive arguments—"can nevertheless be applied indirectly, provided the additional knowledge is, at least approximately, irrelevant for the hypothesis in question."[27] I have tried to

---

26. Carnap, "On the Application of Inductive Logic," p. 139.
27. Carnap, loc. cit., p. 494.

show elsewhere[28] that empirical science does indeed present us with various explanatory and predictive arguments of a fairly simple statistical character which meet the requirement of total evidence at least in an intuitively clear sense.

As was noted earlier, Toulmin, too, invokes a principle of total evidence: While he insists that all quasi-syllogisms in his sense are valid—their validity, like that of deductive syllogisms is said to be "manifest" and "surely not open to doubt"[29]—he later remarks that "quasi-syllogisms can properly be advanced only if the initial data from which we argue state all that we know of relevance to the question at issue. If they represent no more than a part of our relevant knowledge, we shall be required to argue not categorically but hypothetically— 'Given only the information that Petersen is a Swede, we might conclude that the chances of his being a Roman Catholic were slight ...' "[30] It is not made very clear what is meant by validity here nor in what sense and for what reasons a quasi-syllogism, though valid, "can properly be advanced" only if it meets the requirement of total evidence. The latter part of the passage just quoted seems to suggest that in Toulmin's opinion the conclusion of a quasi-syllogism (including its qualifier 'probably', 'almost certainly', etc.) can be unconditionally asserted if that requirement is met. But then his allegedly nonrelative probability statements would seem to amount to elliptically stated relative probability statements referring to the total evidence available; and on this construal, his quasi-syllogisms would normally be invalid, as was shown in section 3. But, as we have noted, Toulmin rejects the interpretation of his probability statements as elliptic and holds instead that the support which the total evidence gives to a hypothesis provides the best *estimate* of *the* probability of the hypothesis. But this leaves us with the question what it is that is supposedly estimated in this manner; and, as was mentioned earlier, it remains obscure precisely what meanings Toulmin attributes to such locutions as '*h* is almost certain', '*h* is probable', 'the probability of *h*', and 'the client's 'real' chance of living to eighty'.[31]

5. INCONSISTENCIES GENERATED BY ELEMENTARY INDUCTION RULES

Let us now turn to another class of presumptive induction rules that generate inconsistencies. These rules are of special interest because they are widely thought to represent the most elementary and fundamental modes of inductive reasoning: we will therefore refer to them as "elementary induction rules."

28. Hempel, "Deductive-Nomological *vs.* Statistical Explanation," section 11; "Aspects of Scientific Explanation," section 3.

29. Toulmin, *loc. cit.*, pp. 131, 132.

30. Toulmin, *loc. cit.*, p. 140.

31. Toulmin, *loc. cit.*, p. 71.

Here are two examples, the first of which expresses the presumptive form of inductive reasoning by simple enumeration:

(5.1) To argue from *All examined instances of A's have been B* to *All A's are B*.[32]

(5.2) If among the n observed instances of A's, m have been found to be instances of B, expect that m/n A's are B. Meanwhile, however, continue to search for further instances of A and constantly modify the estimated ratio (m/n) as new data accumulate.[33]

Suppose now that in order to ascertain how a certain physical magnitude y (e.g., the length of a metal bar) varies with another physical magnitude x (e.g., the temperature of the bar), the associated values of x and y have been measured in n cases: let (x_1, y_1), (x_2, y_2), . . ., (x_n, y_n) be the pairs of associated values thus established. Then the n points whose Cartesian coordinates are given by these number pairs can be connected by infinitely many different curves $C_1, C_2, . . .,$ each of which represents the values of y as a certain function of the values of x; let us say, $y = F_1(x); y = F_2(x); . . .$ Now let A be the class of all the pairs of physically associated values of the magnitudes x and $y;$ then, on our assumptions, it is true to say:

(5.3) All of the n examined instances of A's satisfy the formula '$y = F_1(x)$'.

Hence, rule (5.1) directs us to infer the general law

(5.3a) All A's satisfy the formula '$y = F_1(x)$'.

But on our assumptions, it is equally true to say:

(5.4) All of the n examined instances of A's satisfy the formula '$y = F_2(x)$'

which by (5.1), yields the conclusion

(5.4a) All A's satisfy the formula '$y = F_2(x)$';

and so forth.

Thus, on the basis of the same empirical data, namely, the n measurements of physically associated values of x and y, the rule (5.1) yields infinitely many different presumptive laws, each representing y as a certain mathematical function of x. Furthermore, since no two of the considered functions are identical, there are certain values of x to which F_1 and F_2, for example, assign different values of y; hence, the generalizations (5.3a) and (5.4a) are logically incompatible with each other; and so are any other two of the generalizations obtainable by means of (5.1).

The rule (5.2) yields inductive inconsistencies in the same way. To see this, it suffices to note that (5.2) yields (5.1) for the case where $m = n$; but inconsistencies can also be shown to arise when m is less than n.

Essentially the same argument applies to Reichenbach's basic rule of induction:

32. M. Black, "The Inductive Support of Inductive Rules", p. 196.

33. M. Black, "'Pragmatic' Justifications of Induction", in M. Black, *Problems of Analysis*, p. 164.

(5.5) If an initial section of n elements of a sequence x_i is given, resulting in the frequency f^n, and if, furthermore, nothing is known about the probability of the second level for the occurrence of a certain limit p, we posit that the frequency $f^i(i > n)$ will approach a limit p within $f^n \pm \delta$ when the sequence is continued.[34]

Indeed, let the initial segment consist of our pairs $(x_1, y_1), (x_2, y_2), \ldots, (x_n, y_n)$ obtained by measurement. Among them, the relative frequency of those exhibiting the functional relationship F_1 is 1; but so is the relative frequency of those pairs exhibiting the functional relationships F_2, F_3, and so forth. Hence, assuming that nothing is known as yet about what Reichenbach calls second-level probabilities, the rule directs us to posit that if the measurement of physically associated values of x and y is continued beyond the initial n cases, the proportion of pairs conforming to F_1 will approach a limit which falls within $1—\delta$; and that the same is true of the proportion of pairs conforming to F_2, F_3, and so forth. And though it is not the case that each of these limit statements is logically incompatible with each of the others, it can readily be seen that there still are infinitely many pairs of logically incompatible statements among the posits thus obtained. Thus, rule (5.5), too, leads from true premises to a logically inconsistent set of conclusions.

The inconsistencies here noted are of significance also for the idea that all inductive reasoning presupposes a principle of the uniformity of nature which, when used as a supreme major premise, can turn inductive arguments into deductive or "quasi-deductive" ones.[35] It is well known that attempts to give a suitable formulation of the principle in question encounter serious difficulties. The statement, for example, that what has happened in the past will, under the same circumstances, happen again in the future, is clearly inadequate. If it is understood to require full identity of all attending circumstances, then the rule is inapplicable since the same circumstances simply do not recur; if sameness of only the 'relevant' circumstances is required, the principle is a truism, for any apparent departure from it can then be attributed to a difference in some relevant factor not recognized as such. A formulation which avoids these shortcomings and which also would seem to express much more precisely the intent of the uniformity principle is this:

34. H. Reichenbach, *The Theory of Probability* (University of California Press, 1944), p. 446.

35. The idea, which is familiar from Mill's work, has recently been advocated, for example, by H. G. Alexander in his contribution to the symposium "Convention, Falsification and Induction" in *The Aristotelian Society*, Supplementary Volume 34 (London, 1960). Alexander stresses, however, that several such presuppositions are involved in inductive resaoning, and he suggests that if these are taken into account, inductive reasoning in science would take a "quasi-deductive form: 'Quasi-deductive' because it is impossible to state these presuppositions in a completely precise form." (*loc. cit.*, p. 140).

(5.6) A generalization which has been borne out in all instances so far examined
      will be borne out also in all further instances.

But this principle is self-contradictory. For when applied to our example, it
implies that all the pairs of physically associated values of x and y satisfy the formula '$y = F_1(x)$', but also the formula '$y = F_2(x)$', and so forth, since the n pairs
so far measured satisfy all of those formulas.

The method we used to generate inconsistencies by means of elementary induction rules is akin to that employed by Goodman in posing his "new riddle of
induction."[36] One of the examples characteristic of his approach is this: Suppose
that according to our total evidence at a certain time t, all emeralds that have
been examined so far (i.e., before t) are green. Then, according to standard conceptions of confirmation, the total evidence supports the generalization h_1: 'All
emeralds are green'. Now let 'grue' be a predicate that applies to objects examined
before t just in case they are green and to other objects just in case they are blue.
Then, according to the total evidence at t, all emeralds observed so far are grue;
hence, the total evidence also supports the generalization h_2: 'All emeralds are
grue'. But when applied to emeralds examined after t, the two hypotheses thus
supported yield the conflicting predictions that all those emeralds will be green,
and that they will all be grue and hence blue. Goodman remarks: "Thus although we are well aware which of the two incompatible predictions is genuinely
confirmed, they are equally well confirmed according to our present definition.[37]
He suggests that the total evidence genuinely confirms h_1 rather than h_2 because
the former is a "lawlike statement" (i.e., has the characteristics of a law except
for possibly being false), whereas the latter is not; and because only a statement that is lawlike is capable of receiving confirmation from its established
instances. Thus, there arises the new riddle of induction, namely the problem
of stating clearly "what distinguishes lawlike or confirmable hypotheses from
accidental or non-confirmable ones."[38] Goodman notes that only to the extent
that this problem is solved can we make a distinction between valid and invalid
inductive inferences; and he then outlines his "theory of projection" which distinguishes between confirmable and nonconfirmable hypotheses in terms of the
"entrenchment" of the predicates used in their formulation.[39]

   While Goodman couches his discussion in terms of confirmation rules,
it is readily seen that his hypothesis–pairs can also be used to show that the
elementary induction rules mentioned above can lead from a consistent body
of total evidence to an inconsistent set of conclusions: herein lies the affinity

---

36. See N. Goodman, *Fact, Fiction, and Forecast* (Harvard University Press, 1955), pp. 73ff.
37. Goodman, *loc. cit.*, p. 75.
38. Goodman, *loc. cit.*, p. 80.
39. Goodman, *loc. cit.*, chap. IV.

between Goodman's argument and the one we used at the beginning of the present section. The latter, however, seems to add a new facet to the important problem raised by Goodman. For one may well be inclined to agree that a generalization such as 'All emeralds are grue' is not lawlike, and that its applicability to as yet unexamined cases is not attested to by its previously established instances; but among the conflicting generalizations obtainable in the manner of our earlier example, there are many which would seem to be equally lawlike, and thus equally capable of confirmation by their instances; and if this is so, then none of these incompatible generalizations would be ruled out by restricting permissible inductive conclusions to lawlike statements. (And indeed, Goodman's rules are not intended to arbitrate between well-confirmed but incompatible lawlike hypotheses.)

Suppose, for example, that the pairs of associated values of x and y measured so far are: $(0,-1)$; $(1, 0)$; $(2, 1)$. These satisfy the following generalizations, among others:

(5.7)
$$y = (x-1); y = (x-1)^3; y = (x-1)^5; \ldots$$

$$y = \cos \pi \left(1 - \frac{x}{2}\right); y = (x-1)^2 \cos \pi \left(1 - \frac{x}{2}\right); \ldots$$

$$y = (x-1)^4 \cos \pi \left(1 - \frac{x}{2}\right); \ldots$$

Each of these pairwise incompatible generalizations represents, I think, a perfectly good lawlike statement, capable of confirmation by established instances. Hence by restricting the use of our elementary induction rules to the cases where the conclusion is a lawlike statement, we may well eliminate inductive inconsistencies of the kind constructed by Goodman, but we will still be left with inconsistent sets of hypotheses of the kind illustrated by (5.7).

In philosophical discussions of the justifiability of inductive procedures, rules of the kind considered in this section are often treated as essentially adequate, if perhaps somewhat oversimplified, formulations of norms of inductive reasoning;[40] we now see that the problem of justification does not even arise for those elementary induction rules; for they lead into logical inconsistencies and thus violate what surely is the very minimum requirement that any proposed rule of scientific procedure must meet before the question of its justification can be raised.

---

40. Black, for example, formulates his various rules of induction in order to provide a clear characterization of the principles or policies whose justifiability is in question; and Reichenbach's ingenious argument aimed at a justification of induction deals specifically with his rule considered above, which is held to represent the fundamental principle of inductive procedure.

Are the inconsistencies here encountered attributable again to a violation of the requirement of total evidence? At first glance, this seems implausible; for the rules (5.1) and (5.2), as well as the principle (5.6), include what appears to be a simple version of that requirement, namely, the proviso that the given information must cover all the instances so far examined; and rule (5.5) may be understood as presupposing that condition as well. And in the examples just considered of contradictions generated by elementary induction rules, the proviso in question was always assumed to be satisfied.

However, as is illustrated by the paradoxes of confirmation,[41] the concept of the 'instances' of a nonsingular hypothesis is by no means as clear as it may seem, and there are good reasons to think, therefore, that the requirement of total evidence cannot be adequately expressed by the condition that the evidence must include all the instances so far observed. And indeed, in reference to two other examples constructed by Goodman, Carnap has argued that they do involve a violation of the requirement of total evidence.[42] For the example mentioned above, Carnap's objection would take this form: In the case of the prediction that the next emerald will be grue, *more* is known than that the emeralds so far observed were all grue, i.e., that they were either examined before t and were green or were not examined before t and were blue: it is known that they were all examined before t. And failure to include this information in the evidence violates the requirement of total evidence.

But an inductive logic constructed in accordance with Carnap's conception would avoid our inconsistencies for yet another reason: According to that conception, as was pointed out in section 3 above, an inductive argument must be construed as showing that the information given in the evidence, which forms the premises, lends more or less strong inductive support to the conclusion; and thus construed, inductive inference does not lend itself to the categorical establishment of the conclusion even if the premises are known to be, or are accepted as, true statements. Hence, the possibility of positing or accepting incompatible statements as the result of inductive inferences does not arise.

But perhaps, in an inductive logic thus conceived, the difficulty posed by the inconsistencies would simply appear in a different form? For example, if the information on the many emeralds observed so far shows them all to have been both green and grue, does it not stand to reason that this information should

41. Cf. C. G. Hempel, "Studies in the Logic of Confirmation," *Mind* 54: 1-26 and 97-121 (1945); especially section 5. (Reprinted in this volume.)

42. Cf. N. Goodman, "A Query on Confirmation," *The Journal of Philospohy* 43: 383-85 (1946); Carnap, "On the Application of Inductive Logic," section 3: and Goodman's reply, "On Infirmities of Confirmation Theory," *Philosophy and Phenomenological Research* 8: 149-51 (1947).

confer a high probability on each of the two incompatible predictions 'the first emerald examined after *t* will be green' and 'the first emerald examined after *t* will be grue'? Again, the answer is in the negative. For as a consequence of the basic postulates for inductive probability, the sum of the probabilities which a logically consistent set of statements—e.g., the total evidence at *t*—confers upon two logically incompatible hypotheses is at most 1; hence, if one of the probabilities is close to 1, the other must be close to 0.

6. ON RULES OF RATIONAL DECISION AND BELIEF

The elementary induction rules considered in the previous section construe inductive reasoning as leading to the acquisition of new statements on the basis of given ones. In this respect, they accord well with the familiar conception that inductive procedures, at the common sense and at the scientific levels, lead to the *acceptance* of certain empirical hypotheses on the basis of evidence that gives them more or less strong, but not, as a rule, logically conclusive, support. The body of scientific knowledge at a given time would then be represented by the set of all statements accepted by science at that time. Membership in this set would be granted to a hypothesis, however well confirmed, only until further notice, i.e., with the understanding that the privilege may be withdrawn if evidence unfavorable to the hypothesis should appear in the future.

The rejection of our elementary induction rules thus naturally suggests the question whether there is not some consistent alternative way of construing this conception of scientific knowledge and, more specifically, the notion of rules authorizing the addition of sufficiently supported "new" empirical hypotheses to the set of previously accepted ones. This question clearly belongs to what Carnap calls the methodology of induction: it concerns the application of inductive logic to the formation of rational beliefs. It seems of interest, therefore, to inquire whether the question might not be treated as a special case of another, very general, problem of application which has received a great deal of attention in recent years, namely, the problem of formulating rules for rational choice or decision in the face of several alternatives: the acceptance of a hypothesis might then be construable as a case of theoretical choice between alternative hypotheses.

The problem of rational decision rules has recently been dealt with in the statistical theory of decision–making and the theory of games, which do not make use of the concept of inductive probability, and it has also been investigated from the point of view of inductive logic. Here, I will limit myself to a brief consideration of Carnap's approach to the question. On the assumption that a system of inductive logic in Carnap's sense is available, the problem of rational choice can be posed in the following schematic form: An agent *X* has to choose one out of n courses of action, A_1, A_2,. . ., A_n, which, on his total evidence e, logically exclude each other and jointly exhaust all the possibilities open to him. The agent contemplates a set O_1, O_2,. . ., O_m of different possible "outcomes" which, on e, are mutually exclusive and jointly exhaustive (i.e., e logically implies that exactly one of these outcomes will come about). Then, for any one of those actions, say A_j, and any one of those outcomes, say O_k, the given system of inductive logic determines a probability for the hypothesis that, given e, A_j will lead to the outcome O_k. Indeed, if a_j and o_k are statements describing A_j and O_k respectively, that probability is given by $c\,(o_k, e \cdot a_j)$.

What course of action it is rational for X to choose in the given circumstances will depend, of course, on what his objectives are; or, putting it more broadly, what value or disvalue he attaches to the various outcomes that might occur as a result of his action. In many theoretical studies of rational decision-making, and in particular in Carnap's treatment of the problem, it is assumed that the values and disvalues in question can be represented by a quantitative concept of utility, i.e., a function u assigning to each possible outcome O_k a real number $u(O_k)$, or briefly u_k, which indicates the utility of outcome O_k for X. The task of specifying operational criteria for this concept of utility—i.e., in effect, of specifying methods of measuring the utilities of possible outcomes (which may be very complex) for a given person—raises difficult problems, which have been the object of much theoretical and experimental work in recent years;[43] in the present context however, we need not enter into these issues.

The problem to be solved now calls for the formulation of a general decision rule such that, given any e and any set of A_j and O_k which meet the conditions mentioned above, and given also the utilities attached to the O_k, the rule will determine which of the available courses of action it is rational to adopt in the given circumstances. Carnap adopts a rule which directs the agent to choose an action which offers him the highest expectation of utility. The expectation value, or the probability-estimate, of the utility associated with action A_j is given by the formula

(6.1) $u'(A_j, e) = c(o_1, e \cdot a_j) \cdot u_1 + \ldots + c(o_m, e \cdot a_j) \cdot u_m,$

and Carnap's rule may be stated as follows:

(6.2) *Rule of maximizing the estimated utility:* In the specified circumstances, choose a course of action for which the estimate of the resulting utility is

---

43. For details and further bibliographic references see, for example, Carnap, *Logical Foundations of Probability*, section 51; J. von Neumann and O. Morgenstern, *Theory of Games and Economic Behavior* (Princeton University Press, 2nd ed., 1947); L. J. Savage, *The Foundations of Statistics* (New York, Wiley, 1954), chap. 5; R. D. Luce and H. Raiffa, *Games and Decisions* (New York, Wiley, 1957), chap. 2; R. B. Braithwaite, *Scientific Explanation* (Cambridge University Press, 1953), chap. VII.

a maximum, i.e., is not exceeded by the utility estimates associated with any of the alternative courses of action.[44]

In an attempt to apply this maxim to the problem of acceptance rules for scientific hypotheses, let us suppose now that a scientist has at his disposal the set of all statements accepted by science at the time, which we may assume to be expressed in the form of one complicated sentence e; that he has invented, or has been presented with, a set of n hypotheses, $h_1, h_2, \ldots, h_n$, which, on e, are pairwise incompatible while jointly exhausting all possibilities (i.e., e logically implies the negation of the conjunction of any two of the hypotheses, as well as the disjunction of all of them); and that he has to choose one from among the following $n + 1$ courses of action: To accept h_1 and add it to e; ...; to accept h_n and add it to e; to accept none of the n hypotheses and thus to leave e unchanged. The problem is to construct a rule that will determine which choice it is rational to make. Clearly, this approach to the problem of rules for rational inductive acceptance does not involve the kind of narrowly inductivist conception of scientific research which, though hardly espoused nowadays, has been made a flogging horse by some writers on scientific procedure; more specifically, we are not envisaging a rule which, given some empirical evidence, will make it possible inductively to *infer* "the," or even a, hypothesis or theory that will account for, or explain, the given evidence. Rather, it is assumed here that several rival hypotheses have been proposed; the invention of such hypotheses requires, in general, scientific inventiveness and, in important cases, great genius; it cannot be achieved by the use of mechanical induction rules. The inductive problem here considered is rather that of deciding, on the available evidence— which may include the results of extensive tests—which, if any, of the proposed hypotheses is to be accepted and thus to be added to the *corpus* of scientific knowledge.

Now, Carnap's decision principle (and analogously also such policies as the minimax principle developed in the theory of games and statistical decisions[45]) requires, as a basis for a rational decision, a specification both of the total evidence and of the utilities attached to the various possible outcomes of the contemplated actions. In our case, the possible outcomes may be described as: enlarging e by h_1 where h_1 is true; enlarging e by h_1 where h_1 is false; ...; enlarging e by h_n where h_n is true; enlarging e by h_n where h_n is false; leaving e unchanged. What utilities are we to assign to these outcomes? This much is clear: the utilities should reflect the value or disvalue which the different outcomes have from the point of view of pure scientific research rather than the practical advantages or disadvantages

44. Cf. Carnap, *Logical Foundations of Probability*, p. 269.
45. Cf. Carnap's remarks in section 98 of *Logical Foundations of Probability*, and the literature listed in note 43.

that might result from the application of an accepted hypothesis, according as the latter is true or false. Let me refer to the kind of utilities thus vaguely characterized as *purely scientific*, or *epistemic, utilities*.

Construing the proverbial "pursuit of truth" in science as aimed at the establishment of a maximal system of true statements, we might try as a first step to measure the utility of adding a hypothesis h to e in terms of the strength of that part of the information contained in h which is not contained in e, and which thus goes beyond what has been previously established. This new information contained in h is expressed by the sentence $h \vee -e$. For h is equivalent to $(h \vee e) \cdot (h \vee -e)$; the first of the two conjoined sentences follows from h as well as from e and thus represents information given by h as well as by e; the second of the conjoined sentences follows from h and thus expresses part of the information given by h, but it has no content in common with e since its disjunction with e is a logical truth.

To represent the amount, or the strength, of the information given by a sentence, we use the concept of a *content measure* for the sentences of a (suitably formalized) language L. By such a content measure, we understand any function m which assigns to every sentence s of L a number $m(s)$ in such a way that (i) $m(s)$ is a number in the interval from 0 to 1, inclusive of the endpoints; (ii) $m(s)$ $= 1$ if s is logically false (self-contradictory); (iii) if s_1 and s_2 have no common content—i.e., if the sentence $s_1 \vee s_2$, which expresses their common content, is a logical truth—then $m(s_1.s_2) = m(s_1) + m(s_2)$; (iv) if s_1 and s_2 are logically equivalent then $m(s_1) = m(s_2)$. Content measures in this sense can readily be constructed for certain kinds of formalized language.[46]

Suppose now that m is a content measure for a formalized language of empirical science. Then we might tentatively set the utility of adding h to e equal to $m(h \vee -e)$ if h is true, and equal to $- m(h \vee -e)$ if h is false. More generally, taking account of the principle of diminishing marginal utility, we might set the utility of adding h to e directly proportional to the amount of new information provided by h, or to the negative value of that amount, according as h is true or false; and inversely proportional to the amount of information already contained in e. This would yield the following definition:

(6.3) *Relative–content measure of purely scientific utility:* The purely scientific utility of adding h to e is $k.m(h \vee -e)/m(e)$ when h is true, and the negative of this value when h is false; k being some positive constant.

46. For specific examples see C. G. Hempel and P. Oppenheim, "Studies in the Logic of Explanation," *Philosophy of Science* 15: 135-75 (1948) (reprinted in this volume), especially sections 8 and 9; and R. Carnap and Y. Bar-Hillel, "An Outline of a Theory of Semantic Information," Massachusetts Institute of Technology, Research Laboratory of Electronics. Technical Report No. 247 (1952). As background, see also Carnap, *Logical Foundations of Probability*, section 73.

It can be shown[47] that if this utility measure is adopted—no matter which of the many possible measure functions m might be—then Carnap's principle of maximizing the estimated utility yields the following decision rule for the case, characterized above, of a choice between the $n + 1$ alternatives of accepting $h_1, \ldots,$ accepting h_n, and accepting none of the alternative hypotheses:

(6.4) *Acceptance rule based on relative–content measure of utility.*
    Of the n hypotheses, at most one can have a probability on e which exceeds $\frac{1}{2}$; if there is one, accept it. Otherwise, there may be at most two hypotheses with a probability of $\frac{1}{2}$; in this case, accept one of these, or, alternatively, accept none of the n hypotheses. Finally, if each of the n hypotheses has a probability of less than $\frac{1}{2}$ on e, accept none of them. (In the first case, the estimated utility will be positive, in all other cases, zero.)

Thus, if epistemic utility is construed in the manner of (6.3), then Carnap's general principle of maximizing the estimated utility yields a rule which makes the acceptance of one or none of the n rival hypotheses depend solely on the probabilities which these hypotheses possess on the total evidence e. This rule cannot lead into inductive inconsistencies since the accepted hypothesis must have a probability of at least $\frac{1}{2}$ on the total evidence and thus cannot be incompatible with the latter: and the total evidence, it will be recalled, represents in our case the set of *all* statements accepted in science at the time. Nevertheless, rule (6.4) is unsatisfactory; in particular, it is much too lenient to be suitable as a general rule of scientific procedure. This must not be taken to prove, however, that Carnap's rule for rational choice simply cannot yield a reasonable acceptance rule for scientific hypotheses: quite likely, our crude definition of epistemic utility is at fault.

And indeed, apart from providing true or false new information, the addition of a hypothesis h to e has other aspects which are of importance to pure science, and which have to be taken into account in an attempt to define a concept of purely scientific utility. For example, if h has the character of a general law or of a theoretical principle, its explanatory power with respect to relevant data included in e will strongly influence the potential utility of accepting h. A closely related factor would no doubt be the gain in logical simplicity which would accrue to the total system of accepted statements as a result of incorporating h into it. If factors such as these are to be taken into account they will have to be given clear and precise definitions. Some initial steps towards this end have been

47. The proof, which will be omitted here, is a generalization of the argument used to establish a more limited result in section 12 of my essay "Deductive-Nomological *vs.* Statistical Explanation."

taken in recent years,[48] but a great deal of further work is needed if a reasonably adequate general concept of epistemic utility is to be attained.

The approach just outlined to the problem of inductive acceptance rules construes the formation of rational empirical belief and the establishment of scientific knowledge as involving the use of certain inductive principles which, under specified conditions, authorize the (provisional) acceptance of a hypothesis on a given body of total evidence, rather than simply determine its degree of confirmation. As an alternative, it would be interesting to investigate possible ways of construing the logic of rational belief and of scientific knowledge without assuming acceptance rules. The only inductive principles invoked in such a construal would then be, broadly speaking, probabilistic in character; for example, they might be inductive rules of the kind envisaged by Carnap and might take such forms as (3.4) and 3.5);[49] or they might be of some different character, perhaps in accordance with statistical decision theories.

In fact, it has recently been argued, especially by writers on statistical decision procedures and on the theory of games, that it makes no clear sense to speak of the acceptance of a scientific hypothesis *per se*, without specification of a course of action to be based on it; and that, in particular, what in decision theory is referred to as the acceptance of a given hypothesis always amounts to the adoption of a certain course of action. On this view, one would have to construe the notion of scientific knowledge without using the idea of acceptance at all; or, at best, one would have to construe acceptance as a pragmatic concept that has no counterpart in the logic of science. However, as I have tried to show elsewhere,[50] this view, though supported by some very plausible arguments, faces difficulties of its own.[51]

At present, it seems to me an open question whether the idea of inductive acceptance of a hypothesis in pure science can be given a clear and methodologically illuminating construal, and correlatively, whether there are any good reasons

---

48. For a definition of the explanatory power of hypotheses expressible in certain simple kinds of formalized languages, see Hempel and Oppenheim, *loc. cit.*, sections 8 and 9. On the subject of simplicity in the sense here referred to, see K. Popper, *The Logic of Scientific Discovery* (London: Hutchinson, 1959), chap. VII and *passim*; and cf. also the lucid discussion and tentative explication in S. Barker, *Induction and Hypothesis*, where further bibliographic references, especially to the work of Kemeny, will be found.

49. In this connection, cf. Carnap's remarks in *Logical Foundations of Probability*, p. 206.

50. Cf. Hempel, "Deductive-Nomological *vs.* Statistical Explanation," section 12.

51. The considerations here outlined seem to me to cast doubt upon the view that the question "whether to *accept* a certain hypothesis– whether to *believe* it – is . . . easier to answer than the question of whether to *act upon* it". This view is set forth by R. Chisholm in his book *Perceiving: A Philosophical Study* (Cornell University Press, 1957), pp. 10–11 (author's italics). Part I of this book, entitled "The Ethics of Belief," contains many illuminating observations on issues discussed in the present essay.

for preserving the familiar notion of scientific induction rules that authorize the acceptance of a hypothesis on the basis of suitable evidence. For the further clarification of these issues, it will be necessary to elaborate more fully and precisely the alternative conceptions of scientific knowledge briefly considered in this section: and this calls for additional philosophical analysis in Carnap's sense, aimed at a logical explication[52] of the concepts central to the problem.

52. See Carnap, *Logical Foundations of Probability*, chap. I.

3. SCIENCE AND

HUMAN VALUES

1. THE PROBLEM

OUR AGE is often called an age of science and of scientific technology, and with good reason: the advances made during the past few centuries by the natural sciences, and more recently by the psychological and sociological disciplines, have enormously broadened our knowledge and deepened our understanding of the world we live in and of our fellow men; and the practical application of scientific insights is giving us an ever increasing measure of control over the forces of nature and the minds of men. As a result, we have grown quite accustomed, not only to the idea of a physico-chemical and biological technology based on the results of the natural sciences, but also to the concept, and indeed the practice, of a psychological and sociological technology that utilizes the theories and methods developed by behavioral research.

This growth of scientific knowledge and its applications has vastly reduced the threat of some of man's oldest and most formidable scourges, among them famine and pestilence; it has raised man's material level of living, and it has put within his reach the realization of visions which even a few decades ago would have appeared utterly fantastic, such as the active exploration of interplanetary space.

But in achieving these results, scientific technology has given rise to a host of new and profoundly disturbing problems: The control of nuclear fission has brought us not only the comforting prospect of a vast new reservoir of energy,

This article first appeared in R. E. Spiller (ed.), *Social Control in a Free Society*. Philadelphia: University of Pennsylvania Press, 1960, pp. 39–64. It is here reprinted, with some deletions and some additions, by the kind permission of the University of Pennsylvania Press.

but also the constant threat of the atom bomb and of grave damage, to the present and to future generations, from the radioactive by-products of the fission process, even in its peaceful uses. And the very progress in biological and medical knowledge and technology which has so strikingly reduced infant mortality and increased man's life expectancy in large areas of our globe has significantly contributed to the threat of the "population explosion," the rapid growth of the earth's population which we are facing today, and which, again, is a matter of grave concern to all those who have the welfare of future generations at heart.

Clearly, the advances of scientific technology on which we pride ourselves, and which have left their characteristic imprint on every aspect of this "age of science," have brought in their train many new and grave problems which urgently demand a solution. It is only natural that, in his desire to cope with these new issues, man should turn to science and scientific technology for further help. But a moment's reflection shows that the problems that need to be dealt with are not straightforward technological questions but intricate complexes of technological and moral issues. Take the case of the population explosion, for example. To be sure, it does pose specific technological problems. One of these is the task of satisfying at least the basic material needs of a rapidly growing population by means of limited resources; another is the question of means by which population growth itself may be kept under control. Yet these technical questions do not exhaust the problem. For after all, even now we have at our disposal various ways of counteracting population growth; but some of these, notably contraceptive methods, have been and continue to be the subject of intense controversy on moral and religious grounds, which shows that an adequate solution of the problem at hand requires, not only knowledge of technical means of control, but also standards for evaluating the alternative means at our disposal; and this second requirement clearly raises moral issues.

There is no need to extend the list of illustrations: any means of technical control that science makes available to us may be employed in many different ways, and a decision as to what use to make of it involves us in questions of moral valuation. And here arises a fundamental problem to which I would now like to turn: Can such valuational questions be answered by means of the objective methods of empirical science, which have been so successful in giving us reliable, and often practically applicable, knowledge of our world? Can those methods serve to establish objective criteria of right and wrong and thus to provide valid moral norms for the proper conduct of our individual and social affairs?

2. SCIENTIFIC TESTING

Let us approach this question by considering first, if only in brief and sketchy outline, the way in which objective scientific knowledge is arrived at. We may leave aside here the question of *ways of discovery;* i.e., the problem of how a new scientific idea arises, how a novel hypothesis or theory is first conceived; for our purposes it will suffice to consider the scientific *ways of validation;* i.e., the manner in which empirical science goes about examining a proposed new hypothesis and determines whether it is to be accepted or rejected. I will use the word 'hypothesis' here to refer quite broadly to any statements or set of statements in empirical science, no matter whether it deals with some particular event or purports to set forth a general law or perhaps a more or less complex theory.

As is well known, empirical science decides upon the acceptability of a proposed hypothesis by means of suitable tests. Sometimes such a test may involve nothing more than what might be called direct observation of pertinent facts. This procedure may be used, for example, in testing such statements as "It is raining outside," "All the marbles in this urn are blue," "The needle of this ammeter will stop at the scale point marked 6," and so forth. Here a few direct observations will usually suffice to decide whether the hypothesis at hand is to be accepted as true or to be rejected as false.

But most of the important hypotheses in empirical science cannot be tested in this simple manner. Direct observation does not suffice to decide, for example, whether to accept or to reject the hypotheses that the earth is a sphere, that hereditary characteristics are transmitted by genes, that all Indo-European languages developed from one common ancestral language, that light is an electromagnetic wave process, and so forth. With hypotheses such as these, science resorts to indirect methods of test and validation. While these methods vary greatly in procedural detail, they all have the same basic structure and rationale. First, from the hypothesis under test, suitable other statements are inferred which describe certain directly observable phenomena that should be found to occur under specifiable circumstances if the hypothesis is true; then those inferred statements are tested directly; i.e., by checking whether the specified phenomena do in fact occur; finally, the proposed hypothesis is accepted or rejected in the light of the outcome of these tests. For example, the hypothesis that the earth is spherical in shape is not directly testable by observation, but it permits us to infer that a ship moving away from the observer should appear to be gradually dropping below the horizon; that circumnavigation of the earth should be possible by following a straight course; that high-altitude photographs should show the curving of the earth's surface; that certain geodetic and astronomical measurements should yield such and such results; and so forth. Inferred statements such as these can be tested more or less directly; and as an increasing number and variety of them are actually borne out, the hypothesis becomes increasingly confirmed. Eventually, a hypothesis may be so well confirmed by the available evidence that it is accepted as having been established beyond reasonable doubt. Yet no scientific hypothesis is ever proved completely and definitively; there is always at least the theoretical possibility that new evidence will be discovered which conflicts with some of the observational statements inferred from the hypothesis, and which thus leads to its rejection. The history of science records many instances in which a once accepted hypothesis was subsequently abandoned in the light of adverse evidence.

3. INSTRUMENTAL JUDGMENTS OF VALUE

We now turn to the question whether this method of test and validation may be used to establish moral judgements of value, and particularly judgments to the effect that a specified course of action is good or right or proper, or that it is better than certain alternative courses of action, or that we ought—or ought not—to act in certain specified ways.

By way of illustration, consider the view that it is good to raise children permissively and bad to bring them up in a restrictive manner. It might seem that, at least in principle, this view could be scientifically confirmed by appropriate empirical investigations. Suppose, for example, that careful research had established (1) that restrictive upbringing tends to generate resentment and aggression against parents and other persons exercising educational authority, and that this leads to guilt and anxiety and an eventual stunting of the child's initiative and creative potentialities; whereas (2) permissive upbringing avoids these consequences, makes for happier interpersonal relations, encourages resourcefulness and self-reliance, and enables the child to develop and enjoy his potentialities. These statements, especially when suitably amplified, come within the purview of scientific investigation; and though our knowledge in the matter is in fact quite limited, let us assume, for the sake of the argument, that they had actually been strongly confirmed by careful tests. Would not scientific research then have objectively shown that it is indeed better to raise children in a permissive rather than in a restrictive manner?

A moment's reflection shows that this is not so. What would have been established is rather a conditional statement; namely, that *if* our children are to become happy, emotionally secure, creative individuals rather than guilt-ridden and troubled souls *then* it is better to raise them in a permissive than in a restrictive fashion. A statement like this represents a *relative, or instrumental, judgment of value*. Generally, a relative judgment of value states that a certain kind of action, M, is good (or that it is better than a given alternative M_1) *if* a specified goal G is to be attained; or more accurately, that M is good, or appropriate, for the attainment of goal G. But to say this is tantamount to asserting either that, in the circumstances at hand, course of action M will definitely (or probably) lead to the attainment of G, or that failure to embark on course of action M will definitely (or probably) lead to the nonattainment of G. In other words, the instrumental value judgment asserts either that M is a (definitely or probably) sufficient means for attaining the end or goal G, or that it is a (definitely or probably) necessary means for attaining it. Thus, a relative, or instrumental, judgment of value can be reformulated as a statement which expresses a universal or a probabilistic kind of means-ends relationship, and which contains no terms of moral discourse—such as 'good,' 'better,' 'ought to'— at all. And a statement of this kind surely is an empirical assertion capable of scientific test

4. CATEGORICAL JUDGMENTS OF VALUE

Unfortunately, this does not completely solve our problem; for after a relative judgment of value referring to a certain goal G has been tested and, let us assume, well confirmed, we are still left with the question of whether the goal G ought to be pursued, or whether it would be better to aim at some alternative goal instead. Empirical science can establish the conditional statement, for example, that if we wish to deliver an incurably ill person from intolerable suffering, then a large dose of morphine affords a means of doing so; but it may also indicate ways of prolonging the patient's life, if also his suffering. This leaves us with the question whether it is right to give the goal of avoiding hopeless human suffering precedence over that of preserving human life. And this question calls, not for a relative but for an *absolute, or categorical, judgment of value* to the effect that a certain state of affairs (which may have been proposed as a goal or end) is good, or that it is better than some specified alternative. Are such categorical value judgments capable of empirical test and confirmation?

Consider, for example, the sentence "Killing is evil." It expresses a categorical judgment of value which, by implication, would also categorically qualify euthanasia as evil. Evidently, the sentence does not express an assertion that can be directly tested by observation; it does not purport to describe a directly observable fact. Can it be indirectly tested, then, by inferring from it statements to the effect that under specified test conditions such and such observable phenomena will occur? Again, the answer is clearly in the negative. Indeed, the sentence 'Killing is evil' does not have the function of expressing an assertion that can be qualified as true or false; rather, it serves to express a standard for moral appraisal or a norm for conduct. A categorical judgment of value may have other functions as well; for example, it may serve to convey the utterer's approval or disapproval of a certain kind of action, or his commitment to the standards of conduct expressed by the value judgment. Descriptive empirical import, however, is absent; in this respect a sentence such as 'Killing is evil' differs strongly from, say, 'Killing is condemned as evil by many religions', which expresses a factual assertion capable of empirical test.

Categorical judgements of value, then, are not amenable to scientific test and confirmation or disconfirmation; for they do not express assertions but rather standards or norms for conduct. It was Max Weber, I believe, who expressed essentially the same idea by remarking that science is like a map: it can tell us how to get to a given place, but it cannot tell us where to go. Gunnar Myrdal, in his book *An American Dilemma* (p. 1052), stresses in a similar vein that "factual or theoretical studies alone cannot logically lead to a practical recommendation. A practical or valuational conclusion can be derived only when there is at least one valuation among the premises."

Nevertheless, there have been many attempts to base systems of moral standards on the findings of empirical science; and it would be of interest to examine in some detail the reasoning which underlies those procedures. In the present context, however, there is room for only a few brief remarks on this subject.

It might seem promising, for example, to derive judgments of value from the results of an objective study of human needs. But no cogent derivation of this sort is possible. For this procedure would presuppose that it is right, or good, to satisfy human needs—and this presupposition is itself a categorical judgment of value: it would play the role of a valuational premise in the sense of Myrdal's statement. Furthermore, since there are a great many different, and partly conflicting, needs of individuals and of groups, we would require not just the general maxim that human needs ought to be satisfied, but a detailed set of rules as to the preferential order and degree in which different needs are to be met, and how conflicting claims are to be settled; thus, the valuational premise required for this undertaking would actually have to be a complex system of norms; hence, a derivation of valuational standards simply from a factual study of needs is out of the question.

Several systems of ethics have claimed the theory of evolution as their basis; but they are in serious conflict with each other even in regard to their most fundamental tenets. Some of the major variants are illuminatingly surveyed in a chapter of G. G. Simpson's book, *The Meaning of Evolution*. One type, which Simpson calls a "tooth-and-claw ethics," glorifies a struggle for existence that should lead to a survival of the fittest. A second urges the harmonious adjustment of groups or individuals to one another so as to enhance the probability of their survival, while still other systems hold up as an ultimate standard the increased aggregation of organic units into higher levels of organization, sometimes with the implication that the welfare of the state is to be placed above that of the individuals belonging to it. It is obvious that these conflicting principles could not have been validly inferred from the theory of evolution—unless indeed that theory were self-contradictory, which does not seem very likely.

But if science cannot provide us with categorical judgments of value, what then can serve as a source of unconditional valuations? This question may either be understood in a pragmatic sense, as concerned with the sources from which human beings do in fact obtain their basic values. Or it may be understood as concerned with a systematic aspect of valuation; namely, with the question where a proper system of basic values is to be found on which all other valuations may then be grounded.

The pragmatic question comes within the purview of empirical science. Without entering into details, we may say here that a person's values—both those he professes to espouse and those he actually conforms to—are largely absorbed from the society in which he lives, and especially from certain influential subgroups to which he belongs, such as his family, his schoolmates, his associates on the job, his church, clubs, unions, and other groups. Indeed his values may vary from case to case depending on which of these groups dominates the situation in which he happens to find himself. In general, then, a person's basic valuations are no more the result of careful scrutiny and critical appraisal of possible alternatives than is his religious affiliation. Conformity to the standards of certain groups plays a very important role here, and only rarely are basic values seriously questioned. Indeed, in many situations, we decide and act unreflectively in an even stronger sense; namely, without any attempt to base our decisions on some set of explicit, consciously adopted, moral standards.

Now, it might be held that this answer to the pragmatic version of our question reflects a regrettable human inclination to intellectual and moral inertia; but that the really important side of our question is the systematic one: If we do want to justify our decisions, we need moral standards of conduct of the unconditional type—but how can such standards be established? If science cannot provide categorical value judgments, are there any other sources from which they might be obtained? Could we not, for example, validate a system of categorical judgments of value by pointing out that it represents the moral standards held up by the Bible, or by the Koran, or by some inspiring thinker or social leader? Clearly, this procedure must fail, for the factual information here adduced could serve to validate the value judgments in question only if we were to use, in addition, a valuational presupposition to the effect that the moral directives stemming from the source invoked *ought* to be complied with. Thus, if the process of justifying a given decision or a moral judgment is ever to be completed, certain judgments of value have to be accepted without any further justification, just as the proof of a theorem in geometry requires that some propositions be accepted as postulates, without proof. The quest for a justification of *all* our valuations overlooks this basic characteristic of the logic of validation and of justification. The value judgments accepted without further justification in a given context need not, however, be accepted once and for all, with a commitment never to question them again. This point will be elaborated further in the final section of this essay.

As will hardly be necessary to stress, in concluding the present phase of our discussion, the ideas set forth in the preceding pages do not imply or advocate moral anarchy; in particular, they do not imply that any system of values is just as good, or just as valid, as any other, or that everyone should adopt the moral principles that best suit his convenience. For all such maxims have the character of categorical value judgments and cannot, therefore, be implied by the preceding considerations, which are purely descriptive of certain logical, psychological, and social aspects of moral valuation.

5. RATIONAL CHOICE: EMPIRICAL AND VALUATIONAL COMPONENTS

To gain further insight into the relevance of scientific inquiry for categorical valuation let us ask what help we might receive, in dealing with a moral problem, from science in an ideal state such as that represented by Laplace's conception of a superior scientific intelligence, sometimes referred to as Laplace's demon. This fiction was used by Laplace, early in the nineteenth century, to give a vivid characterization of the idea of universal causal determinism. The demon is conceived as a perfect observer, capable of ascertaining with infinite speed and accuracy all that goes on in the universe at a given moment; he is also an ideal theoretician who knows all the laws of nature and has combined them into one universal formula; and finally, he is a perfect mathematician who, by means of that universal formula, is able to infer, from the observed state of the universe at the given moment, the total state of the universe at any other moment; thus past and future are present before his eyes. Surely, it is difficult to imagine that science could ever achieve a higher degree of perfection!

Let us assume, then, that, faced with a moral decision, we are able to call upon the Laplacean demon as a consultant. What help might we get from him? Suppose that we have to choose one of several alternative courses of action open to us, and that we want to know which of these we *ought* to follow. The demon would then be able to tell us, for any contemplated choice, what its consequences would be for the future course of the universe, down to the most minute detail, however remote in space and time. But, having done this for each of the alternative courses of action under consideration, the demon would have completed his task: he would have given us all the information that an ideal science might provide under the circumstances. And yet he would not have resolved our moral problem, for this requires a decision as to which of the several alternative sets of consequences mapped out by the demon as attainable to us is the best; which of them we ought to bring about. And the burden of this decision would still fall upon our shoulders: it is we who would have to commit ourselves to an unconditional judgment of value by singling out one of the sets of consequences as superior to its alternatives. Even Laplace's demon, or the ideal science he stands for, cannot relieve us of this responsibility.

In drawing this picture of the Laplacean demon as a consultant in decision-making, I have cheated a little; for if the world were as strictly deterministic as Laplace's fiction assumes, then the demon would know in advance what choice we were going to make, and he might disabuse us of the idea that there were several courses of action open to us. However that may be, contemporary physical theory has cast considerable doubt on the classical conception of the universe as a strictly deterministic system: the fundamental laws of nature are now assumed to have a statistical or probabilistic rather than a strictly universal, deterministic, character.

But whatever may be the form and the scope of the laws that hold in our universe, we will obviously never attain a perfect state of knowledge concerning them; confronted with a choice, we never have more than a very incomplete knowledge of the laws of nature and of the state of the world at the time when we must act. Our decisions must therefore always be made on the basis of incomplete information, a state which enables us to anticipate the consequences of alternative choices at best with probability. Science can render an indispensable service by providing us with increasingly extensive and reliable information relevant to our purpose; but again it remains for us to *evaluate* the various probable sets of consequences of the alternative choices under consideration. And this requires the adoption of pertinent valuational standards which are not objectively determined by the empirical facts.

This basic point is reflected also in the contemporary mathematical theories of decision-making. One of the objectives of these theories is the formulation of decision rules which will determine an optimal choice in situations where several courses of action are available. For the formulation of decision rules, these theories require that at least two conditions be met: (1) Factual information must be provided specifying the available courses of action and indicating for each of these its different possible outcomes—plus, if feasible, the probabilities of their occurrence; (2) there must be a specification of the values—often prosaically referred to as utilities—that are attached to the different possible outcomes. Only when these factual and valuational specifications have been provided does it make sense to ask which of the available choices is the best, considering the values attaching to their possible results.

In mathematical decision theory, several criteria of optimal choice have been proposed. In case the probabilities for the different outcomes of each action are given, one standard criterion qualifies a choice as optimal if the probabilistically expectable utility of its outcome is at least as great as that of any alternative choice. Other rules, such as the maximin and the maximax principles, provide criteria that are applicable even when the probabilities of the outcomes are not available. But interestingly, the various criteria conflict with each other in the sense that, for one and the same situation, they will often select different choices as optimal.

The policies expressed by the conflicting criteria may be regarded as reflecting different attitudes towards the world, different degrees of optimism or pessimism, of venturesomeness or caution. It may be said therefore that the analysis offered by current mathematical models indicates two points at which decision-making calls not solely for factual information, but for categorical valuation, namely, in the assignment of utilities to the different possible outcomes and in the adoption of one among many competing decision rules or criteria of optimal choice. (This topic is developed in more detail in section 10.2 of the essay "Aspects of Scientific Explanation" in this volume.)

6. VALUATIONAL "PRESUPPOSITIONS" OF SCIENCE

The preceding three sections have been concerned mainly with the question whether, or to what extent, valuation and decision presuppose scientific investigation and scientific knowledge. This problem has a counterpart which deserves some attention in a discussion of science and valuation; namely, the question whether scientific knowledge and method presuppose valuation.

The word "presuppose" may be understood in a number of different senses which require separate consideration here. First of all, when a person decides to devote himself to scientific work rather than to some other career, and again, when a scientist chooses some particular topic of investigation, these choices will presumably be determined to a large extent by his preferences, i.e., by how highly he values scientific research in comparison with the alternatives open to him, and by the importance he attaches to the problems he proposes to investigate. In this explanatory, quasi-causal sense the scientific *activities* of human beings may certainly be said to presuppose valuations.

Much more intriguing problems arise, however, when we ask whether judgments of value are presupposed by the body of scientific *knowledge*, which might be represented by a system of statements accepted in accordance with the rules of scientific inquiry. Here presupposing has to be understood in a systematic-logical sense. One such sense is invoked when we say, for example, that the statement 'Henry's brother-in-law is an engineer' presupposes that Henry has a wife or a sister: in this sense, a statement presupposes whatever can be logically inferred from it. But, as was noted earlier, no set of scientific statements logically implies an unconditional judgment of value; hence, scientific knowledge does not, in this sense, presuppose valuation.

There is another logical sense of presupposing, however. We might say, for example, that in Euclidean geometry the angle–sum theorem for triangles presupposes the postulate of the parallels in the sense that that postulate is an essential part of the basic assumptions from which the theorem is deduced. Now, the hypotheses and theories of empirical science are not normally validated by deduction from supporting evidence (though it may happen that a scientific statement, such as a prediction, is established by deduction from a previously ascertained, more inclusive set of statements); rather, as was mentioned in section 2, they are usually accepted on the basis of evidence that lends them only partial, or "inductive," support. But in any event it might be asked whether the statements representing scientific knowledge presuppose valuation in the sense that the grounds on which they are accepted include, sometimes or always, certain unconditional judgments of value. Again the answer is in the negative. The grounds on which scientific hypotheses are accepted or rejected are provided by empirical evidence, which may include observational findings as well as previously established laws and theories, but surely no value judgments. Suppose for example that, in support of the hypothesis that a radiation belt of a specified kind surrounds the earth, a scientist were to adduce, first, certain observational data, obtained perhaps by rocket-borne instruments; second, certain previously accepted theories invoked in the interpretation of those data; and finally, certain judgments of value, such as 'it is good to ascertain the truth'. Clearly, the judgments of value would then be dismissed as lacking all logical relevance to the proposed hypothesis since they can contribute neither to its support nor to its disconfirmation.

But the question whether science presupposes valuation in a logical sense can be raised, and recently has been raised, in yet another way, referring more specifically to valuational presuppositions of scientific *method*. In the preceding considerations, scientific knowledge was represented by a system of statements which are sufficiently supported by available evidence to be accepted in accordance with the principles of scientific test and validation. We noted that as a rule the observational evidence on which a scientific hypothesis is accepted is far from sufficient to establish that hypothesis conclusively. For example, Galileo's law refers not only to past instances of free fall near the earth, but also to all future ones; and the latter surely are not covered by our present evidence. Hence, Galileo's law, and similarly any other law in empirical science, is accepted on the basis of incomplete evidence. Such acceptance carries with it the "inductive risk" that the presumptive law may not hold in full generality, and that future evidence may lead scientists to modify or abandon it.

A precise statement of this conception of scientific knowledge would require, among other things, the formulation of rules of two kinds: First, *rules of confirmation*, which would specify what kind of evidence is confirmatory, what kind disconfirmatory for a given hypothesis. Perhaps they would also determine a numerical *degree* of evidential support (or confirmation, or inductive probability) which a given body of evidence could be said to confer upon a proposed hypothesis. Secondly, there would have to be *rules of acceptance:* these would specify how strong the evidential support for a given hypothesis has to be if the hypothesis is to be accepted into the system of scientific knowledge; or, more generally, under what conditions a proposed hypothesis is to be accepted, under what conditions it is to be rejected by science on the basis of a given body of evidence.

Recent studies of inductive inference and statistical testing have devoted a great deal of effort to the formulation of adequate rules of either kind. In particular, rules of acceptance have been treated in many of these investigations as special instances of decision rules of the sort mentioned in the preceding section. The decisions in question are here either to accept or to reject a proposed hypothesis on the basis of given evidence. As was noted earlier, the formulation of "adequate" decision rules requires, in any case, the antecedent specification of valuations that can then serve as standards of adequacy. The requisite valuations, as will be recalled, concern the different possible outcomes of the choices which the decision rules are to govern. Now, when a scientific rule of acceptance is applied to a specified hypothesis on the basis of a given body of evidence, the possible "outcomes" of the resulting decision may be divided into four major types: (1) the hypothesis is accepted (as presumably true) in accordance with the rule and is in fact true; (2) the hypothesis is rejected (as presumably false) in accordance with the rule and is in fact false; (3) the hypothesis is accepted in accordance with the rule, but is in fact false; (4) the hypothesis is rejected in accordance with the rule, but is in fact true. The former two cases are what science aims to achieve; the possibility of the latter two represents the inductive risk that any acceptance rule must involve. And the problem of formulating adequate rules of acceptance and rejection has no clear meaning unless standards of adequacy have been provided by assigning definite values or disvalues to those different possible "outcomes" of acceptance or rejection. It is in this sense that the method of establishing scientific hypotheses "presupposes" valuation: the justification of the rules of acceptance and rejection requires reference to value judgments.

In the cases where the hypothesis under test, if accepted, is to be made the basis of a specific course of action, the possible outcomes may lead to success or failure of the intended practical application; in these cases, the values and disvalues at stake may well be expressible in terms of monetary gains or losses; and for situations of this sort, the theory of decision functions has developed various decision rules for use in practical contexts such as industrial quality control. But when it comes to decision rules for the acceptance of hypotheses in pure scientific research, where no practical applications are contemplated, the question of how to assign values to the four types of outcome mentioned earlier becomes considerably more problematic. But in a general way, it seems clear that the standards governing the inductive procedures of pure science reflect the objective of obtaining a certain goal, which might be described somewhat vaguely as the attainment of an increasingly reliable, extensive, and theoretically systematized body of information about the world. Note that if we were concerned, instead, to form a system of beliefs or a world view that is emotionally reassuring or esthetically satisfying to us, then it would not be reasonable at all to insist, as science does, on a close accord between the beliefs we accept and our empirical evidence; and the standards of objective testability and confirmation by publicly ascertainable evidence would have to be replaced by acceptance standards of an entirely different kind. The standards of procedure must in each case be formed in consideration of the goals to be attained; their justification must be relative to those goals and must, in this sense, presuppose them.

7. CONCLUDING COMPARISONS

If, as has been argued in section 4, science cannot provide a validation of categorical value judgments, can scientific method and knowledge play any role at all in clarifying and resolving problems of moral valuation and decision? The answer is emphatically in the affirmative. I will try to show this in a brief survey of the principal contributions science has to offer in this context.

First of all, science can provide factual information required for the resolution of moral issues. Such information will always be needed, for no matter what system of moral values we may espouse—whether it be egoistic or altruistic, hedonistic or utilitarian, or of any other kind—surely the specific course of action it enjoins us to follow in a given situation will depend upon the facts about that situation; and it is scientific knowledge and investigation that must provide the factual information which is needed for the application of our moral standards.

More specifically, factual information is needed, for example, to ascertain (a) whether a contemplated objective can be attained in a given situation; (b) if it can be attained, by what alternative means and with what probabilities ;(c) what side effects and ulterior consequences the choice of a given means may have apart from probably yielding the desired end; (d) whether several proposed ends are jointly realizable, or whether they are incompatible in the sense that the realization of some of them will definitely or probably prevent the realization of others.

By thus giving us information which is indispensable as a factual basis for rational and responsible decision, scientific research may well motivate us to change some of our valuations. If we were to discover, for example, that a certain kind of goal which we had so far valued very highly could be attained only at the price of seriously undesirable side effects and ulterior consequences, we might well come to place a less high value upon that goal. Thus, more extensive scientific information may lead to a change in our basic valuations—not by "disconfirming" them, of course, but rather by motivating a change in our total appraisal of the issues in question.

Secondly, and in a quite different manner, science can illuminate certain problems of valuation by an objective psychological and sociological study of the factors that affect the values espoused by an individual or a group; of the ways in which such valuational commitments change; and perhaps of the manner in which the espousal of a given value system may contribute to the emotional security of an individual or to the functional stability of a group.

Psychological, anthropological, and sociological studies of valuational behavior cannot, of course, "validate" any system of moral standards. But their results can psychologically effect changes in our outlook on moral issues by broadening our horizons, by making us aware of alternatives not envisaged, or not embraced, by our own group, and by thus providing some safeguard against moral dogmatism or parochialism.

Finally, a comparison with certain fundamental aspects of scientific knowledge may help to illuminate some further questions concerning valuation.

If we grant that scientific hypotheses and theories are always open to revision in the light of new empirical evidence, are we not obliged to assume that there is another class of scientific statements which cannot be open to doubt and reconsideration, namely, the observational statements describing experiential findings that serve to test scientific theories? Those simple, straightforward reports of what has been directly observed in the laboratory or in scientific field work, for example—must they not be regarded as immune from any conceivable revision, as irrevocable once they have been established by direct observation? Reports on directly observed phenomena have indeed often been considered as an unshakable bedrock foundation for all scientific hypotheses and theories. Yet this conception is untenable; even here, we find no definitive, unquestionable certainty.

For, first of all, accounts of what has been directly observed are subject to error that may spring from various physiological and psychological sources.

Indeed, it is often possible to check on the accuracy of a given observation report by comparing it with the reports made by other observers, or with relevant data obtained by some indirect procedure, such as a motion picture taken of the finish of a horse race; and such comparison may lead to the rejection of what had previously been considered as a correct description of a directly observed phenomenon. We even have theories that enable us to explain and anticipate some types of observational error, and in such cases, there is no hesitation to question and to reject certain statements that purport simply to record what has been directly observed.

Sometimes relatively isolated experimental findings may conflict with a theory that is strongly supported by a large number and variety of other data; in this case, it may well happen that part of the conflicting data, rather than the theory, is refused admission into the system of accepted scientific statements— even if no satisfactory explanation of the presumptive error of observation is available. In such cases it is not the isolated observational finding which decides whether the theory is to remain in good standing, but it is the previously well-substantiated theory which determines whether a purported observation report is to be regarded as describing an actual empirical occurrence. For example, a report that during a spiritualistic séance, a piece of furniture freely floated above the floor would normally be rejected because of its conflict with extremely well confirmed physical principles, even in the absence of some specific explanation of the report, say, in terms of deliberate fraud by the medium, or of high suggestibility on the part of the observer. Similarly, the experimental findings reported by the physicist Ehrenhaft, which were claimed to refute the principle that all electric charges are integral multiples of the charge of the electron, did not lead to the overthrow, nor even to a slight modification, of that principle, which is an integral part of a theory with extremely strong and diversified experimental support. Needless to say, such rejection of alleged observation reports by reason of their conflict with well-established theories requires considerable caution; otherwise, a theory, once accepted, could be used to reject all adverse evidence that might subsequently be found—a dogmatic procedure entirely irreconcilable with the objectives and the spirit of scientific inquiry.

Even reports on directly observed phenomena, then, are not irrevocable; they provide no bedrock foundation for the entire system of scientific knowledge. But this by no means precludes the possibility of testing scientific theories by reference to data obtained through direct observation. As we noted, the results obtained by such direct checking cannot be considered as absolutely unquestionable and irrevocable; they are themselves amenable to further tests which may be carried out if there is reason for doubt. But obviously if we are ever to form any beliefs about the world, if we are ever to accept or to reject, even provisionally, some hypothesis or theory, then we must stop the testing process somewhere; we must accept some evidential statements as sufficiently trustworthy not to require further investigation for the time being. And on the basis of such evidence, we can then decide what credence to give to the hypothesis under test, and whether to accept or to reject it.

This aspect of scientific investigation seems to me to have a parallel in the case of sound valuation and rational decision. In order to make a rational choice between several courses of action, we have to consider, first of all, what consequences each of the different alternative choices is likely to have. This affords a basis for certain relative judgments of value that are relevant to our problem. If *this* set of results is to be attained, this course of action ought to be chosen; if *that other* set of results is to be realized, we should choose such and such another course; and so forth. But in order to arrive at a decision, we still have to decide upon the relative values of the alternative sets of consequences attainable to us; and this, as was noted earlier, calls for the acceptance of an unconditional judgment of value, which will then determine our choice. But such acceptance need not be regarded as definitive and irrevocable, as forever binding for all our future decisions: an unconditional judgment of value, once accepted, still remains open to reconsideration and to change. Suppose, for example, that we have to choose, as voters or as members of a city administration, between several alternative social policies, some of which are designed to improve certain material conditions of living, whereas others aim at satisfying cultural needs of various kinds. If we are to arrive at a decision at all, we will have to commit ourselves to assigning a higher value to one or the other of those objectives. But while the judgment thus accepted serves as an unconditional and basic judgment of value for the decision at hand, we are not for that reason committed to it forever—we may well reconsider our standards and reverse our judgment later on; and though this cannot undo the earlier decision, it will lead to different decisions in the future. Thus, if we are to arrive at a decision concerning a moral issue, we have to accept some unconditional judgments of value; but these need not be regarded as ultimate in the absolute sense of being forever binding for all our decisions, any more than the evidence statements relied on in the test of a scientific hypothesis need to be regarded as forever irrevocable. All that is needed in either context are *relative* ultimates, as it were: a set of judgments—moral or descriptive—which are accepted at the time as not in need of further scrutiny. These relative ultimates permit us to keep an open mind in regard to the possibility of making changes in our heretofore unquestioned commitments and beliefs; and surely the experience of the past suggests that if we are to meet the challenge of the present and the future, we will more than ever need undogmatic, critical, and open minds.

II.

CONCEPTIONS

OF COGNITIVE

SIGNIFICANCE

4. EMPIRICIST CRITERIA

OF COGNITIVE SIGNIFICANCE:

PROBLEMS AND CHANGES

1. THE GENERAL EMPIRICIST CONCEPTION OF COGNITIVE AND EMPIRICAL SIGNIFICANCE

It is a basic principle of contemporary empiricism that a sentence makes a cognitively significant assertion, and thus can be said to be either true or false, if and only if either (1) it is analytic or contradictory—in which case it is said to have purely logical meaning or significance—or else (2) it is capable, at least potentially, of test by experiential evidence—in which case it is said to have empirical meaning or significance. The basic tenet of this principle, and especially of its second part, the so-called testability criterion of empirical meaning (or better: meaningfulness), is not peculiar to empiricism alone: it is characteristic also of contemporary operationism, and in a sense of pragmatism as well; for the pragmatist maxim that a difference must make a difference to be a difference may well be construed as insisting that a verbal difference between two sentences must make a difference in experiential implications if it is to reflect a difference in meaning.

How this general conception of cognitively significant discourse led to the rejection, as devoid of logical and empirical meaning, of various formulations in speculative metaphysics, and even of certain hypotheses offered within

This essay combines, with certain omissions and some other changes, the contents of two articles: "Problems and Changes in the Empiricist Criterion of Meaning," *Revue Internationale de Philosophie* No. 11, pp. 41–63 (January, 1950); and "The Concept of Cognitive Significance: A Reconsideration," *Proceedings of the American Academy of Arts and Sciences* 80, No. 1, pp. 61–77 (1951). This material is reprinted with kind permission of the Director of *Revue Internationale de Philosophie* and of the American Academy of Arts and Sciences.

empirical science, is too well known to require recounting. I think that the general intent of the empiricist criterion of meaning is basically sound, and that notwithstanding much oversimplification in its use, its critical application has been, on the whole, enlightening and salutary. I feel less confident, however, about the possibility of restating the general idea in the form of precise and general criteria which establish sharp dividing lines (a) between statements of purely logical and statements of empirical significance, and (b) between those sentences which do have cognitive significance and those which do not.

In the present paper, I propose to reconsider these distinctions as conceived in recent empiricism, and to point out some of the difficulties they present. The discussion will concern mainly the second of the two distinctions; in regard to the first, I shall limit myself to a few brief remarks.

2. THE EARLIER TESTABILITY CRITERIA OF MEANING AND THEIR SHORTCOMINGS

Let us note first that any general criterion of cognitive significance will have to meet certain requirements if it is to be at all acceptable. Of these, we note one, which we shall consider here as expressing a necessary, though by no means sufficient, *condition of adequacy* for criteria of cognitive significance.

(A) If under a given criterion of cognitive significance, a sentence *N* is nonsignificant, then so must be all truth-functional compound sentences in which *N* occurs nonvacuously as a component. For if *N* cannot be significantly assigned a truth value, then it is impossible to assign truth values to the compound sentences containing *N;* hence, they should be qualified as nonsignificant as well.

We note two corollaries of requirement (A):

(A1) If under a given criterion of cognitive significance, a sentence *S* is nonsignificant, then so must be its negation, $\sim S$.

(A2) If under a given criterion of cognitive significance, a sentence *N* is nonsignificant, then so must be any conjunction $N \cdot S$ and any disjunction $N v S$, no matter whether *S* is significant under the given criterion or not.

We now turn to the initial attempts made in recent empiricism to establish general criteria of cognitive significance. Those attempts were governed by the consideration that a sentence, to make an empirical assertion must be capable of being borne out by, or conflicting with, phenomena which are potentially capable of being directly observed. Sentences describing such potentially observable phenomena—no matter whether the latter do actually occur or not—may be called observation sentences. More specifically, an *observation sentence* might be construed as a sentence—no matter whether true or false—which asserts or denies that a specified object, or group of objects, of macroscopic size has a particular *observable characteristic*, i.e., a characteristic whose presence or absence can, under favorable circumstances, be ascertained by direct observation.[1]

The task of setting up criteria of empirical significance is thus transformed into the problem of characterizing in a precise manner the relationship which obtains between a hypothesis and one or more observation sentences whenever the phenomena described by the latter either confirm or disconfirm the hypothesis in question. The ability of a given sentence to enter into that relationship to some set of observation sentences would then characterize its testability-in-principle, and thus its empirical significance. Let us now briefly examine the major attempts that have been made to obtain criteria of significance in this manner.

One of the earliest criteria is expressed in the so-called *verifiability requirement*. According to it, a sentence is empirically significant if and only if it is not analytic and is capable, at least in principle, of complete verification by observational evidence; i.e., if observational evidence can be described which, if actually obtained, would conclusively establish the truth of the sentence.[2] With the

---

1. Observation sentences of this kind belong to what Carnap has called the thing-language, cf., e.g., (1938), pp. 52-53. That they are adequate to formulate the data which serve as the basis for empirical tests is clear in particular for the intersubjective testing procedures used in science as well as in large areas of empirical inquiry on the common-sense level. In epistemological discussions, it is frequently assumed that the ultimate evidence for beliefs about empirical matters consists in perceptions and sensations whose description calls for a phenomenalistic type of language. The specific problems connected with the phenomenalistic approach cannot be discussed here; but it should be mentioned that at any rate all the critical considerations presented in this article in regard to the testability criterion are applicable, *mutatis mutandis*, to the case of a phenomenalistic basis as well.

2. Originally, the permissible evidence was meant to be restricted to what is observable by the speaker and perhaps his fellow beings during their life times. Thus construed, the criterion rules out, as cognitively meaningless, all statements about the distant future or the remote past, as has been pointed out, among others, by Ayer (1946), chapter I; by Pap (1949), chapter 13, esp. pp. 333 ff.; and by Russell (1948), pp. 445-47. This difficulty is avoided, however, if we permit the evidence to consist of any finite set of "logically possible observation data", each of them formulated in an observation sentence. Thus, e.g., the sentence S_1, "The tongue of the largest dinosaur in New York's Museum of Natural History was blue or black" is completely verifiable in our sense; for it is a logical consequence of the sentence S_2, "The tongue of the largest dinosaur in New York's Museum of Natural History was blue"; and this is an observation sentence, in the sense just indicated.

And if the concept of *verifiability in principle* and the more general concept of *confirmability in principle*, which will be considered later, are construed as referring to *logically possible evidence* as expressed by observation sentences, then it follows similarly that the class of statements which are verifiable, or at least confirmable, in principle include such assertions as that the planet Neptune and the Antarctic Continent existed before they were discovered, and that atomic warfare, if not checked, will lead to the extermination of this planet. The objections which Russell (1948), pp. 445 and 447, raises against the verifiability criterion by reference to those examples do not apply therefore if the criterion is understood in the manner here suggested.

(continued overleaf)

help of the concept of observation sentence, we can restate this requirement as follows: A sentence S has empirical meaning if and only if it is possible to indicate a finite set of observation sentences, O_1, O_2,. . ., O_n, such that if these are true, then S is necessarily true, too. As stated, however, this condition is satisfied also if S is an analytic sentence or if the given observation sentences are logically incompatible with each other. By the following formulation, we rule these cases out and at the same time express the intended criterion more precisely:

(2.1) REQUIREMENT OF COMPLETE VERIFIABILITY IN PRINCIPLE. A sentence has empirical meaning if and only if it is not analytic and follows logically from some finite and logically consistent class of observation sentences.[3] These observation sentences need not be true, for what the criterion is to explicate is testability by "potentially observable phenomena," or testability "in principle."

In accordance with the general conception of cognitive significance outlined earlier, a sentence will now be classified as cognitively significant if either it is analytic or contradictory, or it satisfies the verifiability requirement.

This criterion, however, has several serious defects. One of them has been noted by several writers:

a. Let us assume that the properties of being a stork and of being red-legged

3. As has frequently been emphasized in the empiricist literature, the term "verifiability" is to indicate, of course, the conceivability, or better, the logical possibility, of evidence of an observational kind which, if actually encountered, would constitute conclusive evidence for the given sentence; it is not intended to mean the technical possibility of performing the tests needed to obtain such evidence, and even less the possibility of actually finding directly observable phenomena which constitute conclusive evidence for that sentence—which would be tantamount to the actual existence of such evidence and would thus imply the truth of the given sentence. Analogous remarks apply to the terms "falsifiability" and "confirmability". This point has clearly been disregarded in some critical discussions of the verifiability criterion. Thus, e.g., Russell (1948), p. 448 construes verifiability as the actual existence of a set of conclusively verifying occurrences. This conception, which has never been advocated by any logical empiricist, must naturally turn out to be inadequate since according to it the empirical meaningfulness of a sentence could not be established without gathering empirical evidence, and moreover enough of it to permit a conclusive proof of the sentence in question! It is not surprising, therefore, that his extraordinary interpretation of verifiability leads Russell to the conclusion: "In fact, that a proposition is verifiable is itself not verifiable" (*l.c.*). Actually, under the empiricist interpretation of complete verifiability, any statement asserting the verifiability of some sentence S whose text is quoted, is either analytic or contradictory; for the decision whether there exists a class of observation sentences which entail S, i.e., whether such observation sentences can be formulated, no matter whether they are true or false—that decision is a purely logical matter.

Incidentally, statements of the kind mentioned by Russell, which are not actually verifiable by any human being, were explicitly recognized as cognitively significant already by Schlick (1936), Part V, who argued that the impossibility of verifying them was "merely empirical." The characterization of verifiability with the help of the concept of observation sentence as suggested here might serve as a more explicit and rigorous statement of that conception.

are both observable characteristics, and that the former does not logically entail the latter. Then the sentence

(S1)   All storks are red-legged

is neither analytic nor contradictory; and clearly, it is not deducible from a finite set of observation sentences. Hence, under the contemplated criterion, $S1$ is devoid of empirical significance; and so are all other sentences purporting to express universal regularities or general laws. And since sentences of this type constitute an integral part of scientific theories, the verifiability requirement must be regarded as overly restrictive in this respect.

Similarly, the criterion disqualifies all sentences such as 'For any substance there exists some solvent', which contain both universal and existential quantifiers (i.e., occurrences of the terms 'all' and 'some' or their equivalents); for no sentences of this kind can be logically deduced from any finite set of observation sentences.

Two further defects of the verifiability requirement do not seem to have been widely noticed:

b. As is readily seen, the negation of $S1$

($\sim S1$)   There exists at least one stork that is not red-legged

is deducible from any two observation sentences of the type 'a is a stork' and 'a is not red-legged'. Hence, $\sim S1$ is cognitively significant under our criterion, but $S1$ is not, and this constitutes a violation of condition (A1).

c. Let S be a sentence which does, and N a sentence which does not satisfy the verifiability requirement. Then S is deducible from some set of observation sentences; hence, by a familiar rule of logic, SvN is deducible from the same set, and therefore cognitively significant according to our criterion. This violates condition (A2) above.[4]

Strictly analogous considerations apply to an alternative criterion, which

4. The arguments here adduced against the verifiability criterion also prove the inadequacy of a view closely related to it, namely that two sentences have the same cognitive significance if any set of observation sentences which would verify one of them would also verify the other, and conversely. Thus, e.g., under this criterion, any two general laws would have to be assigned the same cognitive significance, for no general law is verified by any set of observation sentences. The view just referred to must be clearly distinguished from a position which Russell examines in his critical discussion of the positivistic meaning criterion. It is "the theory that two propositions whose verified consequences are identical have the same significance" (1948), p. 448. This view is untenable indeed, for what consequences of a statement have actually been verified at a given time is obviously a matter of historical accident which cannot possibly serve to establish identity of cognitive significance. But I am not aware that any logical empiricist ever subscribed to that "theory."

makes complete falsifiability in principle the defining characteristic of empirical significance. Let us formulate this criterion as follows:

(2.2) REQUIREMENT OF COMPLETE FALSIFIABILITY IN PRINCIPLE. A sentence has empirical meaning if and only if its negation is not analytic and follows logically from some finite logically consistent class of observation sentences.

This criterion qualifies a sentence as empirically meaningful if its negation satisfies the requirement of complete verifiability; as it is to be expected, it is therefore inadequate on similar grounds as the latter:

(a) It denies cognitive significance to purely existential hypotheses, such as 'There exists at least one unicorn', and all sentences whose formulation calls for mixed—i.e., universal and existential—quantification, such as 'For every compound there exists some solvent', for none of these can possibly be conclusively falsified by a finite number of observation sentences.

(b) If 'P' is an observation predicate, then the assertion that all things have the property P is qualified as significant, but its negation, being equivalent to a purely existential hypothesis, is disqualified [cf. (a)]. Hence, criterion (2.2) gives rise to the same dilemma as (2.1).

(c) If a sentence S is completely falsifiable whereas N is a sentence which is not, then their conjunction, $S \cdot N$ (i.e., the expression obtained by connecting the two sentences by the word 'and') is completely falsifiable; for if the negation of S is entailed by a class of observation sentences, then the negation of $S \cdot N$ is, *a fortiori*, entailed by the same class. Thus, the criterion allows empirical significance to many sentences which an adequate empiricist criterion should rule out, such as 'All swans are white and the absolute is perfect.'

In sum, then, interpretations of the testability criterion in terms of complete verifiability or of complete falsifiability are inadequate because they are overly restrictive in one direction and overly inclusive in another, and because both of them violate the fundamental requirement A.

Several attempts have been made to avoid these difficulties by construing the testability criterion as demanding merely a partial and possibly indirect confirmability of empirical hypotheses by observational evidence.

A formulation suggested by Ayer[5] is characteristic of these attempts to set up a clear and sufficiently comprehensive criterion of confirmability. It states, in effect, that a sentence S has empirical import if from S in conjunction with suitable subsidiary hypotheses it is possible to derive observation sentences which are not derivable from the subsidiary hypotheses alone.

This condition is suggested by a closer consideration of the logical structure of

---

5. (1936, 1946), Chap. I. The case against the requirements of verifiability and of falsifiability, and in favor of a requirement of partial confirmability and disconfirmability, is very clearly presented also by Pap (1949), chapter 13.

scientific testing; but it is much too liberal as it stands. Indeed, as Ayer himself has pointed out in the second edition of his book, *Language , Truth, and Logic*,[6] his criterion allows empirical import to any sentence whatever. Thus, e.g., if *S* is the sentence 'The absolute is perfect', it suffices to choose as a subsidiary hypothesis the sentence 'If the absolute is perfect then this apple is red' in order to make possible the deduction of the observation sentence 'This apple is red', which clearly does not follow from the subsidiary hypothesis alone.

To meet this objection, Ayer proposed a modified version of his testability criterion. In effect, the modification restricts the subsidiary hypotheses mentioned in the previous version to sentences which either are analytic or can independently be shown to be testable in the sense of the modified criterion.[7]

But it can readily be shown that this new criterion, like the requirement of complete falsifiability, allows empirical significance to any conjunction $S \cdot N$, where *S* satisfies Ayer's criterion while *N* is a sentence such as 'The absolute is perfect', which is to be disqualified by that criterion. Indeed, whatever consequences can be deduced from *S* with the help of permissible subsidiary hypotheses can also be deduced from $S \cdot N$ by means of the same subsidiary hypotheses; and as Ayer's new criterion is formulated essentially in terms of the deducibility of a certain type of consequence from the given sentence, it countenances $S \cdot N$ together with *S*. Another difficulty has been pointed out by Church, who has shown[8] that if there are any three observation sentences none of which alone entails any of the others, then it follows for any sentence *S* whatsoever that either it or its denial has empirical import according to Ayer's revised criterion.

All the criteria considered so far attempt to explicate the concept of empirical significance by specifying certain logical connections which must obtain between a significant sentence and suitable observation sentences. It seems now that this type of approach offers little hope for the attainment of precise criteria of meaningfulness: this conclusion is suggested by the preceding survey of some representative attempts, and it receives additional support from certain further considerations, some of which will be presented in the following sections.

3. CHARACTERIZATION OF SIGNIFICANT SENTENCES BY CRITERIA FOR THEIR CONSTITUENT TERMS

An alternative procedure suggests itself which again seems to reflect well

6. (1946), 2d ed., pp. 11–12.

7. This restriction is expressed in recursive form and involves no vicious circle. For the full statement of Ayer's criterion, see Ayer (1946), p. 13.

8. Church (1949). An alternative criterion recently suggested by O'Connor (1950) as a revision of Ayer's formulation is subject to a slight variant of Church's stricture: It can be shown that if there are three observation sentences none of which entails any of the others, and if *S* is any noncompound sentence, then either *S* or $\sim S$ is significant under O'Connor's criterion.

the general viewpoint of empiricism: It might be possible to characterize cognitively significant sentences by certain conditions which their constituent terms have to satisfy. Specifically, it would seem reasonable to say that all extralogical terms[9] in a significant sentence must have experiential reference, and that therefore their meanings must be capable of explication by reference to observables exclusively.[10] In order to exhibit certain analogies between this approach and the previous one, we adopt the following terminological conventions:

Any term that may occur in a cognitively significant sentence will be called a *cognitively significant term*. Furthermore, we shall understand by an *observation term* any term which either (a) is an *observation predicate*, i.e., signifies some observable characteristic (as do the terms 'blue', 'warm', 'soft', 'coincident with', 'of greater apparent brightness than') or (b) names some physical object of macroscopic size (as do the terms 'the needle of this instrument', 'the Moon', 'Krakatoa Volcano', 'Greenwich, England', 'Julius Caesar').

Now while the testability criteria of meaning aimed at characterizing the cognitively significant sentences by means of certain inferential connections in which they must stand to some observation sentences, the alternative approach under consideration would instead try to specify the vocabulary that may be used in forming significant sentences. This vocabulary, the class of significant terms, would be characterized by the condition that each of its elements is either a logical term or else a term with empirical significance; in the latter case, it has to stand in certain definitional or explicative connections to some observation terms. This approach certainly avoids any violations of our earlier conditions of adequacy. Thus, e.g., if S is a significant sentence, i.e., contains cognitively significant terms only, then so is its denial, since the denial sign, and its verbal equivalents, belong to the vocabulary of logic and are thus significant. Again, if N is a sentence containing a non-significant term, then so is any compound sentence which contains N.

But this is not sufficient, of course. Rather, we shall now have to consider a crucial question analogous to that raised by the previous approach: Precisely how are the logical connections between empirically significant terms and observation terms to be construed if an adequate criterion of cognitive significance is to result? Let us consider some possibilities.

9. An extralogical term is one that does not belong to the specific vocabulary of logic. The following phrases, and those definable by means of them, are typical examples of logical terms: 'not', 'or', 'if...then', 'all', 'some', '... is an element of class...'. Whether it is possible to make a sharp theoretical distinction between logical and extra-logical terms is a controversial issue related to the problem of discriminating between analytic and synthetic sentences. For the purpose at hand, we may simply assume that the logical vocabulary is given by enumeration.

10. For a detailed exposition and critical discussion of this idea, see H. Feigl's stimulating and enlightening article (1950).

(3.1) The simplest criterion that suggests itself might be called the *requirement of definability*. It would demand that any term with empirical significance must be explicitly definable by means of observation terms.

This criterion would seem to accord well with the maxim of operationism that all significant terms of empirical science must be introduced by operational definitions. However, the requirement of definability is vastly too restrictive, for many important terms of scientific and even pre-scientific discourse cannot be explicitly defined by means of observation terms.

In fact, as Carnap[11] has pointed out, an attempt to provide explicit definitions in terms of observables encounters serious difficulties as soon as disposition terms, such as 'soluble', 'malleable', 'electric conductor', etc., have to be accounted for; and many of these occur even on the pre-scientific level of discourse.

Consider, for example, the word 'fragile'. One might try to define it by saying that an object x is fragile if and only if it satisfies the following condition: If at any time t the object is sharply struck, then it breaks at that time. But if the statement connectives in this phrasing are construed truth-functionally, so that the definition can be symbolized by

$$(D) \qquad Fx \equiv (t)\,(Sxt \supset Bxt)$$

then the predicate 'F' thus defined does not have the intended meaning. For let a be any object which is not fragile (e.g., a raindrop or a rubber band), but which happens not to be sharply struck at any time throughout its existence. Then 'Sat' is false and hence '$Sat \supset Bat$' is true for all values of 't'; consequently, 'Fa' is true though a is not fragile.

To remedy this defect, one might construe the phrase 'if... then...' in the original definiens as having a more restrictive meaning than the truth-functional conditional. This meaning might be suggested by the subjunctive phrasing 'If x were to be sharply struck at any time t, then x would break at t.' But a satisfactory elaboration of this construal would require a clarification of the meaning and the logic of counterfactual and subjunctive conditionals, which is a thorny problem.[12]

An alternative procedure was suggested by Carnap in his theory of reduction sentences.[13] These are sentences which, unlike definitions, specify the meaning of a term only conditionally or partially. The term 'fragile', for example, might be introduced by the following reduction sentence:

$$(R) \qquad (x)\,(t)\,[Sxt \supset (Fx \equiv Bxt)]$$

11. Cf. (1936–37), especially section 7.

12. On this subject, see for example Langford (1941); Lewis (1946), pp. 210–30; Chisholm (1946); Goodman (1947); Reichenbach (1947), Chapter VIII; Hempel and Oppenheim (1948), Part III; Popper (1949); and especially Goodman's further analysis (1955).

13. Cf. Carnap, *loc. cit.* note 11. For a brief elementary presentation of the main idea, see Carnap (1938), Part III. The sentence R here formulated for the predicate 'F' illustrates only the simplest type of reduction sentence, the so-called bilateral reduction sentence.

which specifies that if x is sharply struck at any time t, then x is fragile if and only if x breaks at t.

Our earlier difficulty is now avoided, for if a is a nonfragile object that is never sharply struck, then that expression in R which follows the quantifiers is true of a; but this does not imply that 'Fa' is true. But the reduction sentence R specifies the meaning of 'F' only for application to those objects which meet the "test condition" of being sharply struck at some time; for these it states that fragility then amounts to breaking. For objects that fail to meet the test condition, the meaning of 'F' is left undetermined. In this sense, reduction sentences have the character of partial or conditional definitions.

Reduction sentences provide a satisfactory interpretation of the experiential import of a large class of disposition terms and permit a more adequate formulation of so-called operational definitions, which, in general, are not complete definitions at all. These considerations suggest a greatly liberalized alternative to the requirement of definability:

(3.2) *The requirement of reducibility.* Every term with empirical significance must be capable of introduction, on the basis of observation terms, through chains of reduction sentences.

This requirement is characteristic of the liberalized versions of positivism and physicalism which, since about 1936, have superseded the older, overly narrow conception of a full definability of all terms of empirical science by means of observables,[14] and it avoids many of the shortcomings of the latter. Yet, reduction sentences do not seem to offer an adequate means for the introduction of the central terms of advanced scientific theories, often referred to as theoretical constructs. This is indicated by the following considerations: A chain of reduction sentences provides a necessary and a sufficient condition for the applicability of the term it introduces. (When the two conditions coincide, the chain is tantamount to an explicit definition.) But now take, for example, the concept of length as used in classical physical theory. Here, the length in centimeters of the distance between two points may assume any positive real number as its value; yet it is clearly impossible to formulate, by means of observation terms, a sufficient condition for the applicability of such expressions as 'having a length of $\sqrt{2}$ cm' and 'having a length of $\sqrt{2} + 10^{-100}$ cm'; for such conditions would provide a possibility for discrimination, in observational terms, between two lengths which differ by only 10^{-100} cm.[15]

14. Cf. the analysis in Carnap (1936–37), especially section 15; also see the briefer presentation of the liberalized point of view in Carnap (1938).

15. (Added in 1964.) This is not strictly correct. For a more circumspect statement, see note 12 in "A Logical Appraisal of Operationism" and the fuller discussion in section 7 of the essay "The Theoretician's Dilemma." Both of these pieces are reprinted in the present volume.

It would be ill-advised to argue that for this reason, we ought to permit only such values of the magnitude, length, as permit the statement of sufficient conditions in terms of observables. For this would rule out, among others, all irrational numbers and would prevent us from assigning, to the diagonal of a square with sides of length 1, the length $\sqrt{2}$, which is required by Euclidean geometry. Hence, the principles of Euclidean geometry would not be universally applicable in physics. Similarly, the principles of the calculus would become inapplicable, and the system of scientific theory as we know it today would be reduced to a clumsy, unmanageable torso. This, then, is no way of meeting the difficulty. Rather, we shall have to analyze more closely the function of constructs in scientific theories, with a view to obtaining through such an analysis a more adequate characterization of cognitively significant terms.

Theoretical constructs occur in the formulation of scientific theories. These may be conceived of, in their advanced stages, as being stated in the form of deductively developed axiomatized systems. Classical mechanics, or Euclidean or some Non-Euclidean form of geometry in physical interpretation, present examples of such systems. The extralogical terms used in a theory of this kind may be divided, in familiar manner, into primitive or basic terms, which are not defined within the theory, and defined terms, which are explicitly defined by means of the primitives. Thus, e.g., in Hilbert's axiomatization of Euclidean geometry, the terms 'point', 'straight line', 'between' are among the primitives, while 'line segment', 'angle', 'triangle', 'length' are among the defined terms. The basic and the defined terms together with the terms of logic constitute the vocabulary out of which all the sentences of the theory are constructed. The latter are divided, in an axiomatic presentation, into primitive statements (also called postulates or basic statements) which, in the theory, are not derived from any other statements, and derived ones, which are obtained by logical deduction from the primitive statements.

From its primitive terms and sentences, an axiomatized theory can be developed by means of purely formal principles of definition and deduction, without any consideration of the empirical significance of its extralogical terms. Indeed, this is the standard procedure employed in the axiomatic development of uninterpreted mathematical theories such as those of abstract groups or rings or lattices, or any form of pure (i.e., noninterpreted) geometry.

However, a deductively developed system of this sort can constitute a scientific theory only if it has received an empirical interpretation[16] which

---

16. The interpretation of formal theories has been studied extensively by Reichenbach, especially in his pioneer analyses of space and time in classical and in relativistic physics. He describes such interpretation as the establishment of *coordinating definitions* (Zuordnungsdefinitionen) for certain terms of the formal theory. See, for example, Reichenbach (1928). More recently,

(continued overleaf)

renders it relevant to the phenomena of our experience. Such interpretation is given by assigning a meaning, in terms of observables, to certain terms or sentences of the formalized theory. Frequently, an interpretation is given not for the primitive terms or statements but rather for some of the terms definable by means of the primitives, or for some of the sentences deducible from the postulates.[17] Furthermore, interpretation may amount to only a partial assignment of meaning. Thus, e.g., the rules for the measurement of length by means of a standard rod may be considered as providing a *partial* empirical interpretation for the term 'the length, in centimeters, of interval *i*', or alternatively, for some sentences of the form 'the length of interval *i* is *r* centimeters'. For the method is applicable only to intervals of a certain medium size, and even for the latter it does not constitute a full interpretation since the use of a standard rod does not constitute the only way of determining length: various alternative procedures are available involving the measurement of other magnitudes which are connected, by general laws, with the length that is to be determined.

This last observation, concerning the possibility of an indirect measurement of length by virtue of certain laws, suggests an important reminder. It is not correct to speak, as is often done, of "the experiential meaning" of a term or a sentence in isolation. In the language of science, and for similar reasons even in pre-scientific discourse, a single statement usually has no experiential implications. A single sentence in a scientific theory does not, as a rule, entail any observation sentences; consequences asserting the occurrence of certain observable phenomena can be derived from it only by conjoining it with a set of other, subsidiary, hypotheses. Of the latter, some will usually be observation sentences, others will be previously accepted theoretical statements. Thus, e.g., the relativistic theory of the deflection of light rays in the gravitational field of the sun entails assertions about observable phenomena only if it is conjoined with a considerable body of astronomical and optical theory as well as a large number of specific statements about the instruments used in those observations of solar eclipses which serve to test the hypothesis in question.

Hence, the phrase, 'the experiential meaning of expression *E*' is elliptical: What

---

17. A somewhat fuller account of this type of interpretation may be found in Carnap (1939), §24. The articles by Spence (1944) and by MacCorquodale and Meehl (1948) provide enlightening illustrations of the use of theoretical constructs in a field outside that of the physical sciences, and of the difficulties encountered in an attempt to analyze in detail their function and interpretation.

Northrop [cf. (1947), Chap. VII, and also the detailed study of the use of deductively formulated theories in science, ibid., Chaps. IV, V, VI] and H. Margenau [cf., for example, (1935)] have discussed certain aspects of this process under the title of *epistemic correlation*.

a given expression "means" in regard to potential empirical data is relative to two factors, namely:

I. *the linguistic framework L* to which the expression belongs. Its rules determine, in particular, what sentences—observational or otherwise—may be inferred from a given statement or class of statements;

II. the theoretical context in which the expression occurs, i.e., the class of those statements in *L* which are available as subsidiary hypotheses.

Thus, the sentence formulating Newton's law of gravitation has no experiential meaning by itself; but when used in a language whose logical apparatus permits the development of the calculus, and when combined with a suitable system of other hypotheses—including sentences which connect some of the theoretical terms with observation terms and thus establish a partial interpretation—then it has a bearing on observable phenomena in a large variety of fields. Analogous considerations are applicable to the term 'gravitational field', for example. It can be considered as having experiential meaning only within the context of a theory, which must be at least partially interpreted; and the experiential meaning of the term—as expressed, say, in the form of operational criteria for its application—will depend again on the theoretical system at hand, and on the logical characteristics of the language within which it is formulated.

4. COGNITIVE SIGNIFICANCE AS A CHARACTERISTIC OF INTERPRETED SYSTEMS

The preceding considerations point to the conclusion that a satisfactory criterion of cognitive significance cannot be reached through the second avenue of approach here considered, namely by means of specific requirements for the terms which make up significant sentences. This result accords with a general characteristic of scientific (and, in principle, even pre-scientific) theorizing: Theory formation and concept formation go hand in hand; neither can be carried on successfully in isolation from the other.

If, therefore, cognitive significance can be attributed to anything, then only to entire theoretical systems formulated in a language with a well-determined structure. And the decisive mark of cognitive significance in such a system appears to be the existence of an interpretation for it in terms of observables. Such an interpretation might be formulated, for example, by means of conditional or biconditional sentences connecting nonobservational terms of the system with observation terms in the given language; the latter as well as the connecting sentences may or may not belong to the theoretical system.

But the requirement of partial interpretation is extremely liberal; it is satisfied, for example, by the system consisting of contemporary physical theory combined with some set of principles of speculative metaphysics, even if the latter have no empirical interpretation at all. Within the total system, these metaphysical principles play the role of what K. Reach and also O. Neurath liked to call *isolated sentences:* They are neither purely formal truths or falsehoods, demonstrable or refutable by means of the logical rules of the given language system; nor do they have any experiential bearing; i.e., their omission from the theoretical system would have no effect on its explanatory and predictive power in regard to potentially observable phenomena (i.e., the kind of phenomena described by observation sentences). Should we not, therefore, require that a cognitively significant system contain no isolated sentences? The following criterion suggests itself:

(4.1) A theoretical system is cognitively significant if and only if it is partially interpreted to at least such an extent that none of its primitive sentences is isolated.

But this requirement may bar from a theoretical system certain sentences which might well be viewed as permissible and indeed desirable. By way of a simple illustration, let us assume that our theoretical system T contains the primitive sentence

$$(S1) \qquad (x)\, [P_1 x \supset (Qx \equiv P_2 x)]$$

where 'P_1' and 'P_2' are observation predicates in the given language L, while 'Q' functions in T somewhat in the manner of a theoretical construct and occurs in only one primitive sentence of T, namely $S1$. Now $S1$ is not a truth or falsehood of formal logic; and furthermore, if $S1$ is omitted from the set of primitive sentences of T, then the resulting system, T', possesses exactly the same systematic, i.e., explanatory and predictive, power as T. Our contemplated criterion would therefore qualify $S1$ as an isolated sentence which has to be eliminated—excised by means of Occam's razor, as it were—if the theoretical system at hand is to be cognitively significant.

But it is possible to take a much more liberal view of $S1$ by treating it as a partial definition for the theoretical term 'Q'. Thus conceived, $S1$ specifies that in all cases where the observable characteristic P_1 is present, 'Q' is applicable if and only if the observable characteristic P_2 is present as well. In fact, $S1$ is an instance of those partial, or conditional, definitions which Carnap calls bilateral reduction sentences. These sentences are explicitly qualified by Carnap as analytic (though not, of course, as truths of formal logic), essentially on the ground that all their consequences which are expressible by means of observation predicates (and logical terms) alone are truths of formal logic.[18]

Let us pursue this line of thought a little further. This will lead us to some observations on analytic sentences and then back to the question of the adequacy of (4.1).

18. Cf. Carnap (1936-37), especially sections 8 and 10.

Suppose that we add to our system T the further sentence

$$(S2) \qquad (x)[P_3x \supset (Qx \equiv P_4x)]$$

where 'P_3', 'P_4' are additional observation predicates. Then, on the view that "every bilateral reduction sentence is analytic", [19] $S2$ would be analytic as well as $S1$. Yet, the two sentences jointly entail non-analytic consequences which are expressible in terms of observation predicates alone, such as[20]

$$(O) \qquad (x)\,[\sim(P_1x \cdot P_2x \cdot Px_3 \cdot \sim P_4x) \cdot \sim(P_1x \cdot \sim P_2x \cdot P_3x \cdot P_4x)]$$

But one would hardly want to admit the consequence that the conjunction of two analytic sentences may be synthetic. Hence if the concept of analyticity can be applied at all to the sentences of interpreted deductive systems, then it will have to be relativized with respect to the theoretical context at hand. Thus, e.g., $S1$ might be qualified as analytic relative to the system T, whose remaining postulates do not contain the term 'Q', but as synthetic relative to the system T enriched by $S2$. Strictly speaking, the concept of analyticity has to be relativized also in regard to the rules of the language at hand, for the latter determine what observational or other consequences are entailed by a given sentence. This need for at least a twofold relativization of the concept of analyticity was almost to be expected in view of those considerations which required the same twofold relativization for the concept of experiential meaning of a sentence.

If, on the other hand, we decide not to permit $S1$ in the role of a partial definition and instead reject it as an isolated sentence, then we are led to an analogous conclusion: Whether a sentence is isolated or not will depend on the linguistic frame and on the theoretical context at hand: While $S1$ is isolated relative to T (and the language in which both are formulated), it acquires definite experiential implications when T is enlarged by $S2$.

Thus we find, on the level of interpreted theoretical systems, a peculiar rapprochement, and partial fusion, of some of the problems pertaining to the concepts of cognitive significance and of analyticity: Both concepts need to be relativized; and a large class of sentences may be viewed, apparently with equal right, as analytic in a given context, or as isolated, or nonsignificant, in respect to it.

In addition to barring, as isolated in a given context, certain sentences which could just as well be construed as partial definitions, the criterion (4.1) has another serious defect. Of two logically equivalent formulations of a theoretical system it may qualify one as significant while barring the other as containing

19. Carnap (1936-37), p. 452.
20. The sentence O is what Carnap calls the *representative sentence* of the couple consisting of the sentences $S1$ and $S2$; see (1936-37), pp. 450-53.

an isolated sentence among its primitives. For assume that a certain theoretical system $T1$ contains among its primitive sentences $S',$ $S'',$ . . . exactly one, $S',$ which is isolated. Then $T1$ is not significant under (4.1). But now consider the theoretical system $T2$ obtained from $T1$ by replacing the two first primitive sentences, $S',$ $S'',$ by one, namely their conjunction. Then, under our assumptions, none of the primitive sentences of $T2$ is isolated, and $T2$, though equivalent to $T1$, is qualified as significant by (4.1). In order to do justice to the intent of (4.1), we would therefore have to lay down the following stricter requirement:

(4.2) A theoretical system is cognitively significant if and only if it is partially interpreted to such an extent that in no system equivalent to it at least one primitive sentence is isolated.

Let us apply this requirement to some theoretical system whose postulates include the two sentences $S1$ and $S2$ considered before, and whose other postulates do not contain 'Q' at all. Since the sentences $S1$ and $S2$ together entail the sentence O, the set consisting of $S1$ and $S2$ is logically equivalent to the set consisting of $S1$, $S2$ and O. Hence, if we replace the former set by the latter, we obtain a theoretical system equivalent to the given one. In this new system, both $S1$ and $S2$ are isolated since, as can be shown, their removal does not affect the explanatory and predictive power of the system in reference to observable phenomena. To put it intuitively, the systematic power of $S1$ and $S2$ is the same as that of O. Hence, the original system is disqualified by (4.2). From the viewpoint of a strictly sensationalist positivism as perhaps envisaged by Mach, this result might be hailed as a sound repudiation of theories making reference to fictitious entities, and as a strict insistence on theories couched exclusively in terms of observables. But from a contemporary vantage point, we shall have to say that such a procedure overlooks or misjudges the important function of constructs in scientific theory: The history of scientific endeavor shows that if we wish to arrive at precise, comprehensive, and well-confirmed general laws, we have to rise above the level of direct observation. The phenomena directly accessible to our experience are not connected by general laws of great scope and rigor. Theoretical constructs are needed for the formulation of such higher-level laws. One of the most important functions of a well-chosen construct is its potential ability to serve as a constituent in ever new general connections that may be discovered; and to such connections we would blind ourselves if we insisted on banning from scientific theories all those terms and sentences which could be "dispensed with" in the sense indicated in (4.2). In following such a narrowly phenomenalistic or positivistic course, we would deprive ourselves of the tremendous fertility of theoretical constructs, and we would often render the formal structure of the expurgated theory clumsy and inefficient.

Criterion (4.2), then, must be abandoned, and considerations such as those outlined in this paper seem to lend strong support to the conjecture that no adequate alternative to it can be found; i.e., that it is not possible to formulate general and precise criteria which would separate those partially interpreted systems whose isolated sentences might be said to have a significant function from those in which the isolated sentences are, so to speak, mere useless append-ages.

We concluded earlier that cognitive significance in the sense intended by recent empiricism and operationism can at best be attributed to sentences forming a theoretical system, and perhaps rather to such systems as wholes. Now, rather than try to replace (4.2) by some alternative, we will have to recognize further that cognitive significance in a system is a matter of degree: Significant systems range from those whose entire extralogical vocabulary consists of observation terms, through theories whose formulation relies heavily on theoretical con-structs, on to systems with hardly any bearing on potential empirical findings. Instead of dichotomizing this array into significant and non-significant systems it would seem less arbitrary and more promising to appraise or compare different theoretical systems in regard to such characteristics as these:

a. the clarity and precision with which the theories are formulated, and with which the logical relationships of their elements to each other and to expressions couched in observational terms have been made explicit;

b. the systematic, i.e., explanatory and predictive, power of the systems in regard to observable phenomena;

c. the formal simplicity of the theoretical system with which a certain systematic power is attained;

d. the extent to which the theories have been confirmed by experiential evidence.

Many of the speculative philosophical approaches to cosmology, biology, or history, for example, would make a poor showing on practically all of these counts and would thus prove no matches to available rival theories, or would be recognized as so unpromising as not to warrant further study or development.

If the procedure here suggested is to be carried out in detail, so as to become applicable also in less obvious cases, then it will be necessary, of course, to develop general standards, and theories pertaining to them, for the appraisal and compari-son of theoretical systems in the various respects just mentioned. To what extent this can be done with rigor and precision cannot well be judged in advance. In recent years, a considerable amount of work has been done towards a definition and theory of the concept of degree of confirmation, or logical probability, of a theoretical system;[21] and several contributions have been made towards the

21. Cf., for example, Carnap (1945)1 and (1945)2, and especially (1950). Also see Helmer and Oppenheim (1945).

clarification of some of the other ideas referred to above.[22] The continuation of this research represents a challenge for further constructive work in the logical and methodological analysis of scientific knowledge.

22. On simplicity, cf. especially Popper (1935), Chap. V; Reichenbach (1938), § 42; Goodman (1949)1, (1949)2, (1950); on explanatory and predictive power, cf. Hempel and Oppenheim (1948), Part IV.

REFERENCES

Ayer, A. J., *Language, Truth and Logic*, London, 1936; 2nd ed. 1946.

Carnap, R., "Testability and Meaning," *Philosophy of Science*, 3 (1936) and 4 (1937).

Carnap, R., "Logical Foundations of the Unity of Science," in: *International Encyclopedia of Unified Science*, I, 1; Chicago, 1938.

Carnap, R., *Foundations of Logic and Mathematics*, Chicago, 1939.

Carnap, R., "On Inductive Logic," *Philosophy of Science*, 12 (1945). Referred to as (1945)1 in this article.

Carnap, R., "The Two Concepts of Probability," *Philosophy and Phenomenological Research*, 5 (1945). Referred to as (1945)2 in this article.

Carnap, R., *Logical Foundations of Probability*, Chicago, 1950.

Chisholm, R. M., "The Contrary-to-Fact Conditional," *Mind*, 55 (1946).

Church, A., Review of Ayer (1946), *The Journal of Symbolic Logic*, 14 (1949), 52–53.

Feigl, H., "Existential Hypotheses: Realistic vs. Phenomenalistic Interpretations," *Philosophy of Science*, 17 (1950).

Goodman, N., "The Problem of Counterfactual Conditionals," *The Journal of Philosophy*, 44 (1947).

Goodman, N., "The Logical Simplicity of Predicates," *The Journal of Symbolic Logic*, 14 (1949). Referred to as (1949)1 in this article.

Goodman, N., "Some Reflections on the Theory of Systems," *Philosophy and Phenomenological Research*, 9 (1949). Referred to as (1949)2 in this article.

Goodman, N., "An Improvement in the Theory of Simplicity," *The Journal of Symbolic Logic*, 15 (1950).

Goodman, N., *Fact, Fiction, and Forecast*, Cambridge, Massachusetts, 1955.

Helmer, O. and P. Oppenheim, "A Syntactical Definition of Probability and of Degree of Confirmation." *The Journal of Symbolic Logic*, 10 (1945).

Hempel, C. G. and P. Oppenheim, "Studies in the Logic of Explanation," *Philosophy of Science*, 15 (1948). (Reprinted in this volume.)

Langford, C. H., Review in *The Journal of Symbolic Logic*, 6 (1941), 67–68.

Lewis, C. I., *An Analysis of Knowledge and Valuation*, La Salle, Ill., 1946.

MacCorquodale, K. and P. E. Meehl, "On a Distinction Between Hypothetical Constructs and Intervening Variables," *Psychological Review*, 55 (1948).

Margenau, H., "Methodology of Modern Physics," *Philosophy of Science*, 2 (1935).

Northrop, F. S. C., *The Logic of the Sciences and the Humanities*, New York, 1947.

O'Connor, D. J., "Some Consequences of Professor A. J. Ayer's Verification Principle," *Analysis*, 10 (1950).

Pap, A., *Elements of Analytic Philosophy*, New York, 1949.

Popper, K., *Logik der Forschung*, Wien, 1935.

Popper, K., "A Note on Natural Laws and So-Called 'Contrary-to-Fact Conditionals'," *Mind*, 58 (1949).

Reichenbach, H., *Philosophie der Raum-Zeit-Lehre*, Berlin, 1928.

Reichenbach, H., *Elements of Symbolic Logic*, New York, 1947.

Russell, B., *Human Knowledge*, New York, 1948.

Schlick, M., "Meaning and Verification," *Philosophical Review*, 45 (1936). Also reprinted in Feigl, H. and W. Sellars, (eds.) *Readings in Philosophical Analysis*, New York, 1949.

Spence, Kenneth W., "The Nature of Theory Construction in Contemporary Psychology," *Psychological Review*, 51 (1944).

POSTSCRIPT (1964) *ON*

COGNITIVE SIGNIFICANCE

The preceding essay is a conflation of two articles: "Problems and Changes in the Empiricist Criterion of Meaning," *Revue Internationale de Philosophie* No. 11 (1950), and "The Concept of Cognitive Significance: A Reconsideration," *Proceedings of the American Academy of Arts and Sciences* 80 (1951). In combining the two, I omitted particularly some parts of the first article, which had been largely superseded by the second one;[1] I also made a few minor changes in the remaining text. Some of the general problems raised in the combined essay are pursued further elsewhere in this volume, especially in "The Theoretician's Dilemma." In this Postscript, I propose simply to note some second thoughts concerning particular points in the preceding essay.

(i) The objections 2.1(c) and 2.2(c) against the requirements of complete verifiability and of complete falsifiability are, I think, of questionable force. For S v N can properly be said to be entailed by S, and S in turn by $S \cdot N$, only if N as well as S is a declarative sentence and thus is either true or false. But if the criterion of cognitive significance is understood to delimit the class of sentences which make significant assertions, and which are thus either true or false, then the sentence N invoked in the objections is not declarative, and neither are S v N or $S \cdot N$; hence the alleged inferences from $S \cdot N$ to S and from S to S v N are inadmissible.[2]

1. The basic ideas presented in the earlier articles and in the present conflated version are penetratingly examined by I. Scheffler in *The Anatomy of Inquiry*, New York, 1963. Part II of his book deals in detail with the concept of cognitive significance.

2. I owe this correction to graduate students who put forth the above criticism in one of my seminars. The same point has recently been stated very clearly by D. Rynin in "Vindication of L*G*C*L P*S*T*V*SM", *Proceedings and Addresses of the American Philosophical Association*, 30 (1957); see especially pp. 57-58.

My objection retains its force, however, against the use of falsifiability, not as a criterion of significance, but as a "criterion of demarcation." This use would draw a dividing line "between the statements, or systems of statements, of the empirical sciences, and all other statements—whether they are of a religious or of a metaphysical character, or simply pseudo-scientific."[3] For the argument 2.2(c) shows that the conjunction of a scientific statement S with a nonscientific statement N is falsifiable and thus qualifies as a scientific statement; and this would defeat the intended purpose of the criterion of demarcation.

(ii) My assertion, in 2.1(a) and 2.2(a), that the requirements of verifiability and of falsifiability would rule out *all* hypotheses of mixed quantificational form is false. Consider the hypothesis 'All ravens are black and something is white', or, in symbolic notation

$$(x)\,(Rx \supset Bx) \cdot (\exists y)\,Wy,$$

which is equivalent to

$$(x)\,(\exists y)[(Rx \supset Bx) \cdot Wy]$$

This sentence satisfies the falsifiability requirement because it implies the purely universal hypothesis '$(x)\,(Rx \supset Bx)$', which would be falsified, for example, by the following set of observation sentences: $\{`Ra`,\ `{\sim}Ba`\}$. Similarly, the sentence

$$(\exists x)\,(y)\,(Rx \vee Wy)$$

is verifiable since it is implied, for example, by 'Ra'.

The essential point of the objection remains unaffected, however: Many scientific hypotheses of mixed quantificational form are neither verifiable nor falsifiable; these would therefore be disqualified by the requirement of verifiability as well as by that of falsifiability; and if the latter is used as a criterion of demarcation rather than of significance, it excludes those hypotheses from the class of scientific statements. These consequences are unacceptable.

(iii) An even stronger criticism of the criteria of verifiability and of falsifiability results from condition (A1), which is stated early in section 2, and which demands in effect that any acceptable criterion of significance which admits a sentence as significant must also admit its negation. That this condition must be met is clear, for since a significant sentence is one that is either true or false, its negation can be held nonsignificant only on pain of violating a fundamental principle of logic. And even if the falsifiability criterion is used as a criterion of demarcation rather than of cognitive significance, satisfaction of (A1) seems imperative. Otherwise, a scientist reporting that he had succeeded in refuting a scientific hypothesis S of universal form would be making a nonscientific

3. K. R. Popper, "Philosophy of Science: A Personal Report," In C. A. Mace, ed., *British Philosophy in the Mid-Century*, London, 1957; pp. 155-91; quotations from pp. 163, 162.

statement if he were to say: "Hence, it is not the case that S holds," for this statement would not be falsifiable. More generally, formally valid deductive logical inference would often lead from scientific premises to nonscientific conclusions—e.g., from '$Ra \cdot \sim Ba$' to '$(\exists x)(Rx \cdot \sim Bx)$'; and, surely, this is intolerable.

But when the requirement of verifiability, or that of falsifiability, is combined with condition (A1), then a sentence qualifies as cognitively significant just in case it and its negation are verifiable, or just in case it and its negation are falsifiable. These two criteria now demand the same thing of a significant sentence, namely, that it be both verifiable and falsifiable. This characterization admits, besides all truth-functional compounds of observation sentences, also certain sentences containing quantifiers. For example, '$Pa \lor (x)Qx$' is verifiable by 'Pa' and falsifiable by {'$\sim Pa$', '$\sim Qb$'}; and as is readily seen, '$Pa \cdot (\exists x)Qx$' equally meets the combined requirement. But this requirement excludes all strictly general hypotheses, i.e., those containing essential occurrences of quantifiers but not of individual constants; such as '$(x)(Rx \supset Bx)$', '$(x)(\exists y)(Rxy \supset Sxy)$', and so forth. Again, this consequence is surely unacceptable, no matter whether the criterion is meant to delimit the class of significant sentences or the class of statements of empirical science.

5. A LOGICAL APPRAISAL

OF OPERATIONISM

1. BASIC TENETS OF OPERATIONISM

OPERATIONISM, in its fundamental tenets, is closely akin to logical empiricism. Both schools of thought have put much emphasis on definite experiential meaning or import as a necessary condition of objectively significant discourse, and both have made strong efforts to establish explicit criteria of experiential significance. But logical empiricism has treated experiential import as a characteristic of statements—namely, as their susceptibility to test by experiment or observation—whereas operationism has tended to construe experiential meaning as a characteristic of concepts or of the terms representing them—namely, as their susceptibility to operational definition.

BASIC IDEAS OF OPERATIONAL ANALYSIS. An operational definition of a term is conceived as a rule to the effect that the term is to apply to a particular case if the performance of specified operations in that case yields a certain characteristic result. For example, the term 'harder than' might be operationally defined by the rule that a piece of mineral, x, is to be called harder than another piece of mineral, y, if the operation of drawing a sharp point of x across the surface of y results in a scratch mark on the latter. Similarly, the different numerical values of a quantity such as length are thought of as operationally definable by reference to the outcomes of specified measuring operations. To safeguard the objectivity of science, all operations invoked in this kind of definition are

This article is a slightly modified version of an article with the same title that appeared in *Scientific Monthly* 79, pp. 215–20 (1954). It is here reprinted by kind permission of the Editor of *Science*.

required to be intersubjective in the sense that different observers must be able to perform "the same operation" with reasonable agreement in their results.[1]

P. W. Bridgman, the originator of operational analysis, distinguishes several kinds of operation that may be invoked in specifying the meanings of scientific terms.[2] The principal ones are (i) what he calls *instrumental operations*. These consist in the use of various devices of observation and measurement, and (ii) paper-and-pencil operations, verbal operations, mental experiments, and the like—this group is meant to include, among other things, the techniques of mathematical and logical inference as well as the use of experiments–in–imagination. For brevity, but also by way of suggesting a fundamental similarity among the procedures of the second kind, I shall refer to them as *symbolic operations*.

The concepts of operation and of operational definition serve to state the basic principles of operational analysis, of which the following are of special importance.

1) "Meanings are operational." To understand the meaning of a term, we must know the operational criteria of its application,[3] and every meaningful scientific term must therefore permit of an operational definition. Such definition may refer to certain symbolic operations and it always must ultimately make reference to some instrumental operation.[4]

2) To avoid ambiguity, every scientific term should be defined by means of one unique operational criterion. Even when two different operational procedures (for instance, the optical and the tactual ways of measuring length) have been found to yield the same results, they still must be considered as defining different concepts (for example, optical and tactual length), and these should be distinguished terminologically because the presumed coincidence of the results is inferred from experimental evidence, and it is "not safe" to forget that the presumption may be shown to be spurious by new, and perhaps more precise, experimental data.[5]

3) The insistence that scientific terms should have unambiguously specifiable operational meanings serves to insure the possibility of an objective test for the

1. P. W. Bridgman, "Some General Principles of Operational Analysis" and "Rejoinders and Second Thoughts," *Psychological Review*, 52, 246 and 281 (1945); "The Nature of Some of our Physical Concepts," *British Journal for the Philosophy of Science* 1, 258 (1951).

2. ———"Operational Analysis," *Philosophy of Science* 5, 123 (1938); *British Journal for the Philosophy of Science* 1, 258 (1951).

3. ——— *Philosophy of Science* 5, 116 (1938).

4. ——— *British Journal for the Philosophy of Science* 1, 260 (1951).

5. ——— *The Logic of Modern Physics*, New York, Macmillan, 1927, pp. 6, 23–24; *Philosophy of Science* 5, 121 (1938); *Psychological Review*, 52, 247 (1945); "The Operational Aspect of Meaning," *Synthèse* 8, 255 (1950–51).

hypotheses formulated by means of those terms[6]. Hypotheses incapable of operational test or, rather, questions involving untestable formulations, are rejected as meaningless: "If a specific question has meaning, it must be possible to find operations by which an answer may be given to it. It will be found in many cases that the operations cannot exist, and the question therefore has no meaning."[7]

The emphasis on "operational meaning" in scientifically significant discourse has unquestionably afforded a salutary critique of certain types of procedure in philosophy and in empirical science and has provided a strong stimulus for methodological thinking. Yet, the central ideas of operational analysis as stated by their proponents are so vague that they constitute not a theory concerning the nature of scientific concepts but rather a program for the development of such a theory. They share this characteristic with the insistence of logical empiricism that all significant scientific statements must have experiential import, that the latter consists in testability by suitable data of direct observation, and that sentences which are entirely incapable of any test must be ruled out as meaningless "pseudo-hypotheses." These ideas, too, constitute not so much a thesis or a theory as a program for a theory that needs to be formulated and amplified in precise terms.

An attempt to develop an operationist theory of scientific concepts will have to deal with at least two major issues: the problem of giving a more precise explication of the concept of operational definition; and the question whether operational definition in the explicated sense is indeed necessary for, and adequate to, the introduction of all nonobservational terms in empirical science.

I wish to present here in brief outline some considerations that bear on these problems. The discussion will be limited to the descriptive, or extralogical, vocabulary of empirical science and will not deal, therefore, with Bridgman's ideas concerning the status of logic and mathematics.

2. A BROADENED CONCEPTION OF OPERATIONAL DEFINITION AND OF THE PROGRAM OF OPERATIONAL ANALYSIS

The terms 'operational meaning' and 'operational definition', as well as many of the pronouncements made in operationist writings, convey the suggestion that the criteria of application for any scientific term must ultimately refer to the outcome of some specified type of manipulation of the subject matter under investigation. Such emphasis would evidently be overly restrictive. An operational definition gives experiential meaning to the term it introduces because it enables us to decide on the applicability of that term to a given case by observing the response the case shows under specifiable test conditions. Whether

6. P. W. Bridgman, *Psychological Review* 52, 246 (1945).
7. ———— *The Logic of Modern Physics*, p. 28.

these conditions can be brought about at will by "instrumental operations" or whether we have to wait for their occurrence is of great interest for the practice of scientific research, but is it inessential to securing experiental import for the defined term; what matters for this latter purpose is simply that the relevant test conditions and the requisite response be of such kind that different investigators can ascertain, by direct observation and with reasonably good agreement, whether, in a given case, the test conditions are realized and whether the characteristic response does occur.

Thus, an operational definition of the simplest kind—one that, roughly speaking, refers to instrumental operations only—will have to be construed more broadly as introducing a term by the stipulation that it is to apply to all and only those cases which, under specified observable conditions S, show a characteristic observable response R.

However, an operational definition cannot be conceived as specifying that the term in question is to apply to a given case only if S and R actually occur in that case. Physical bodies, for example, are asserted to have masses, temperatures, charges, and so on, even at times when these magnitudes are not being measured. Hence, an operational definition of a concept will have to be understood as ascribing the concept to all those cases that *would* exhibit the characteristic response if the test conditions *should* be realized. A concept thus characterized is clearly not "synonymous with the corresponding set of operations".[8] It constitutes not a manifest but a potential character, namely, a disposition to exhibit a certain characteristic response under specified test conditions.

But to attribute a disposition of this kind to a case in which the specified test condition is not realized (for example, to attribute solubility-in-water to a lump of sugar that is not actually put into water) is to make a generalization, and this involves an inductive risk. Thus, the application of an operationally defined term to an instance of the kind here considered would have to be adjudged "not safe" in precisely the same sense in which Bridgman insists it is "not safe" to assume that two procedures of measurement that have yielded the same results in the past will continue to do so in the future. It is now clear that if we were to reject any procedure that involves an inductive risk, we would be prevented not only from using more than one operational criterion in introducing a given term but also from ever applying a disposition term to any case in which the characteristic manifest conditions of application are not realized; thus, the use of dispositional concepts would, in effect, be prohibited.

8. P. W. Bridgman, ibid., p. 5; subsequently qualified by Bridgman in his reply, *Philosophy of Science* 5, 117 (1938), to R. B. Lindsay, "A Critique of Operationalism in Physics," *Philosophy of Science* 4, (1937). The qualification was essentially on the ground, quite different from that given in the present paper, that operational meaning is only a necessary, but presumably not a sufficient characteristic of scientific concepts.

A few remarks might be added here concerning the noninstrumental operations countenanced for the introduction especially of theoretical terms. In operationist writings, those symbolic procedures have been characterized so vaguely as to permit the introduction, by a suitable choice of "verbal" or "mental" operations, of virtually all those ideas that operational analysis was to prohibit as devoid of meaning. To meet this difficulty, Bridgman has suggested a distinction between "good" and "bad" operations;[9] but he has not provided a clear criterion for this distinction. Consequently, this idea fails to plug the hole in the operationist dike.

If the principles of operationism are to admit the theoretical constructs of science but to rule out certain other kinds of terms as lacking experiential, or operational, meaning, then the vague requirement of definability by reference to instrumental and "good" symbolic operations must be replaced by a precise characterization of the kinds of sentences that may be used to introduce, or specify the meanings of, "meaningful" nonobservational terms on the basis of the observational vocabulary of science. Such a characterization would eliminate the psychologistic notion of mental operations in favor of a specification of the logico-mathematical concepts and procedures to be permitted in the context of operational definition.

The reference just made to the observational vocabulary of science is essential to the idea of operational definition; for it is in terms of this vocabulary that the test conditions and the characteristic response specified in an operational definition are described and by means of which, therefore, the meanings of operationally defined terms are ultimately characterized. Hence, the intent of the original operationist insistence on intersubjective repeatability of the defining operations will be respected if we require that the terms included in the observational vocabulary must refer to features that are directly and publicly observable—that is, whose presence or absence can be ascertained, under suitable conditions, by direct observation, and with good agreement among different observers.[10]

9. P. W. Bridgman, *Philosophy of Science* 5, 126 (1938); "Some Implications of Recent Points of View in Physics," *Revue Internationale de Philosophie* 3, 484 (1949). The intended distinction between good and bad operations is further obscured by the fact that in Bridgman's discussion the meaning of "good operation" shifts from what might be described as "operation whose use in operational definition insures experiential meaning and testability" to "scientific procedure—in some very broad sense—which leads us to correct predictions."

10. The condition thus imposed upon the observational vocabulary of science is of a pragmatic character: it demands that each term included in that vocabulary be of such a kind that under suitable conditions, different observers can, by means of direct observation, arrive at a high degree of agreement on whether the term applies to a given situation. The expression 'coincides with' as applicable to instrument needles and marks on scales of instruments is an example of a term meeting this condition. That human beings are capable of developing observational vocabularies that satisfy the given requirement is a fortunate circumstance: without it, science as an intersubjective enterprise would be impossible.

In sum, then, a precise statement and elaboration of the basic tenets of operationism requires an explication of the logical relationships between theoretical and observational terms, just as a precise statement and elaboration of the basic tenets of empiricism requires an explication of the logical relationships connecting theoretical sentences with observation sentences describing potential data of direct observation.

3. SPECIFICATION OF MEANING BY EXPLICIT DEFINITION AND BY REDUCTION

Initially, it may appear plausible to assume that all theoretical terms used in science can be fully defined by means of the observational vocabulary. There are various reasons, however, to doubt this assumption.

First of all, there exists a difficulty concerning the definition of the scientific terms that refer to dispositions—and, as is noted in a foregoing paragraph, all the terms introduced by operational definition have to be viewed as dispositional in character. Recent logical studies strongly suggest that dispositions can be defined by reference to manifest characteristics, such as those presented by the observational vocabulary, only with help of some "nomological modality" such as the concept of nomological truth, that is, truth by virtue of general laws of nature.[11] But a concept of this kind is presumably inadmissible under operationist standards, since it is neither a directly observable characteristic nor definable in terms of such characteristics.

Another difficulty arises when we attempt to give full definitions, in terms of observables, for quantitative terms such as 'length in centimeters', 'duration in seconds', 'temperature in degrees Celsius'. In scientific theory, each of these is allowed to assume any real-number value within a certain interval; and the

---

11. To illustrate briefly, it seems reasonable, *prima facie*, to define 'x is soluble in water' by 'if x is put in water then x dissolves', But if the phrase 'if . . . then . . .', is here construed as the truth-functional, or "material," conditional, then the objects qualified as soluble by the definition include, among others, all those things that are never put in water—no matter whether or not they are actually soluble in water. This consequence—one aspect of the "paradoxes of material implication"—can be avoided only if our conditional definiens is construed in a more restrictive fashion. The idea suggests itself of construing 'x is soluble in water' as short for 'by virtue of some general laws of nature, x dissolves if x is put in water', or briefly, 'it is nomologically true that if x is put in water then x dissolves', The phrase 'if. . . then. . .', may now be understood in the truth-functional sense again. However, the acceptability of this analysis depends, of course, upon whether nomological truth can be considered as a sufficiently clear concept. For a fuller discussion of this problem complex, see especially R. Carnap, "Testability and Meaning," *Philosophy of Science* 3 (1936) and 4 (1937) and N. Goodman, "The Problem of Counterfactual Conditionals," *Journal of Philosophy* 44 (1947).

question therefore arises whether each of the infinitely many permissible values, say of length, is capable of an operational specification of meaning. It can be shown that it is impossible to characterize every one of the permissible numerical values by some truth-functional combination of observable characteristics, since the existence of a threshold of discrimination in all areas of observation allows for only a finite number of nonequivalent combinations of this kind.[12]

Difficulties such as these suggest the question whether it is not possible to conceive of methods more general and more flexible than definition for the introduction of scientific terms on the basis of the observational vocabulary. One such method has been developed by Carnap. It makes use of so-called reduction sentences, which constitute a considerably generalized version of definition sentences and are especially well suited for a precise reformulation of the intent of operational definitions. As we noted earlier, an operational definition of the simplest kind stipulates that the concept it introduces, say C, is to apply to those and only those cases which, under specified test conditions S, show a certain characteristic response R. In Carnap's theory this stipulation is replaced by the sentence

(1)
$$Sx \rightarrow (Cx \equiv Rx)$$

or, in words: If a case x satisfies the test condition S, then x is an instance of C if and only if x shows the response R. Formula 1, called a bilateral reduction sentence, is not a full definition (which would have to be of the form '$Cx \equiv \ldots$', with 'Cx' constituting the definiendum); it specifies the meaning of 'Cx', not for all cases, but only for those that satisfy the condition S. In this sense, it con-

---

12. In other words, it is not possible to provide, for every theoretically permissible value r of the length $l(x)$ of a rod x, a definition of the form

$$[l(x) = r] =_{df} C(P_1 x, P_2 x, \ldots, P_n x)$$

where $P_1, P_2, \ldots, P_n$ are observable characteristics, and the definiens is an expression formed from '$P_1 x$', '$P_2 x$', '. . . ., '$P_n x$' by means of the connective words 'and', 'or,' and 'not' alone.

It is worth noting, however, that if the logical constants allowed in the definiens include, in addition to truth-functional connectives, also quantifiers and the identity sign, then a finite observational vocabulary may permit the explicit definition of a denumerable infinity of further terms. For instance, if 'x spatially contains y' and 'y is an apple' are included in the observational vocabulary, then it is possible to define the expressions 'x contains 0 apples', 'x contains exactly 1 apple', 'x contains exactly 2 apples', and so forth, in accordance with the Frege-Russell definition of natural numbers. Yet even if definitions of this type are countenanced—and no doubt they are in accord with the intent of operationist analysis—there remain serious obstacles for an operationist account of the totality of real numbers which are permitted as theoretical values of length, mass, and so forth. On this point, see C. G. Hempel, *Fundamentals of Concept Formation in Empirical Science* (Chicago: University of Chicago Press, 1952), sec. 7.

stitutes only a partial, or conditional, definition for C.[13] If 'S' and 'R' belong to the observational vocabulary of science, formula 1 schematizes the simplest type of operational definition, which invokes (almost) exclusively instrumental operations or, better, experiential findings. Operational definitions that also utilize symbolic operations would be represented by chains of reduction sentences containing logical or mathematical symbols. Some such symbols occur even in formula 1, however; and clearly, there can be no operational definition that makes use of no logical concepts at all.

4. INTERPRETATIVE SYSTEMS

Once the idea of a partial specification of meaning is granted, it appears unnecessarily restrictive, however, to limit the sentences effecting such partial interpretation to reduction sentences in Carnap's sense. A partial specification of the meanings of a set of nonobservational terms might be expressed, more generally, by one or more sentences that connect those terms with the observational vocabulary but do not have the form of reduction sentences. And it seems well to countenance, for the same purpose, even stipulations expressed by sentences containing only nonobservational terms; for example, the stipulation that two theoretical terms are to be mutually exclusive may be regarded as a limitation and, in this sense, a partial specification of their meanings.

Generally, then, a set of one or more theoretical terms, $t_1, t_2, \ldots, t_n$, might be introduced by any set M of sentences such that (i) M contains no extralogical terms other than $t_1, t_2, \ldots, t_n$, and observation terms, (ii) M is logically consistent, and (iii) M is not equivalent to a truth of formal logic. The last two of these conditions serve merely to exclude trivial extreme cases. A set of M of this kind will be referred to briefly as an *interpretative system*, its elements as *interpretative sentences*.

Explicit definitions and reduction sentences are special types of interpretative sentences, and so are the meaning postulates recently suggested by Kemeny and Carnap.[14]

13. The use of reduction sentences circumvents one of the difficulties encountered in the attempt to give explicit and, thus, complete definitions of disposition terms: the conditional and biconditional signs occurring in formula 1 may be construed truth-functionally without giving rise to undesirable consequences of the kind characterized in footnote 11. For details, see R. Carnap, "Testability and Meaning," sections 5–10; also C. G. Hempel, *Fundamentals of Concept Formation in Empirical Science*, sections 6 and 8. Incidentally, the use of nomological concepts is not entirely avoided in Carnap's procedure; the reduction sentences that are permitted for the introduction of new terms are required to satisfy certain conditions of logical or of nomological validity. See R. Carnap, "Testability and Meaning," pp. 442–443.

14. J. G. Kemeny, "Extension of the Methods of Inductive Logic," *Philosophical Studies* 3 (1952); R. Carnap, "Meaning Postulates," *ibid.* 3 (1952).

The interpretative sentences used in a given theory may be viewed simply as postulates of that theory,[15] with all the observation terms, as well as the terms introduced by the interpretative system, being treated as primitives. Thus construed, the specification of the meanings of nonobservational terms in science resembles what has sometimes been called the implicit definition of the primitives of an axiomatized theory by its postulates. In this latter procedure, the primitives are all uninterpreted, and the postulates then impose restrictions on any interpretation of the primitives that can turn the postulates into true sentences. Such restrictions may be viewed as partial specifications of meaning. The use of interpretative systems as here envisaged has this distinctive peculiarity, however: the primitives include a set of terms—the observation terms—which are antecedently understood and thus not in need of any interpretation, and by reference to which the postulates effect a partial specification of meaning for the remaining, nonobservational, primitives. This partial specification again consists in limiting those interpretations of the nonobservational terms that will render the postulates true.

5. IMPLICATIONS FOR THE IDEA OF EXPERIENTIAL MEANING AND FOR THE DISTINCTION OF ANALYTIC AND SYNTHETIC SENTENCES IN SCIENCE

If the introduction of nonobservational terms is conceived in this broader fashion, which appears to accord with the needs of a formal reconstruction of the language of empirical science, then it becomes pointless to ask for the operational definition or the experiential import of any one theoretical term. Explicit definition by means of observables is no longer generally available, and experiential—or operational—meaning can be attributed only to the set of all the nonobservational terms functioning in a given theory.

Furthermore, there remains no satisfactory general way of dividing all conceivable systems of theoretical terms into two classes: those that are scientifically significant and those that are not; those that have experiential import and those that lack it. Rather, experiential, or operational, significance appears as capable of gradations. To begin with one extreme possibility: the interpretative system M introducing the given terms may simply be a set of sentences in the form of explicit definitions that provide an observational equivalent for each of those terms. In this case, the terms introduced by M have maximal experiential significance, as it were. In another case, M might consist of reduction sentences for the theoretical terms; these will enable us to formulate, in terms of obser-

---

15. For the case of Carnap's reduction sentences, the postulational interpretation was suggested to me by N. Goodman and by A. Church.

vables, a necessary and a (different) sufficient condition of application for each of the introduced terms. Again M might contain sentences in the form of definitions or reduction sentences for only some of the nonobservational terms it introduces. And finally, none of the sentences in M might have the form of a definition or of a reduction sentence; and yet, a theory whose terms are introduced by an interpretative system of this kind may well permit of test by observational findings, and in this sense, the system of its nonobservational terms may possess experiential import.[16]

Thus, experiental significance presents itself as capable of degrees, and any attempt to set up a dichotomy allowing only experientially meaningful and experientially meaningless concept systems appears as too crude to be adequate for a logical analysis of scientific concepts and theories.

Interpretative systems afford a more inclusive method of introducing theoretical terms than the method of meaning postulates developed by Carnap and Kemeny. For although meaning postulates are conceived as analytic and hence as implying only analytic consequences, an interpretative system may imply certain sentences which contain observation terms but no theoretical terms and which are neither formal truths of logic nor analytic in the customary sense. Consider, for example, the following two interpretative sentences, which form what Carnap calls a reduction pair, and which interpret 'C' by means of observation predicates, 'R_1', 'S_1', 'R_2', 'S_2':

(2.1) $$S_1 x \rightarrow (R_1 x \rightarrow Cx)$$
(2.2) $$S_2 x \rightarrow (R_2 x \rightarrow {\sim} Cx).$$

Since in no case the sufficient conditions for C and for ${\sim}C$ (non-C) can be satisfied jointly, the two sentences imply the consequence [17] that, for every case x,

---

16. This is illustrated by the following simple model case: The theory T consists of the sentence '$(x) ((C_1 x . C_2 x) \rightarrow C_3 x)$' and its logical consequences; the three "theoretical" terms occurring in it are introduced by the interpretative set M consisting of the sentences '$O_1 x \rightarrow (C_1 x . C_2 x)$' and '$(C_1 x . C_2 x) \rightarrow (O_2 x \vee O_3 x)$', where '$O_1$', '$O_2$', '$O_3$' belong to the observational vocabulary. As is readily seen, T permits, by virtue of M, the "prediction" that if an object has the observable proberty O_1 but lacks the observable property O_2, then it will have the observable property O_3. Thus T is susceptible to experiential test, although M provides for none of its constituent terms both a necessary and a sufficient observational, or operational, criterion of application.

17. Carnap calls it the representative sentence of the pair of formulas 2.1 and 2.2. See R. Carnap, "Testability and Meaning," p. 444 and p. 451. Generally, when a term is introduced by several reduction sentences representing different operational criteria of application, then the agreement among the results of the corresponding procedures, which must be presupposed if the reduction sentences are all to be compatible with one another, is expressed by the representative sentence associated with the given set of reduction sentences. The representative sentence reflects, therefore, the inductive risk which, as Bridgman has stressed, is incurred by using more than one operational criterion for a given term.

(3) $$\sim(S_1 x \cdot R_1 x \cdot S_2 x \cdot R_2 x)$$

that is, no case x exhibits the attributes S_1, R_1, S_2, R_2 jointly. Now, an assertion of this kind is not a truth of formal logic, nor can it generally be viewed as true solely by virtue of the meanings of its constituent terms. Carnap therefore treats this consequence of formulas 2.1 and 2.2 as empirical and as expressing the factual content of the reduction pair from which it was derived. Occurrences of this kind are by no means limited to reduction sentences, and we see that in the use of interpretative systems, specification of meaning and statement of empirical fact—two functions of language often considered as completely distinct—become so intimately bound up with each other as to raise serious doubt about the advisability or even the possibility of preserving that distinction in a logical reconstruction of science. This consideration suggests that we dispense with the distinction, so far maintained for expository purposes, between the interpretative sentences, included in M, and the balance of the sentences constituting a scientific theory: we may simply conceive of the two sets of sentences as constituting one "interpreted theory."

The results obtained in this brief analysis of the operationist view of significant scientific concepts are closely analogous to those obtainable by a similar study of the logical empiricist view of significant scientific statements, or hypotheses.[18] In the latter case, the original requirement of full verifiability or full falsifiability by experiental data has to give way to the more liberal demand for confirmability—that is, partial verifiability. This demand can be shown to be properly applicable to entire theoretical systems rather than to individual hypotheses—a point emphasized, in effect, already by Pierre Duhem. Experiential significance is then seen to be a matter of degree, so that the originally intended sharp distinction between cognitively meaningful and cognitively meaningless hypotheses (or systems of such) has to be abandoned; and it even appears doubtful whether the distinction between analytic and synthetic sentences can be effectively maintained in reference to the language of empirical science.

---

18. Cf. the essay "Empiricist Criteria of Cognitive Significance: Problems and Changes" in the present volume. On the notion of analyticity, see W. V. Quine, "Two Dogmas of Empiricism", *Philosophical Review*, 60 (1951).

III.

STRUCTURE AND FUNCTION

OF SCIENTIFIC CONCEPTS

AND THEORIES

6. FUNDAMENTALS OF

TAXONOMY

1. INTRODUCTION

THIS PAPER[1] attempts to provide a systematic background for a discussion of the taxonomy[2] of mental disorders. To this end, it analyzes the basic logical and methodological aspects of the classificatory procedures used in various branches of empirical science and indicates some implications which that analysis seems to suggest for the taxonomic problems of psychiatry.

2. CLASSES AND CONCEPTS

A classification, as is well known, divides a given set or class of objects into subclasses. The objects are called the *elements* or *members* of the given set; the set itself will also be referred to as the *universe of discourse*, especially when it is assumed to contain as its elements all the objects with which a given investigation is concerned.

The objects of a classification may be concrete things such as stars, crystals,

1. The following is the substance of a paper read at the Work Conference on Field Studies in the Mental Disorders held in New York in February, 1959, under the auspices of the American Psychopathological Association. The present text incorporates some changes I made in the original version as a result of the discussion of my paper. The papers read at the Conference, some of which I refer to by the names of their authors, were published in Zubin (1961), which also contains a record of the discussion.

2. The term 'taxonomy' often serves as a synonym for 'classification'; but I will here use the words 'taxonomy' and 'taxonomic' primarily to refer to the *theory* of classificatory procedures and systems. The two concepts thus distinguished are more fully characterized in the foreword of Gregg's study (1954), where "taxonomy proper" is contrasted with "methodological taxonomy".

organisms, books, and so on; or they may be abstract entities such as numbers, kinship systems, political ideologies, religions, or philosophical doctrines.

Each of the subclasses provided for in a given classification may be thought of as defined by the specification of necessary and sufficient conditions of membership in it, i.e., by stating certain characteristics which all and only the members of this class possess. Each subclass is thus defined by means of (more precisely, as the extension of) a certain *concept*, which represents the complex of characteristics essential for membership in that subclass. For example, in the division of positive integers into prime and composite numbers, the condition of membership in the former of these subclasses is that the number in question be greater than 1 and be an integral multiple only of 1 and of itself. These characteristics determine the concept of prime number, and the corresponding class is the extension of this concept.

Similarly, each of the hierarchically ordered groups (cohorts, orders, families, tribes, genera, species, etc.) in a classification of mammals may be regarded as the extension of a corresponding concept, such as the concepts of marsupial, bat, primate, and so on.

Analogously, the subclasses established by a particular taxonomic system of mental disorders are determined by the different kinds of mental illness conceptually distinguished in the system; for example, in the system of the *Diagnostic and Statistical Manual* of the American Psychiatric Association, the specification of the concept of psychotic depressive reaction serves to determine the class of those individuals to whom the concept applies, i.e., who suffer from that type of reaction. As this example illustrates, the objects of classification in psychiatric taxonomy are not the various kinds of mental disorder, but individual cases, which are assigned to various classes according to the kinds of mental disorder they exemplify. This construal accords perfectly with the conception of *diagnosis* as the assignment of individual cases to particular classes in a taxonomic system of diseases; and it is definitely called for by the use made of psychiatric classifications in medical statistics, which is concerned with the distribution of individual cases over the various classes provided in a classificatory system, such as that of the *International Statistical Classification of Diseases* or that of the *Diagnostic and Statistical Manual.*

An individual case of the kind here referred to is best understood to be a particular human being at a given time, or during a given time span, in his life history: this construal allows for the possibility that a person may belong to a class representing a certain illness at some time, but not at all times, during his life. (By contrast, the elements classified by a taxonomic system in biology are best considered to be individual organisms during their total life spans.)

Alternative ways of dividing a given universe of discourse into subclasses correspond to the use of alternative sets of concepts in singling out similarities and differences among the objects under consideration. Thus, the different typologies of physique and of temperament which have been developed from antiquity to the present employ different sets of concepts to classify or to type a given person. For example, one system of classifying individuals according to their temperaments is based on the concepts of extraversion and introversion, another on those of cerebrotonia, viscerotonia and somatotonia; another on the concepts of cycloid and schizoid temperaments, and so on; and the resulting classificatory or typological schemes differ accordingly.

Thus, the specification of a classificatory system requires a corresponding set of classificatory concepts: Each class provided for in the system is the *extension* of one of these concepts; i.e., it consists of just those objects in the universe of discourse which possess the specific characteristics which the concept represents. Hence, the establishment of a suitable system of classification in a given domain of investigation may be considered as a special kind of scientific concept formation. It seems reasonable therefore, in a methodological study of taxonomy, first to examine the basic functions of scientific concepts in general and then to consider what demands those intended functions impose upon classificatory concepts.

In our discussion, we will distinguish, in a manner widely accepted in contemporary logic, between *concepts* and the *terms* that stand for them; for example, the term 'soluble in alcohol' which is a linguistic expression, stands for the concept of solubility in alcohol, which is a property of certain substances. Collectively, the terms used by empirical science in general or by one of its branches will be referred to as its *vocabulary*.

3. DESCRIPTION AND THEORETICAL SYSTEMATIZATION AS TWO BASIC FUNCTIONS OF SCIENTIFIC CONCEPTS

Broadly speaking, the vocabulary of science has two basic functions: first, to permit an adequate *description* of the things and events that are the objects of scientific investigation; second, to permit the establishment of general laws or theories by means of which particular events may be *explained* and *predicted* and thus *scientifically understood*; for to understand a phenomenon scientifically is to show that it occurs in accordance with general laws or theoretical principles.

In fact, granting some oversimplification, the development of a scientific discipline may often be said to proceed from an initial "natural history" stage,[3]

3. This suggestive term is borrowed from Northrop (1947), especially chapters 3 and 4, where a distinction is drawn between "the natural history stage of inquiry" and the "stage of deductively formulated theory".

which primarily seeks to describe the phenomena under study and to establish simple empirical generalizations concerning them, to subsequent more and more "theoretical" stages, in which increasing emphasis is placed upon the attainment of comprehensive theoretical accounts of the empirical subject matter under investigation. The vocabulary required in the early stages of this development will be largely observational: It will be chosen so as to permit the description of those aspects of the subject matter which are ascertainable fairly directly by observation. The shift toward theoretical systematization is marked by the introduction of new, "theoretical" terms, which refer to various theoretically postulated entities, their characteristics, and the processes in which they are involved; all these are more or less removed from the level of directly observable things and events. For example, the electric and magnetic fields of physics, and the propagation of waves in them; chemical valences; molecular and atomic structures; elementary physical particles; quantum states: all these are typical of the sorts of things and processes to which the theoretical vocabulary of physics and of chemistry refers.

In medical science, the development from a predominantly descriptive to an increasingly theoretical emphasis is reflected, for example, in the transition from a largely symptomatological to a more and more etiological point of view. Etiology should not be conceived as dealing with the "causes" of disease in a narrow sense of that term. In the physical sciences, the search for causes in that sense has been replaced by a search for explanatory laws and theories; and etiology has been moving in the same direction. Indeed, the various theoretical approaches to disease have brought with them a variety of theoretical concepts. For example, the *Diagnostic and Statistical Manual* characterizes the concept of conversion reaction as follows:

> Instead of being experienced consciously, . . . the impulse causing the anxiety is "converted" into functional symptoms in organs or parts of the body, usually those that are mainly under voluntary control. The symptoms serve to lessen conscious (felt) anxiety and ordinarily are symbolic of the underlying mental conflict. Such reactions usually meet immediate needs of the patient and are, therefore, associated with more or less obvious "secondary gain." (pp. 32-33.)

Clearly, several of the terms used in this passage refer neither to directly observable phenomena, such as overt behavior, nor to responses that can be elicited by suitable stimuli, but rather to theoretically assumed psychodynamic factors. Those terms have a distinct meaning and function only in the context of a corresponding theory; just as the terms 'gravitational field', 'gravitational potential', and so on have a definite meaning and function only in the context of a corresponding theory of gravitation.

Let us now survey some of the requirements which the two major objectives of description and theoretical systematization impose upon scientific concepts, and in particular upon concepts used for classifactory purposes.

4. EMPIRICAL IMPORT OF SCIENTIFIC TERMS: OPERATIONAL DEFINITION

Science aims at knowledge that is *objective* in the sense of being intersubjectively certifiable, independently of individual opinion or preference, on the basis of data obtainable by suitable experiments or observations. This requires that the terms used in formulating scientific statements have clearly specified meanings and be understood in the same sense by all those who use them. One of the main objections against various types of contemporary psychodynamic theories, for example, is that their central concepts lack clear and uniform criteria of application, and that, as a consequence, there are no definite and unequivocal ways of putting the theories to a test by applying them to concrete cases.

A method that has been widely recommended to avoid this kind of deficiency is the use of so-called *operational definitions* for scientific terms. The idea was first set forth very explicitly by the physicist P. W. Bridgman in his book, *The Logic of Modern Physics*. An operational definition for a given term is conceived as providing objective criteria by means of which any scientific investigator can decide, for any particular case, whether the term does or does not apply. To this end, the operational definition specifies a testing "operation" T that can be performed on any case to which the given term could conceivably apply, and a certain outcome O of the testing operation, whose occurrence is to count as the criterion for the applicability of the term to the given case. Schematically, an operational definition of a scientific term S is a stipulation to the effect that S is to apply to all and only those cases for which performance of test operation T yields the specified outcome O. To illustrate: A simple operational definition of the term *harder than* as used in mineralogy might specify that a piece of mineral x is called harder than another piece of mineral y if the operation of drawing a sharp point of x under pressure across a smooth surface of y has as its outcome a scratch on y, whereas y does not thus scratch x. Similarly, an operational definition of length has to specify rules for the measurement of length in terms of publicly performable operations, such as the appropriate use of measuring rods. Again, phenylpyruvic oligophrenia might be operationally defined by reference to the "operation" of chemically testing the urine of the person concerned for the presence of phenylpyruvic acid; the "outcome" indicating the presence of the condition (and thus the applicability of the corresponding term) is simply a positive result of the test. Most diagnostic procedures used in medicine are based on operational criteria of application for corresponding diagnostic categories.

There are exceptions, however: For example, it has been suggested that the occurrence of a characteristic "praecox-feeling" in the investigator may count as one indication of dementia praecox in the patient he is examining; but this idea does not meet the requirements of operationism because the occurrence of the specified outcome, the praecox-feeling in regard to a given patient, is *not* independent of the examiner.

Bridgman argues in effect that if the meanings of the terms used in a scientific discipline are operationally specified then the assertions made by that discipline are capable of objective test. If, on the other hand, a proposed problem or hypothesis is couched in terms some of which are not thus tied to the firm ground of operationally ascertainable data, operationism rejects it as scientifically meaningless because no empirical test can have any bearing on it, so that the proposed formulation in turn can have no possible bearing on empirical subject matter and thus lacks empirical import.[4] The operationist insistence that meaningful scientific terms should have definite public criteria of application is thus closely akin to the empiricist insistence that meaningful scientific hypotheses and theories should be capable, in principle, of intersubjective test by observational data.

The methodological tenets of operationism and empiricism have met with especially keen, and largely favorable, interest in psychology and sociology. Here, an operational specification of meaning is often achieved by formulating definite testing procedures that are to govern the application of terms such as '*IQ*' and of terms pertaining to various aptitudes and attitudes.

The concern of many psychologists and social scientists with the *reliability* of their terms reflects the importance attributed to objectivity of use: The reliability of a concept (or of the corresponding term) is usually understood as an indicator of two things: the consistency shown in its use by one observer, and the agreement in the use made of it by different observers. The former feature is often expressed in terms of the correlation between the judgments made by the same observer when he is asked to judge the same case on several occasions; the latter feature is expressed in terms of the correlations obtaining among the judgments of several observers judging the same cases; the "judgments" here referred to being made in terms of the concept whose reliability is under consideration.

The operationist emphasis on clear and precise public criteria of application for scientific terms is no doubt sound and salutary. But the customary formulations of operationism require certain qualifications, two of which will be briefly mentioned here because they are relevant to the subject matter of this paper.

4. Cf., for example, Bridgman, p. 28.

First, the operational criteria of application available for a term often amount to less than a full definition. For example, criteria of application for the term *temperature* may be specified by reference to the operation of putting a mercury thermometer into the appropriate place and noting its response; or by similar use of an alcohol thermometer, or of a thermocouple, and so on. These instruments have different, though partly overlapping, ranges within which they can be used, and none covers the full range of theoretically possible temperatures. Each of them thus provides a *partial definition*, or better, a *partial criterion of application*, for the term under consideration (or for the corresponding concept). Such partial criteria of application for the terms occurring in a given hypothesis or theory will often suffice to make an empirical test possible. Indeed, there are reasons to doubt the possibility of providing *full* operational definitions for all theoretical terms in science, and the operationist program needs therefore to be liberalized, so as to call only for the specification of partial criteria of application.[5]

Secondly, if the insistence on an *operational* specification of meaning for scientific terms is not to be unduly restrictive, the idea of operation has to be taken in a very liberal sense which does not require manipulation of the objects under consideration: the mere observation of an object, for example, must be allowed to count as an operation. For criteria of application for a term may well be specified by reference to certain characteristics which can be ascertained without any testing procedure more complicated than direct observation. Consider, for example, the check list of characteristics which Sheldon gives for dominant endomorphy. That list includes such directly observable features as roundness and softness of body; central concentration of mass; high, square shoulders with soft contours; short neck; short tapering limbs.[6] This is a satisfactory way of determining the concept of predominant endomorphy and thus the class of predominantly endomorphic individuals, provided that the terms used to specify the distinctive characteristics of endomorphs have a reasonably precise meaning and are used, by all investigators concerned, with high intersubjective uniformity; i.e., provided that, for any given subject, there is a high degree of agreement among different observers as to whether or not the subject has soft body contours, a short neck, tapering limbs, and so on. And indeed, Bridgman's insistence on operational tests and their outcomes is no doubt basically aimed at making sure that the criteria of application for scientific concepts be expressed in terms which have a very high uniformity of usage.

It would be unreasonable to demand, however, that *all* the terms used in a

---

5. For a more detailed discussion of these issues, see Hempel (1958).

6. See Sheldon, Stevens, and Tucker (1940), p. 37. For detailed somatotyping, measurement of a number of diameters on the body surface, and thus the "operation" of applying suitable measuring devices, is required; cf. *loc. cit.*, chapter 3.

given scientific discipline be given an operational specification of meaning; for then, the process of specifying the meanings of the defining terms, and so forth, would lead to an infinite regress. In any definitional context (quite independently of the issue of operationism), some terms must be antecedently understood; and the objectivity of science demands that the terms which thus serve as a basis for the introduction of other scientific terms should be among those used with a high degree of uniformity by different investigators in the field.

For just this reason, the operational criteria of application for psychological terms are usually formulated by reference to publicly observable aspects of the behavior a subject shows in response to a specified publicly observable stimulus situation, and this does indeed seem to be the most satisfactory way of meeting the demands of scientific objectivity. Reference to "operations" of a highly introspective and subjective character does not meet the requirements of scientific concept formation; for example, the operational reformulation of psychoanalytic concepts proposed by Ellis,[7] which relies on such "operations" as thinking, remembering, emoting, and perceiving (in an enormously comprehensive sense) provides no clear criteria of application for the terms of psychoanalysis and no objective ways of testing psychoanalytic hypotheses.

To apply the preceding considerations to the taxonomy of mental disorders: If a classificatory scheme is to be used with a high degree of uniformity by different investigators, the concepts determining the various subclasses will have to possess clear criteria of application that can be stated in terms of publically ascertainable characteristics. The importance of objective criteria of classification, or of objective diagnostic criteria, seems to me to be strikingly illustrated by observations made in some of the other papers prepared for this conference. For example, Professor Stengel[8] mentions in his contribution that among the cases admitted to mental hospitals in England and Wales during 1949, a quite improbably small fraction were assigned to the categories 315 to 317 (psychoneuroses with somatic symptoms) of the *International Statistical Classification of Diseases;* and the question arises whether lack of clearly specified criteria of application may not account in part for this apparent anomaly. Another case in point is Professor Greenberg's observation that not infrequently, technicians, assistants, and even coinvestigators engaged in a common research project differ among each other in their interpretations of the meanings of terms, disease conditions, and procedures when these are not specified in writing. In a similar vein, Professor Strömgren notes that many of the controversies between research workers in psychiatric demography can easily be traced back to inconsistencies of definition.

But while the formulation of more reliable criteria of application is certainly

7. Cf. Ellis (1956).
8. This contribution and others, soon to be cited, are included in Zubin (1961).

very desirable, it is not, I am sure, always an easy task. Professor Strömgren gives some illustrations of this point in his paper. It would therefore be unreasonable and self-defeating to insist on the highest standards of precision from the beginning; but it is important to aim at increasingly reliable criteria of application for the various categories distinguished in a classification of mental disorders.

In the interest of this objective, it may be worth considering whether, or to what extent, criteria with valuational overtones are used in the specification of psychiatric concepts. Consider, for example, the characterization of the category "Inadequate personality" as given in the *Diagnostic and Statistical Manual* (p. 35): "Such individuals are characterized by inadequate response to intellectual, emotional, social, and physical demands. They are neither physically nor mentally grossly deficient on examination, but they do show inadaptibility, ineptness, poor judgment, lack of physical and emotional stamina, and social incompatibility." Such notions as inadequacy of response, inadaptability, ineptness, and poor judgment clearly have valuational aspects, and it is to be expected that their use in concrete cases will be influenced by the idiosyncrasies of the investigator; this will reduce the reliability of these concepts and of those for which they serve as partial criteria of application.

One interesting way of increasing uniformity in the intersubjective use of certain classificatory terms has been pointed out by Lazarsfeld and Barton: Some kinds of classificatory judgment become more reliable when the "indicators," the criteria that serve to assign individual cases to specific classes, are broken down into several components. For example, when several classifiers judge children's adjustment, reliability will be increased by simply specifying certain aspects to which the classifiers are to pay attention, such as appearance (which in turn may be further characterized by means of such sub-indicators as excessively untidy hair and clothing, chewed fingernails, rigid facial expression); response to interviews; attitude towards others and toward self. The authors add, significantly, that despite the increase in objectivity thus achieved, there "is still required, however, a certain body of common training and experience, such as might be found among trained child psychologists, to make a vague procedure work at all well."[9]

Another factor that may affect the reliability of classificatory criteria is illustrated by the Rorschach test, the thematic apperception test, and similar procedures, all of which may be regarded as providing operational criteria for diagnostic purposes. These tests differ from, say, intelligence or aptitude tests of the customary kind in that they require a good deal of interpretation, and that

9. See Lazarsfeld and Barton (1951), especially pp. 166-167.

there is no simple routine—performable, in principle, by a machine, as it were—of noting the subject's responses and combining them into an unequivocal diagnosis that assigns the subject to some particular class.

Similar observations apply to Sheldon's typology of temperaments. For diagnostic assignment of an individual subject to one of the various types distinguished in the system, the examiner has to rate the subject with respect to a specified list of traits; and while there is likely to be rather close agreement among the ratings made by different examiners, Sheldon and Stevens[10] add this comment on the procedure:

> The later (diagnostic) use of the traits, considering the traits individually, is perhaps about as objective and systematic as medical diagnosis. That is to say, we admit freely that a subjective element is present—that no machine has been built which can make a diagnosis of temperament.

However, the objectivity, or intersubjectivity, here under discussion is of course a matter of degree, and it should be remembered that also the results of such "operations" as observing an object by microscope or telescope, or a lung via fluoroscope or indirectly through an X-ray photograph, show intersubjective variation even among expert observers.[11] What matters is, I think, to be aware of the extent to which subjective factors enter into the application of a given set of concepts, and to aim at a gradual reduction of their influence.

5. SYSTEMATIC IMPORT AND "NATURAL" CLASSIFICATION

But clear and objective criteria of application are not enough: to be scientifically useful a concept must lend itself to the formulation of general laws or theoretical principles which reflect uniformities in the subject matter under study, and which thus provide a basis for explanation, prediction, and generally scientific understanding. This aspect of a set of scientific concepts will be called its *systematic import*, for it represents the contribution the concepts make to the systematization of knowledge in the given field by means of laws or theories.

The requirement of systematic import applies, in particular, also to the concepts that determine scientific classifications. Indeed, the familiar vague distinction between "natural" and "artificial" classifications may well be explicated as referring to the difference between classifications that are scientifically fruitful and those that are not: in a classification of the former kind, those characteristics of the elements which serve as criteria of membership in a given class are associated, universally or with high probability, with more or less extensive clusters of

---

10. Sheldon and Stevens (1942), p. 426.
11. See Chapter 1 of Hanson (1958) for an instructive discussion of scientific seeing and observing as "theory-laden" undertakings.

other characteristics. For example, the two sets of primary sex characteristics which determine the division of humans into male and female are each associated, by general laws or by statistical connections, with a large variety of concomitant physical, physiological, and psychological traits. It is understandable that a classification of this sort should be viewed as somehow having objective existence in nature, as "carving nature at the joints," in contradistinction to "artificial" classifications, in which the defining characteristics have few explanatory or predictive connections with other traits; as is the case, for example, in the division of humans into those weighing less than one hundred pounds, and all others. (This is not to deny that the latter distinction, as well as other, similarly "artificial" ones, may be very useful for certain special practical purposes, as is, for example, the classification of fingerprints for the identification of individuals, although the systematic import of the system would seem to be quite small.)

Similarly, as W. S. Jevons pointed out (before the periodic system had been published), the elements potassium, sodium, caesium, rubidium, and lithium, which are grouped together as forming the class of alkali metals, have a great many characteristics in common: they all combine energetically with oxygen, decompose in water at various temperatures, and form strongly basic oxides that are highly soluble in water; their carbonates are soluble in water, and so forth.[12] Perhaps the most striking example of a classification reflecting general laws is the periodic system of the elements, on which Mendeleev based a set of highly specific predictions, which were impressively confirmed by subsequent research. As a result of more recent advances, the system, in a somewhat revised form, has been given a deeper theoretical foundation by showing that it reflects, in the classes represented by the columns of the periodic table, certain similarities and differences in the atomic structure of the elements.

A similar development has taken place in the taxonomic methods of biology. Even in the early taxonomic systems, which are based on more or less directly observable (largely morphological) characteristics, each class represents of course a large bundle of empirically associated traits; but, as an outgrowth of the theory of evolution, the morphological basis of classification came to be replaced by one more deeply imbedded in theory, namely a phylogenetic basis. The various species, for example, are "theoretically defined, at least in principle, in phylogenetic and genetic terms,"[13] and the morphological characteristics

---

12. Jevons (1877), p. 675. See also Jevons' illuminating general discussion in Chapter 30 of his book.

13. Simpson (1945), p. 13. See also the lucid exposition of the same subject in Chapter 19, "The principles of classification," in Simpson, Pittendrigh, and Tiffany (1957). Concerning the systematic import of classificatory concepts in biological taxonomy, see the essays by Huxley and by Gilmour in Huxley (1940).

now provide simply the observational criteria for the assignment of individuals to a species which is construed in phylogenetic terms.

In psychological and psychopathological research the typological systems of Kretschmer[14] and of Sheldon and his associates, to mention two characteristic examples, illustrate the strong interest in concepts reflecting empirical uniformities and statistical associations. In Sheldon's system the three "primary components of temperament"—viscerotonia, cerebrotonia, and somatotonia—are characterized by means of three corresponding clusters of traits which were selected, on the basis of much empirical trial and error, in such a way that the traits in each group would intercorrelate positively with each other and show a negative correlation with all or nearly all the traits in the other groups.[15] In addition, one of the principal claims to scientific significance that are suggested for the system rests on the correlation between the three components of temperament on the one hand and various other psychological and somatic traits on the other; in regard to the latter, certain statistical connections are indicated between the basic components of temperament and the basic components of physique—endomorphy, ectomorphy, and mesomorphy—which are distinguished in Sheldon's theory of somatic types.[16] Kretschmer's typology of character and physique has similar objectives; and both systems attempt to exhibit some connections between somatic characteristics and a disposition to certain kinds of mental disturbance. Whatever the merits of these and similar systems may prove to be, they are mentioned here as instances of a deliberate effort to develop classificatory systems (more precisely: typologies in the sense to be discussed in the next section) whose conceptual basis has definite systematic import.

In accordance with the requirement of systematic import, the concepts used in a given field of scientific inquiry will change with the systematic advances made in that field: the formation of concepts will go hand in hand with the formulation of laws and, eventually, of theories. As was mentioned earlier, the laws may at first express simple uniform or statistical connections among observables; they will then be formulated in terms of the observational vocabulary of the discipline to which they belong. Further systematic progress, however, will call for the formulation of principles expressed in theoretical terms which refer to various kinds of unobservable entities and their characteristics. In the course of such development, classifications defined by reference to manifest, observable characteristics will tend to give way to systems based on theoretical

14. See Kretschmer (1925).
15. See Sheldon and Stevens (1942), chapter 2.
16. See Sheldon, Stevens, and Tucker (1940), especially chapter 7, and Sheldon and Stevens (1942), chapter 7.

concepts. This process is illustrated, for example, by the shift from an observational-phenomenal characterization and classification of chemical elements and compounds to theoretical modes of defining and differentiating them by reference to their atomic and molecular structures. To be unequivocally applicable to concrete cases, the theoretically specified concepts must, of course, possess clear-cut empirical, or "operational," criteria of application; but these can no longer be regarded as their defining characteristics: the specified outcome of the operational test just constitutes a readily observable *symptom* for the presence of the traits or processes represented by the theoretical concepts; the "meanings" of the latter are not fully reflected by operational-symptomatic criteria of application (diagnosis) alone, but quite importantly also by the theoretical system to which they belong.

The emphasis on systematic import in concept formation has been clearly in evidence in the development of classificatory systems for mental disorders. The concepts determining the various classes or categories distinguished now are no longer defined just in terms of symptoms, but rather in terms of the key concepts of *theories* which are intended to *explain* the observable behavior, including the symptoms in question; just as molecular and atomic theory accounts for the more directly observable characteristics that served as defining characteristics in an earlier stage of chemical concept formation. The trend is nicely illustrated by several of the characterizations of mental disorders given in the *Diagnostic and Statistical Manual*, where an enumeration of certain symptoms is combined with an etiological or generally theoretical account: the characterizations of the various categories of psychoneurotic disorders (pp. 31-34 of the *Manual*) are clear cases in point.

In a classificatory system with a theoretical basis, two individuals with similar symptoms may then come to be assigned to quite different classes; for some of the kinds of mental disturbance distinguished at the etiologic-theoretical level may well partially overlap in the associated syndromes, just as two different chemical compounds may have various directly observable characteristics in common. Similarly, in taxonomic systems of biology which have a phylogenetic-evolutionary basis, two phenomenally very similar specimens may be assigned to species far removed from each other in the evolutionary hierarchy, such as the species Wolf (*Canis*) and Tasmanian Wolf (*Thylacinus*).[17]

The preceding considerations have some bearing on the question whether prognostic prospects and therapeutic possibilities may—or perhaps even ought to—be properly included among the defining characteristics of a mental illness.

17. For this and other examples see chapter 19 of Simpson, Pittendrigh, and Tiffany (1957).

It is certainly conceivable—and indeed to be hoped for as a result of further research—that concepts representing mental disorders should be used in a theoretical context which carries certain prognostic implications. In this case, the concepts in question might be defined, within the framework of the theory, by means of characteristics some of which are prognostic in character. On the other hand, it would defeat the practical purposes of diagnosis and therapy if the operational criteria of application for those concepts, i.e., the criteria forming the basis of medical diagnosis, required postponement of the diagnosis until after the illness had run its course. If they are to meet those practical needs, the criteria of application will therefore have to be couched in terms of characteristics that can be ascertained more or less immediately. To mention a parallel from physics: It would be unfortunate if the application of the term *radium* depended on the criterion that the half-life of radium is approximately 1800 years; though this half-life is certainly an important characteristic of radium.

We should note, however, that the distinction here assumed between prognostic and nonprognostic criteria of application is a matter of degree. Operational definitions, for example, imply conditional prognoses concerning the outcome of certain test operations: If x is a harder piece of mineral than y then the scratch test will result in a scratch mark on the surface of y; if a current of one ampere is flowing through that wire, the needle of a properly connected ammeter will respond accordingly; and so forth. Similarly, the Schick test, which provides an operational criterion of application for the concept of immunity to diphtheria, involves a short-range prognosis concerning a skin reaction. And in certain cases, response to particular forms of therapy might be resorted to as a diagnostic criterion. But it seems reasonable to expect that advances in theoretical understanding will increasingly provide us with etiological or structural accounts of physical and mental illness, and that these in turn will imply diagnostic criteria in terms of antecedent conditions or presently ascertainable physical or mental characteristics.

It is very likely, I think, that classifications of mental disorders will increasingly reflect theoretical considerations. It is not for me to speculate on the direction that theoretical developments in this field may take and especially on whether the major theories will be couched in biophysiological or biochemical terms or rather in psychodynamic terms that lack an over-all physiological or physiochemical interpretation. Theoretical systems of either kind can satisfy the basic requirements for scientific theories. In brief and schematic outline, these requirements call for (1) a clear specification of the basic concepts used to represent the theoretical entities (objects, states, processes, characteristics, and so on) in terms of which the theory proposes to interpret, and account for, the empirical phenomena in its domain of investigation; (2) a set of theoretical assumptions (basic laws, fundamental hypotheses) couched in theoretical terms and asserting certain interrelations among the corresponding theoretical entities; (3) an empirical interpretation of the theory, which might take the form of operational criteria for the theoretical terms or, more generally, the form of a set of laws, statistical or strictly universal in character, connecting the theoretical traits, states, or processes with observable phenomena; (4) testability-in-principle of the theory thus specified; i.e., the theory together with its interpretation, must imply, deductively or inductively, definite assertions about observable phenomena that should be found to occur under specifiable test conditions if the theory is correct: the occurrence or nonoccurrence of these phenomena will then provide confirming or disconfirming evidence concerning the theory. If a proposed theory has no such implications at all, it clearly has no possible bearing on empirical subject matter and thus cannot qualify as a significant theory in empirical science (not even as an unsound or false one: for these latter attributes presuppose a conflict between the theory and relevant experimental or observational evidence).[18]

This requirement of testability by reference to observable phenomena rules out, for example, the neo-vitalistic conception of biological processes as being determined, at least in part, by vital forces or entelechies; for the available statements of this conception yield no experimentally testable implications.

6. FROM CLASSIFICATORY TO COMPARATIVE AND QUANTITATIVE CONCEPTS

While it is not possible to predict the substantive changes that the concepts and theories of mental disorder will undergo as a result of further research, I think that certain changes in their logical character may well be anticipated. In this concluding section, I will attempt briefly to indicate the nature of these changes.

Classification, strictly speaking, is a yes-or-no, an either-or affair: A class is determined by some concept representing its defining characteristics, and a given object falls either into this class or outside, depending on whether it has or lacks the defining characteristics.

In scientific research, however, the objects under study are often found to resist a tidy pigeonholing of this kind. More precisely: those characteristics of the subject matter which, in the given context of investigation, suggest themselves as a fruitful basis of classification often cannot well be treated as properties which a given object *either* has *or* lacks; rather, they have the character of traits

18. For a fuller account of these principal requirements and a critical analysis of some of their consequences, see Hempel (1952), (1958).

which are capable of gradations, and which a given object may therefore exhibit *more or less* markedly. As a result, some of the objects under study will present the investigator with borderline cases, which do not fit unequivocally into one or another of several neatly bounded compartments, but which exhibit to some degree the characteristics of *different* classes. For example, Professor Strömgren refers in his paper to the difficulties of finding a natural border line separating the whole group of neuroses and psychopathies from that which does not belong to it, and he remarks that the transitions are gradual in all directions. Typologies of physique and of temperament provide another good illustration, and one in which the gradual character of the transition has recently received some special methodological attention. The proponents of typological systems often emphasize that "pure" instances of the basic types they distinguish are rarely, if ever, encountered in experience, and that concrete individuals usually represent mixtures of several types. Sometimes, the basic types acquire the status of ideal reference points which mark, as it were, the ends of a scale along which concrete cases can be arranged. Thus, Kretschmer[19] states:

> We never, even in the most definite cases, come across a pure example in the strictest sense of the word, but always the peculiar individual instances of a type, that is the type itself mixed with slight accretions out of a heterogeneous inheritance. This mixture, in the guise of which the type appears to us in any individual instance, we call the *constitutional alloy*.

Metaphorical statements of this kind are suggestive; but they are not sufficient for the formulation of a theory that is to take explicit and objective account of those impure cases. A conceptual apparatus is needed to describe and distinguish constitutional alloys in which the characteristics of the pure types are represented with different strengths. For example, to give a clear, objective meaning to the notion of a pure type, say A, which different individuals may represent in different degrees, objective criteria are required which will determine for any two individuals whether they represent type A with equal strength, and if not, which of them represents A more strongly than does the other. Suitable criteria of this kind will effect, not a division of the universe of discourse into two classes, A and *non-A*, but a simple (quasi-linear) ordering of the universe. In this ordering, two individuals will "coincide," i.e., occupy the same place, if, in the sense of the criteria, they exhibit A with equal strength; whereas individual x will precede individual y if, in the sense of the criteria, x is a less pronounced case of A than is y.

A parallel from physics may serve to illustrate the point: A simple ordering of minerals according to increasing hardness can be effected by means of the

19. Kretschmer (1925), p. 93.

scratch-test criterion mentioned earlier: if a sharp point of y scratches a surface of x, but not vice versa, y is harder than x and thus follows x in the order of increasing hardness; if neither y is harder than x nor x harder than y, both minerals are assigned the same place in the quasi-linear order. This example illustrates two elementary but important points: (1) The "diagnostic" criteria which serve to place individual cases in the scheme are not criteria of class-membership, as they would be in a strictly classificatory system; rather, they are criteria of precedence and coincidence in a quasi-linear order. (2) such criteria can be quite objective and rather precise without presupposing quantitative measurement.[20]

We noted that recent typological systems have, in effect, replaced a strictly classificatory procedure by an ordering one (even though some of them use a classificatory terminology and supplement it by speaking metaphorically of borderline cases, mixtures, transitional forms, and the like). Such reliance on concepts and methods of an ordering character is illustrated not only by Kretschmer's system, but also, to mention just a few other examples, by C. G. Jung's distinction of the extraverted and introverted types, by E. R. Jaensch's typology[21] and by the system developed more recently by Sheldon in collaboration with Stevens and others. This latter theory, however, makes the ordering character of its basic concepts quite explicit and seeks to satisfy the requirement of objectivity (in the sense discussed earlier) for the diagnostic criteria it sets down.

Since each of the types distinguished in a typological theory will represent at least one quasi-linear ordering, typological systems usually provide for an arrangement of individuals along several axes, and thus replace classificatory schemes by reference "spaces" of several "dimensions."

The advantages of ordering over classification can be considerable. In particular, ordering allows for subtler distinctions than classification; furthermore, ordering may take the special form of a quantitative procedure, in which each dimension is represented by a quantitative characteristic. And quantitative concepts not only allow for a fineness and precision of distinction unparalleled on the levels of classification and of nonquantitative ordering, but also provide a basis for the use of the powerful tools of quantitative mathematics: laws and theories can be expressed in terms of functions connecting several variables, and consequences can be derived from them, for purposes of prediction or of test, by means of mathematical techniques.

The considerations presented in this section and in the preceding one suggest that the development of taxonomic concepts in the study of mental disorder will

20. For a detailed analysis of ordering procedures, with special reference to typological theories, see Hempel and Oppenheim (1936); a short general account of the logic of classification, ordering and measurement is given in Hempel (1952), Part III.

21. See, for example, Jung (1921), Jaensch (1933).

probably show two trends: First, a continuation of the shift from systems defined by reference to observable characteristics to systems based on theoretical concepts; and second, a gradual shift from classificatory concepts and methods to ordering concepts and procedures, both of the non-quantitative and of the quantitative varieties.

REFERENCES

American Psychiatric Association, *Diagnostic and Statistical Manual: Mental Disorders.* Washington, D. C., 1952.

Bridgman, P. W., *The Logic of Modern Physics.* New York, Macmillan, 1927.

Ellis, Albert, "An Operational Reformulation of Some of the Basic Principles of Psychoanalyis." In Feigl, H., and Scriven, M., eds., *Minnesota Studies in the Philosophy of Science,* vol. I. Minneapolis, University of Minnesota Press, 1956, pp. 131-154.

Gregg, John R., *The Language of Taxonomy,* New York, Columbia University Press, 1954.

Hanson, N. R., *Patterns of Discovery.* London, Cambridge University Press, 1958.

Hempel, Carl G., *Fundamentals of Concept Formation in Empirical Science.* Chicago, University of Chicago Press, 1952.

Hempel, Carl G., "The Theoretician's Dilemma." In Feigl, H., Scriven, M., and Maxwell G., eds., *Minnesota Studies in the Philosophy of Science,* vol. II. Minneapolis, University of Minnesota Press, 1958, pp. 37-98 (Reprinted in this volume).

Hempel, Carl G., and Oppenheim, P., *Der Typusbegriff im Lichte der neuen Logik.* Leiden, Sitjhoff, 1936.

Huxley, J., *The New Systematics.* Oxford, Clarendon Press, 1940.

Jaensch, E. R., *Die Eidetik und die typologische Forschungsmethode.* Leipzig, Quelle und Meyer, 1933.

Jevons, W. S., *The Principles of Science,* 2nd ed., 1877; reprinted, with a new introduction by Ernest Nagel. New York, Dover Publications, 1958.

Jung, C. G., *Psychologische Typen.* Zurich, Rascher, 1921.

Kretschmer, E., *Physique and Character.* Translated from second German edition by W. J. H. Sprott. New York, Harcourt, Brace and Co., 1925.

Lazarsfeld, P., and Barton, A. H., "Qualitative Measurement in the Social Sciences: Classification, Typologies, and Indices" In: Terner, D., and Lasswell, H. eds., *The Policy Sciences.* Stanford: Stanford Univ. Press, 1951, pp. 155-192.

Northrop, F. S. C., *The Logic of the Sciences and the Humanities.* New York, Macmillan, 1947.

Sheldon, W. H., and Stevens, S. S., *The Varieties of Temperament.* New York, Harper & Brothers, 1942.

Sheldon, W. H., and Tucker, W. B., *The Varieties of Human Physique.* New York, Harper & Brothers, 1940.

Simpson, George G., *The Principles of Classification and a Classification of Mammals.* Bulletin of the American Museum of Natural History, vol. 45. New York, 1945.

Simpson, George G., Pittendrigh, C. S., and Tiffany, L. H., *Life: An Introduction to Biology.* New York, Harcourt, Brace and Co., 1957.

Zubin, J., ed., *Field Studies in the Mental Disorders.* New York, Grune and Stratton, 1961.

7. TYPOLOGICAL METHODS

IN THE NATURAL AND

THE SOCIAL SCIENCES

1. INTRODUCTION

THE CONCEPT of type has played a significant role in various phases of the development of empirical science. Many of its uses are by now of historical interest only; but some branches of research, especially psychology and the social sciences, have continued up to the present to employ typological concepts for descriptive and for theoretical purposes. In particular, various typologies of character and physique have been propounded as providing fruitful approaches to the study of personality; the investigation of "extreme" or "pure" types of physical and mental constitution has been advocated as a source of insight into the functioning of "normal" individuals; and as for social science, the use of ideal types has been declared one of the methodological characteristics which distinguish it essentially from natural science.

Considering these recent uses of typological concepts and the various claims concerning their peculiar significance, it appears to be a matter of some interest and importance to have a reasonably clear understanding of their logical status and their methodological function. Now, there exists a voluminous literature on the subject, but a large part of it suffers from a definite inadequacy of the logical apparatus used for the analysis of the issues at hand. In particular, many of the studies devoted to the logic of typological concepts use only the concepts and principles of classical logic, which is essentially a logic of properties or classes, and cannot deal adequately with relations and with quantitative concepts. It is illustrative of this situation that Max Weber, who so eloquently champions the method of ideal types in the social sciences, makes a clear negative statement about their logical status: they cannot be defined by *genus proximum* and *differentia*

Reprinted, by kind permission of the publisher, from a volume of symposium papers published under the auspices of the American Philosophical Association, Eastern Division, under the title *Science, Language,* and *Human Rights*. Philadelphia: University of Pennsylvania Press, 1952.

specifica, and concrete cases cannot be subsumed under them as instances[1] i.e., they are not simply class, or property, concepts; but when it comes to a positive characterization, he resorts to much less precise, and often metaphorical, language. An ideal type, according to Weber, is a mental construct formed by the synthesis of many diffuse, more or less present and occasionally absent, concrete individual phenomena, which are arranged, according to certain one-sidedly accentuated points of view, into a unified analytical construct, which in its conceptual purity cannot be found in reality; it is a utopia, a limiting concept, with which concrete phenomena can only be compared for the purpose of explicating some of their significant components.[2] This characterization, and many similar accounts which Weber and others have given of the nature of ideal types, are certainly suggestive, but they lack clarity and rigor and thus call for further logical analysis.

In addition to the logical status of typological concepts, some of the methodological claims which have been made for them appear to me to warrant reexamination.

The present paper, then, is an attempt to explicate in outline the logical and methodological character of typological concepts, and to appraise their potential significance for the purposes they are intended to serve.

The term 'type' has been used in several quite different senses. I propose to distinguish here three main kinds of type concepts, which for brief reference, and pending further clarification, will be called classificatory, extreme, and ideal types. These will now be considered in turn.

2. CLASSIFICATORY TYPES

The classificatory use of type concepts is illustrated by Ernst Kretschmer's rather influential typological theory of character and physique,[3] in which types are construed as classes. In this case, the logic of typological procedure is the familiar logic of classification, which requires no discussion here. Methodologically, classificatory type formation, like any other kind of classification in empirical science, is subject to the requirement of systematic fruitfulness: The characteristics which serve to define the different types should not merely provide neat pigeonholes to accommodate all the individual cases in the domain

1. Max Weber, *On the Methodology of the Social Sciences*, trans. and ed. E. A. Shils and H. A. Finch (New York, The Free Press of Glencoe, 1949), p. 93.

2. *loc. cit.*, pp. 90-93.

3. Ernst Kretschmer, *Physique and Character*, trans. W. J. H. Sprott (New York, Harcourt, Brace & World, 1936).

On the theory and technique of classificatory type formation in contemporary social research, see Paul F. Lazarsfeld and Allen H. Barton, "Qualitative Measurement in the Social Sciences: Classification, Typologies, and Indices," in Daniel Lerner and Harold D. Lasswell (eds.), *The Policy Sciences*, (Stanford, Stanford University Press, 1951).

of inquiry, but should lend themselves to sound generalization and thus offer a basis for prediction. Thus, e.g., constitutional typologies often aim at defining their types by reference to certain physical properties which are empirically associated with a variety of psychological traits, so that every type represents a cluster of concomitant characteristics. This objective is the methodological kernel of the search for "natural" as distinguished from "artificial" classes or types.

In connection with classificatory types, brief reference should be made to the use of the term 'typical' in the sense of average, for that use evidently presupposes a classification. Thus, the statement that the typical American college undergraduate is, say, 18.9 years old, purports to state the average value of a certain magnitude for a specified class. But since there are different kinds of average, and since none of these provides much information without an added measure of dispersion, it is clear that for any serious scientific purpose this use of the term 'typical' has to be supplanted by a more precise formulation in statistical terms.

3. EXTREME TYPES

Attempts at typological classification in empirical science are often frustrated, however, by the realization that those characteristics of the subject matter which are to provide the defining basis of the classification cannot fruitfully be construed as simple property concepts determining, as their extensions, classes with neatly demarcated boundaries. Thus, e.g., if we try to formulate explicit and precise criteria for the distinction of extravert and introvert personalities it soon becomes clear that the adoption of classificatory criteria drawing a precise boundary line between the two categories would prove an "artificial", theoretically sterile, procedure: it appears much more natural, much more promising systematically, to construe the two concepts as capable of gradations, so that a given individual will not be qualified either as extravert or as introvert, but as exhibiting each of the two traits to a certain extent. The purely extravert and the purely introvert personalities thus come to be conceived as "extreme" or "pure" types, of which concrete instances are rarely if ever found, but which may serve as conceptual points of reference or "poles," between which all actual occurrences can be ordered in a serial array. This general conception underlies several of the recent and contemporary systems of psychological and physical types, such as Sheldon's theory of physique and temperament.[4]

What is the logical form of these "extreme" or "pure" type concepts?

---

4. W. H. Sheldon, S. S. Stevens, and W. B. Tucker, *The Varieties of Human Physique* (New York and London, Harper and Row, 1940), and W. H. Sheldon and S. S. Stevens, *The Varieties of Temperament* (New York and London, Harper and Row, 1942).

Clearly, they cannot be construed as class concepts: individual cases cannot be subsumed under them as instances, but can only be characterized as to the extent to which they approximate them. In other words, if the term T is an extreme type, an individual a cannot be said either to be T or to be non-T; rather, a may be, so to speak, "more or less T." But exactly how is this "more or less" to be objectively defined? A description, however vivid, of an extreme type with which concrete cases are to be compared does not by itself provide standards for such comparison; at best, it may suggest a program of research, focusing attention upon certain empirical phenomena and regularities and stimulating efforts toward the development of a precise conceptual apparatus suited for their description and theoretical interpretation. But if an extreme type is to function as a legitimate scientific concept in scientific statements with clear objective meaning, then explicit criteria for the "more or less" of comparison must be provided. These criteria may take a nonnumerical, "purely comparative" form, or they may be based on quantitative devices such as rating scales or measurement.

The formally simplest, purely comparative, form of an extreme-type concept T can be specified by laying down criteria which determine, for any two individual cases a, b in the domain under investigation, whether (i) a is more T than b, or (ii) b is more T than a, or (iii) a is just as much T as is b. For the concept of pure introversion as an extreme type, for example, this would require objective criteria determining for any two individuals a, b whether they are equally introverted and, if not, which of them is the more introverted. Thus, an extreme type T of the purely comparative or ordering kind is defined, not by *genus* and *differentia* in the manner of a class concept, but by specifying two dyadic relations, "more T than" and "as much T as." Now, if the criteria defining those relations are to yield an ordering of all particular cases in a linear array reflecting increasing T-ness, then they must meet certain formal requirements: "more T than" must be an asymmetrical and transitive relation, "as much T as" must be symmetrical and transitive, and the two together must satisfy a trichotomy law to the effect that any two particular cases a, b meet the defining conditions for exactly one of the three alternatives (i), (ii), (iii) mentioned above.[5]

The kind of ordering concept here characterized is well illustrated by the definition, in mineralogy, of a purely comparative concept of hardness by reference to the scratch test: A mineral a is said to be harder than another, b, if a sharp point of a sample of a will scratch the surface of a sample of b, but not conversely. If neither of the minerals is harder than the other, they are said to

---

5. For details, see Carl G. Hempel and Paul Oppenheim, *Der Typusbegriff im Lichte der neuen Logik* (Leiden, Holland, Sijthoff, 1936), chapter III.

be of the same hardness. The two relations thus defined might be said to determine a purely comparative extreme type of hardness; but this terminology would tend to obscure rather than clarify the logic of the procedure, and it is not actually used.

In psychology and the social sciences it is difficult, to say the least, to find fruitful objective criteria, analogous to those based on the scratch test, which will determine a purely comparative typological order. We find therefore that proponents of extreme-type concepts, insofar as they provide precise criteria and not merely suggestive programmatic characterizations, either end by construing their types as classes after all or else specify their typological orders by reference to rating scales or measuring procedures, which define a numerical "degree of T-ness," as it were. The first course is illustrated by Kretschmer's typology of physique and character: it uses the parlance of pure types for an intuitive characterization of the material to be investigated, while for exact formulations, it construes each of the main types as a class and accommodates the intermediate cases in some additional classes, designated as "mixed types." The second course is exemplified by Sheldon's typology of physique, which assigns to each individual a specific position on each of three seven-point scales representing the basic type traits of the theory: endomorphy, mesomorphy, and ectomorphy.

But once suitable "operational" criteria of a strictly comparative or of a quantitative kind have been specified, the pure types lose their special importance: they simply represent extreme places in the range defined by the given criteria, and from a systematic point of view, the typological terminology is no more significant than it would be to say that the specific electric conductivity of a given material indicated how close it came to the extreme, or pure, type of a perfect conductor.

The use of extreme-type concepts of the kind here considered reflects an attempt to proceed from the classificatory, qualitative level of concept formation to the quantitative one; ordering concepts of the purely comparative kind represent a logically intermediate stage. As long as explicit criteria for their use are lacking, they have, as we noted, essentially a programmatic but no systematic status; and once suitable criteria have been specified, the parlance of extreme types becomes unnecessary, for there are no logical peculiarities which differentiate extreme-type concepts from the other comparative and quantitative concepts of empirical science; their logic is the logic of ordering relations and of measurement; henceforth, we will therefore refer to them also as *ordering types.*

Ordering as well as classificatory typologies belong, as a rule, to an early stage in the growth of a scientific discipline, a stage which is concerned with the development of a largely "empirical" concept system and with its use for description and for low-grade generalization. Systematic fruitfulness, which is an essential requirement for all stages of concept formation, here consists, in the simplest case, in a high correlation between the criteria which "operationally define" a typological order (such as certain anthropometric indices, for example) and a variety of other graded traits (such as further anatomical and physiological indices or psychological characteristics). For quantitative scales, such correlations may assume, in favorable cases, the form of a proportionality of several variables (analogous to the proportionality, at constant temperature, of the specific electric and thermic conductivities of metals), or they may consist in other invariant relationships expressible in terms of mathematical functions.[6]

4. IDEAL TYPES AND EXPLANATION IN THE SOCIAL SCIENCES

As was mentioned in the first section, ideal types, too, are usually presented as the results of isolating and exaggerating certain aspects of concrete empirical phenomena, as limiting concepts which are not fully exemplified but at best approximated in reality.[7] Despite the suggestion conveyed by this description, I think that an adequate logical reconstruction has to assign to ideal types a status different from that of the extreme or pure types discussed above. For ideal types—or, as Howard Becker aptly calls them, constructed types—are usually introduced without even an attempt at specifying appropriate criteria of order, and they are not used for the kind of generalization characteristic of ordering

6. A fuller discussion of the logic and methodology of ordering and quantitative procedures may be found in Carl G. Hempel, *Fundamentals of Concept Formation in Empirical Science* (Chicago, The University of Chicago Press, 1952), especially section 11.

On the use of such procedures in typological studies, cf. Lazarsfeld and Barton, *op. cit.*, Hempel and Oppenheim, *op. cit.*, and R. F. Winch, "Heuristic and Empirical Typologies: A Job for Factor Analysis," *American Sociological Review*, 12 (1947), 68-75.

7. For detailed exposition and critical discussion of the concept of ideal type as used in social science, see especially the following works, which have served as guides in the present attempt at analysis and reconstruction:

Max Weber, *On the Methodology of the Social Sciences* (see note 1).

Max Weber, *The Theory of Social and Economic Organization*, trans. A. M. Henderson and Talcott Parsons (New York, Oxford University Press, 1947).

Alexander von Schelting, *Max Weber's Wissenschaftslehre* (Tübinger, J. C. B. Mohr, 1934).

Talcott Parsons, *The Structure of Social Action* (New York, McGraw-Hill Book Company, 1937), chapter XVI.

Howard Becker, *Through Values to Social Interpretation* (Durham, N. C., Duke University Press, 1950).

Further stimulating critical discussions of the concept of ideal type may be found in:

Felix Kaufmann, *Methodenlehre der Sozialwissenschaften* (Wien, Springer, 1936), especially section 6 of the second part.

J. W. N. Watkins, "Ideal Types and Historical Explanation," *The British Journal for the Philosophy of Science*, 3 (1952), 22-43.

types; rather, they are invoked as a specific device for the explanation of social and historical phenomena. I shall try to argue now that this conception reflects an attempt to advance concept formation in sociology from the stage of description and "empirical generalization," which is exemplified by most classificatory and ordering types, to the construction of theoretical systems or models. In order to amplify and substantiate this view, it will be necessary to examine more closely the character and function of ideal types as conceived by its proponents.

According to Max Weber and some writers holding similar views, the use of ideal types makes it possible to explain concrete social or historical phenomena, such as the caste system in India or the development of modern capitalism, in their individuality and uniqueness. Such understanding is held to consist in grasping the particular causal relationships which interconnect the relevant elements of the total occurrence under examination. If such relationships are to afford a sociologically significant explanation they must be, according to this view, not only "causally adequate" but also meaningful, i.e., they must refer to aspects of human behavior which are intelligibly actuated by valuation or other motivating factors. Weber characterizes the principles expressing those connections as "general empirical rules" concerning the ways in which human beings are prone to react in given situations; the "nomological knowledge" conveyed by them is said to be derived from our own experience and from our knowledge of the conduct of others. Weber mentions Gresham's law as a generalization of this kind: it is empirically well substantiated by the pertinent information available, and it is" a rationally clear interpretation of human action under certain conditions and under the assumption that it will follow a purely rational course."[8]

As for specific ways of discovering meaningful explanatory principles, Weber mentions the method of empathic understanding but adds the reminder that it is neither universally applicable nor always dependable. And indeed, the subjective experience of empathic identification with a historical figure, and of an immediate—almost self-evidently certain—insight into his motivations, constitutes no knowledge, no scientific understanding at all, though it may be a guide in the search for explicit general hypotheses of the kind required for a systematic explanation. In fact, the occurrence of an empathic state in the interpreter is neither a necessary nor a sufficient condition of sound interpretation or understanding in the scientific sense: not necessary, for an appropriate theory of psychopathic behavior may provide the historian with an explanation of some phases of Hitler's actions even in the absence of empathic identification;

8. *The Theory of Social and Economic Organization*, p. 98; cf. also pp. 107-9.

not sufficient, for the motivational hypotheses suggested by the empathic experience may be factually unsound.

Weber himself stresses that verification of subjective interpretation is always indispensable; he adds that in the absence of adequate experimental or observational data, "there is available only the dangerous and uncertain procedure of the 'imaginary experiment' which consists in thinking away certain elements of a chain of motivation and working out the course of action which would then probably ensue, thus arriving at a causal judgment."[9] By thus suggesting what *would* have happened *if* certain specified constituents of the situation had been different, this method yields "judgments of objective possibility," which form the basis of causal imputation in the social sciences. Those judgments evidently have the form of contrary-to-fact conditionals, and students of the currently much discussed logic of counterfactuals might be interested in Weber's fascinating illustration of the proposed method by reference to interpretative problems of historiography, among them the question of the significance of the Persian Wars for the development of Western culture;[10] Weber's discussion of these topics shows how well he was aware of the close connection between contrary-to-fact conditionals and general laws.

An ideal type, then, is meant to serve as an interpretative or explanatory schema embodying a set of "general empirical rules" which establish "subjectively meaningful" connections between different aspects of some kind of phenomenon, such as purely rational economic behavior, a capitalistic society, a handicraft economy, a religious sect, or the like. But then, in intent at least, ideal types represent not concepts properly speaking, but rather theories; and the idea suggests itself that if those theories are to serve their purpose, they must have a character similar to that of the theory of ideal gases, for example.[11] To elaborate and substantiate this conception, I will first try to show that the alleged differences between the explanatory use of ideal types and the method of explanation in natural science are spurious; then I will attempt a brief comparative analysis of the status of "idealized" concepts, and the corresponding theories, in natural and in social science.

In natural science, to explain an individual event is to explain the occurrence of some general, or repeatable, characteristic (i.e., one that may have other

9. *loc. cit.*, p. 97.

10. *The Methodology of the Social Sciences*, pp. 164–88. An illuminating amplification and examination of Weber's analysis may be found in von Schelting, *op. cit.*, pp. 269–81.

11. Parallels between ideal types and certain idealizations in physics have often been drawn, of course (cf., e.g., Weber, *The Theory of Social and Economic Organization*, p. 110; Becker, *op. cit.*, p. 125). It seems important, however, to make explicit the similarities involved and to show that they do not accord with the claim of a status *sui generis* for ideal-type concepts in the social sciences.

instances; for example, a rise in temperature, the presence of corrosion, a drop in blood pressure, etc.) in a particular case, i.e., at a specified place or in a specified object at a given moment or during a certain period of time (for example, the air in New Haven during the morning hours of September 5, 1952; the hull of a specified ship; patient John Doe at a given time). Explanation of an individual event does not and cannot reasonably mean an account of *all* the general characteristics of a given particular, say *b*. For the latter include the fact that in such and such directions and at such and such spatiotemporal distances from *b*, there are particulars having such and such general properties; as a consequence, to explain *all* the general aspects of *b* is tantamount to explaining every individual fact in the universe—past, present, and future. Evidently this kind of explaining a particular occurrence "in its uniqueness" is no more accessible to sociology than it is to physics; in fact, even its precise *meaning* is quite problematic. Thus, all that can be significantly sought is the explanation of the occurrence of some repeatable characteristic U (which may be quite complex, of course) in a given particular *b*. The task of explaining Western capitalism in its uniqueness, for example, has to be construed in this fashion if it is to be at all significant; and it is then analogous to the problem of explaining the solar eclipse of March 18, 1950. In either case, there are certain characteristics—their combination is referred to as U above—for whose occurrence an explanation is sought (in the case of the eclipse, those characteristics might include the fact that the eclipse was annular, not visible in the United States, of a duration of 4 hours and 42 minutes, etc.), but there are innumerable other characteristics for which no account is intended (such as the number of newspapers in which the event was described). It is worth noting here that the event thus to be explained, $U(b)$ for short, is still unique in the sense that the particular *b* is unrepeatable: While the existence of other instances of U is at least logically possible, none of them can have the same spatiotemporal location as *b*.

In the natural sciences a particular event is explained by showing that its occurrence can be inferred by means of laws or theoretical principles from other, usually antecedent or simultaneous, particular circumstances. As Max Weber's writings make clear, an adequate explanation of a particular event in sociology or historiography has to be of essentially the same character. Empathic insight and subjective understanding provide no warrant of objective validity, no basis for the systematic prediction or explanation of specific phenomena; the latter procedures have to be based on general empirical principles, on nomological knowledge. Weber's limitation of the explanatory principles of sociology to "meaningful" rules of intelligible behavior, on the other hand, is untenable: many, if not all, occurrences of interest to the social scientist require for their explanation reference to factors which are "devoid of subjective meaning," and thus to "non-understandable uniformities," to use Weber's terminology. Weber acknowledges that the sociologist must accept such facts as causally significant data, but he insists that this does "not in the least alter the specific task of sociological analysis . . ., which is the interpretation of action in terms of its subjective meaning."[12] But this conception bars from the field of sociology any theory of behavior which foregoes the use of "subjectively meaningful" motivational concepts. This means either an arbitrary restriction of the concept of sociology—which, as a result, might eventually become inapplicable to any branch of scientific research—or else it amounts to an *a priori* judgment as to the character of any system of concepts that can possibly yield an explanatory sociological theory. Clearly, such an *a priori* verdict is indefensible; and indeed, the more recent development of psychological and social theory indicates that it is possible to formulate explanatory principles for purposive action in purely behavioristic, nonintrospective terms.

In discussing, next, the role of experiments-in-imagination, which are, of course, well known also in the natural sciences, it will be useful to distinguish *two kinds of imaginary experiment: the intuitive and the theoretical.* An intuitive experiment-in-imagination is aimed at anticipating the outcome of an experimental procedure which is just imagined, but which may well be capable of being actually performed. Prediction is guided here by past experience concerning particular phenomena and their regularities, and occasionally by belief in certain general principles which are accepted as if they were *a priori* truths. Thus, in explaining the equidistribution of results obtained in rolling a regular die, or in anticipating similar results for a game with a regular homogeneous dodecahedron, certain rules of symmetry, such as the principle of insufficient reason, are often invoked; and similar principles are sometimes adduced in imaginary experiments involving levers and other physical systems with certain symmetry features. Imaginary experiments of this kind are intuitive in the sense that the assumptions and data underlying the prediction are not made explicit and indeed may not even enter into the conscious process of anticipation at all: past experience and the—possibly unconscious—belief in certain general principles function here as suggestive guides for imaginative anticipation rather than as a theoretical basis for systematic prediction.

The theoretical kind of imaginary experiment, on the other hand, presupposes a set of explicitly stated general principles—such as laws of nature—and it anticipates the outcome of the experiment by deductive or probabilistic inference from those principles in combination with suitable boundary conditions representing the relevant aspects of the imagined experimental situation. Sometimes,

12. *The Theory of Social and Economic Organization*, p. 94.

the latter is not actually realizable, as when the laws for an ideal mathematical pendulum or for perfectly elastic impact are deduced from more general principles of theoretical mechanics. The question what *would* happen *if*, say, the thread of a pendulum were infinitely thin and perfectly rigid and *if* the mass of the pendulum were concentrated in the free end point of the thread is answered here, not by "thinking away" those aspects of a physical pendulum that are at variance with this assumption and then trying to envisage the outcome, but by rigorous deduction from available theoretical principles. Imagination does not enter here; the experiment is imaginary only in the sense that the situation it refers to is not actually realized and may indeed be technically incapable of realization.

The two types of experiment-in-imagination here distinguished constitute extreme types, as it were, which are rarely realized in their pure form: in many cases, the empirical assumptions and the reasoning underlying an imaginary experiment are made highly, but not fully, explicit. Galileo's dialogues contain excellent examples of this procedure, which show how fruitful the method can be in suggesting general theoretical insights. But, of course, intuitive experiments-in-imagination are no substitute for the collection of empirical data by actual experimental or observational procedures. This is well illustrated by the numerous, intuitively quite plausible, imaginary experiments which have been adduced in an effort to refute the special theory of relativity; and as for imaginary experimentation in the social sciences, its outcome is liable to be affected by preconceived ideas, stereotypes, and other disturbing factors. In his review of Stouffer's *The American Soldier*, Lazarsfeld[13] lists a number of psychological and sociological assumptions which might seem to be so obviously true as to require no further investigation, but which were in fact strongly disconfirmed by the findings of Stouffer's group; for example, that among American soldiers during the war, better educated men showed more psychoneurotic symptoms than those with less education; that Southerners were better able to stand the climate in the hot South Sea Islands than Northern soldiers, and so forth. Beliefs such as these could evidently affect the outcome and defeat the purpose of intuitive thought-experiments in sociology. Such experiments, then, cannot provide evidence pertinent to the test of sociological hypotheses. At best, they can serve a heuristic function: they may *suggest* hypotheses, which must then be subjected, however, to appropriate objective tests.

The imaginary experiments mentioned by such writers as Max Weber and Howard Becker as a method of sociological inquiry are obviously of the intuitive variety; their heuristic function is to aid in the discovery of regular connections

13. *Public Opinion Quarterly*, 13 (1949), pp. 377-404.

between various constituents of some social structure or process. These connections can then be incorporated into an ideal type and thus provide the basis for
the explanatory use of the latter.

5. IDEAL TYPES AND THEORETICAL MODELS

We have argued that since ideal types are intended to provide explanations,
they must be construed as theoretical systems embodying testable general
hypotheses. To what extent is this conception reconcilable with the frequent
insistence, on the part of proponents of the method, that ideal types are not
meant to be hypotheses to be verified by empirical evidence, that deviation from
concrete fact is of their very essence? Let us consider more closely how those who
hold such views conceive of the application of ideal-type concepts to concrete
phenomena. There are few precise statements on this subject; perhaps the most
explicit formulation has been given by Howard Becker, in an effort to develop
what he terms "a logical formula for typology." Becker suggests that ideal, or
constructed, types function in hypotheses of the form 'If P then Q', where P
is the type invoked, and Q is some more or less complex characteristic.[14] Concerning the application of such hypotheses to empirical data, Becker says: "In
the very nature of type construction, however, the consequent seldom if ever
follows empirically, and the antecedent is then empirically 'false.' If Q' then P'."[15]
By this deviation from empirical fact, by the occurrence of Q' rather than Q,
a constructed type acquires what Becker calls "negative utility": it initiates a
search for factors other than those embodied in P to account for the discrepancy.[16]
In this manner, according to Becker, "constructive typology makes planned
use of the proviso 'All other conditions being equal or irrelevant' for the purpose
of determining the 'inequality' or 'relevance' of the 'other conditions'."[17]
This view calls for closer analysis, for it suggests—perhaps unintentionally—
the use of the *ceteris paribus* clause for a conventionalistic defense of typological

---

14. *Op. cit.*, pp. 259-64. Becker describes the connection between P and Q as one of
"objective probability." But since he uses the expression 'If P then Q' in an inference of the
modus tollens form, which does not hold for probabilistic implication—i.e., for statements
of the form, 'If P then probably Q'—it seems more adequate to construe Becker's remark as
meaning that 'If P then Q' is a typological hypothesis expressing an empirical generalization
in Weber's sense. Such a generalization, like any other empirical hypothesis, can of course be
only probable, and never certain, relative to any body of pertinent factual evidence.

15. *Op. cit.*, p. 262.

16. Max Weber has similarly pointed to the heuristic utility of ideal types; cf., e.g.,
The Methodology of the Social Sciences, pp. 90, 101-103; *The Theory of Social and Economic
Organization*, p. 111.

17. Howard Becker, *op. cit.*, p. 264.

hypotheses against any conceivable disconfirming evidence.[18] To illustrate this point, imagine a physicist propounding the hypothesis that under ideal conditions, namely in a vacuum near the surface of the Earth, a body falling freely for t seconds will cover a distance of exactly $16t^2$ feet. Suppose now that a careful experiment yields results differing from those required by the hypothesis. Then clearly the physicist cannot be content simply to infer that the requisite ideal conditions were not realized: in addition to this possibility, he has to allow for the alternative that the hypothesis under test is not correct. To state the point now in terms of Becker's general schema: we could infer that P is not realized only if, in addition to the observational finding Q', we could take the truth of the hypothesis 'If P then Q' for granted; but for this assumption, we surely have no warrant; in fact, it would make the entire test pointless. Thus, from the occurrence of Q', we can infer only that either P was not realized or the hypothesis, 'If P then Q', is false.

Now, it might seem that we may with assurance assert our typological hypothesis if only we qualify it by an appropriate *ceteris paribus* clause and thus give it the form: 'All other factors being equal or irrelevant, Q will be realized whenever P is realized'. Evidently, no empirical evidence can ever disconfirm a hypothesis of this form since an apparently unfavorable finding can always be attributed to a violation of the *ceteris paribus* clause by the interference of factors other than those specifically included in P. In other words, the qualified hypothesis can be made unexceptionable by the convention to plead violation of the *ceteris paribus* clause whenever an occurrence of P is not accompanied by an occurrence of Q. But the very convention that renders the hypothesis irrefutable also drains it of all empirical content and thus of explanatory power: since the protective clause does not specify *what* factors other than P have to be equal (i.e., constant) or irrelevant if the prediction of Q is to be warranted, the hypothesis is not capable of predictive application to concrete phenomena. Similarly, the idea of testing the given hypothesis becomes pointless. It is significant to note here by contrast that in the formulation of physical hypotheses, the *ceteris paribus* clause is never used: all the factors considered relevant are explicitly stated (as in Newton's law of gravitation or in Maxwell's laws) or are clearly understood (as in the familiar formulation of Galileo's law, which is understood to refer to free fall in a vacuum near the surface of the Earth); all other factors are asserted, by implication, to be irrelevant. Empirical test is therefore significant, and the discovery of discordant evidence requires appropriate revisions either by modifying the presumed functional connections between the variables

18. On the use of the *ceteris paribus* clause, see also the excellent discussion in Felix Kauf-mann, *Methodology of the Social Sciences* (New York, Oxford University Press, 1944), 84ff. and 213ff.

singled out as relevant, or by explicitly introducing new relevant variables. Ideal-type hypotheses will have to follow the same pattern if they are to afford a theoretical explanation of historical and social phenomena rather than an empirically vacuous conceptual schematism.

But is it not true that in physics as well there are theories, such as those of ideal gases, of perfectly elastic impact, of the mathematical pendulum, of the statistical aspects of a game played with perfect dice, etc., which are not held to be invalidated by the fact that they possess no precise exemplification in the empirical world? And could not ideal types claim the same status as the central concepts of those "idealized" theories? Those concepts refer to physical systems satisfying certain extreme conditions which cannot be met fully, but only approximately, by concrete empirical phenomena. Their scientific significance lies, I think, in the following points: (a) The laws governing the behavior of the ideal physical systems are deducible from more comprehensive theoretical principles, which are well confirmed by empirical evidence; the deduction usually takes the form of assigning certain extreme values to some of the parameters of the comprehensive theory. Thus, e.g., the laws for an ideal gas are obtainable from more inclusive principles of the kinetic theory of gases by "assuming" that the volumes of the gas molecules vanish and that there are no forces of attraction among the molecules—i.e., by setting the appropriate parameters equal to zero. (b) The extreme conditions characterizing the ideal case can at least be approximated empirically, and whenever this is the case in a concrete instance, the ideal laws in question are empirically confirmed. Thus, e.g., the Boyle-Charles law for ideal gases is rather closely satisfied by a large variety of gases within wide, specifiable ranges of pressure and temperature (for a fixed mass of gas), and it is for this reason that the law can be significantly invoked for explanatory purposes.

The preceding analysis suggests the following observations on the ideal and the empirical aspects of ideal-type concepts in the social sciences:

(i) Ideal constructs have the character not of concepts in the narrower sense, but of theoretical systems. The introduction of such a construct into a theoretical context requires, therefore, not definition by *genus* and *differentia*, but the specification of a set of characteristics (such as pressure, temperature, and volume in the case of an ideal gas) *and* of a set of general hypotheses connecting those characteristics.

(ii) An idealized concept P does *not*, therefore, function in hypotheses of the simple form 'If P then Q'. Thus, e.g., the hypothesis 'If a substance is an ideal gas then it satisfies Boyle's law', which is of that form, is an analytic statement entailed by the definition of an ideal gas; it cannot serve explanatory purposes. Rather, the hypotheses characterizing the concept of ideal gas connect certain quantitative characteristics of a gas, and when they are applied to concrete physical systems, they make specific empirical predictions. Thus, to put the point in a somewhat oversimplified form, what enters into physical theory is not the concept of ideal gas at all, but rather the concepts representing the various characteristics dealt with in the theory of ideal gases; only they are mentioned in the principles of thermodynamics.

(iii) In the natural sciences at least, a set of hypotheses is considered as characterizing an ideal system only if they represent what might be called *theoretical*, rather than *intuitive*, idealizations; i.e., if they are obtainable, within the framework of a given theory, as special cases of more inclusive principles. Thus, e.g., the formula for the mathematical pendulum as empirically discovered by Galileo did not constitute a theoretical idealization until after the establishment of more comprehensive hypotheses which (a) have independent empirical confirmation, (b) entail the pendulum formula as a special case, (c) enable us to judge the degree of idealization involved in the latter by giving an account of additional factors which are relevant for the motion of a physical pendulum, but whose influence is fairly small in the case of those physical systems to which the formula is customarily applied.

No theory, of course, however inclusive, can claim to give a completely accurate account of any class of empirical phenomena; it is always possible that even a very comprehensive and well-confirmed theory may be improved in the future by the inclusion of further parameters and appropriate laws: the most comprehensive theory of today may be but a systematic idealization within the broader theoretical framework of tomorrow.

Among the ideal-type concepts of social theory, those used in analytical economics approximate most closely the status of idealizations in natural science: the concepts of perfectly free competition, of monopoly, of economically rational behavior on the part of an individual or a firm, etc., all represent schemata for the interpretation of certain aspects of human behavior and involve the idealizing assumption that noneconomic factors of the sort that do in fact influence human actions may be neglected for the purposes at hand. In the context of rigorous theory construction, those ideal constructs are given a precise meaning in the form of hypotheses which postulate specified mathematical connections between certain economic variables; frequently, such postulates characterize the ideal type of behavior as maximizing a given function of those variables (e.g., profit).

In two important respects, however, idealizations in economics seem to me to differ from those of the natural sciences: first of all, they are intuitive rather than theoretical idealizations in the sense that the corresponding postulates are not deduced, as special cases, from a broader theory which covers also the non-rational and noneconomic factors affecting human conduct. No suitable more general theory is available at present, and thus there is no theoretical basis for an appraisal of the idealization involved in applying the economic constructs to concrete situations. This takes us to the second point of difference: the class of concrete behavioral phenomena for which the idealized principles of economic theory are meant to constitute at least approximately correct generalizations is not always clearly specified. This of course hampers the significant explanatory use of those principles: an ideal theoretical system, as indeed any theoretical system at all, can assume the status of an explanatory and predictive apparatus only if its area of application has been specified; in other words, if its constituent concepts have been given an empirical interpretation which, directly or at least mediately, links them to observable phenomena. Thus, e.g., the area of application for the theory of ideal gases might be indicated, roughly speaking, by interpreting the theoretical parameters 'P', 'V', 'T', in terms of the "operationally defined" magnitudes of pressure, volume, and temperature of gases at moderate or low pressures and at moderate or high temperatures. Similarly, the empirical applicability of the principles of an ideal economic system requires an interpretation in empirical terms which does not render those principles analytic; hence the interpretation must not amount to the statement that the propositions of theory hold in all cases of economically rational behavior—that would be simply a tautology; rather, it has to characterize, by criteria logically independent of the theory, those kinds of individual or group behavior to which the theory is claimed to be applicable. In reference to these, it has then to attach a reasonably definite operational interpretation to the theoretical parameters, such as 'money', 'price', 'cost', 'profit', 'utility', etc. In this fashion, the propositions of the theory acquire empirical import: they become capable of test and thus susceptible to disconfirmation—and this is an essential characteristic of all potential explanatory systems.

The results of the preceding comparison between the ideal constructs of economics with those of physics should not be considered, however, as indicating an essential methodological difference between the two fields. For in regard to the first of our two points of comparison, it need only be remembered that much effort in sociological theorizing at present is directed toward the development of a comprehensive theory of social action, relative to which the ideal constructs of economics, in so far as they permit of empirical application, might then have the status of theoretical rather than intuitive idealizations. And quite apart from the attainability of that ambitious goal, it is clear that an interpretation is required for any theoretical system which is to have empirical import—in the social no less than in the natural sciences.

The ideal types invoked in other fields of social science lack the clarity and precision of the constructions used in theoretical economics. The behavioral regularities which are meant to define a given ideal type are usually stated only in more or less intuitive terms, and the parameters they are meant to connect are not explicitly specified; finally, there is no clear indication of the area of empirical applicability and consequent testability claimed for the typological system. In fact, the demand for such testability is often rejected in a sweeping manner which, I think, the preceding discussion has shown to be inconsistent with the claim that ideal types provide an understanding of certain empirical phenomena.

If the analysis here outlined is essentially sound, then surely ideal types can serve their purpose only if they are introduced as interpreted theoretical systems, i.e., by (a) specifying a list of characteristics with which the theory is to deal, (b) formulating a set of hypotheses in terms of those characteristics, (c) giving those characteristics an empirical interpretation, which assigns to the theory a specific domain of application, and (d), as a long-range objective, incorporating the theoretical system, as a special case, into a more comprehensive theory. To what extent these objectives can be attained cannot be decided by logical analysis; but it would be self-deception to believe that any conceptual procedure essentially lacking in the first three respects can give theoretical understanding in any field of scientific inquiry. And to the extent that the program here outlined can actually be carried through, the use of ideal types is at best an unimportant terminological aspect, rather than a distinctive methodological characteristic, of the social sciences: the method of ideal types becomes indistinguishable from the methods used by other scientific disciplines in the formation and application of explanatory concepts and theories.

6. CONCLUSION

In sum, then, the various uses of type concepts in psychology and the social sciences, when freed from certain misleading connotations, prove to be of basically the same character as the methods of classification, ordering, measurement, empirical correlation, and theory formation used in the natural sciences. In leading to this result, the analysis of typological procedures exhibits an important logical and methodological similarity between divers branches of empirical science.

8. THE THEORETICIAN'S DILEMMA:

A STUDY IN THE LOGIC

OF THEORY CONSTRUCTION

1. DEDUCTIVE AND INDUCTIVE SYSTEMATIZATION

SCIENTIFIC RESEARCH in its various branches seeks not merely to record particular occurrences in the world of our experience: it tries to discover regularities in the flux of events and thus to establish general laws which may be used for prediction, postdiction,[1] and explanation.

The principles of Newtonian mechanics, for example, make it possible, given the present positions and momenta of the celestial objects that make up the solar system, to predict their positions and momenta for a specified future time or to postdict them for a specified time in the past; similarly, those principles permit an explanation of the present positions and momenta by reference to those at some earlier time. In addition to thus accounting for particular facts, the principles of Newtonian mechanics also explain certain "general facts,"

---

1. This term was suggested by a passage in Reichenbach (1944), where the word 'postdictability' is used to refer to the possibility of determining "past data in terms of given observations" (p. 13). In a similar context, Ryle uses the term 'retrodict' (see for example 1949, p. 124), and Walsh speaks of the historian's business "to 'retrodict' the past: to establish, on the basis of present evidence, what the past must have been like" (1951, p. 41). According to a remark in Acton's review of Walsh's book (*Mind*, vol. 62 (1953), pp. 564–65), the word 'retrodiction' was used in this sense already by J. M. Robertson in *Buckle and his Critics* (1895).

This article is reprinted, with some changes, by kind permission of the publisher, from *Minnesota Studies in the Philosophy of Science*, vol. II. Edited by Herbert Feigl, Michael Scriven, and Grover Maxwell, University of Minnesota Press, Minneapolis. Copyright 1958 by the University of Minnesota.

i.e., empirical uniformities such as Kepler's laws of planetary motion; for the latter can be deduced from the former.[2]

Scientific explanation, prediction, and postdiction all have the same logical character: they show that the fact under consideration can be inferred from certain other facts by means of specified general laws. In the simplest case, this type of argument may be schematized as a deductive inference of the following form:

$$(1.1) \quad \frac{\begin{array}{c} C_1, C_2 \ldots C_k \\ L_1, L_2 \ldots L_r \end{array}}{E}$$

Here, $C_1, C_2 \ldots C_k$ are statements of particular occurrences (e.g., of the positions and momenta of certain celestial bodies at a specified time), and $L_1, L_2 \ldots L_r$ are general laws (e.g., those of Newtonian mechanics); finally, E is a sentence stating whatever is being explained, predicted, or postdicted. And the argument has its intended force only if its conclusion, E, follows deductively from the premises.[3]

While explanation, prediction, and postdiction are alike in their logical structure, they differ in certain other respects. For example, an argument of the form (1.1) will qualify as a prediction only if E refers to an occurrence at a time later than that at which the argument is offered; in the case of a postdiction, the event must occur before the presentation of the argument. These differences, however, require no fuller study here, for the purpose of the preceding discussion was simply to point out the role of general laws in scientific explanation prediction, and postdiction.

For these three types of scientific procedure, I will use the common term '(deductive) systematization'. More precisely, that term will be used to refer, first to any argument of the form (1.1) that meets the requirements indicated above, no matter whether it serves as an explanation, a prediction, a postdiction, or in still some other capacity; second, to the procedure of establishing arguments of the kind just characterized.

So far, we have considered only those cases of explanation, prediction, and related procedures which can be construed as deductive arguments. There are many instances of scientific explanation and prediction, however, which do not fall into a strictly deductive pattern. For example, when Johnny comes

_____

2. More accurately: it can be deduced from the principles of Newtonian mechanics that Kepler's laws hold in approximation, namely, on the assumption that the forces exerted upon the planets by celestial objects other than the sun (especially other planets) are negligible.

3. (added in 1964). For a fuller discussion of this schema and for certain qualifications concerning the structural identity of explanatory and predictive arguments, see the essay "Aspects of Scientific Explanation" in this volume.

down with the measles, this might be explained by pointing out that he caught the disease from his sister, who is just recovering from it. The particular antecedent facts here invoked are that of Johnny's exposure and, let us assume, the further fact that Johnny had not had the measles previously. But to connect these with the event to be explained, we cannot adduce a general law to the effect that under the specified circumstances, the measles is invariably transmitted to the exposed person: what can be asserted is only a high probability (in the sense of statistical frequency) of transmission. The same type of argument can be used also for predicting or postdicting the occurrence of a case of the measles.

Similarly, in a psychoanalytic explanation of the neurotic behavior of an adult by reference to certain childhood experiences, the generalizations which might be invoked to connect the antecedent events with those to be explained can be construed at best as establishing more or less high probabilities for the connections at hand, but surely not as expressions of unexceptional uniformities.

Explanations, predictions, and postdictions of the kind here illustrated differ from those previously discussed in two important respects: The laws invoked are of a different form, and the statement to be established does not follow deductively from the explanatory statements adduced. We will now consider these differences somewhat more closely.

The laws referred to in connection with the schema (1.1), such as the laws of Newtonian mechanics, are what we will call *statements of strictly universal form*, or *strictly universal statements*. A statement of this kind is an assertion—which may be true or false—to the effect that all cases which meet certain specified conditions will unexceptionally have such and such further characteristics. For example, the statement 'All crows are black' is a sentence of strictly universal form; and so is Newton's first law of motion, that any material body which is not acted upon by an external force persists in its state of rest or of rectilinear motion at constant speed.

The laws invoked in the second type of explanatory and related arguments, on the other hand, are, as we will say, of *statistical form*; they are *statistical probability statements*. A statement of this kind is an assertion—which may be true or false—to the effect that for cases which meet conditions of a specified kind, the probability of having such and such further characteristics is so-and-so much.[4]

4. The distinction here made concerns, then, exclusively the *form* of the statements under consideration and not their truth status nor the extent to which they are supported by empirical evidence. If it were established, for example, that actually only 80 per cent of all crows are black, this would not show that 'All crows are black', or S_1 for short, was a statistical probability statement, but rather that it was a false statement of strictly universal form, and that 'The probability for a crow to be black is .8,' or S_2 for short, was a true statement of statistical form.

(Continued overleaf)

To put the distinction in a nutshell: A strictly universal statement of the simplest kind has the form 'All cases of P are cases of Q'; a statistical probability statement of the simplest kind has the form 'The probability for a case of P to be a case of Q is r.' While the former implies an assertion about any particular instance of P—namely, that it is also an instance of Q—the latter implies no similar assertion concerning any particular instance of P or even concerning any finite set of such instances.[5] This circumstance gives rise to the second distinctive characteristic mentioned above: the statement E describing the phenomenon being explained, predicted, or postdicted (for example, Johnny's catching the measles) is not logically deducible from the explanatory statements adduced [for example, (C_1) Johnny was exposed to the measles; (C_2) Johnny had not previously had the measles; (L) For persons who have not previously had the measles and are exposed to it, the probability is .92 that they will contract the disease]; rather, on the assumption that the explanatory statements adduced are true, it is very likely, though not certain, that E is true as well. This kind of argument, therefore, is inductive rather than strictly deductive in character: it offers the conclusion E on the basis of other statements which constitute only partial, if strongly supporting, grounds for it. An argument of this kind—no matter whether it is used for explanation, prediction, or postdiction, or for yet another purpose—will be called an *inductive systematization*. In particular, we will assume of an inductive systematization that the conclusion is not logically implied by the premises.[6] Again, the procedure of establishing an argument of the kind just described will also be called inductive systematization.

By way of further illustration, let us note here two explanatory arguments

5. For a fuller discussion of this point, see, for example, Nagel (1939, section 7), Reichenbach (1949, sections 63-67), Cramér (1946, Chapter 13).

6. The explanatory and predictive use of statistical laws constitutes perhaps the most important type of inductive systematization; but the occurrence of such laws among the premises is not required by our general concept of inductive systematization. And indeed, as Carnap (1950, pp. 574-75) has pointed out, it is sometimes possible to make predictions of an inductive character exclusively on the basis of information about a finite set of particular cases, without the mediation of any laws whatever. For example, information to the effect that a large sample of instances of P has been examined, that all of its elements have the characteristic Q, and that a certain case x, not included in the sample, is an instance of P, will lend high inductive support to the prediction that x, too, has the characteristic Q. Also, it is sometimes possible to base an inductive systematization on a set of premises which include one or more strictly universal statements, but no statistical laws. An example of such a systematization will be found in Section 9, in the prediction based on the formulas (9.6)-(9.12).

Furthermore, to be sure, neither S_1 nor S_2 can ever be established conclusively: they can only be more or less well supported by available evidence; each of them thus has a more or less high logical, or inductive, probability, relative to that evidence. But this again does not affect at all the fact that S_1 is of strictly universal and S_2 of statistical form.

which are of the inductive kind just characterized. They are adduced by von Mises in a statement to the effect that the everyday notion of causal explanation will eventually adjust itself to changes in the logical form of scientific theories (especially to the use of statistical probability statements as explanatory principles): "We think," von Mises says, that "people will gradually come to be satisfied by causal statements of this kind: It is *because* the die was loaded that the 'six' shows more frequently (but we do not know what the next number will be); or: *Because* the vacuum was heightened and the voltage increased, the radiation became more intense (but we do not know the precise number of scintillations that will occur in the next minute)."[7] Clearly, both of these statements can be construed as inductive explanations of certain physical phenomena.

All the cases of scientific systematization we have considered share this characteristic: they make use of general laws or general principles either of strictly universal or of statistical form. These general laws have the function of establishing systematic connections among empirical facts in such a way that with their help some empirical occurrences may be inferred, by way of explanation, prediction, or postdiction, from other such occurrences. When, in an explanation, we say that the event described by E occurred "because" of the circumstances detailed in $C_1, C_2 \ldots C_k$, that phrase has significance if it can be construed as referring to general laws which render $C_1, C_2 \ldots C_k$ relevant to E in the sense that, granted the truth of the former, they make the truth of the latter either certain (as in a deductive systematization) or inductively probable (as in an inductive systematization). It is for this reason that the establishment of general laws is of crucial importance in the empirical sciences.

2. OBSERVABLES AND THEORETICAL ENTITIES

Scientific systematization is ultimately aimed at establishing explanatory and predictive order among the bewilderingly complex "data" of our experience, the phenomena that can be "directly observed" by us. It is a remarkable fact, therefore, that the greatest advances in scientific systematization have not been accomplished by means of laws referring explicitly to *observables*, i.e., to things and events which are ascertainable by direct observation, but rather by means of laws that speak of various *hypothetical*, or *theoretical*, *entities*, i.e., presumptive objects, events, and attributes which cannot be perceived or otherwise directly observed by us.

7. Mises (1951, p. 188). Whether it is advisable to refer to explanations of this kind as causal is debatable: since the classical conception of causality is intimately bound up with the idea of strictly universal laws connecting cause and effect, it might be better to reserve the term 'causal explanation' for some of those explanatory arguments of form (1.1) in which all the laws invoked are of strictly universal form.

For a fuller discussion of this point, it will be helpful to refer to the familiar rough distinction between two levels of scientific systematization: the level of *empirical generalization*, and the level of *theory formation*.[8] The early stages in the development of a scientific discipline usually belong to the former level, which is characterized by the search for laws (of universal or statistical form) which establish connections among the directly observable aspects of the subject matter under study. The more advanced stages belong to the second level, where research is aimed at comprehensive laws, in terms of hypothetical entities, which will account for the uniformities established on the first level. On the first level, we find everyday physical generalizations such as 'Where there is light there is heat', 'Iron rusts in damp air', 'Wood floats on water, iron sinks in it'; but we might assign to it also such more precise quantitative laws as Galileo's, Kepler's, Hooke's, and Snell's laws, as well as botanical and zoological generalizations about the concomitance of certain observable anatomical, physical, functional, and other characteristics in the members of a given species; generalizations in psychology that assert correlations among diverse observable aspects of learning, of perception, and so forth; and various descriptive generalizations in economics, sociology, and anthropology. All these generalizations, whether of strictly universal or of statistical form, purport to express regular connections among directly observable phenomena, and they lend themselves, therefore, to explanatory, predictive, and postdictive use.

On the second level, we encounter general statements that refer to electric, magnetic, and gravitational fields, to molecules, atoms, and a variety of sub-atomic particles; or to ego, id, superego, libido, sublimation, fixation, and transference; or to various not directly observable entities invoked in recent learning theories.

In accordance with the distinction here made, we will assume that the (extra-logical) vocabulary of empirical science, or of any of its branches, is divided into two classes: *observational terms* and *theoretical terms*. In regard to an observational term it is possible, under suitable circumstances, to decide by means of direct observation whether the term does or does not apply to a given situation.

Observation may here be construed so broadly as to include not only perception, but also sensation and introspection; or it may be limited to the perception of what in principle is publicly ascertainable, i.e., perceivable also by others. The subsequent discussion will be independent of how narrowly or how liberally the notion of observation is construed; it may be worth noting,

8. Northrop (1947, Chapters III and IV), for example, presents this distinction very suggestively; he refers to the two levels as "the natural history stage of inquiry" and "the stage of deductively formulated theory." A lucid and concise discussion of the idea at hand will be found in Feigl (1948).

however, that empirical science aims for a system of publicly testable statements, and that, accordingly, the observational data whose correct prediction is the hallmark of a successful theory are at least thought of as couched in terms whose applicability in a given situation different individuals can ascertain with high agreement, by means of direct observation. Statements which purport to describe readings of measuring instruments, changes in color or odor accompanying a chemical reaction, verbal or other kinds of overt behavior shown by a given subject under specified observable conditions—these all illustrate the use of *intersubjectively applicable* observational terms.[9]

Theoretical terms, on the other hand, usually purport to refer to not directly observable entities and their characteristics; they function, in a manner soon to be examined more closely, in scientific theories intended to explain empirical generalizations.

The preceding characterization of the two vocabularies is obviously vague; it offers no precise criterion by means of which any scientific term may be unequivocally classified as an observational term or as a theoretical one. But no such precise criterion is needed here; the questions to be examined in this essay are independent of precisely where the dividing line between the terms of the observational and the theoretical vocabularies is drawn.

3. WHY THEORETICAL TERMS?

The use of theoretical terms in science gives rise to a perplexing problem: Why should science resort to the assumption of hypothetical entities when it is interested in establishing predictive and explanatory connections among observables? Would it not be sufficient for the purpose, and much less extravagant at that, to search for a system of general laws mentioning only observables, and thus expressed in terms of the observational vocabulary alone?

Many general statements in terms of observables have indeed been formulated; they constitute the empirical generalizations mentioned in the preceding

9. In his essay on Skinner's analysis of learning (in Estes *et al.* 1945), Verplanck throws an illuminating sidelight on the importance, for the observational vocabulary (the terms of the data-language, as he calls it), of high uniformity of use among different experimenters. Verplanck argues that while much of Skinner's data-language is sound in this respect, it is "contaminated" by two kinds of term that are not suited for the description of objective scientific data. The first kind includes terms "that cannot be successfully used by many others"; the second kind includes certain terms that should properly be treated as higher-order theoretical expressions.

The nonprecise and pragmatic character of the requirement of intersubjective uniformity of use is nicely reflected in Verplanck's conjecture "that if one were to work with Skinner, and read his records with him, he would find himself able to make the same discriminations as does Skinner and hence eventually give some of them at least data-language status" (*loc. cit.*, p. 279n).

section. But, vexingly, many if not all of them suffer from definite short-comings: they usually have a rather limited range of application; and even within that range, they have exceptions, so that actually they are not true general statements. Take for example, one of our earlier illustrations:

(3.1) Wood floats on water; iron sinks in it.

This statement has a narrow range of application in the sense that it refers only to wooden and iron objects and concerns their floating behavior only in regard to water.[10] And, what is even more serious, it has exceptions: certain kinds of wood will sink in water, and a hollow iron sphere of suitable dimensions will float on it.

As the history of science shows, flaws of this kind can often be remedied by attributing to the subject matter under study certain further characteristics which, though not open to direct observation, are connected in specified ways with its observable aspects, and which make it possible to establish systematic connections among the latter. For example, a generalization much more satis-factory than (3.1) is obtained by means of the concept of the specific gravity of a body x, which is definable as the quotient of its weight and its volume:

(3.2) Def. $s(x) = w(x)/v(x)$

Let us assume that w and v have been characterized operationally, i.e., in terms of the directly observable outcomes of specified measuring procedures, and that therefore they are counted among the observables. Then s, as determined by (3.2), might be viewed as a characteristic that is less directly observable; and, just for the sake of obtaining a simple illustration, we will classify s as a hypothetical entity. For s, we may now state the following generalization, which is a corollary of the principle of Archimedes:

(3.3) A solid body floats on a liquid if its specific gravity is less than that of the liquid.

This statement avoids, first of all, the exceptions we noted above as refuting (3.1); it predicts correctly the behavior of a piece of heavy wood and of a hollow iron sphere. Moreover, it has a much wider scope: it refers to any kind of solid object and concerns its floating behavior in regard to any liquid. Even the new

10. It should be mentioned, however, that the idea of the range of application of a general-ization is here used in an intuitive sense which it would be difficult to explicate. The range of application of (3.1), for example, might plausibly be held to be narrower than here indicated: it might be construed as consisting only of wooden-objects-placed-in-water and iron-objects-placed-in-water. On the other hand, (3.1) may be equivalently restated thus: Any object whatever has the two properties of either not being wood or floating on water, and of either not being iron or sinking in water. In this form, the generalization might be said to have the largest possible range of application, the class of all objects whatsoever.

generalization has certain limitations, of course, and thus invites further improvement. But instead of pursuing this process, let us now examine more closely the way in which a systematic connection among observables is achieved by the law (3.3), which involves a detour through the domain of unobservables.

Suppose that we wish to predict whether a certain solid object b will float on a given body l of liquid. We will then first have to ascertain, by appropriate operational procedures, the weight and the volume of b and l. Let the results of these measurements be expressed by the following four statements O_1, O_2, O_3, O_4:

$$(3.4) \quad \begin{array}{llll} O_1: & w(b) = w_1; & O_2: & v(b) = v_1 \\ O_3: & w(l) = w_2; & O_4: & v(l) = v_2 \end{array}$$

where w_1, w_2, v_1, v_2, are certain positive real numbers. By means of the definition (3.2), we can infer, from (3.4), the specific gravities of b and l:

$$(3.5) \quad s(b) = w_1/v_1; s(l) = w_2/v_2$$

Suppose now that the first of these values is less than the second; then (3.4), via (3.5) implies that

$$(3.6) \quad s(b) < s(l)$$

By means of the law (3.3), we can now infer that

$$(3.7) \quad b \text{ floats on } l$$

This sentence will also be called O_5. The sentences O_1, O_2, O_3, O_4, O_5 then share the characteristic that they are expressed entirely in terms of the observational vocabulary; for on our assumption, 'w' and 'v' are observational terms, and so are 'b' and 'l', which name certain observable bodies; finally, 'floats on' is an observational term because under suitable circumstances, direct observation will show whether a given observable object floats on a given observable liquid. On the other hand, the sentences (3.2), (3.3), (3.5), and (3.6) lack that characteristic, for they all contain the term 's', which, in our illustration, belongs to the theoretical vocabulary.

The systematic transition from the "observational data" listed in (3.4) to the prediction (3.7) of an observable phenomenon is schematized in the accompanying diagram. Here, an arrow represents a deductive inference; mention,

$$(3.8) \quad \left. \begin{array}{l} O_1 \\ O_2 \end{array} \right\} \xrightarrow{\;(3.2)\;} s(b) = v_1/w_1 \\ \left. \begin{array}{l} O_3 \\ O_4 \end{array} \right\} \xrightarrow{\;(3.2)\;} s(l) = v_2/w_2 \quad \left. \begin{array}{c} \\ \\ \\ \end{array} \right\} \xrightarrow{\;(3.3)\;} s(b) < s(l) \xrightarrow{\;(3.3)\;} O_5$$

Data described in terms of observables	Systematic connection effected by statements making reference to nonobservables	Prediction in terms of observables

above an arrow, of a further sentence indicates that the deduction is effected by means of that sentence, i.e., that the conclusion stated at the right end follows logically from the premises listed at the left, taken in conjunction with the sentence mentioned above the arrow. Note that the argument just considered illustrates the schema (1.1), with O_1, O_2, O_3, O_4 constituting the statements of particular facts, the sentences (3.2) and (3.3) taking the place of the general laws, and O_5 that of E.[11]

Thus, the assumption of nonobservable entities serves the purposes of systematization: it provides connections among observables in the form of laws containing theoretical terms, and this detour via the domain of hypothetical entities offers certain advantages, some of which were indicated above.

In the case of our illustration, however, brief reflection will show that the advantages obtained by the "theoretical detour" could just as well have been obtained without ever resorting to the use of a theoretical term. Indeed, by virtue of the definition (3.2), the law (3.3) can be restated as follows:

(3.3).   A solid body floats on a liquid if the quotient of its weight and its volume is less than the corresponding quotient for the liquid.

This alternative version clearly shares the advantages we found (3.3) to have over the crude generalization (3.1); and, of course, it permits the deductive transition from O_1, O_2, O_3, O_4 to O_5 just as well as does (3.3) in conjunction with (3.2).

The question arises therefore whether the systematization achieved by general principles containing theoretical terms can always be duplicated by means of general statements couched exclusively in observational terms. To prepare for an examination of this problem, we must first consider more closely the form and function of a scientific theory.

4. STRUCTURE AND INTERPRETATION OF A THEORY

Formally, a scientific theory may be considered as a set of sentences expressed

---

11. Since (3.2) was presented as a definition, it might be considered inappropriate to include it among the general laws effecting the predictive transition from O_1, O_2, O_3, O_4, to O_5. And indeed, it is quite possible to construe the concept of logical deduction as applied to (1.1) in such a way that it includes the use of any definition as an additional premise. In this case, (3.3) is the only law invoked in the prediction here considered. On the other hand, it is also possible to treat sentences such as (3.2), which are usually classified as purely definitional, on a par with other statements of universal form, which are qualified as general laws. This view is favored by the consideration, for example, that when a theory conflicts with pertinent empirical data, it is sometimes the "laws" and sometimes the "definitions" that are modified in order to accommodate the evidence. Our analysis of deductive systematization is neutral with respect to this issue.

in terms of a specific vocabulary. The vocabulary, V_T, of a theory T will be understood to consist of the extralogical terms of T, i.e., those which do not belong to the vocabulary of pure logic. Usually, some of the terms of V_T are defined by means of others; but, on pain of a circle or an infinite regress, not all of them can be so defined. Hence, V may be assumed to be divided into two subsets: *primitive terms*—those for which no definition is specified—and *defined terms*. Analogously, many of the sentences of a theory are derivable from others by means of the principles of deductive logic (and the definitions of the defined terms); but, on pain of a vicious circle or an infinite regress in the deduction, not all of the theoretical sentences can be thus established. Hence, the set of sentences asserted by T falls into two subsets: *primitive sentences*, or *postulates* (also called *axioms*), and *derivative sentences*, or *theorems*. Henceforth, we will assume that theories are stated in the form of axiomatized systems as here described; i.e., by listing, first the primitive and the derivative terms and the definitions for the latter, second, the postulates. In addition, the theory will always be thought of as formulated within a linguistic framework of a clearly specified logical structure, which determines, in particular, the rules of deductive inference.

The classical paradigms of deductive systems of this kind are the axiomatizations of various mathematical theories, such as Euclidean and various forms of non-Euclidean geometry, and the theory of groups and other branches of abstract algebra;[12] but by now, a number of theories in empirical science have likewise been put into axiomatic form, or approximations thereof; among them, parts of classical and relativistic mechanics,[13] certain segments of biological theory[14] and some theoretical systems in psychology, especially in the field of learning;[15] in economic theory, the concept of utility, among others, has received axiomatic treatment.[16]

12. A lucid elementary discussion of the nature of axiomatized mathematical systems may be found in Cohen and Nagel (1934), Chapter VI; also reprinted in Feigl and Brodbeck (1953). For an analysis in a similar vein, with special emphasis on geometry, see also Hempel (1945). An excellent systematic account of the axiomatic method is given in Tarski (1941, Chapters VI-X); this presentation, which makes use of some concepts of elementary symbolic logic, as developed in earlier chapters, includes several simple illustrations from mathematics. A careful logical study of deductive systems in empirical science with special attention to the role of theoretical terms, is carried out in the first three chapters of Braithwaite (1953) and a logically more advanced exposition of the axiomatic method, coupled with applications to biological theory, has been given by Woodger, especially in (1937) and (1939).

13. See, for example, Hermes (1938); Walker (1943-1949), McKinsey, Sugar, and Suppes (1953); McKinsey and Suppes (1953), Rubin and Suppes (1953), and the further references given in these publications. An important pioneer work in the field is Reichenbach (1924).

14. See expecially Woodger (1937) and (1939).

15. See for example, Hull *et al.* (1940).

16. For example, in von Neumann and Morgenstern (1947), Chapter III and Appendix.

If the primitive terms and the postulates of an axiomatized system have been specified, then the proof of theorems, i.e., the derivation of further sentences from the primitive ones—can be carried out by means of the purely formal canons of deductive logic, and thus, without any reference to the meanings of the terms and sentences at hand; indeed, for the deductive development of an axiomatized system, no meanings need be assigned at all to its expressions, primitive or derived.

However, a deductive system can function as a theory in empirical science only if it has been given an *interpretation* by reference to empirical phenomena. We may think of such interpretation as being effected by the specification of a set of *interpretative sentences*, which connect certain terms of the theoretical vocabulary with observational terms.[17] The character of these sentences will be examined in detail in subsequent sections; at present it may be mentioned as an example that interpretative sentences might take the form of so-called operational definitions, i.e., of statements specifying the meanings of theoretical terms with the help of observational ones; of special importance among these are rules for the measurement of theoretical quantities by reference to observable responses of measuring instruments or other indicators.

The manner in which a theory establishes explanatory and predictive connections among statements couched in observational terms can now be illustrated in outline by the following example. Suppose that the Newtonian theory of mechanics is used to study the motions, under the exclusive influence of their mutual gravitational attraction, of two bodies, such as the components of a double-star system, or the moon and a rocket coasting freely 100 miles above the moon's surface. On the basis of appropriate observational data, each of the two bodies may be assigned a certain mass, and, at a given instant t_0, a certain position and velocity in some specified frame of reference. Thus, a first step is taken which leads, via interpretative sentences in the form of rules of measurement, from certain statements $O_1, O_2 \ldots O_k$ which describe observable in-

---

17. Statements effecting an empirical interpretation of theoretical terms have been discussed in the methodological literature under a variety of names. For example, Reichenbach, who quite early emphasized the importance of the idea with special reference to the relation between pure and physical geometry, speaks of *coordinative definitions* (1928, section 4; also 1951, Chapter VIII); Campbell [1920, Chapter VI; an excerpt from this chapter is reprinted in Feigl and Brodbeck (1953)] and Ramsey (1931, pp. 212-36) assume a *dictionary* connecting theoretical and empirical terms. (See also Section 8 below). Margenau (1950, especially Chapter 4) speaks of *rules of correspondence*, and Carnap (1956) has likewise used the general term 'correspondence rules.' Northrop's *epistemic correlations* (1947, especially Chapter VII) may be viewed as a special kind of interpretative statements. For a discussion of interpretation as a semantical procedure, see Carnap (1939, sections 23, 24, 25), and Hutten (1956, especially Chapter II). A fuller discussion of interpretative statements is included in sections 6, 7, 8 of the present essay.

strument readings, to certain theoretical statements, say $H_1, H_2 \ldots H_6$, which assign to each of the two bodies a specific numerical value of the theoretical quantities mass, position, and velocity. From these statements, the law of gravitation, which is couched entirely in theoretical terms, leads to a further theoretical statement, H_7, which specifies the force of the gravitational attraction the two bodies exert upon each other at t_0; and H_7 in conjunction with the preceding theoretical statements and the laws of Newtonian mechanics implies, via a deductive argument involving the principles of the calculus, certain statements H_8, H_9, H_{10}, H_{11}, which give the positions and velocites of the two objects at a specified later time, say t_1. Finally, use in reverse of the interpretative sentences leads, from the last four theoretical statements, to a set of sentences $O'_1, O'_2 \ldots O'_m$, which describe observable phenomena, namely, instrument readings that are indicative of the predicted positions and velocities.

By means of a schema analogous to (3.8), the procedure may be represented as follows:

$$(4.1) \quad \{O_1, O_2 \ldots O_k\} \xrightarrow{R} \{H_1, H_2 \ldots H_6\} \xrightarrow{G} \{H_1, H_2 \ldots H_6, H_7\}$$
$$\xrightarrow{LM} \{H_8, H_9, H_{10}, H_{11}\} \xrightarrow{R} \{O'_1, O'_2 \ldots O'_m\}$$

Here, R is the set of the rules of measurement for mass, position, and velocity; these rules constitute the interpretative sentences; G is Newton's law of gravitation, and LM are the Newtonian laws of motion.

In reference to psychology, similar schematic analyses of the function of theories or of hypotheses involving "intervening variables" have repeatedly been presented in the methodological literature.[18] Here, the observational data with which the procedure starts usually concern certain observable aspects of an initial state of a given subject, plus certain observable stimuli acting upon the latter; and the final observational statements describe a response made by the subject. The theoretical statements mediating the transition from the former to the latter refer to various hypothetical entities, such as drives, reserves, inhibitions, or whatever other not directly observable characteristics, qualities, or psychological states are postulated by the theory at hand.

5. THE THEORETICIAN'S DILEMMA

The preceding account of the function of theories raises anew the problem encountered in section 3, namely, whether the theoretical detour through a domain of not directly observable things, events, or characteristics cannot be

---

18. A lucid and concise presentation may be found, for example, in Bergmann and Spence (1941).

entirely avoided. Assume, for example, that—as will often be the case—the interpretative sentences as well as the laws asserted by the theory have the form of equations which connect certain expressions in terms of theoretical quantities either with other such expressions, or with expressions in terms of observable quantities. Then the problem can be stated in Hull's succinct formulation: "If you have a secure equational linkage extending from the antecedent observable conditions through to the consequent observable conditions, why, even though to do so might not be positively pernicious, use several equations where one would do?"[19] Skinner makes the same point in more general form when he criticizes the construction, in psychological theories, of causal chains in which a first link consisting of an observable and controllable event is connected with a final ("third") one of the same kind by an intermediate link which usually is not open to observation and control. Skinner argues: "Unless there is a weak spot in our causal chain so that the second link is not lawfully determined by the first, or the third by the second, then the first and third links must be lawfully related. If we must always go back beyond the second link for prediction and control, we may avoid many tiresome and exhausting digressions by examining the third link as a function of the first."[20]

The conclusion suggested by these arguments might be called the *paradox of theorizing*. It asserts that if the terms and the general principles of a scientific theory serve their purpose, i.e., if they establish definite connections among observable phenomena, then they can be dispensed with since any chain of laws and interpretative statements establishing such a connection should then be replaceable by a law which directly links observational antecedents to observational consequents.

By adding to this crucial thesis two further statements which are obviously true, we obtain the premises for an argument in the classical form of a dilemma:

(5.1)   If the terms and principles of a theory serve their purpose they are unnecessary, as just pointed out; and if they do not serve their purpose they are surely unnecessary. But given any theory, its terms and principles either serve their purpose or they do not. Hence, the terms and principles of any theory are unnecessary.

This argument, whose conclusion accords well with the views of extreme methodological behaviorists in psychology, will be called the *theoretician's dilemma*.

However, before yielding to glee or to gloom over the outcome of this argument, it will be well to remember that the considerations adduced so far

19. Hull (1943, p. 284).
20. Skinner (1953, p. 35).

in support of the crucial first premise were formulated rather sketchily. In order to form a more careful judgment on the issue, it will therefore be necessary to inquire whether the sketch can be filled in so as to yield a cogent argument. To this task we now turn.

6. OPERATIONAL DEFINITIONS AND REDUCTION SENTENCES

It will be well to begin by considering more closely the character of interpretative sentences. In the simplest case, such a sentence could be an *explicit definition* of a theoretical expression in terms of observational ones, as illustrated by (3.2). In this case, the theoretical term is unnecessary in the strong sense that it can always be avoided in favor of an observational expression, its definiens. If all the primitives of a theory *T* are thus defined, then clearly *T* can be stated entirely in observational terms, and all its general principles will indeed be laws that directly connect observables with observables.

This would be true, in particular, of any theory that meets the standards of operationism in the narrow sense that each of its terms is introduced by an explicit definition stating an observable response whose occurrence is necessary and sufficient, under specified observable test conditions, for the applicability of the term in question. Suppose, for example, that the theoretical term is a one-place predicate, or property term, 'Q'. Then an operational definition of the kind just mentioned would take the form

(6.1) Def. $Qx \equiv (Cx \supset Ex)$

i.e., an object x has (by definition) the property Q if and only if it is such that if it is under test conditions of kind C then it exhibits an effect, or response, of kind E. Tolman's definition of expectancy of food provides an illustration: "When we assert that a rat expects food at L, what we assert is that *if* (1) he is deprived of food, (2) he has been trained on path P, (3) he is now put on path P, (4) path P is now blocked, and (5) there are other paths which lead away from path P, one of which points directly to location L, *then* he will run down the path which points directly to location L."[21] We can obtain this formulation by replacing, in (6.1), 'Ox' by 'rat x expects food at location L', 'Cx' by the conjunction of the conditions (1), (2), (3), (4), (5) for rat x, and 'Ex' by 'x runs down the path which points directly to location L'.

However, as has been shown by Carnap in a now classical argument,[22] this manner of defining scientific terms, no matter how natural it may seem, en-

---

21. Tolman, Ritchie, and Kalish (1946, p. 15). See the detailed critical analysis of Tolman's characterization of expectancy in MacCorquodale and Meehl (1945, pp. 179-81).
22. See Carnap (1936-37), section 4.

counters a serious difficulty. For on the standard extensional interpretation, a conditional sentence, such as the definiens in (6.1), is false only if its antecedent is true and its consequent false. Hence, for any object which does not satisfy the test conditions C, and for which therefore the antecedent of the definiens is false, the definiens as a whole is true; consequently, such an object will be assigned the property Q. In terms of our illustration: of any rat not exposed to the conditions (1)-(5) just stated, we would have to say that he expected food at L—no matter what kind of behavior the rat might exhibit.

One way out of this difficulty is suggested by the following consideration. In saying that a given rat expects food at L, we intend to attribute to the animal a state or a disposition which, under circumstances (1)-(5), will cause the rat to run down the path pointing directly to L; hence, in a proper operational definition, E must be tied to C nomologically, i.e., by virtue of general laws of the kind expressing causal connections. The extensional 'if . . . then . . .'— which requires neither logical nor nomological necessity of connection— would therefore have to be replaced in (6.1) by a stricter, nomological counterpart which might be worded perhaps as 'if . . . then, with causal necessity, . . .'. However, the idea of causal or of nomological necessity here invoked is not clear enough at present to make this approach seem promising.[23]

Carnap[24] has proposed an alternative way of meeting the difficulty encountered by definitions of the form (6.1); it consists in providing a partial rather than a complete specification of meaning for 'Q'. This is done by means of so-called reduction sentences; in the simplest case, (6.1) would be replaced by the following *bilateral reduction sentence:*

(6.2) $Cx \supset (Qx \equiv Ex)$

This sentence specifies that if an object is under test conditions of kind C, then it has the property Q just in case it exhibits a response of kind E. Here, the use of extensional connectives no longer has the undesirable aspects it exhibited in (6.1). If an object is not under test conditions C, then the entire formula (6.2) is true of it, but this implies nothing as to whether the object does, or does not, have the property Q. On the other hand, while (6.1) offers a full explicit definition of 'Q', (6.2) specifies the meaning of 'Q' only partly, namely, for just those objects that meet condition C; for those which do not, the meaning of 'Q' is left unspecified.

---

23. On this point, and on the general problem of explicating the concept of a law of nature, see Braithwaite (1953), Chapter IX; Burks (1951); Carnap (1956), section 9; Goodman (1955); Hempel and Oppenheim (1948), Part III; Reichenbach (1954).

24. In his theory of reduction sentences, developed in Carnap (1936-37). There is a question, however, whether certain conditions which Carnap imposes upon reduction sentences do not implicitly invoke causal modalities. On this point, see Hempel (1963), section 3.

In our illustration, (6.2) would specify the meaning of 'x expects food at L' only for rats that meet conditions (1)-(5); for them, running down the path which points to L would be a necessary and sufficient condition of food expectancy. In reference to rats that do not meet the test conditions (1)-(5), the meaning of 'x expects food at L' would be left open; it could be further specified by means of additional reduction sentences.

In fact, it is this interpretation which is indicated for Tolman's concept of food expectancy. For while the passage quoted above seems to have exactly the form (6.1), this construal is ruled out by the following sentence which immediately follows the one quoted earlier: "When we assert that he does not expect food at location L, what we assert is that, under the same conditions, he will not run down the path which points directly to location L." The total interpretation thus given to 'rat x expects food at L' is most satisfactorily formulated in terms of a sentence of the form (6.2), in the manner outlined in the preceding paragraph.[25]

As this example illustrates, reduction sentences offer a precise formulation of the intent of operational definitions. By expressing the latter as merely partial specifications of meaning, they treat theoretical concepts as "open"; and the provision for a set of different, and mutually supplementary, reduction sentences for a given term reflects the availability, for most theoretical terms, of different operational criteria of application, pertaining to different contexts.[26]

However, while an analysis in terms of reduction sentences construes theoretical terms as not fully defined by reference to observables, it does not prove that a full explicit definition in observational terms *cannot* be achieved for theoretical expressions. And indeed, it seems questionable whether a *proof* to this effect could even be significantly asked for. The next section deals with this issue in some detail.

7. ON THE DEFINABILITY OF THEORETICAL TERMS BY MEANS OF AN OBSERVATIONAL VOCABULARY

The first, quite general, point to be made here is this: a definition of any term, say 'v', by means of a set V of other terms, say 'v_1', 'v_2' ... v_n', has to specify a necessary and sufficient condition for the applicability of 'v', expressed in terms of some or all of the members of V. And in order to be able to judge whether this can be done in a given case, we will have to know how the terms

---

25. And in fact, the total specification of meaning effected by the passages quoted is then summarized by the authors in their "definition" DF II, which has exactly the form (6.2) of a bilateral reduction sentence for 'rat x expects food at L'. [Tolman, Ritchie, and Kalish (1946, p. 15).]

26. For a fuller discussion, see Carnap (1936-37), section 7 and (1956), section 10.

under consideration are to be understood. For example, the vocabulary consisting of the terms 'male' and 'offspring of' permits the formulation of a necessary and sufficient condition of application for the term 'son of' in its biological, but not in its legal sense. How the given terms are to be understood can be indicated by specifying a set U of sentences which are to be considered as true, and which connect the given terms with each other and perhaps with other terms. Thus, U will be a set of sentences containing 'v', 'v_1' ... 'v_n' and possibly also other extralogical constants. For example, in the case of the biological use of the terms 'son', 'male', and 'offspring', in reference to humans, the following set of sentences —let us call it U_1—might be given: 'Every son is male,' 'No daughter is male,' 'x is an offspring of y if and only if x is a son or a daughter of y'.

Generally, the sentences of U specify just what assumptions are to be made, in the search for a definition, concerning the concepts under consideration; and the problem of definability now turns into the question whether it is possible to formulate, in terms of $v_1, v_2 \ldots v_n$, a condition which, *in virtue of the assumptions included in U*, will be both necessary and sufficient for v. Thus, using an idea set forth and developed technically by Tarski,[27] we see that the concept of definability of 'v' by means of 'v_1', 'v_2' ... 'v_n' acquires a precise meaning only if it is explicitly relativized by reference to a set U of specifying assumptions. That precise meaning may now be stated as follows:

(7.1)   'v' is definable by means of the vocabulary $V = \{$'v_1', 'v_2', ..., 'v_n'$\}$ relative to a finite set U of statements containing, at least, 'v' and all the elements of V if from U there is deducible at least one sentence stating a necessary and sufficient condition for v in terms of no other extralogical constants than the members of V.

If all the terms under study are one-place predicates of the first order, for example, then a sentence of the required kind could most simply be stated in the form

(7.2) $v(x) \equiv D(x, v_1, v_2, \ldots, v_n)$

where the expression on the right-hand side stands for a sentential function whose only free variable is 'x', and which contains no extralogical constant other than those included in V.

Similarly, in the case of our illustration, the set U_1 specified above implies the statement:

x is a son of $y \equiv (x$ is male and x is an offspring of $y)$

so that, relative to U_1, 'son' is definable as 'male offspring'.

A definition that is not simply a convention introducing an abbreviatory notation (such as the convention to let 'x^5' be short for '$x \cdot x \cdot x \cdot x \cdot x$') is usually considered as stating the *synonymy* of two expressions, or, as it is often put, the *identity of their meanings*. Now the question of the definability of a given term 'v' by means of a set V of other terms surely is not simply one of notational fiat; and indeed it will normally be construed as concerning the possibility of expressing the meaning of the term 'v' by reference to the meanings of the members of V. If this conception is adopted, then naturally the information needed to answer the question of definability will concern the *meanings* of 'v' and of the members of V; accordingly, the statements in U which provide this information will then be required not simply to be true, but to be analytic, i.e., true by virtue of the intended meanings of the constituent terms. In this case, the statements in U would have the character of meaning postulates in the sense of Kemeny and Carnap.[28]

But in a study of the definability of theoretical expressions by means of observational terms, it is neither necessary nor even advisable to construe definition in this intensional manner. For, first of all, the idea of meaning, and related notions such as those of analyticity and synonymy, are by no means as clear as they have long been considered to be,[29] and it will be better, therefore, to avoid them when this is possible.

Secondly, even if those concepts are accepted as clearly intelligible, the definability of a theoretical term still cannot be construed exclusively as the existence of a synonymous expression containing only observational terms: it would be quite sufficient if a coextensive (rather than a strictly cointensive, or synonymous) expression in terms of observables were forthcoming. For such an expression would represent an empirically necessary and sufficient observational condition of applicability for the theoretical term; and this is all that is required for our purposes. In fact, the sentence stating the coextensiveness in question, which might have the form (7.2) for example, can then be given the status of a truth-by-definition, by a suitable reformalization of the theory at hand.

It is of interest to note here that a necessary and sufficient observational condition for a theoretical term, say 'Q', might be inductively discovered even if only a partial specification of the meaning of 'Q' in terms of observables were

28 See Kemeny (1951) and (1952); Carnap (1952).

29. On this point, see especially Quine (1951); Goodman (1949); White (1950) and (1956, Part II). The significance of the notion of analyticity in special reference to theoretical statements is critically examined, for example, in Pap (1953) and (1955) and in Hempel (1963). Arguments in defense of concepts such as analyticity and synonymy are advanced in the following articles, among others: Carnap (1952), (1955); Grice and Strawson (1956); Martin (1952); Mates (1951); Wang (1955).

available. Suppose, for example, that a set of alternative conditions of application for 'Q' has been specified by means of bilateral reduction sentences:

$$(7.3) \quad C_1x \supset (Qx \equiv E_1x)$$
$$C_2x \supset (Qx \equiv E_2x)$$
$$\dots\dots\dots\dots\dots$$
$$C_nx \supset (Qx \equiv E_nx)$$

where all predicates except 'Q' are observational. Suppose further that suitable investigations lead to the following empirical generalizations:

$$(7.4) \quad C_1x \supset (Ox \equiv E_1x)$$
$$C_2x \supset (Ox \equiv E_2x)$$
$$\dots\dots\dots\dots\dots$$
$$C_nx \supset (Ox \equiv E_nx)$$

where 'Ox' stands for a sentential function in 'x' which contains no nonobservational extralogical terms. These findings, in combination with (7.3), would inductively support the hypothesis

$$(7.5) \quad Qx \equiv Ox$$

which presents a necessary and sufficient observational condition for Q. However, (7.5) even if true (its acceptance involves the usual "inductive risk") clearly does not express a synonymy; if it did, no empirical investigations would be needed in the first place to establish it. Rather, it states that, as a matter of empirical fact, 'O' is coextensive with 'Q', or, that O is an empirically necessary and sufficient condition for Q. And if we wish, we may then imagine the theory-plus-interpretation at hand to be thrown into the form of a deductive system in which (7.5) becomes a definitional truth, and (7.3) assumes the character of a set of empirical statements equivalent to those listed in (7.4).

It might be mentioned here in passing that a similarly broad extensional interpretation of definability is called for also in the context of the problem whether a given scientific discipline, such as psychology, can be "reduced" to another, such as biology or even physics and chemistry.[30] For one component of this problem is the question whether the terms of the first discipline can be defined by means of those of the latter; and what is wanted for this purpose is again a set of empirical hypotheses providing for each psychological term a neces-

---

30. On the problem of "reducing" the concepts of one discipline to those of another, the following publications have important bearings: Nagel (1949) and (1951); Woodger (1952, pp. 271ff); Kemeny and Oppenheim (1956).

sary and sufficient condition of application expressed in the vocabulary of biology, or of physics and chemistry.

When we say, for example, that the concepts of the various chemical elements are definable in physical terms by a characterization of the specific ways in which their molecules are composed of elementary physical particles, we are clearly referring to results of experimental research rather than of a mere analysis of what is *meant* by the terms naming the various elements. If the latter were the case, it would be quite incomprehensible why the problems pertaining to the definability of scientific terms should present any difficulty, and why they should be the objects of much conjecture and controversy.

The preceding considerations have important implications for our question whether all theoretical terms in empirical science can be defined in terms of observables. First of all, they show that the question as stated is elliptical: to complete it, we have to specify some set U of statements as referred to in (7.1). What set could reasonably be chosen for this purpose? One natural choice would be the set of all statements, in theoretical or observational terms, that are accepted as presumably true by contemporary science. Now, this pragmatic-historical characterization is by no means precise and unambiguous; there is a wide border area containing statements for which it cannot be clearly determined whether they are accepted by contemporary science. But no matter how the claims of these border-area statements are adjudicated, and no matter where—within reason—the borderline between observational and theoretical terms is drawn, it is at least an open question whether the set of presently accepted scientific statements implies for every theoretical term a necessary and sufficient condition of applicability in terms of observables. Certainly those who have asserted such definability have not supported their claim by actually deducing such conditions, or by presenting cogent general reasons for the possibility of doing so.

There is another way in which the claim of definability may be construed, namely as the assertion that as our scientific knowledge becomes more comprehensive, it will eventually be possible to deduce from it necessary and sufficient conditions of the required kind. (This is the sense in which definability is usually understood by those who claim the eventual definability of the concepts of psychology in terms of those of biology or of physics and chemistry; for that all the requisite definition statements—even in an extensional, empirical sense— cannot be deduced from current psychological, biological, physical, and chemical principles seems clear.[31]) But to assert definability of a theoretical term in this sense is to make a twofold claim: first, that the term in question will not

31. This point is discussed more fully in Hempel (1951).

be abandoned in the further development of scientific theorizing; and second, that general laws will be discovered which establish certain necessary and sufficient conditions, expressible in observational terms, for the applicability of the theoretical term at hand. Clearly, the truth of these claims cannot be established by philosophic arguments, but at best by the results of further scientific research.

Despite the precariousness of the problem, various claims and counterclaims have been advanced by philosophers of science and by methodologically interested scientists concerning the possibility of defining theoretical terms by reference to observables.

Some among the philosophers have simply urged that nothing short of explicit definition in terms of a vocabulary that is clearly understood can provide an acceptable method of introducing new terms into the language of science; and the argument supporting this view is to the effect that otherwise the new terms are not intelligible,[32] To this question we will return later. The protagonists of this view do not make an assertion, then, about the actual definability of the theoretical terms used in contemporary empirical science; rather, they stress the importance of clarifying the ideas of science by restating them, as far as possible, in a language with a clear and simple logical structure, and in such a way as to introduce all theoretical terms by means of definitions.

Other writers have argued, in effect, that scientific theories and the way in which they function have certain pervasive logical or methodological characteristics which are not affected by changes in scientific knowledge, and by reference to which the question as to the definability of theoretical terms can be settled without examining all the statements accepted by contemporary science or waiting for the results of further research.

An example of this type of procedure is provided by Carnap's argument, referred to in the beginning of section 6 above, which shows that definitions of the form (6.1) cannot serve to introduce scientific concepts of the kind they are meant to specify. The argument is limited, however, in the sense that it does not show (and does not claim to show) that an explicit definition of theoretical terms by means of observational ones is generally impossible.

More recently,[33] Carnap has extended his examination of the problem in the following direction. Suppose that a given object, b, exhibits this kind of

---

32. One writer who is impelled by his "philosophical conscience" to take this view is Goodman (see 1951, Chapter I; 1955, Chapter II, section 1). A similar position was taken by Russell when he insisted that physical objects should be conceived as "logical constructions" out of sense-data, and thus as definable in terms of the latter (see, for example, 1929, Chapter VIII).

33. See Carnap (1956), especially sections 9, 10.

lawful behavior: whenever b is under conditions of a certain observable kind C, then it shows a response of a specified observable kind E. We then say that b has the disposition to react to C by E; let us call this dispositional property Q for short. Clearly, our earlier discussion in section 6 concerns the problem of precisely defining 'Q' in terms of 'C' and 'E'; we noted there, following Carnap, that we will either have to resign ourselves to a partial specification of meaning for 'Q' by means of the bilateral reduction sentence (6.2); or, if we insist on an explicit complete definition, we will have to use nomological modalities in the definiens.

But no matter which of these alternative courses is chosen, the resulting disposition term 'Q' has this characteristic: if a given object b is under condition C and fails to show response E, or briefly, if Cb but $\sim Eb$, then this establishes conclusively that b lacks the property Q, or briefly that $\sim Qb$. This characteristic, Carnap argues, distinguishes "pure disposition terms," such as 'Q', from the theoretical terms used in science; for though the latter are connected with the observational vocabulary by certain interpretative sentences—Carnap calls them C-rules—those rules will not, in general, permit a set of observational data (such as 'Cb' and '$\sim Eb$' above) to constitute conclusive evidence for or against the applicability of the theoretical term in a given situation. There are two reasons for this assertion. First, the interpretative sentences for a given theoretical term provide an observational interpretation only within a certain limited range; thus, for example, in the case of the theoretical term 'mass', no C-rule is directly applicable to a sentence S_m ascribing a certain value of mass to a given body, if the value is either so small that the body is not directly observable or so large that the observer cannot "manipulate the body."[34]

Secondly, a direct observational interpretation for a theoretical term always involves the tacit understanding that the occurrence or absence of the requisite observable response in the specified test situation is to serve as a criterion only if there are no disturbing factors, or, provided that "the environment is in a normal state."[35] Thus, for example, a rule of correspondence might specify the deflection of a magnetic needle as an observable symptom of an electric current in a nearby wire, but with the tacit understanding that the response of the needle is to count only if there are no disturbing factors, such as, say, a sudden magnetic storm.

Generally, then, Carnap holds that "if a scientist has decided to use a certain term 'M' in such a way, that for certain sentences about M, any possible observational results can never be absolutely conclusive evidence but at best

34. Carnap (1956), section 10.
35. Carnap (1950), section 10.

evidence yielding a high probability," then the appropriate place for 'M' is in the theoretical vocabulary.[36]

Now we should note, first of all, that if Carnap's arguments are sound, they establish that the theoretical terms of science cannot be construed as pure disposition terms, and thus even if, by the use of nomological modalities, explicit definitions of the latter should be achieved, this method would be unavailing for theoretical terms. But the arguments do not show—and are not claimed to show—that theoretical terms can in no way be explicitly defined in terms of observables. In fact, if Carnap's statement quoted in the preceding paragraph is accepted, then many terms that can be explicitly defined by means of the observational vocabulary must be qualified as theoretical. For example, let 'R' be a two-place observational predicate, and let a one-place predicate 'M_1' be defined as follows:

(7.6)   Def. $M_1 x \equiv (\exists y) \, Rxy$

i.e., an object x has the property M_1 just in case it stands in relation R to at least one object y. If, for example, 'Rxy' stands for 'x is less heavy than y', then M_1 is the property of being exceeded in weight by at least one object, or, of not being the heaviest of all objects.

Let us assume, as customary, that the domain of objects under study is infinite or at least has not been assigned any definite maximum number of elements. Consider now the possibility of conclusive observational evidence for or against the sentence '$M_1 a$', which attributes M_1 to a certain object a. Obviously, a single observational finding, to the effect that a bears R to a certain object b, or that Rab, would suffice to verify '$M_1 a$' completely. But no finite set of observational data—'$\sim Raa$', '$\sim Rab$', '$\sim Rac$', and so forth—would suffice for a conclusive refutation of '$M_1 a$'. According to Carnap's criterion, therefore, 'M_1',

---

36. Carnap (1956), section 10. An idea which is similar in spirit, but not quite as clear in its content, has been put forward by Pap in (1953) and in (1955), sections 10-13 and 70, with the claim (not made by Carnap for his argument) that it establishes the "untenability" of the "thesis of explicit definability" of theoretical terms by means of observational ones. (Pap 1953, p. 8). On the other hand, Bergmann holds that many concepts of theoretical physics, including "even the particle notions of classical physics could, in principle, be introduced by explicit definitions. This, by the way, is also true of all the concepts of scientific psychology." (1951a, section 1. In the same context Bergmann mentions that the method of partial interpretation seems to be necessary in order to dissolve some of the puzzles concerning quantum theory). However, this strong assertion is supported chiefly by sketches of some sample definitions. Bergmann suggests, for example, that 'This place is in an electric field' can be defined by a sentence of the form 'If R_1 then R_2' where R_1 stands for a sentence to the effect that there is an electroscope at the place in question, and R_2 stands "for the description of the behavior of the electroscope (in an electric field)." (1951, pp. 98-99.) However, this kind of definition may be questioned on the basis of Carnap's arguments, which have just been considered. And in addition, even if unobjectionable, some examples cannot establish the general thesis at issue. Thus, the question remains unsettled.

though defined in terms of the observational predicate 'R', might have to be classified as a theoretical term.

But possibly, in the passage quoted above, Carnap meant to require of a theoretical term 'M' that for certain sentences about M no observational results can be conclusively verificatory or falsificatory evidence. Yet even terms meeting this requirement can be explicitly defined in terms of observables. Let 'S' be a three-place observational predicate; for example, '$Sxyz$' might stand for 'x is farther away from y than from z.' And let 'M_2' be defined as follows:

(7.7)   Def. $M_2x \equiv (\exists y)(z)[\sim(z = y) \supset Sxyz]$.

In our example, an object x has M_2 just in case there is an object y from which it is farther away than from any other object z. Consider now the sentence 'M_2a'. As is readily seen, no finite set of observational findings (all the relevant ones would have the form '$Sabc$' or '$\sim Sabc$') can be conclusive evidence, either verificatory or falsificatory, concerning 'M_2a'. Hence, though explicitly defined in terms of the observational predicate 'S', the term 'M_2' is theoretical according to the criterion suggested by Carnap.

The preceding discussion illustrates an elementary but important point: when a term, say a one-place predicate 'Q', is defined in terms of observables, its definiens must state a necessary and sufficient condition for the applicability of 'Q', i.e., for the truth of sentences of the form 'Qb'. But even though that condition is then stated completely in observational terms, it still may not enable us to decide, on the basis of a finite number of observational findings, whether 'Q' applies to a given object b; for the truth condition for 'Qb' as characterized by the definiens may not be equivalent to a truth functional compound of sentences each of which expresses a potential observational finding.

To add one more example to those given before: suppose that the property term 'iron object' and the relation terms 'attracts' and 'in the vicinity of' are included in the observational vocabulary. Then the definition

(7.8)   Def. x is a magnet $\equiv$ x attracts every iron object in its vicinity

is in terms of observables; but the criterion it provides for an object b being a magnet cannot be expressed in terms of any finite number of observational findings; for to establish that b is a magnet, we would have to show that any piece of iron which, at any time whatever, is brought into the vicinity of b, will be attracted by b; and this is an assertion about an infinity of cases.

To express the idea more formally, let us assume that our observational vocabulary contains, in addition to individual names for observable objects, just first-order predicates of any degree, representing attributes (i.e., properties or relations) which are observable in the sense that a small number of direct observations will suffice, under suitable conditions, to ascertain whether a given object or group of objects exhibits the attribute in question.

Now let us adopt the following definitions: An *atomic sentence* is a sentence, such as '*Pa*', '*Rcd*', '*Sadg*', which ascribes an observable attribute to a specified object or group of objects. A *basic sentence* is an atomic sentence or the negation of an atomic sentence. A *molecular sentence* is a sentence formed from a finite number of atomic sentences by means of truth-functional connectives. Basic sentences will be considered as included among the molecular sentences.

Basic sentences can be considered as the simplest statements describing potential results of direct observation: they assert that some specified set of (one or more) objects has, or lacks, such and such an observable attribute.

Now for every molecular statement S, there exist certain finite classes of basic statements which imply S, and certain other such classes which imply the negation of S. Thus, the molecular sentence '*Pa* v ($\sim$*Pa·Rab*)' is implied by {'*Pa*'} and also by {'$\sim$*Pa*', '*Rab*'}, for example; whereas its negation is implied by the set {'$\sim$*Pa*', '$\sim$*Rab*'}. Hence, for each molecular sentence S, it is possible to specify a set of basic sentences whose truth would conclusively verify S, and also a set of basic sentences whose truth would verify the negation of S, and would thus conclusively refute S. Thus, a molecular sentence is capable both of conclusive observational verification and of conclusive observational falsification "in principle," i.e., in the sence that potential data can be described whose occurrence would verify the sentence, and others whose occurrence would falsify it; but not of course in the sense that the two kinds of data might occur jointly—indeed, they are incompatible with each other.

There are even some sentences of nonmolecular form, i.e., sentences containing quantifiers nonvacuously, which are both completely verifiable and completely falsifiable in the sense just specified.[37] For example, the sentence '(x) (*Px* v *Qa*)' is implied by {'*Qa*'} and its negation by {'$\sim$*Pb*', '$\sim$*Qa*'}. A similar argument applies to the sentence '($\exists x$) (*Px·Qc*)'.

As a rule, however, nonmolecular sentences are not both verifiable and falsifiable. This holds, in particular, for all nonmolecular sentences of purely general form, i.e., those containing no individual constants at all, such as '(x) (*Px* $\supset$ *Qx*)'; but it is true also of many quantified sentences containing individual constants. Thus, if '*R*' and '*S*' are observational predicates, then sentences of the type '($\exists y$)*Ray*' are not falsifiable and sentences of the types '(y) ($\exists z$)*Sayz*' and '($\exists y$)(z)*Sayz*' are neither verifiable nor falsifiable, as is readily seen.

Explicit definitions of scientific terms by means of an observational vocabulary may accordingly be divided into two kinds: those which provide *finite observational criteria of application* for the defined term, and those which do not. The

---

37. (added in 1964). The present paragraph, and the next few, have been modified so as to correct a mistaken statement made here in the original version of this essay, namely, that only molecular sentences are both verifiable and falsifiable.

former are simply those whose definiens, when applied to a particular case, yields a sentence that is both verifiable and falsifiable. The following definition is of this kind:

(7.9)   Def.   Son $xy \equiv$ Male $x \cdot$ Offspring xy

For application of the definiens to two particular individuals, say a and b, yields the sentence 'Male a . Offspring a b', which is both verifiable and falsifiable and thus provides a finite observational criterion for the application of the term 'Son' to a in relation to b. On the other hand, the definitions (7.6), (7.7), and (7.8) above are among those which afford no finite observational criteria of application for the terms they define; this was pointed out earlier.

However, the circumstance that a term, say 'M', is originally introduced by a definition affording no finite observational criteria for its application does not preclude the possibility that 'M' may in fact be coextensive with some observational predicate, or with a truth-functional compound of such predicates, say 'O_m'; and if this should be found to be the case, then 'M' could, of course, be redefined by 'O_m' and could thus be provided with a finite observational criterion of application.

But granting certain plausible assumptions concerning the observational vocabulary, it can be proved that not all scientific terms are definable in a way that provides them with finite criteria of application. We will assume that the observational vocabulary is finite. It may contain individual names designating certain observable objects; first-order predicate terms with any finite number of places, representing properties and relations of observable objects; and also functors, i.e., terms expressing quantitative aspects—such as weight in grams, volume in cubic centimeters, or age in days—of observable objects. However, we will suppose that each of the functors can take on only a finite number of different values; this corresponds to the assumption that only a finite number of different weights, for example, can be ascertained and distinguished by direct observation.

In contrast to the functors in the observational vocabulary, the theoretical vocabulary of physics, for example, contains a large number of functors whose permissible values range over all real numbers or over all real numbers within a certain interval. Thus, for example, the distance between two points may theoretically have any non-negative value whatever. Now a definition of the required kind for a theoretical functor would have to specify, for each of its permissible values, a finite observational criterion of application. Thus, in the case of the theoretical functor 'length', a necessary and sufficient condition, in the form of a finite observational criterion, would have to be forthcoming for each of the infinitely many statements of the form 'The distance, in centimeters, between points x and y is r' or briefly, '$l(x,y) = r$', where r is some real number.

Hence we would have to specify for each value of 'r' a corresponding finitely ascertainable configuration of observables. But this is impossible because the limits of discrimination in direct observation allow only a finite, though very large, number of finitely observable configurations to be ascertained and distinguished.

However, if we do not require a finite observational criterion of application for each permissible value of a theoretical functor, then an infinity of different values may become available.[38] Consider, for example, the functor 'the number of cells contained in organism y'. If 'x is a cell', 'y is an organism', and 'x is contained in y' are admitted as observational expressions, then it is possible to give a separate criterion of applicability, in terms of observables, for each of the infinitely many values 1, 2, 3 . . . which that functor may theoretically assume.[39] This can be done by means of the Frege-Russell analysis of cardinal numbers. For $n = 1$, for example, the necessary and sufficient condition is the following:

(7.10) $(\exists u)\,(v)\,[y$ is an organism $\cdot\;((v$ is a cell $\cdot\; v$ is contained in $y) \equiv (v = u))]$

Thus, the reach of explicit definition in terms of observables, even in the first-order functional calculus, is greatly extended if quantification is permitted in the definiens. And if stronger logical means are countenanced, considerable further extensions may be obtained. For example, the functor 'the number of cells contained in y' can be explicitly defined by the single expression

(7.11) $\hat{\alpha}\,(\alpha$ sim $\hat{x}\,(x$ is a cell $\cdot\; x$ is contained in $y))$

Here, the circumflex accent is the symbol of class abstraction, and 'sim' the symbol for similarity of classes (in the sense of one-to-one matchability of their elements).

So far, we have examined only functors whose values are integers. Can functors with rational and even irrational values be similarly defined in terms of observables? Consider, for example, the theoretical functor 'length in centimeters'. Is it possible to express, in observational terms, a necessary and sufficient condition for

(7.12) $l(x,y) = r$

for every non-negative value of r? We might try to develop a suitable definition which would correspond to the fundamental method of measuring length

---

38. I am grateful to Herbert Bohnert who, in a conversation, provided the stimulus for the development of the ideas here outlined concerning the definability of functors with infinitely many permissible values. Dr. Bohnert remarked on that occasion that explicit definition of such functors in terms of an observational vocabulary should be possible along lines indicated by the Frege-Russell theory of natural and of real numbers.

39. If it should be objected that 'cell' and 'organism' are theoretical rather than observational terms, then they may be replaced, without affecting the crux of the argument, by terms whose observational character is less controversial, such as 'marble' and 'bag', for example.

by means of rigid rods. And indeed, if our observational vocabulary contains a name for the standard meter bar, and furthermore the (purely qualitative) terms required to describe the fundamental measuring procedure, it is possible to state, for any specified rational or irrational value of r, a necessary and sufficient condition for (7.12). However, the definiens will normally be teeming with symbols of quantification over individuals and over classes and relations of various types and will be far from providing finite observational criteria of application. I will briefly indicate how such definitions may be obtained. Expressions assumed to belong to the observational vocabulary will be italicized.

First, *the segment determined by two points x,y* will be said to have a length of 100 centimeters if it is *congruent* with (i.e., can be made to coincide with) *the segment marked off on the standard meter bar*. Next, consider the observational criterion for a rational value of length, say, $l(x,y) = .25$. It may be stated as follows: there are four *segments*, each *marked off on a rigid body*, such that (i) all four are *congruent* with each other; (ii) their *sum* (i.e., the segment obtained by placing them end to end along a straight line) is *congruent* with *the segment marked off on the standard meter bar;* (iii) each of the four *segments* is *congruent* with the *segment determined by points x,y*. Analogously, an explicit observational definiens can be formulated for any other value of n that is a rational multiple of 100, and hence, for any rational value of n.

Next, the consideration that an irrational number can be construed as the limit of a sequence of rational numbers yields the following necessary and sufficient condition for $l(x,y) = r$, where r is irrational: *the segment determined by the points x,y* contains an infinite sequence of *points* $x_1, x_2, x_3 \ldots$ such that (i) x_1 is *between x* and y, x_2 *between* x_1 and y, and so forth; (ii) given any *segment S* of rational length, there is a *point*, say x_n, in the sequence such that the *segments determined by* x_n and y, x_{n+1} and y, and so forth are all *shorter than S*, (iii) the lengths of the *segments determined by x* and x_1, x and x_2, and so forth, form a sequence of rational numbers with the limit r.

Finally, the idea underlying the preceding definition can be used to formulate an explicit definiens for the expression '$l(x,y)$' in such a way that its range of values is the set of all non-negative numbers.

Definitions of the kind here outlined are attainable only at the cost of using a strong logical apparatus, namely, a logic of sets adequate for the development of the theory of real numbers.[40] This price will be considered too high by nomin-

---

40. The argument can readily be extended to functors taking complex numbers or vectors of any number of components as values. Our reasoning has relied essentially on the Frege-Russell method of defining the various kinds of numbers (integers, rational, irrational, complex numbers, etc.) in terms of the concepts of the logic of sets. For a detailed outline of the procedure, see Russell (1919); fuller technical accounts may be found in works on symbolic logic.

alists, who hold that many of the logical concepts and principles here required, beginning with the general concept of set, are intrinsically obscure and should not, therefore, be used in a purported explication of the meanings of scientific terms. This is not the place to discuss the nominalistic strictures, however, and besides, it would no doubt be generally considered a worthwhile advance in clarification if for a set of theoretical scientific expressions explicit definitions in terms of observables can be constructed at all.

Another objection that might be raised against the definitional procedure here outlined is that it takes a schematic and oversimplified view of the fundamental measurement of length, and that it is rather liberal in construing as observational certain terms needed in the definiens, such as 'rigid body' and 'point'. This is quite true. By including the term 'point' in the observational vocabulary, for example, we construed points as directly observable physical objects; but our observational criterion for two points x, y determining a segment of irrational length required that there should be an infinite sequence of other points between x and y. This condition is never satisfied by the observable "points" in the form of small physical objects, or marks on rigid bodies, which are used in the fundamental measurement of length. As a consequence, the actual performance of fundamental measurement as represented in the above definition will never yield an irrational value for the length of a segment. But this does not show that no meaning has been assigned to irrational lengths; on the contrary, our outline of the definition shows that a meaning can indeed be formulated in observational terms for the assignment of any specified irrational value to the length of a physical line segment, as well as for the function 'length in centimeters' in general.

However, the concept of length thus defined is not adequate for a physical theory which incorporates geometry, say in its Euclidean form. For the latter requires that the length of certain segments which are well accessible to direct measurement—such as the diagonal of a square whose sides have a length of 100 centimeters—be an irrational number; and statements to this effect will always turn out to be false if the criterion just discussed is made strictly definitory of length; for that procedure, as we noted, will always yield a rational value for the length of a given segment.

What the preceding argument about quantitative terms (represented by functors) shows, then, is this: the fact that the set of permissible values of a theoretical functor is infinite need not preclude an explicit definition for it by means of a finite vocabulary containing only qualitative terms which are, by reasonably liberal standards, observational in character. The argument does not show, however, that such a definition is available for every functor term required by science (even our illustrative definition of 'length' turned out not to meet the needs of theoretical physics); and indeed, as was pointed out early in this section, a general proof to this effect cannot be expected.

Some writers have taken the position that even if in principle theoretical terms could be avoided in favor of observational ones, it would be practically impossible or—what is more serious—methodologically disadvantageous or even stultifying to do so.

There is, for example, the answer given by Tolman and by Spence to the problem considered by Hull, which was mentioned in section 5 above: if intervening theoretical variables can establish a secure linkage between antecedent and consequent observable conditions, why should we not use just one functional connection that directly links antecedents and consequents? Spence adduces as one reason, also suggested by Tolman,[41] the following consideration: the mathematical function required to express the connection will be so complex that it is humanly impossible to conceive of it all at once; we can arrive at it only by breaking it down into a sequence of simpler functional connections, mediated by intervening variables. This argument, then, attributes to the introduction of unobservable theoretical entities an important practical role in the context of discovering interdependencies among observables, and presumably also in the context of actually performing the calculations required for the explanation or prediction of specific occurrences on the basis of those interdependencies.

An important methodological function is attributed to hypothetical entities in an essay by Hull on intervening variables in molar behavior theory.[42] Suppose that in order to explain or predict the response of a subject in a given situation, we ascribe to him, for the time t_1 of his response, a certain habit strength, which has the status of a hypothetical entity. That strength is, in Hull's theory, "merely a quantitative representation of the perseverative after-effects" of certain earlier observable events, such as observable stimuli received in temporally remote learning situations. Consequently, if reference to habit strength were avoided by linking the subject's observable response at t_1 directly to the observable stimuli received earlier, then we would be invoking, as causal determinants for the response, certain observable events which at the time of the response have long ceased to exist. And Hull rejects this notion of causal action over a temporal distance: "it is hard to believe that an event such as stimulation in a remote learning situation can be causally active long after it has ceased to act on the receptors. I fully agree with Lewin that all the factors alleged to be causally influential in the determination of any other event must be in existence at the

41. See Tolman (1936), as reprinted in Marx (1951), p. 89; and Spence (1944), p. 65n.
42. Hull (1943).

time of such causal action."[43] Reference to the habit strength of the subject at the time t_1 of his response permits an explanation that accords with this principle.

Though the concluding part of the quoted passage sounds somewhat metaphysical, the basic import of Hull's argument is methodological. It credits the assumption of explanatory hypothetical entities with an accomplishment that is well described by Feigl in another context: "the discontinuous and historical character (action at a spatial and/or temporal distance) of the phenomenalistically restricted account vanishes and is replaced by a spatio-temporally continuous (contiguous) and nomologically coherent formulation on the level of hypothetical construction."[44] Such spatio-temporally continuous theories appear to recommend themselves for at least two reasons: first, they possess a certain formal simplicity, which at present can hardly be characterized in precise terms, but which is reflected, for example, in the possibility of using the powerful and elegant mathematical machinery of the calculus for the deduction, from the postulates of the theory, of explanatory and predictive connections among particular occurrences. And second, as was mentioned in section 3, the past development of empirical science seems to show that explanatory and predictive principles asserting discontinuous connections among (spatio-temporally separated) observable events are likely to be found to have limited scope and various exceptions. Theories in terms of hypothetical entities frequently make it possible to account for such exceptions by means of suitable assumptions concerning the hypothetical entities involved.

Another, more general, argument has been developed by Braithwaite, who gives credit to Ramsey for the basic principle.[45] Braithwaite's main contention is that "theoretical terms can only be defined by means of observable properties on condition that the theory cannot be adapted properly to apply to new situations."[46] He elaborates this idea by reference to a precisely formulated, miniature model of an interpreted theory. Without going into the details of that model, which would require too long a digression here, Braithwaite's claim can be adequately illustrated, it seems, by the following example: Suppose that the term 'temperature' is interpreted, at a certain stage of scientific research, only by reference to the readings of a mercury thermometer. If this observational criterion is taken as just a partial interpretation (namely as a sufficient but not necessary condition), then the possibility is left open of adding further partial interpretations, by reference to other thermometrical substances which are

43. Hull (1943), p. 285.
44. Feigl (1950), p. 40.
45. See the essay "Theories" in Ramsey (1931).
46. Braithwaite (1953), p. 76.

usable above the boiling point or below the freezing point of mercury; this permits a vast increase in the range of application of such laws as those connecting the temperature of a metal rod with its length or with its electric resistance, or the temperature of a gas with its pressure or its volume. If, however, the original criterion is given the status of a complete definiens, then the theory is not capable of such expansion; rather, the original definition has to be abandoned in favor of another one, which is incompatible with the first.[47]

The concept of intelligence lends itself to a similar argument: if test criteria which presuppose, on the part of the subject, the ability to read or at least to use language extensively are accorded the status of full definitions, then difficulties of the sort just indicated arise when the concept and the corresponding theory are to be extended to very young children or to animals.

However, the argument here outlined can hardly be said to establish what is claimed, namely that "A theory which it is hoped may be expanded in the future to explain more generalizations than it was originally designed to explain must allow more freedom to its theoretical terms than would be given them were they to be logical constructions out of observable entities"[48] (and thus defined in terms of the latter). For clearly, the procedure of expanding a theory at the cost of changing the definitions of some theoretical terms is not logically faulty; nor can it even be said to be difficult or inconvenient for the scientist, for the problem at hand is rather one for the methodologist or the logician, who seeks to give a clear "explication" or "logical reconstruction" of the changes involved in expanding a given theory. In the type of case discussed by Braithwaite, for example, this can be done in alternative ways—either in terms of additions to the original partial interpretation, or in terms of a total change of definition for some theoretical expressions. And if it is held that this latter method constitutes, not an expansion of the original theory, but a transition to a new one, this would raise more a terminological question than a methodological objection.

But though the above argument against definition does not have the intended systematic weight, it throws into relief an important heuristic aspect of scientific theorizing: when a scientist introduces theoretical entities such as electric currents, magnetic fields, chemical valences, or subconscious mechanisms, he intends them to serve as explanatory factors which have an existence independent of the observable symptoms by which they manifest themselves; or, to put it in more sober terms: whatever observational criteria of application the scientist may provide are intended by him to describe just symptoms or indications of the

---

47. This point is also made in Carnap (1936-1937), section 7, in a discussion of the advantages of reduction sentences over definitions. Feigl argues in the same vein in his essay (1951), in which the general principle is illustrated by examples from physics and psychology.

48. Braithwaite (1953), p. 76.

presence of the entity in question, but not to give an exhaustive characterization of it. The scientist does indeed wish to leave open the possibility of adding to his theory further statements involving his theoretical terms—statements which may yield new interpretative connections between theoretical and observational terms; and yet he will regard these as additional assumptions about the same hypothetical entities to which the theoretical terms referred before the expansion. This way of looking at theoretical terms appears to have definite heuristic value. It stimulates the invention and use of powerfully explanatory concepts for which only some links with experience can be indicated at the time, but which are fruitful in suggesting further lines of research that may lead to additional connections with the data of direct observation.[49].

The survey made in the present section has yielded no conclusive argument for or against the possibility of explicitly defining all theoretical terms of empirical science by means of a purely observational vocabulary; and in fact we have found strong reasons to doubt that any argument can settle the question once and for all.

As for the theoretical terms currently in use, it is impossible at present to formulate observational definientia for all of them, and thus to make them, in principle, unnecessary. In effect, therefore, most theoretical terms are presently used in science on the basis of only a partial experiential interpretation; and this use, as we noted, appears to offer distinct heuristic advantages.

In view of the importance that thus attaches to the idea of partial interpretation, we will now consider what kind of formal account might be given of it, and we will then turn to the question whether, or in what sense, the verdict of dispensability as proclaimed by the "theoretician's dilemma" applies also to theoretical terms which have been only partially interpreted, and which, therefore, cannot be dispensed with simply by virtue of definition.

8. INTERPRETATIVE SYSTEMS

Carnap's theory of reduction sentences is the first systematic study of the logic of partial definition. The introduction of a term by means of a chain of reduction sentences differs in two significant respects from the use of a chain of definitions. First, it specifies the meaning of the term only partially and thus does not provide a way of eliminating the term from all contexts in which it may occur. Second, as a rule, it does not amount just to a notational convention,

---

49. A concise synopsis of various arguments in favor of invoking "hypothetical constructs" will be found in Feigl (1950), pp. 38–41. Some aspects of the "semantic realism" concerning theoretical terms which Feigl presents in the same article are discussed in section 10 of the present essay.

but involves empirical assertions. If, for example, the term 'Q' is introduced by the two reduction sentences

(8.1) $C_1 x \supset (Qx \equiv E_1 x)$

(8.2) $C_2 x \supset (Qx \equiv E_2 x)$

then the following empirical law is asserted by implication:

(8.3) $(x)[(C_1 x \cdot E_1 x) \supset (C_2 x \supset E_2 x)]$

i.e., roughly speaking: any object that shows a positive response under the first test condition will, when put into the second test condition, show a positive response as well. Thus, a chain of reduction sentences for a given term normally combines two functions of language that are often considered as sharply distinct: the stipulative assignment of meaning, and the assertion or description of empirical fact.

Reduction sentences, as we saw earlier, are very well suited for the formulation of operational criteria of application as partial definitions. But they are subject to rather severe limitations as to logical form and thus they do not seem sufficient to provide a satisfactory general schema for the partial interpretation of theoretical terms.[50] A broader view of interpretation is suggested by Campbell's conception of a physical theory as consisting of a "hypothesis," represented by a set of sentences in theoretical terms, and a "dictionary," which relates the latter to concepts of experimental physics (which must be interconnected by empirical laws).[51] In contrast to the standard conception of a dictionary, Campbell's dictionary is assumed to contain, not definitions for the theoretical terms, but statements to the effect that a theoretical sentence of a certain kind is true if and only if a corresponding empirical sentence of a specified kind is true. Thus, rather than definitions, the dictionary provides rules of translation; and partial rules at that, for no claim is made that a translation must be specified for each theoretical statement or for each empirical statement.

This latter feature accords well, for example, with the consideration that a particular observable macrostate of a given physical system may correspond to a large number of theoretically distinguishable microstates; so that, for a theoretical sentence describing just one of those micro-states, the sentence describing the corresponding macrostate does not express a necessary and sufficient condition, and hence provides no translation.[52]

---

50. This has been pointed out by Carnap himself; see, for example, his (1956).

51. See Campbell (1920), Chapter VI. Important parts of this chapter are reprinted in Feigl and Brodbeck (1953).

52. However, this does not show that there cannot possibly be any necessary and sufficient condition in observational terms for the theoretical sentence: the problem of proving or disproving this latter claim is subject to difficulties analogous to those discussed in section 7 in regard to definability.

The statements in Campbell's dictionary evidently do not have the character of reduction sentences; they might be formulated, however, as biconditionals in which a sentence in theoretical terms is connected, by an "if and only if" clause, with a sentence in observational terms.

In other contexts, neither reduction sentences nor such biconditionals seem to be adequate. For as a rule, the presence of a hypothetical entity H, such as a certain kind of electric field, will have observable symptoms only if certain observational conditions, O_1, are satisfied, such as the presence of suitable detecting devices, which will then have to show observable responses, O_2. A sentence stating this kind of criterion would have the character of a generalized reduction sentence; it might be put into the form.

(8.4) $O_1 \supset (H \supset O_2)$

where 'O_1' and 'O_2' are sentences—possibly quite complex ones—in terms of observables, and 'H' is a sentence which is expressed in theoretical terms.

But there is no good reason to limit interpretative statements to just the three types here considered. In order to obtain a general concept of partial interpretation, we will now admit as interpretative statements any sentences, of whatever logical form, which contain theoretical and observational terms. On the assumption that the theoretical and observational statements of empirical science are formulated within a specified logical framework, this idea can be stated more precisely and explicitly as follows:

(8.5)   Let T be a theory characterized by a set of postulates in terms of a finite *theoretical vocabulary* V_T, and let V_B be a second set of extra-logical terms, to be called the *basic vocabulary*, which shares no term with V_T. By an *interpretative system* for T with the basis V_B we will then understand a set J of sentences which (i) is finite, (ii) is logically compatible with T, (iii) contains no extra-logical term that is not contained in V_T or V_B, (iv) contains every element of V_T and V_B essentially, i.e., is not logically equivalent to some set of sentences in which some term of V_T or V_B does not occur at all.[53]

In applying the concept here defined to the analysis of scientific theories, we will have to assume, of course, that V_B consists of terms which are antecedently understood. They might be observational terms, in the somewhat vague sense

53. The intuitive notion of interpretation, as well as the conception reflected in Campbell's idea of an interpretative dictionary, would seem to call for the following additional condition: (v) Each sentence of J contains essentially terms from V_T as well as terms from V_B. However, this requirement introduces no further restriction of the concept of interpretative system; for any system J that meets conditions (i) to (iv) can be stated in an equivalent form that satisfies (v) as well. To this end, it suffices to replace the member sentences of J by their conjunction; this yields a logically equivalent interpretative system which contains only one sentence, and which satisfies (v) since J satisfies (iv).

explained earlier, but we need not insist on this. One might well take the view, for example, that certain disposition terms such as 'malleable', 'elastic', 'hungry', and 'tired' are not strictly observation terms, and are not known to be explicitly definable by means of observation terms; and yet, such terms might be taken to be well understood in the sense that they are used with a high degree of agreement by competent observers. In this case, it would be quite reasonable to use these terms in interpreting a given theory, i.e., to admit them into V_B.

Campbell's conception of the function of his "dictionary" illustrates this possibility very well and shows that it comes closer to actual scientific procedure. Campbell specifies that the interpretation provided by the dictionary must be in terms of what he calls "concepts," such as the terms 'temperature', 'electrical resistance', 'silver', and 'iron' as used in experimental physics and chemistry. These are hardly observational in the narrow sense, for they are specifically conceived as representing clusters of empirical laws: "Thus, if we say anything about electrical resistance we assume that Ohm's Law is true; bodies for which Ohm's Law is not true, gases for example, have no electrical resistance."[54] But even though one might not wish to qualify these terms as observational, one may still consider them as well understood, and as used with high intersubjective agreement, by scientific experimenters; and thus, they might be admitted into V_B.

Interpretative systems as just defined include as special cases all the types of interpretation we considered earlier, namely, interpretation by explicit definitions for all theoretical terms, by chains of reduction sentences, by biconditional translation statements in the sense of Campbell's dictionary, and by generalized reduction sentences of the form (8.4); but of course they also allow for interpretative statements of many other forms.

Interpretative systems have the same two characteristics which distinguish chains of reduction sentences from chains of definitions: First, an interpretative system normally effects only a partial interpretation of the terms in V_T; i.e., it does not lay down (by explicit statement or by logical implication), for every term in V_T, a necessary and sufficient condition of application in terms of V_B. Second, like a chain of reduction sentences for a given theoretical term, an interpretative system will normally not be purely stipulative in character, but will imply certain statements in terms of V_B alone which are not logical truths, and which, on the conception of V_B as consisting of antecedently understood empirical terms, express empirical assertions. Thus, here again, we find a combination of the stipulative and the descriptive use of language.

54. Campbell (1920), p. 43.

But, to turn to a third point of comparison, an interpretative system need not provide an interpretation—complete or incomplete—for each term in V_T individually. In this respect it differs from a set of definitions, which specifies for each term a necessary and sufficient condition, and from a set of reduction sentences, which provides for each term a necessary and a—usually different— sufficient condition. It is quite possible that an interpretative system provides, for some or even all of the terms in V_T, no necessary or no sufficient condition in terms of V_B, or indeed neither of the two; instead, it might specify, by explicit statement or by logical implication, sufficient or necessary conditions in terms of V_B only for certain expressions containing several terms of V_T—for example, in the manner of Campbell's dictionary.

As a rule, therefore, when a theory T is interpreted by an interpretative system J, the theoretical terms are not dispensable in the narrow sense of being replaceable in all contexts by defining expressions in terms of V_B. Nor are they generally dispensable in the sense that J provides, for every sentence H that can be formed by means of V_T, a "translation" into terms of V_B, i.e., a sentence O in terms of V_B such that the biconditional $H \equiv O$[55] is logically deducible from J.

Are theoretical terms, then, altogether indispensable on this broad conception of interpretation, so that the "paradox of theorizing" formulated in section 5 no longer applies to them? We consider this question in the next section.

9. FUNCTIONAL REPLACEABILITY OF THEORETICAL TERMS

The systematizing function of a theory T interpreted by an interpretative system J will consist in permitting inferences from given "data" in terms of V_B to certain other (e.g., predictive) statements in terms of V_B. If O_1 is the statement expressing the data, O_2 the inferred statement, then the connection may be symbolized thus:

(9.1) $(O_1 \cdot T \cdot J) \longrightarrow O_2$

Here, as in similar contexts below, 'T' stands for the set of postulates of the theory at hand; the arrow represents deductive implication.

Now, (9.1) holds if and only if $T \cdot J$ implies the sentence $O_1 \supset O_2$; so that (9.1) is tantamount to

(9.2) $(T \cdot J) \longrightarrow (O_1 \supset O_2)$

55. Here, and on some subsequent occasions where there is no danger of misunderstandings, logical connectives are used autonomously; the expression '$H \equiv O$', for example, represents the sentence obtained by placing the triple-bar symbol (for 'if and only if') between the sentences of which 'H' and 'O' are names.

Whatever systematization is achieved among the V_B-sentences is clearly accomplished by T in conjunction with J. It will be convenient therefore to consider the postulates of T together with the sentences of J as the postulates of a deductive system T', which will be called an *interpreted theory*. Its vocabulary $V_{T'}$ will be the sum of V_T and V_B.

What was noted in connection with (9.1) and (9.2) may now be restated thus: If an interpreted theory T' establishes a deductive transition from O_1 to O_2, i.e., if

(9.3) $(O_1 \cdot T') \longrightarrow O_2$

then

(9.4) $T' \longrightarrow (O_1 \supset O_2)$

and conversely, where T' is the set of postulates of the interpreted theory.

Now it can readily be shown that an interpreted theory T' establishes exactly the same deductive connections among V_B-sentences as does the set of all those theorems of T' which are expressible in terms of V_B alone; we will call this the set of V_B-*theorems*, or V_B-*consequences*, of T', and will designate it by '$O_{T'}$'. This means that for all purposes of deductive systematization, T' is, as we will say, *functionally equivalent* to the set $\underline{O_T}'$ which contains not a single theoretical term.

The proof is as follows: The deductive transition, represented in (9.3), from O_1 to O_2 can be achieved just as well by using, instead of T', simply the sentence $O_1 \supset O_2$, which by virtue of (9.4) belongs to $O_{T'}$; for we have, by *modus ponens*,

(9.5) $[O_1 \cdot (O_1 \supset O_2)] \longrightarrow O_2$

And since $O_{T'}$ surely contains all the V_B-sentences of the form $O_1 \supset O_2$ that are implied by T', the set $O_{T'}$ suffices to effect all the deductive systematizations achievable by means of T'. On the other hand, $O_{T'}$ is no stronger in this respect than T'; for $O_{T'}$ permits the deductive transition from O_1 to O_2 only if it implies $O_1 \supset O_2$; but in this case T', too, implies $O_1 \supset O_2$, which means, in view of the equivalence of (9.4) with (9.3), that T' will permit the deductive transition from O_1 to O_2.

Thus, *the deductive systematization that an interpreted theory T' achieves among sentences expressed in terms of a basic vocabulary V_B is exactly the same as that accomplished by the set $O_{T'}$ of those statements (theorems) of T' which can be expressed in terms of V_B alone*. In this sense, the theoretical terms used in T can be dispensed with.

But $O_{T'}$ is normally an unwieldy infinite set of statements, and the question arises therefore whether there is some generally applicable method of making it more manageable and perspicuous by putting it into the form of an axiomatized theoretical system T'_B, which would be formulated in terms of V_B alone. A theorem in formal logic proved by Craig shows that this is indeed the case, provided only that T' satisfies certain extremely liberal and unconfining conditions.[56]

Thus Craig's theorem has a definite bearing upon the problems raised by the "paradox of theorizing," which was stated in section 5 in somewhat vague terms. The theorem indicates one way in which the "paradox" can be given a clear and precise interpretation and a rigorous proof: It shows that for any theory T' using both theoretical terms and nontheoretical, previously understood ones,

56. Craig's paper (1953) contains the first published account of this important theorem. A less condensed and less technical presentation, with explicit through brief references to applications such as the one here considered, is given in Craig (1956).

In application to the issue we are discussing, the result obtained by Craig may be briefly stated as follows: Let the set $V_{T'}$ of primitive terms of T' and the set of postulates of T' be specified effectively, i.e., in a manner providing a general procedure which, for any given expression, will decide in a finite number of steps whether or not the expression is a primitive term (or a postulate) of T'. Let $V_{T'}$ be divided, by an effective criterion that may otherwise be chosen at will, into two mutually exclusive vocabularies, V_T and V_B. Finally, let the rules of the logic used be such that there is an effective method of determining, for any given finite sequence of expressions, whether it is a valid deduction according to those rules.

Then there exists a general method (i.e., a method applicable in all cases meeting the conditions just outlined) of effectively constructing (i.e., effectively characterizing the postulates and the rules of inference of) a new system T'_B whose set of primitives is V_B and whose theorems are exactly those theorems of T' which contain no extralogical constants other than those contained in V_B.

Note that the theorem permits us to draw the dividing line between V_T and V_B wherever we please, as long as the criterion used to effect the division permits us to decide in a finite number of steps to which of the two sets a given term belongs. This condition as well as the requirement of an effective characterization of $V_{T'}$ will be trivially satisfied, for example, if $V_{T'}$ is finite and its member terms as well as those of V_B and V_T are specified simply by enumerating them individually.

The further requirement of an effective characterization of the postulates and the rules of logic for T' are so liberal that no doubt any scientific theory that has yet been considered can be formalized in a manner that satisfies them—as long as the connections between theoretical and observational expressions can be assumed to be expressible in the form of definite statements. The only important case I am aware of in which this condition would be violated is that of a theory for which no definite rules of interpretation are specified—say, on the ground that the criteria of application for theoretical expressions always have to be left somewhat vague. A conception of this kind may have been intended, for example, by A. Wald's remark "In order to apply [a scientific] theory to real phenomena, we need some rules for establishing the correspondence between the idealized objects of the theory and those of the real world. These rules will always be somewhat vague and can never form a part of the theory itself." Wald (1942), p. 1.

The conditions of Craig's theorem are satisfiable, however, if the vagueness here referred to is reflected in definite rules. Thus, for example, the interpretative sentences for a given theory might take the form of statistical probability statements (a possibility mentioned in Carnap (1956), section 5), or perhaps of logical probability statements (each specifying the logical probability of some theoretical sentence relative to a specified sentence in observational terms, or vice versa). Either of these procedures would yield an interpretation of a more general kind than that characterized by the definition of an interpretative system given in section 8 of the present essay. Yet even to theories which are interpreted in this wider sense, Craig's theorem can be applied.

there exists, under certain very widely satisfied conditions, an axiomatized theoretical system T'_B which uses only the nontheoretical terms of T' and yet is functionally equivalent with T' in the sense of effecting, among the sentences expressible in the nontheoretical vocabulary, exactly the same deductive connections as T'.

Should empirical science then avail itself of this method and replace all its theories involving assumptions about hypothetical entities by functionally equivalent theoretical systems couched exclusively in terms which have direct observational reference or which are, at any rate, clearly understood? There are various reasons which make this inadvisable in consideration of the objectives of scientific theorizing.

To begin with, let us consider the general character of Craig's method. Disregarding many subtle points of detail, the procedure may be described as follows: By means of a constructive procedure, Craig arranges all the V_B-theorems of T' in a sequence. This sequence is highly redundant, for it contains, for any sentence occurring in it, also all its logical equivalents (as far as they are expressible in V_B). Craig prescribes a procedure for eliminating many, though not all, of these duplications. The remaining sequence therefore still contains each V_B-theorem of T' in at least one of its various equivalent formulations. Finally, all the sentences in this remaining sequence are made postulates of T'_B. Thus, the set of V_B-theorems of T' is "axiomatized" in T'_B only in a rather Pickwickian sense, namely by making every sentence of the set, in some of its many equivalent formulations, a postulate of T'_B. Normally, the axiomatization of a set of sentences selects as postulates just a small subset from which the rest can then be logically derived as theorems; thus, the axiomatization presents the content of the whole set "in a form which is psychologically or mathematically more perspicuous."[57] And since Craig's method in effect includes all sentences that are to be axiomatized among the postulates of T', the latter, as Craig himself puts it, "fail to simplify or to provide genuine insight."[58]

The loss in simplicity which results from discarding the theoretical terms of T' is reflected in the circumstance that the set of postulates which Craig's method yields for T'_B is always infinite. Even in cases where actually there exists some finite subset of $O_{T'}$ of V_B-theorems of T' from which all the rest can be deduced,

57. Craig (1956), p. 49. It may be well to note briefly two further points which were established by Craig, in the studies here referred to: (i) A theory T' may have a set of V_B-consequences that cannot be axiomatized by means of a *finite* set of postulates expressible in terms of V_B. (ii) There is no general method that permits an effective decision, for every theory T', as to whether its V_B-consequences can, or cannot, be axiomatized by means of a finite set of postulates.

58. Craig (1956), p. 49. This fact does not detract in the least, of course, from the importance and interest of Craig's result as a theorem in logic.

Craig's procedure will not yield such a subset: that is the price of its universal applicability.

Now there are cases where an infinity of postulates may not be excessively unwieldy; notably when the axioms are specified by means of axiom-schemata,[59] i.e., by stipulations to the effect that any sentence that has one of a finite number of specified forms (such as '$x = x$,' for example) is to count as an axiom. But the manner in which postulates of T'_B are specified by Craig's method is vastly more intricate, and the resulting system would be practically unmanageable— to say nothing of the loss in heuristic fertility and suggestiveness which results from the elimination of the theoretical concepts and hypotheses. For empirical science, therefore, this method of dispensing with theoretical expressions would be quite unsatisfactory.

So far, we have examined the eliminability of theoretical concepts and assumptions only in the context of deductive systematization: we considered an interpreted theory T' exclusively as a vehicle of establishing deductive transitions among observational sentences. However, such theories may also afford means of inductive systematization in the sense outlined in section 1; an analysis of this function will yield a further argument against the elimination of theoretical expressions by means of Craig's method.

By way of illustration I will use an example which is deliberately oversimplified in order the more clearly to exhibit the essentials. Let us assume that V_T contains the term 'white phosphorus', or 'P' for short, and that the interpretative system incorporated into T' states no sufficient observational conditions of application for it, but several necessary ones. These will be taken to be independent of each other in the sense that, though in the case of white phosphorus they occur jointly, any one of them occurs in certain other cases in the absence of one or more of the others. Let those necessary conditions be the following: white phosphorus has a garlic-like odor; it is soluble in turpentine, in vegetable oils, and in ether; it produces skin burns. In symbolic notation:

(9.6) $(x)\,(Px \supset Gx)$

(9.7) $(x)\,(Px \supset Tx)$

(9.8) $(x)\,(Px \supset Vx)$

(9.9) $(x)\,(Px \supset Ex)$

(9.10) $(x)\,(Px \supset Sx)$

All predicates other than 'P' that occur in these sentences will belong, then, to V_B.

Now let V_T contain just one term in addition to 'P', namely 'has an ignition temperature of $30°$ C', or 'I' for short; and let there be exactly one interpretative sentence for 'I', to the effect that if an object has the property I then it will burst

59. On this method, first used by von Neumann, see Carnap (1937), pp. 29–30 and p. 96, where further references to the literature are given.

into flame if surrounded by air in which a thermometer shows a reading above 30° C. This property will be considered as observable and will be represented by the predicate 'F' in V_B. The interpretative sentence for 'I', then, is

(9.11) $(x) (Ix \supset Fx)$

Finally, we will assume that the theoretical part of T' contains one single postulate, namely,

(9.12) $(x) (Px \supset Ix)$

which states that white phosphorus has an ignition temperature of 30° C. Let the seven sentences (9.6)-(9.12) represent the total content of T'.

Then, as is readily seen, T' has no consequences in terms of V_B except for purely logical truths; consequently, T' will permit a deductive transition from one V_B-sentence to another only if the latter is logically implied by the former, so that T' is not required to establish the connection. In other words: T' effects no deductive systematization among V_B-sentences at all. Nevertheless, T' may play an essential role in establishing certain explanatory or predictive connections of an inductive kind among the V_B-sentences. Suppose, for example, that a certain object b has been found to have all the characteristics G, T, V, E, S. In view of the sentences (9.6)-(9.10), according to which these characteristics are symptomatic of P, it might then well be inferred that b is white phosphorus. This inference would be inductive rather than deductive, and part of its strength would derive from the mutual independence which we assumed to exist among those five observable symptoms of white phosphorus. The sentence 'Pb' which has thus been inductively accepted leads, via (9.12), to the prediction 'Ib', which in turn, in virtue of (9.11), yields the forecast 'Fb'. Thus, T' permits the transition from the observational data 'Gb', 'Tb', 'Vb', 'Eb', 'Sb' to the observational prediction 'Fb'. But the transition requires an inductive step, consisting of the acceptance of 'Pb' on the strength of the five data sentences, which support, but do not logically imply, 'Pb'.

On the other hand, the system T'_B obtained by Craig's method does not lend itself to this inductive use; in fact, all its sentences are logical truths and thus T'_B makes no empirical assertion at all, for, as was noted above, all the V_B-theorems of T' are logically true statements.

Thus, if the systematizing use of an interpreted theory T' is conceived as involving inductive as well as deductive procedures, then the corresponding system T'_B cannot, in general, replace T'.

An intuitively simpler method of obtaining a functional equivalent, in observational terms, of a given interpreted theory T' is provided by an idea of Ramsey's. In effect, the method amounts to treating all theoretical terms as existentially quantified variables, so that all the extralogical constants that occur in Ramsey's manner of formulating a theory belong to the observational vocabulary.[60] Thus, the interpreted theory determined by the formulas (9.6)-(9.12) would be expressed by the following sentence, which we will call the *Ramsey-sentence associated with the given theory*:

(9.13) $(\exists \phi)\,(\exists \psi)\,(x)\,[(\phi x \supset (Gx \cdot Tx \cdot Vx \cdot Ex \cdot Sx)) \cdot (\psi x \supset Fx) \cdot (\phi x \supset \psi x)]$

This sentence is equivalent to the expression obtained by conjoining the sentences (9.6)-(9.12), replacing '*P*' and '*I*' throughout by the variables 'ϕ' and 'ψ' respectively, and prefixing existential quantifiers with regard to the latter. Thus, (9.13) asserts that there are two properties, ϕ and ψ, otherwise unspecified, such that any object with the property ϕ also has the observable properties G, T, V, E, S; any object with the property ψ also has the observable property E; and any object with the property ϕ also has the property ψ.

An interpreted theory T' is not, of course, logically equivalent with its associated Ramsey-sentence any more than it is logically equivalent with the associated Craig-system T'_B; in fact, each of the two is implied by, but does not in turn imply, T'. But though the Ramsey-sentence contains, apart from variables and logical constants, only terms from V_B, it can be shown to imply exactly the same V-sentences as does T'; hence, it establishes exactly the same deductive transitions among V_B-sentences as does T'. In this respect then, the Ramsey-sentence associated with T' is on a par with the Craig-system T'_B obtainable from T'. But its logical apparatus is more extravagant than that required by T' or by T'_B. In our illustration, for example, T' and T'_B contain variables and quantifiers only with respect to individuals (physical objects), whereas the Ramsey-sentence (9.13) contains variables and quantifiers also for properties of individuals; thus, while T' and T'_B require only a first-order functional calculus, the Ramsey-sentence calls for a second-order functional calculus.

But this means that the Ramsey-sentence associated with an interpreted theory T' avoids reference to hypothetical entities only in letter—replacing Latin constants by Greek variables—rather than in spirit. For it still asserts the existence of certain entities of the kind postulated by T', without guaranteeing any more than does T' that those entities are observables or at least fully characterizable in terms of observables. Hence, Ramsey-sentences provide no satisfactory way of avoiding theoretical concepts.

And indeed, Ramsey himself made no such claim. Rather, his construal of theoretical terms as existentially quantified variables appears to have been motivated by considerations of the following kind: If theoretical terms are treated as constants which are not fully defined in terms of antecedently understood observational terms, then the sentences that can formally be constructed out of them do not have the character of assertions with fully specified meanings,

60. Ramsey (1931), pp. 212-15, 231.

which can be significantly held to be either true or false; rather, their status is comparable to that of sentential functions, with the theoretical terms playing the role of variables. But of a theory we want to be able to predicate truth or falsity, and the construal of theoretical terms as existentially quantified variables yields a formulation which meets this requirement and at the same time retains all the intended empirical implications of the theory.

This consideration raises a further problem, which will be discussed in the next section.

10. ON MEANING AND TRUTH OF SCIENTIFIC THEORIES

The problem suggested by Ramsey's approach is this: If, in the manner of section 8, we construe the theoretical terms of a theory as extralogical constants for which the system J provides only a partial interpretation in terms of the antecedently understood vocabulary V_B, can the sentences formed by means of the theoretical vocabulary nevertheless be considered as meaningful sentences which make definite assertions, and which are either true or false?

The question might seem to come under the jurisdiction of semantics, and more specifically, of the semantical theory of truth. But this is not the case. What the semantical theory of truth provides (under certain conditions) is a general definition of truth for the sentences of a given language L. That definition is stated in a suitable metalanguage, M, of L and permits the formulation of a necessary and sufficient condition of truth for any sentence S of L. This condition is expressed by a translation of S into M.[61] (To be suited for its purpose, M must therefore contain a translation of every sentence of L and must meet certain other conditions which are specified in the semantical theory of truth.) But if the truth criteria thus stated in M are to be intelligible at all, then clearly all the translations of L-statements into M must be assumed to be significant to begin with. Instead of deciding the question as to the meaningfulness of L-sentences, the semantical definition of truth presupposes that it has been settled antecedently.

For analogous reasons, semantics does not enable us to decide whether the theoretical terms in a given system T' do or do not have semantical, or factual, or ontological reference—a characteristic which some writers have considered as distinguishing genuinely theoretical constructs from auxiliary or intervening theoretical terms.[62] One difficulty with the claims and counterclaims that have been made in this connection lies in the failure of the discussants to indicate clearly what they wish to assert by attributing ontological reference to a given

---

61. See Tarski (1944), section 9.
62. On this point, see for example, MacCorquodale and Meehl (1948); Lindzey (1953); Feigl (1950), (1950a); Hempel (1950); Rozeboom (1956).

term. From a purely semantical point of view, it is possible to attribute semantical reference to any term of a language L that is taken to be understood: the referent can be specified in the same manner as the truth condition of a given sentence in L, namely by translation into a suitable metalanguage. For example, using English as a metalanguage, we might say, in reference to Freud's terminology, that 'Verdraengung' designates repression, 'Sublimierung', sublimation, and so on. Plainly, this kind of information is unilluminating for those who wish to use existential reference as a distinctive characteristic of a certain kind of theoretical term; nor does it help those who want to know whether, or in what sense, the entities designated by theoretical terms can be said actually to exist— a question to which we will return shortly.

Semantics, then, does not answer the question raised at the beginning of this section; we have to look elsewhere for criteria of significance for theoretical expressions.

Generally speaking, we might qualify a theoretical expression as intelligible or significant if it has been adequately explained in terms which we consider as antecedently understood. In our earlier discussion, such terms were represented by the vocabulary V_B (plus the terms of logic). But now the question arises: What constitutes an "adequate" explanation? No generally binding standards can be specified: the answer is ultimately determined by one's philosophical conscience. The logical and epistemological puritan might declare intelligible only what has been explicitly defined in terms of V_B; and he might impose further restrictions—in a nominalistic vein, for example—on the logical apparatus that may be used in formulating the definitions. Others will find terms introduced by reduction sentences quite intelligible, and still others will even countenance an interpretation as tenuous as that afforded by an interpretative system. One of the most important advantages of definition lies in the fact that it ensures the possibility of an equivalent restatement of any theoretical sentence in terms of V_B. Partial interpretation does not guarantee this; consequently it does not provide, for every sentence expressible in theoretical terms, a necessary and sufficient condition of truth that can be stated in terms which are antecedently understood. This, no doubt, is the basic difficulty that critics find with the method of partial interpretation.

In defense of partial interpretation, on the other hand, it can be said that to understand an expression is to know how to use it, and in a formal reconstruction the "how to" is expressed by means of rules. Partial interpretation as we have construed it provides such rules. These show, for example, what sentences in terms of V_B alone may be inferred from sentences containing theoretical terms; and thus they specify a set of V_B-sentences that are implied, and hence indirectly asserted, by an interpreted theory T'. (If the set is empty, the theory does not fall within the domain of empirical science.) Conversely, the rules also show what sentences in theoretical terms may be inferred from V_B-sentences. Thus, there are close resemblances between our theoretical sentences and those sentences which are intelligible in the narrower sense of being expressible entirely in terms of V_B—a circumstance which militates in favor of admitting theoretical sentences into the class of significant statements.

It should be mentioned that if this policy is adopted, then we will have to recognize as significant (though not, of course, as interesting or worth investigating) certain interpreted systems which surely would not qualify as potential scientific theories. For example, let L be the conjunction of some finite number of empirical generalizations about learning behavior, formulated in terms of an observational vocabulary V_B, and let P be the conjunction of a finite number of arbitrary sentences formed out of a set V_T of arbitrarily chosen uninterpreted terms (for example, P might be the conjunction of the postulates of some axiomatization of elliptic geometry). Then, by making P the postulates of T and by choosing the sentence $P \supset L$ as the only member of our interpretative system J, we obtain an interpreted theory T' which explains in a trivial way all the given empirical generalizations, since $T \cdot J$ plainly implies L. Yet, needless to say, T' would not be considered a satisfactory learning theory.[63] The characteristic here illustrated does not vitiate our analysis of partial interpretation, since the latter does not claim that every partially interpreted theoretical system is a potentially interesting theory; and indeed, even the requirement of full definition of all theoretical terms by means of V_B still leaves room for similarly unrewarding "theories." Examples like our mock "learning theory" simply remind us that, in addition to having an empirical interpretation (which is necessary if there are to be any empirically testable consequences) a good scientific theory must satisfy various important further conditions; its V_B-consequences must be empirically well confirmed; it must effect a logically simple systematization of the pertinent V_B-sentences, it must suggest further empirical laws, and so forth.

If the sentences of a partially interpreted theory T' are granted the status of significant statements, they can be said to be either true or false. And then the question, touched upon earlier in this section, as to the factual reference of theoretical terms, can be dealt with in a quite straightforward manner: To assert that the terms of a given theory have factual reference, that the entities they purport to refer to actually exist, is tantamount to asserting that what the theory tells us is true; and this in turn is tantamount to asserting the theory.

---

63. It is of interest to note here that if in addition to the conditions specified in section 8, an interpreted theory were also required to meet the criteria of significance for theoretical terms and sentences that have recently been proposed by Carnap (1956 sections 6, 7, 8), then the terms and the sentences of our mock "learning theory" would be ruled out as nonsignificant.

When we say, for example, that the elementary particles of contemporary physical theory actually exist, we assert that there occur in the universe particles of the various kinds indicated by physical theory, governed by specified physical laws, and showing certain specific kinds of observable symptoms of their presence in certain specified circumstances. But this is tantamount to asserting the truth of the (interpreted) physical theory of elementary particles. Similarly, asserting the existence of the drives, reserves, habit strengths, and the like postulated by a given theory of learning amounts to affirming the truth of the system consisting of the statements of the theory and its empirical interpretation.[64]

Thus understood, the existence of hypothetical entities with specified characteristics and interrelations, as assumed by a given theory, can be examined inductively in the same sense in which the truth of the theory itself can be examined, namely, by empirical tests of its V_B-consequences.

According to the conception just outlined, we have to attribute factual reference to all the (extra-logical) terms of a theory if that theory is true; hence, this characteristic provides no basis for a semantic dichotomy in the theoretical vocabulary. Also, the factual reference, as here construed, of theoretical terms does not depend on whether those terms are avoidable in favor of expressions couched in terms of V_B alone. Even if all the theoretical terms of a theory T' are explicitly defined in terms of V_B, so that their use affords a convenient shorthand way of saying what could also be said by means of V_B alone, they will still have factual reference if what the theory says is true.

The preceding observations on truth and factual reference in regard to partially interpreted theories rest on the assumption that the sentences of such theories are accorded the status of statements. For those who find this assumption unacceptable, there are at least two other ways of construing what we have called an interpreted theory. The first of these is Ramsey's method, which was described in the previous section. It has the very attractive feature of representing an interpreted theory in the form of a bona fide statement, which contains no extra-logical constants other than those contained in V_B, and which has exactly the same V_B-consequences as the theory stated in terms of incompletely inter-

---

64. More precisely, the assertion that there exist entities of the various kinds (such as hypothetical objects and events and their various qualitative and quantitative properties and relations) postulated by an interpreted theory T' is expressed by the Ramsey-sentence associated with T'. It is obtained by replacing all theoretical constants in the conjunction of the postulates of T' by variables and binding all these by existential quantifiers placed before the resulting expression. The sentence thus obtained is a logical consequence of the postulates of T'; but the converse does not hold; hence strictly speaking, the assertion of the existence of the various hypothetical entities assumed in a theory is logically weaker than the theory itself.

For suggestive observations on the question of the reality of theoretical entities, see, for example, Toulmin (1953), pp. 134–139 and Smart (1956).

preted theoretical constants. It is perhaps the most satisfactory way of conceiving the logical character of a scientific theory, and it will be objectionable mainly, or perhaps only, to those who, on philosophical grounds, are opposed to the ontological commitments[65] involved in countenancing variables that range over domains other than that of the individuals of the theory (such as, for example the set of all quantitative characteristics of physical objects, or the set of all dyadic relations among them, or sets of such sets, and so forth).

Those finally, who, like the contemporary nominalists, reject such strong ontological commitments, may adopt a conception of scientific theories, not as significant statements, but as intricate devices for inferring, from intelligible initial statements, expressed in terms of an antecedently understood vocabulary V_B, certain other, again intelligible, statements in terms of that vocabulary.[66] The nominalistically inclined may then construe theoretical terms as meaningless auxiliary marks, which serve as convenient symbolic devices in the transition from one set of experiential statements to another. To be sure, the conception of laws and theories as extralogical principles of inference does not reflect the way in which they are used by theoretical scientists. In publications dealing with problems of theoretical physics, or biology, or psychology, for example, sentences containing theoretical terms are normally treated on a par with those which serve to describe empirical data: together with the latter, they function as premises and as conclusions of deductive and of inductive arguments. And indeed, for the working scientist the actual formulation and use of theoretical principles as complex extralogical rules of inference would be a hindrance rather than a help. However, the purpose of those who suggest this conception is not, of course, to facilitate the work of the scientist but rather to clarify the import of his formulations; and from the viewpoint of a philosophical analyst with nominalistic inclinations the proposed view of scientific sentences which by his standards are not admissible as statements does represent an advance in clarification.

---

65. The concept is used here in Quine's sense, according to which a theory is ontologically committed to those entities which must be included in the domains over which its bound variables range if the theory is to be true. Quine develops and defends this idea in several of the essays comprising his book (1953).

66. The conception of laws or theories as inferential principles has been suggested, but by no means generally from a nominalistic point of view, by several authors; among them Schlick (1931), pp. 151 and 155; Ramsey (1931), p. 241; Ryle (1949), especially pp. 120-25; and Toulmin (1953), Chapters III and IV. (Toulmin remarks, however, that to think of laws of nature as rules or licenses "reflects only a part of their nature" (*loc. cit.*, p. 105).) See also Braithwaite's discussion of the issue in (1953), pp. 85-87. Finally, Popper's essay (1956) contains several critical and constructive comments that bear on this issue and on some of the other questions discussed in the present study.

However, the question posed by the theoretician's dilemma can be raised also in regard to the two alternative conceptions of the status of a theory. Concerning Ramsey's formulation, we may ask whether it is not possible to dispense altogether with the existentially quantified variables which represent the theoretical terms, and thus to avoid the ontological commitment they require, without sacrificing any of the deductive connections that the Ramsey-sentence establishes among V_B-sentences. And in regard to theories conceived as inferential devices, we may ask whether they cannot be replaced by a functionally equivalent set of rules—i.e., one establishing exactly the same inferential transitions among V_B-sentences—which uses none of the "meaningless marks."

To both questions, Craig's theorem gives an affirmative answer by providing a general method for constructing the desired kind of equivalent. But again, in both cases, the result has the shortcomings mentioned in section 8. First, the method would replace the Ramsey-sentence by an infinite set of postulates, or the body of inferential rules by an infinite set of rules, in terms of V_B, and would thus lead to a loss of economy. Second, the resulting system of postulates or of inferential rules would not lend itself to inductive prediction and explanation. And third, it would have the pragmatic defect, partly reflected already in the second point, of being less fruitful heuristically than the system using theoretical terms.

Our argument (5.1), the theoretician's dilemma, took it to be the sole purpose of a theory to establish deductive connections among observation sentences. If this were the case, theoretical terms would indeed be unnecessary. But if it is recognized that a satisfactory theory should provide possibilities also for inductive explanatory and predictive use and that it should achieve systematic economy and heuristic fertility, then it is clear that theoretical formulations cannot be replaced by expressions in terms of observables only; the theoretician's dilemma, with its conclusion to the contrary, is seen to rest on a false premise.

REFERENCES

Bergmann, Gustav. "The Logic of Psychological Concepts," *Philosophy of Science*, 18:93-110 (1951).

Bergmann, Gustav. "Comments on Professor Hempel's 'The Concept of Cognitive Significance'," *Proceedings of the American Academy of Arts and Sciences*, 80 (No. 1): 78-86 (1951). Reprinted in Gustav Bergmann, *The Metaphysics of Logical Positivism*. New York: Longmans, Green and Co., 1954. Referred to in this essay as (1951a).

Bergmann, Gustav, and Kenneth Spence. "Operationism and Theory in Psychology," *Psychological Review*, 48:1-14 (1941). Reprinted in Marx (1951).

Braithwaite, R. B. *Scientific Explanation.* Cambridge, England: Cambridge University Press, 1953.

Bridgman, P. W. *The Logic of Modern Physics.* New York: Macmillan, 1927.

Burks, Arthur W. "The Logic of Causal Propositions," *Mind,* 60:363-382 (1951).

Campbell, Norman R. *Physics: The Elements.* Cambridge: Cambridge University Press, 1920. Republished under the title *Foundations of Science.* New York: Dover, 1957.

Carnap, Rudolf. "Testability and Meaning," *Philosophy of Science,* 3:420-468 (1936); 4:1-40 (1937). Reprinted as a monograph by Whitlock's Inc., New Haven, Conn., 1950. Excerpts reprinted in Feigl and Brodbeck (1953).

Carnap, Rudolf. *The Logical Syntax of Language.* London: Routledge and Kegan Paul, 1937.

Carnap, Rudolf. *Foundations of Logic and Mathematics.* Chicago: University of Chicago Press, 1939.

Carnap, Rudolf. *Logical Foundations of Probability.* Chicago: University of Chicago Press, 1950.

Carnap, Rudolf. "Meaning Postulates," *Philosophical Studies,* 3:65-73 (1952).

Carnap, Rudolf. "Meaning and Synonymy in Natural Languages," *Philosophical Studies,* 6:33-47 (1955).

Carnap, Rudolf. "The Methodological Character of Theoretical Concepts," in H. Feigl and M. Scriven (eds.), *The Foundations of Science and the Concepts of Psychology and Psychoanalysis,* pp. 38-76. Minneapolis: University of Minnesota Press, 1956.

Cohen, M. R., and E. Nagel. *Introduction to Logic and Scientific Method.* New York: Harcourt, Brace, 1934.

Craig, William. "On Axiomatizability within a System," *Journal of Symbolic Logic,* 18:30-32 (1953).

Craig, William. "Replacement of Auxiliary Expressions," *Philosophical Review,* 65:38-55 (1956).

Cramér, Harald. *Mathematical Methods of Statistics.* Princeton: Princeton University Press, 1946.

Estes, W. K., S. Koch, K. MacCorquodale, P. E. Meehl, C. G. Mueller, W. S. Schoenfeld, and W. S. Verplanck. *Modern Learning Theory.* New York; Appleton-Century-Crofts, 1954.

Feigl, Herbert. "Some Remarks on the Meaning of Scientific Explanation," (A slightly modified version of comments first published in *Psychological Review,* 52(1948)), in Feigl and Sellars (1949), pp. 510-514.

Feigl, Herbert. "Existential Hypotheses," *Philosophy of Science,* 17:35-62 (1950).

Feigl, Herbert. "Logical Reconstruction, Realism, and Pure Semiotic," *Philosophy of Science,* 17:186-195 (1950). Referred to in this essay as (1950a).

Feigl, Herbert. "Principles and Problems of Theory Construction in Psychology," in W. Dennis (ed.), *Current Trends in Psychological Theory,* pp. 179-213. Pittsburgh: University of Pittsburgh Press, 1951.

Feigl, Herbert, and May Brodbeck (eds.). *Readings in the Philosophy of Science.* New York: Appleton-Century-Crofts, 1953.

Feigl, Herbert, and Wilfred Sellars (eds.). *Readings in Philosophical Analysis.* New York: Appleton-Century-Crofts, 1949.

Goodman, Nelson. "On Likeness of Meaning," *Analysis,* 10:1-7 (1949). Reprinted in a revised form in Linsky (1952).

Goodman, Nelson. *The Structure of Appearance*. Cambridge, Mass.: Harvard University Press,1951.

Goodman, Nelson. *Fact, Fiction, and Forecast*. Cambridge, Mass.: Harvard University Press, 1955.

Grice, H. P., and P. F. Strawson. "In Defense of a Dogma," *Philosophical Review*, 65:141-158 (1956).

Hempel, Carl G. "Geometry and Empirical Science," *American Mathematical Monthly*, 52:7-17 (1945). Reprinted in Feigl and Sellars (1949), in Wiener (1953), and in James R. Newman (ed.), *The World of Mathematics*. New York: Simon and Schuster, 1956.

Hempel, Carl G. "A Note on Semantic Realism," *Philosophy of Science*, 17: 169-173 (1950).

Hempel, Carl G. "General System Theory and the Unity of Science," *Human Biology*, 23:313-322 (1951).

Hempel, Carl G. *Fundamentals of Concept Formation in Empirical Science*. Chicago: University of Chicago Press, 1952.

Hempel, Carl G. "Implications of Carnap's Work for the Philosophy of Science," in P. A. Schilpp (ed.), *The Philosophy of Rudolf Carnap*. La Salle, Ill.: Open Court Publishing Co., 1963.

Hempel, Carl G. "The Concept of Cognitive Significance: A Reconsideration," *Proceedings of the American Academy of Arts and Sciences*, 80 (No. 1):61-77 (1951).

Hempel, Carl G., and Paul Oppenheim. "Studies in the Logic of Explanation," *Philosophy of Science*, 15:135-175 (1948). Reprinted in the present volume.

Hermes, H. "Eine Axiomatisierung der allgemeinen Mechanik," *Forschungen zur Logik und Grundlegung der exakten Wissenschaften*. Neue Folge, Heft 3. Leipzig, 1938.

Hull, C. L. "The Problem of Intervening Variables in Molar Behavior Theory," *Psychological Review*, 50:273-291 (1943). Reprinted in Marx (1951).

Hull, C. L., C. I. Hovland, R. T. Ross, M. Hall, D. T. Perkins, and F. B. Fitch. *Mathematico-Deductive Theory of Rote Learning*. New Haven: Yale University Press, 1940.

Hutten, Ernest H. *The Language of Modern Physics*: An *Introduction to the Philosophy of Science*. London and New York: Macmillan, 1956.

Kemeny, John G. Review of Carnap (1950). *The Journal of Symbolic Logic*, 16:205-207 (1951).

Kemeny, John G. "Extension of the Methods of Inductive Logic," *Philosophical Studies*, 3:38-42 (1952).

Kemeny, John G., and Paul Oppenheim. "On Reduction," *Philosophical Studies*, 7:6-19 (1956).

Lindzey, Gardner. "Hypothetical Constructs, Conventional Constructs, and the Use of Physiological Data in Psychological Theory," *Psychiatry*, 16:27-33 (1953).

Linsky, Leonard (ed.). *Semantics and the Philosophy of Language*. Urbana, Ill.: University of Illinois Press, 1952.

MacCorquodale, K., and P. Meehl. "On a Distinction between Hypothetical Constructs and Intervening Variables," *Psychological Review*, 55:95-107 (1948). Reprinted in Feigl and Brodbeck (1953) and, with omissions, in Marx (1951).

MacCorquodale, K., and P. Meehl. "Edward C. Tolman," in Estes *et al.* (1954), 177-266.

Margenau, Henry. *The Nature of Physical Reality*. New York: McGraw-Hill Book Co., 1950.

Martin, R. M. "On 'Analytic'," *Philosophical Studies*, 3:42-47 (1952).

Marx, Melvin H. (ed.). *Psychological Theory*. New York: Macmillan, 1951.

Mates, Benson. "Analytic Sentences," *Philosophical Review*, 60:525-534 (1951).

McKinsey, J. C. C., A. C. Sugar, and P. Suppes. "Axiomatic Foundations of Classical Particle Mechanics," *Journal of Rational Mechanics and Analysis*, 2:253-272 (1953).

McKinsey, J. C. C., and P. Suppes. "Transformations of Systems of Classical Particle Mechanics," *Journal of Rational Mechanics and Analysis*, 2:273-289 (1953).

Mises, R. von. *Positivism: A Study in Human Understanding*. Cambridge, Mass.: Harvard University Press, 1951.

Nagel, Ernest. *Principles of the Theory of Probability*. Chicago: University of Chicago Press, 1939.

Nagel, Ernest. "The Meaning of Reduction in the Natural Sciences," in Robert C. Stauffer (ed.), *Science and Civilization*. Madison, Wis.: University of Winconsin Press, 1949. Reprinted in Wiener (1953).

Nagel, Ernest. "Mechanistic Explanation and Organismic Biology," *Philosophy and Phenomenological Research*. 11:327-338 (1951).

Neumann, John von, and Oskar Morgenstern. *Theory of Games and Economic Behavior*, 2d ed. Princeton: Princeton University Press, 1947.

Northrop, F. S. C. *The Logic of the Sciences and the Humanities*. New York: Macmillan, 1947.

Pap, Arthur. "Reduction Sentences and Open Concepts," *Methodos*, 5:3-28 (1953).

Pap, Arthur. *Analytische Erkenntnistheorie*. Wien: J. Springer, 1955.

Popper, Karl. *Logik der Forschung*. Wien: J. Springer, 1935.

Popper, Karl. *The Open Society and its Enemies*. London: G. Routledge & Sons, 1945.

Popper, Karl. "Three Views Concerning Human Knowledge," in H. D. Lewis (ed.), *Contemporary British Philosophy: Personal Statements*. New York: Macmillan, 1956.

Quine, W. V. "Two Dogmas of Empiricism," *Philosophical Review*, 60:20-43 (1951). Reprinted in Quine (1953).

Quine, W. V. *From a Logical Point of View*. Cambridge, Mass.: Harvard University Press, 1953.

Ramsey, Frank Plumpton. *The Foundation of Mathematics and other Logical Essays*. London: Kegan Paul, and New York: Harcourt Brace, 1931.

Reichenbach, Hans. *Axiomatik der relativistischen Raum-Zeit-Lehre*. Braunschweig: F. Vieweg & Sohn, 1924.

Reichenbach, Hans. *Philosophie der Raum-Zeit-Lehre*. Berlin: W. de Gruyter & Co., 1928.

Reichenbach, Hans. *Philosophic Foundations of Quantum Mechanics*. Berkeley and Los Angeles: University of California Press, 1944.

Reichenbach, Hans. *The Theory of Probability*. Berkeley: University of California Press, 1949.

Reichenbach, Hans. *The Rise of Scientific Philosophy*. Berkeley and Los Angeles: University of California Press, 1951.

Reichenbach, Hans. *Nomological Statements and Admissible Operations*. Amsterdam: North Holland Publishing Co., 1954.

Rozeboom, William W. "Mediation Variables in Scientific Theory," *Psychological Review*, 63:249-264 (1956).

Rubin, H., and P. Suppes. *Transformations of Systems of Relativistic Particle Mechanics*. Technical Report No. 2. Prepared under contract for Office of Naval Research. Stanford University, Stanford, 1953.

Russell, Bertrand. *Introduction to Mathematical Philosophy*. London and New York: Macmillan, 1919.

Russell, Bertrand. *Mysticism and Logic*. New York: W. W. Norton & Co., 1929.

Ryle, Gilbert. *The Concept of Mind*. London: Hutchinson's University Library, 1949.

Schlick, M. "Die Kausalitaet in der gegenwaertigen Physik," *Die Naturwissenschaften*, 19:145-162 (1931).

Skinner, B. F. *Science and Human Behavior*. New York: Macmillan, 1953.

Smart, J. J. C. "The Reality of Theoretical Entities," *Australasisan Journal of Philosophy*, 34:1-12 (1956).

Spence, Kenneth W. "The Nature of Theory Construction in Contemporary Psychology," *Psychological Review*, 51:47-68 (1944). Reprinted in Marx (1951).

Tarski, Alfred. "Einige methodologische Untersuchungen über die Definierbarkeit der Begriffe," *Erkenntnis* 5:80-100 (1935). English translation in Tarski (1956).

Tarski, Alfred. *Introduction to Logic and to the Methodology of Deductive Sciences*. New York: Oxford University Press, 1941.

Tarski, Alfred, "The Semantic Conception of Truth," *Philosophy and Phenomenological Research*, 4:341-375 (1944). Reprinted in Feigl and Sellars (1949) and in Linsky (1952).

Tarski, Alfred, *Logic, Semantics, Metamathematics*. Tr. by J. H. Woodger. Oxford: The Clarendon Press, 1956.

Tolman, E. C. "Operational Behaviorism and Current Trends in Psychology," *Proceedings of the 25th Anniversary Celebration of the Inauguration of Graduate Study*, Los Angeles, 1936, pp. 89-103. Reprinted in Marx (1951).

Tolman, E. C., B. F. Ritchie, and D. Kalish. "Studies in Spatial Learning. I. Orientation and the Short-Cut." *Journal of Experimental Psychology*, 36: 13-24 (1946).

Toulmin, Stephen. *The Philosophy of Science*. London: Hutchinson's University Library, 1953.

Verplanck, W. S. "Burrhus F. Skinner," in Estes *et al.* (1954), 267-316.

Wald, A. *On the Principles of Statistical Inference*. Notre Dame: University of Notre Dame Press, 1942.

Walker, A. G. "Foundations of Relativity: Parts I and II," *Proceedings of the Royal Society of Edinburgh*, 62:319-335 (1943-1949).

Walsh, W. H. *An Introduction to Philosophy of History*. London: Hutchinson's University Library, 1951.

Wang, Hao. "Notes on the Analytic-Synthetic Distinction," *Theoria*, 21:158-178 (1955).

White, Morton G. "The Analytic and the Synthetic: An Untenable Dualism," in S. Hook (ed.), *John Dewey: Philosopher of Science and of Freedom*. New York: Dial Press, 1950. Reprinted in Linsky (1952).

White, Morton G. *Toward Reunion in Philosophy*. Cambridge, Mass.: Harvard University Press, 1956.

Wiener, Philip P. (ed.). *Readings in Philosophy of Science*. New York: Scribner, 1953.

Woodger, J. H. *The Axiomatic Method in Biology*. Cambridge: Cambridge University Press, 1937.

Woodger, J. H. *The Technique of Theory Construction*. Chicago: University of Chicago Press, 1939.

Woodger, J. H. *Biology and Language*. Cambridge: Cambridge University Press, 1952.

IV.

SCIENTIFIC

EXPLANATION

9. THE FUNCTION OF

GENERAL LAWS IN HISTORY

1. It is a rather widely held opinion that history, in contradistinction to the so-called physical sciences, is concerned with the description of particular events of the past rather than with the search for general laws which might govern those events. As a characterization of the type of problem in which some historians are mainly interested, this view probably can not be denied; as a statement of the theoretical function of general laws in scientific historical research, it is certainly unacceptable. The following considerations are an attempt to substantiate this point by showing in some detail that general laws have quite analogous functions in history and in the natural sciences, that they form an indispensable instrument of historical research, and that they even constitute the common basis of various procedures which are often considered as characteristic of the social in contradistinction to the natural sciences.

By a general law, we shall here understand a statement of universal conditional form which is capable of being confirmed or disconfirmed by suitable empirical findings. The term 'law' suggests the idea that the statement in question is actually well confirmed by the relevant evidence available; as this qualification is, in many cases, irrelevant for our purpose, we shall frequently use the term 'hypothesis of universal form' or briefly 'universal hypothesis' instead of 'general law', and state the condition of satisfactory confirmation separately, if necessary. In the context of this paper, a universal hypothesis may be assumed to assert a regularity of the following type: In every case where an event of a specified kind C occurs at a certain place and time, an event of a

This article is a slightly modified version of the original text, which appeared in *The Journal of Philosophy* 39, pp. 35-48 (1942). It is reprinted with kind permission of the Editor.

specified kind E will occur at a place and time which is related in a specified manner to the place and time of the occurrence of the first event. (The symbols 'C' and 'E' have been chosen to suggest the terms 'cause' and 'effect', which are often, though by no means always, applied to events related by a law of the above kind.)

2.1 The main function of general laws in the natural sciences is to connect events in patterns which are usually referred to as *explanation* and *prediction*.

The explanation of the occurrence of an event of some specific kind E at a certain place and time consists, as it is usually expressed, in indicating the causes or determining factors of E. Now the assertion that a set of events—say, of the kinds $C_1, C_2, \ldots, C_n$—have caused the event to be explained, amounts to the statement that, according to certain general laws, a set of events of the kinds mentioned is regularly accompanied by an event of kind E. Thus, the scientific explanation of the event in question consists of

(1) a set of statements asserting the occurrence of certain events $C_1, \ldots C_n$ at certain times and places,

(2) a set of universal hypotheses, such that

   (a) the statements of both groups are reasonably well confirmed by empirical evidence,

   (b) from the two groups of statements the sentence asserting the occurrence of event E can be logically deduced.

In a physical explanation, group (1) would describe the initial and boundary conditions for the occurrence of the final event; generally, we shall say that group (1) states the *determining conditions* for the event to be explained, while group (2) contains the general laws on which the explanation is based; they imply the statement that whenever events of the kind described in the first group occur, an event of the kind to be explained will take place.

Illustration: Let the event to be explained consist in the cracking of an automobile radiator during a cold night. The sentences of group (1) may state the following initial and boundary conditions: The car was left in the street all night. Its radiator, which consists of iron, was completely filled with water, and the lid was screwed on tightly. The temperature during the night dropped from 39° F. in the evening to 25° F. in the morning; the air pressure was normal. The bursting pressure of the radiator material is so and so much. Group (2) would contain empirical laws such as the following: Below 32° F., under normal atmospheric pressure, water freezes. Below 39.2° F., the pressure of a mass of water increases with decreasing temperature, if the volume remains constant or decreases; when the water freezes, the pressure again increases. Finally, this group would have to include a quantitative law concerning the change of pressure of water as a function of its temperature and volume.

From statements of these two kinds, the conclusion that the radiator cracked during the night can be deduced by logical reasoning; an explanation of the considered event has been established.

2.2 It is important to bear in mind that the symbols 'E', 'C', 'C_1', 'C_2', etc., which were used above, stand for kinds or properties of events, not for what is sometimes called individual events. For the object of description and explanation in every branch of empirical science is always the occurrence of an event of a certain *kind* (such as a drop in temperature by 14° F., an eclipse of the moon, a cell-division, an earthquake, an increase in employment, a political assassination) at a given place and time, or in a given empirical object (such as the radiator of a certain car, the planetary system, a specified historical personality, etc.) at a certain time.

What is sometimes called the *complete description* of an individual event (such as the earthquake of San Francisco in 1906 or the assassination of Julius Caesar) would require a statement of all the properties exhibited by the spatial region or the individual object involved, for the period of time occupied by the event in question. Such a task can never be completely accomplished.

A fortiori, it is impossible to give a *complete explanation* of an individual event in the sense of accounting for *all* its characteristics by means of universal hypotheses, although the explanation of what happened at a specified place and time may gradually be made more and more specific and comprehensive.

But there is no difference, in this respect, between history and the natural sciences: both can give an account of their subject-matter only in terms of general concepts, and history can "grasp the unique individuality" of its objects of study no more and no less than can physics or chemistry.

3. The following points result more or less directly from the above study of scientific explanation and are of special importance for the questions here to be discussed.

3.1 A set of events can be said to have caused the event to be explained only if general laws can be indicated which connect "causes" and "effect" in the manner characterized above.

3.2 No matter whether the cause-effect terminology is used or not, a scientific explanation has been achieved only if empirical laws of the kind mentioned under (2) in 2.1 have been applied.[1]

3.3 The use of universal empirical hypotheses as explanatory principles dis-

---

1. Maurice Mandelbaum, in his generally very clarifying analysis of relevance and causation in history (*The Problem of Historical Knowledge*, New York, 1938, Chs. 7, 8) seems to hold that there is a difference between the "causal analysis" or "causal explanation" of an event and the establishment of scientific laws governing it in the sense stated above. He argues that "scientific laws can only be formulated on the basis of causal analysis," but that "they are not substitutes for full causal explanations" (*l.c.*, p. 238). For the reasons outlined above, this distinction does not appear to be justifiable: every "causal explanation" is an "explanation by scientific laws"; for in no other way than by reference to empirical laws can the assertion of a causal connection between events be scientifically substantiated.

tinguishes genuine from pseudo-explanation, such as, say, the attempt to account for certain features of organic behavior by reference to an entelechy, for whose functioning no laws are offered, or the explanation of the achievements of a given person in terms of his "mission in history", his "predestined fate,"or similar notions. Accounts of this type are based on metaphors rather than laws; they convey pictorial and emotional appeals instead of insight into factual connections; they substitute vague analogies and intuitive "plausibility" for deduction from testable statements and are therefore unacceptable as scientific explanations.

Any explanation of scientific character is amenable to objective checks; these include

(a) an empirical test of the sentences which state the determining conditions;

(b) an empirical test of the universal hypotheses on which the explanation rests;

(c) an investigation of whether the explanation is logically conclusive in the sense that the sentence describing the events to be explained follows from the statements of groups (1) and (2).

4. The function of general laws in *scientific prediction* can now be stated very briefly. Quite generally, prediction in empirical science consists in deriving a statement about a certain future event (for example, the relative position of the planets to the sun, at a future date) from (1) statements describing certain known (past or present) conditions (for example, the positions and momenta of the planets at a past or present moment), and (2) suitable general laws (for example, the laws of celestial mechanics). Thus, the logical structure of a scientific prediction is the same as that of a scientific explanation, which has been described in 2.1. In particular, prediction no less than explanation throughout empirical science involves reference to universal empirical hypotheses.

The customary distinction between explanation and prediction rests mainly on a pragmatic difference between the two: While in the case of an explanation, the final event is known to have happened, and its determining conditions have to be sought, the situation is reversed in the case of a prediction: here, the initial conditions are given, and their "effect"—which, in the typical case, has not yet taken place—is to be determined.

In view of the structural equality of explanation and prediction, it may be said that an explanation as characterized in 2.1 is not complete unless it might as well have functioned as a prediction: If the final event can be derived from the initial conditions and universal hypotheses stated in the explanation, then it might as well have been predicted, before it actually happened, on the basis of a knowledge of the initial conditions and the general laws. Thus, e.g., those initial conditions and general laws which the astronomer would adduce in explanation of a certain eclipse of the sun are such that they might also have served as a sufficient basis for a forecast of the eclipse before it took place.

However, only rarely, if ever, are explanations stated so completely as to exhibit this predictive character (which the test referred to under (c) in 3.3 would serve to reveal). Quite commonly, the explanation offered for the occurrence of an event is incomplete. Thus, we may hear the explanation that a barn burnt down "because" a burning cigarette was dropped in the hay, or that a certain political movement has spectacular success "because" it takes advantage of widespread racial prejudices. Similarly, in the case of the broken radiator, the customary way of formulating an explanation would be restricted to pointing out that the car was left in the cold, and the radiator was filled with water. In explanatory statements like these, the general laws which confer upon the stated conditions the character of "causes" or "determining factors" are completely omitted (sometimes, perhaps, as a "matter of course"), and, furthermore, the enumeration of the determining conditions of group (1) is incomplete; this is illustrated by the preceding examples, but also by the earlier analysis of the broken radiator case: as a closer examination would reveal, even that much more detailed statement of determining conditions and universal hypotheses would require amplification in order to serve as a sufficient basis for the deduction of the conclusion that the radiator broke during the night.

In some instances, the incompleteness of a given explanation may be considered as inessential. Thus, e.g., we may feel that the explanation referred to in the last example could be made complete if we so desired; for we have reasons to assume that we know the kind of determining conditions and of general laws which are relevant in this context.

Very frequently, however, we encounter "explanations" whose incompleteness can not simply be dismissed as inessential. The methodological consequences of this situation will be discussed later (especially in 5.3 and 5.4).

5.1 The preceding considerations apply to *explanation in history* as well as in any other branch of empirical science. Historical explanation, too, aims at showing that the event in question was not "a matter of chance," but was to be expected in view of certain antecedent or simultaneous conditions. The expectation referred to is not prophecy or divination, but rational scientific anticipation which rests on the assumption of general laws.

If this view is correct, it would seem strange that while most historians do suggest explanations of historical events, many of them deny the possibility of resorting to any general laws in history. It is possible, however, to account for this situation by a closer study of explanation in history, as may become clear in the course of the following analysis.

5.2 In some cases, the universal hypotheses underlying a historical explanation are rather explicitly stated, as is illustrated by the italicized passages in the following attempt to explain the tendency of government agencies to perpetuate themselves and to expand:

> As the activities of the government are enlarged, more people develop a vested interest in the continuation and expansion of governmental functions. *People who have jobs do not like to lose them; those who are habituated to certain skills do not welcome change; those who have become accustomed to the exercise of a certain kind of power do not like to relinquish their control—if anything, they want to develop greater power and correspondingly greater prestige. . . .*
> Thus, government offices and bureaus, once created, in turn institute drives, not only to fortify themselves against assault, but to enlarge the scope of their operations.[2]

Most explanations offered in history or sociology, however, fail to include an explicit statement of the general regularities they presuppose; and there seem to be at least two reasons which account for this:

First, the universal hypotheses in question frequently relate to individual or social psychology, which somehow is supposed to be familiar to everybody through his everyday experience; thus, they are tacitly taken for granted. This is a situation quite similar to that characterized in section 4.

Second, it would often be very difficult to formulate the underlying assumptions explicitly with sufficient precision and at the same time in such a way that they are in agreement with all the relevant empirical evidence available. It is highly instructive, in examining the adequacy of a suggested explanation, to attempt a reconstruction of the universal hypotheses on which it rests. Particularly, such terms as "hence," "therefore," "consequently," "because," "naturally," "obviously," etc., are often indicative of the tacit presupposition of some general law: they are used to tie up the initial conditions with the event to be explained; but that the latter was "naturally" to be expected as a "consequence" of the stated conditions follows only if suitable general laws are presupposed. Consider, for example, the statement that the Dust Bowl farmers migrated to California "because" continual drought and sandstorms made their existence increasingly precarious, and because California seemed to them to offer so much better living conditions. This explanation rests on some such universal hypothesis as that populations will tend to migrate to regions which offer better living conditions. But it would obviously be difficult accurately to state this hypothesis in the form of a general law which is reasonably well confirmed by all the relevant evidence available. Similarly, if a particular revolution is explained by reference to the growing discontent, on the part of a large part of the population, with certain prevailing conditions, it is clear that a general

2. Donald W. McConnell *et al., Economic Behavior;* New York, 1939; pp. 894–95. (Italics supplied.)

regularity is assumed in this explanation, but we are hardly in a position to state just what extent and what specific form the discontent has to assume, and what the environmental conditions have to be, to bring about a revolution. Analogous remarks apply to all historical explanations in terms of class struggle, economic or geographic conditions, vested interests of certain groups, tendency to conspicuous consumption, etc.: all of them rest on the assumption of universal hypotheses[3] which connect certain characteristics of individual or group life with others; but in many cases, the content of the hypotheses which are tacitly assumed in a given explanation can be reconstructed only quite approximately.

5.3 It might be argued that the phenomena covered by the type of explanation just mentioned are of a statistical character, and that therefore only probability hypotheses need to be assumed in their explanation, so that the question as to the "underlying general laws" would be based on a false premise. And indeed, it seems possible and justifiable to construe certain explanations offered in history as based on the assumption of probability hypotheses rather than of general "deterministic" laws, i.e., laws in the form of universal conditionals. This claim may be extended to many of the explanations offered in other fields of empirical science as well. Thus, e.g., if Tommy comes down with the measles two weeks after his brother, and if he has not been in the company of other persons having the measles, we accept the explanation that he caught the disease from his brother. Now, there is a general hypothesis underlying this explanation; but it can hardly be said to be a general law to the effect that any person who has not had the measles before will get it without fail if he stays in the company of somebody else who has the measles; that contagion will occur can be asserted only with high probability.

Many an explanation offered in history seems to admit of an analysis of this kind: if fully and explicitly formulated, it would state certain initial conditions, and certain probability hypotheses,[4] such that the occurrence of the event to be explained is made highly probable by the initial conditions in view of the probability hypotheses. But no matter whether explanations in history be construed as causal or as probabilistic, it remains true that in general the initial conditions

---

3. What is sometimes misleadingly called an explanation by means of a certain *concept* is, in empirical science, actually an explanation in terms of *universal hypotheses* containing that concept. "Explanations" involving concepts which do not function in empirically testable hypotheses—such as "entelechy" in biology, "historic destination of a race" or "self-unfolding of absolute reason" in history—are mere metaphors without cognitive content.

4. E. Zilsel, in a stimulating paper on "Physics and the Problem of Historico-Sociological Laws" (*Philosophy of Science*, Vol. 8, 1941, pp. 567-79), suggests that all specifically historical laws are of a statistical character similar to that of the "macro-laws" of physics. The above remarks, however, are not restricted to specifically historical laws since explanation in history rests to a large extent on nonhistorical laws (cf. section 8 of this paper).

and especially the universal hypotheses involved are not clearly indicated, and can not unambiguously be supplemented. (In the case of probability hypotheses, for example, the probability values involved will at best be known quite roughly.)

5.4 What the explanatory analyses of historical events offer is, then, in most cases not an explanation in one of the senses indicated above, but something that might be called an *explanation sketch*. Such a sketch consists of a more or less vague indication of the laws and initial conditions considered as relevant, and it needs "filling out" in order to turn into a full-fledged explanation. This filling-out requires further empirical research, for which the sketch suggests the direction. (Explanation sketches are common also outside of history; many explanations in psychoanalysis, for instance, illustrate this point.)

Obviously, an explanation sketch does not admit of an empirical test to the same extent as does a complete explanation; and yet, there is a difference between a scientifically acceptable explanation sketch and a pseudo-explanation (or a pseudo-explanation sketch). A scientifically acceptable explanation sketch needs to be filled out by more specific statements; but it points into the direction where these statements are to be found; and concrete research may tend to confirm or to infirm those indications; i.e., it may show that the kind of initial conditions suggested are actually relevant; or it may reveal that factors of a quite different nature have to be taken into account in order to arrive at a satisfactory explanation.

The filling-out process required by an explanation sketch will in general effect a gradual increase in the precision of the formulations involved; but at any stage of this process, those formulations will have some empirical import: it will be possible to indicate, at least roughly, what kind of evidence would be relevant in testing them, and what findings would tend to confirm them. In the case of nonempirical explanations or explanation sketches, on the other hand—say, by reference to the historical destiny of a certain race, or to a prinicple of historical justice—the use of empirically meaningless terms makes it impossible even roughly to indicate the type of investigation that would have a bearing upon those formulations, and that might lead to evidence either confirming or infirming the suggested explanation.

5.5 In trying to appraise the soundness of a given explanation, one will first have to attempt to reconstruct as completely as possible the argument constituting the explanation or the explanation sketch. In particular, it is important to realize what the underlying explanatory hypotheses are, and to appraise their scope and empirical foundation. A resuscitation of the assumptions buried under the gravestones 'hence', 'therefore', 'because', and the like will often reveal that the explanation offered is poorly founded or downright unacceptable. In many cases, this procedure will bring to light the fallacy of claiming that a large number of details of an event have been explained when, even on a very liberal interpretation, only some broad characteristics of it have been accounted for. Thus, for example, the geographic or economic conditions under which a group lives may account for certain general features of, say, its art or its moral codes; but to grant this does not mean that the artistic achievements of the group or its system of morals has thus been explained in detail; for this would imply that from a description of the prevalent geographic or economic conditions alone, a detailed account of certain aspects of the cultural life of the group can be deduced by means of specifiable general laws.

A related error consists in singling out one of several important groups of factors which would have to be stated in the initial conditions, and then claiming that the phenomenon in question is "determined" by that one group of factors and thus can be explained in terms of it.

Occasionally, the adherents of some particular school of explanation or interpretation in history will adduce, as evidence in favor of their approach, a successful historical prediction which was made by a representative of their school. But though the predictive success of a theory is certainly relevant evidence of its soundness, it is important to make sure that the successful prediction is in fact obtainable by means of the theory in question. It happens sometimes that the prediction is actually an ingenious guess which may have been influenced by the theoretical outlook of its author, but which can not be arrived at by means of his theory alone. Thus, an adherent of a quite metaphysical "theory" of history may have a sound feeling for historical developments and may be able to make correct predictions, which he will even couch in the terminology of his theory, though they could not have been attained by means of it. To guard against such pseudo-confirming cases would be one of the functions of test (c) in 3.3.

6. We have tried to show that in history no less than in any other branch of empirical inquiry, scientific explanation can be achieved only by means of suitable general hypotheses, or by theories, which are bodies of systematically related hypotheses. This thesis is clearly in contrast with the familiar view that genuine explanation in history is obtained by a method which characteristically distinguishes the social from the natural sciences, namely, *the method of empathic understanding:* The historian, we are told, imagines himself in the place of the persons involved in the events which he wants to explain; he tries to realize as completely as possible the circumstances under which they acted and the motives which influenced their actions; and by this imaginary self-identification with his heroes, he arrives at an understanding and thus at an adequate explanation of the events with which he is concerned.

This method of empathy is, no doubt, frequently applied by laymen and by experts in history. But it does not in itself constitute an explanation; it rather is essentially a heuristic device; its function is to suggest psychological hypotheses which might serve as explanatory principles in the case under consideration. Stated in crude terms, the idea underlying this function is the following: The historian tries to realize how he himself would act under the given conditions, and under the particular motivations of his heroes; he tentatively generalizes his findings into a general rule and uses the latter as an explanatory principle in accounting for the actions of the persons involved. Now, this procedure may sometimes prove heuristically helpful; but it does not guarantee the soundness of the historical explanation to which it leads. The latter rather depends upon the factual correctness of the generalizations which the method of understanding may have suggested.

Nor is the use of this method indispensable for historical explanation. A historian may, for example, be incapable of feeling himself into the role of a paranoiac historic personality, and yet he may well be able to explain certain of his actions by reference to the principles of abnormal psychology. Thus, whether the historian is or is not in a position to identify himself with his historical hero is irrelevant for the correctness of his explanation; what counts is the soundness of the general hypotheses involved, no matter whether they were suggested by empathy or by a strictly behavioristic procedure. Much of the appeal of the "method of understanding" seems to be due to the fact that it tends to present the phenomena in question as somehow "plausible" or "natural" to us;[5] this is often done by means of persuasive metaphors. But the kind of "understanding" thus conveyed must clearly be separated from scientific understanding. In history as anywhere else in empirical science, the explanation of a phenomenon consists in subsuming it under general empirical laws; and the criterion of its soundness is not whether it appeals to our imagination, whether it is presented in terms of suggestive analogies or is otherwise made to appear plausible—all this may occur in pseudo-explanations as well—but exclusively whether it rests on empirically well confirmed assumptions concerning initial conditions and general laws.

7.1 So far, we have discussed the importance of general laws for explanation and prediction, and for so-called understanding in history. Let us now survey more briefly some other procedures in historical research which involve the assumption of universal hypotheses.

Closely related to explanation and understanding is the so-called *interpretation of historical phenomena* in terms of some particular approach or theory. The interpretations which are actually offered in history consist either in subsuming the phenomena in question under a scientific explanation or explanation sketch; or

---

5. For a criticism of this kind of plausibility, cf. Zilsel, *l.c.*, pp. 577-78, and sections 7 and 8 in the same author's "Problems of Empiricism," in *International Encyclopedia of Unified Science*, Vol. II, 8 (Chicago: University of Chicago Press, 1941).

in an attempt to subsume them under some general idea which is not amenable to any empirical test. In the former case, interpretation clearly is explanation by means of universal hypotheses; in the latter, it amounts to a pseudo-explanation which may have emotive appeal and evoke vivid pictorial associations, but which does not further our theoretical understanding of the phenomena under consideration.

7.2 Analogous remarks apply to the procedure of ascertaining the *"meaning"* of given historical events; its scientific import consists in determining what other events are relevantly connected with the event in question, be it as "causes," or as "effects"; and the statement of the relevant connections assumes, again, the form of explanations or explanation sketches which involve universal hypotheses; this will be seen more clearly in the next subsection.

7.3 In the historical explanation of some social institutions great emphasis is laid upon an analysis of the *development* of the institution up to the stage under consideration. Critics of this approach have objected that a mere description of this kind is not a genuine explanation. This argument may be given a slightly different form in terms of the preceding reflections: An account of the development of an institution is obviously not simply a description of *all* the events which temporally preceded it; only those events are meant to be included which are *"relevant"* to the formation of that institution. And whether an event is relevant to that development is not a matter of evaluative opinion, but an objective question depending upon what is sometimes called a causal analysis of the rise of that institution.[6] Now, the causal analysis of an event establishes an explanation for it, and since this requires reference to general hypotheses, so do assumptions about relevance, and, consequently, so does the adequate analysis of the historical development of an institution.

7.4 Similarly, the use of the notions of *determination* and of *dependence* in the empirical sciences, including history, involves reference to general laws.[7] Thus,

---

6. See the detailed and clear exposition of this point in M. Mandelbaum's book, chapters 6–8.

7. According to Mandelbaum, history, in contradistinction to the physical sciences, consists "not in the formulation of laws of which the particular case is an instance, but in the description of the events in their actual determining relationships to each other; in seeing events as the products and producers of change" (*l.c.*, pp. 13-14). This is, in effect, a conception whose untenability has been pointed out already by Hume, namely, that a careful examination of two specific events alone, without any reference to similar cases and to general regularities, can reveal that one of the events produces or determines the other. This thesis does not only run counter to the scientific meaning of the concept of determination which clearly rests on that of general law, but it even fails to provide any objective criteria which would be indicative of the intended relationship of determination or production. Thus, to speak of empirical determination independently of any reference to general laws is to use a metaphor without cognitive content.

e.g., we may say that the pressure of a gas depends upon its temperature and volume, or that temperature and volume determine the pressure, in virtue of Boyle's law. But unless the underlying laws are stated explicitly, the assertion of a relation of dependence or of determination between certain magnitudes or characteristics amounts at best to claiming that they are connected by some unspecified empirical law; and that is a very meager assertion indeed: If, for example, we know only that there is some empirical law connecting two metrical magnitudes (such as length and temperature of a metal bar), we can not even be sure that a change of one of the two will be accompanied by a change of the other (for the law may connect the same value of the "dependent" or "determined" magnitude with different values of the other), but only that with any specific value of one of the variables, there will always be associated one and the same value of the other; and this is obviously much less than most authors mean to assert when they speak of determination or dependence in historical analysis.

Therefore, the sweeping assertion that economic (or geographic, or any other kind of) conditions "determine" the development and change of all other aspects of human society, has explanatory value only in so far as it can be substantiated by explicit laws which state just what kind of change in human culture will regularly follow upon specific changes in the economic (geographic, etc.) conditions. Only the establishment of specific laws can fill the general thesis with scientific content, make it amenable to empirical tests, and confer upon it an explanatory function. The elaboration of such laws with as much precision as possible seems clearly to be the direction in which progress in scientific explanation and understanding has to be sought.

8. The considerations developed in this paper are entirely neutral with respect to the problem of "*specifically historical laws*": they do not presuppose a particular way of distinguishing historical from sociological and other laws, nor do they imply or deny the assumption that empirical laws can be found which are historical in some specific sense, and which are well confirmed by empirical evidence.

But it may be worth mentioning here that those universal hypotheses to which historians explicitly or tacitly refer in offering explanations, predictions, interpretations, judgments of relevance, etc., are taken from *various* fields of scientific research, in so far as they are not pre-scientific generalizations of everyday experiences. Many of the universal hypotheses underlying historical explanation, for instance, would commonly be classified as psychological, economical, sociological, and partly perhaps as historical laws; in addition, historical research has frequently to resort to general laws established in physics, chemistry, and biology. Thus, e.g., the explanation of the defeat of an army by reference to lack of food, adverse weather conditions, disease, and the like, is based on a—

usually tacit—assumption of such laws. The use of tree rings in dating events in history rests on the application of certain biological regularities. Various methods of testing the authenticity of documents, paintings, coins, etc., make use of physical and chemical theories.

The last two examples illustrate another point which is relevant in this context: Even if a historian should propose to restrict his research to a "pure description" of the past, without any attempt at offering explanations or statements about relevance and determination, he would continually have to make use of general laws. For the object of his studies would be the past—forever inaccessible to his direct examination. He would have to establish his knowledge by indirect methods: by the use of universal hypotheses which connect his present data with those past events. This fact has been obscured partly because some of the regularities involved are so familiar that they are not considered worth mentioning at all; and partly because of the habit of relegating the various hypotheses and theories which are used to ascertain knowledge about past events, to the "auxiliary sciences" of history. Quite probably, some of the historians who tend to minimize, if not to deny, the importance of general laws for history, are prompted by the feeling that only "genuinely historical laws" would be of interest for history. But once it is realized that the discovery of historical laws (in some specified sense of this very vague notion) would not make history methodologically autonomous and independent of the other branches of scientific research, it would seem that the problem of the existence of historical laws ought to lose some of its importance.

The remarks made in this section are but special illustrations of two broader principles of the theory of science: first, the separation of "pure description" and "hypothetical generalization and theory-construction" in empirical science is unwarranted; in the building of scientific knowledge the two are inseparably linked. And, second, it is similarly unwarranted and futile to attempt the demarcation of sharp boundary lines between the different fields of scientific research, and an autonomous development of each of the fields. The necessity, in historical inquiry, to make extensive use of universal hypotheses of which at least the overwhelming majority come from fields of research traditionally distinguished from history is just one of the aspects of what may be called the methodological unity of empirical science.

10. STUDIES IN THE

LOGIC OF EXPLANATION[1]

1. INTRODUCTION

TO EXPLAIN the phenomena in the world of our experience, to answer the question "why?" rather than only the question "what?" is one of the foremost objectives of empirical science. While there is rather general agreement on this point there exists considerable difference of opinion as to the function and the essential characteristics of scientific explanation. The present essay is an attempt to shed some light on these issues by means of an elementary survey of the basic pattern of scientific explanation and a subsequent more rigorous analysis of the concept of law and the logical structure of explanatory arguments.

1. This essay grew out of discussions with Dr. Paul Oppenheim; it was published in co-authorship with him and is here reprinted with his permission. Our individual contributions cannot be separated in detail; the present author is responsible, however, for the substance of Part IV and for the final formulation of the entire text.

Some of the ideas set forth in Part II originated with our common friend, Dr. Kurt Grelling, who suggested them to us in a discussion carried on by correspondence. Grelling and his wife subsequently became victims of the Nazi terror during the Second World War; by including in this essay at least some of Grelling's contributions, which are explicitly identified, we hope to realize his wish that his ideas on this subject might not entirely fall into oblivion.

Paul Oppenheim and I are much indebted to Professors Rudolf Carnap, Herbert Feigl, Nelson Goodman, and W. V. Quine for stimulating discussions and constructive criticism.

This article was published in *Philosophy of Science*, vol. 15, pp. 135-75. Copyright © 1948. The Williams and Wilkins Co., Baltimore 2, Md., U.S.A. It is reprinted, with some changes, by kind permission of the publisher.

The elementary survey is presented in Part I; Part II contains an analysis of the concept of emergence; Part III seeks to exhibit and to clarify in a more rigorous manner some of the peculiar and perplexing logical problems to which the familiar elementary analysis of explanation gives rise. Part IV, finally, deals with the idea of explanatory power of a theory; an explicit definition and a formal theory of this concept are developed for the case of a scientific language of simple logical structure.

PART I. ELEMENTARY SURVEY OF SCIENTIFIC EXPLANATION

2. SOME ILLUSTRATIONS. A mercury thermometer is rapidly immersed in hot water; there occurs a temporary drop of the mercury column, which is then followed by a swift rise. How is this phenomenon to be explained? The increase in temperature affects at first only the glass tube of the thermometer; it expands and thus provides a larger space for the mercury inside, whose surface therefore drops. As soon as by heat conduction the rise in temperature reaches the mercury, however, the latter expands, and as its coefficient of expansion is considerably larger than that of glass, a rise of the mercury level results. – This account consists of statements of two kinds. Those of the first kind indicate certain conditions which are realized prior to, or at the same time as, the phenomenon to be explained; we shall refer to them briefly as antecedent conditions. In our illustration, the antecedent conditions include, among others, the fact that the thermometer consists of a glass tube which is partly filled with mercury, and that it is immersed into hot water. The statements of the second kind express certain general laws; in our case, these include the laws of the thermic expansion of mercury and of glass, and a statement about the small thermic conductivity of glass. The two sets of statements, if adequately and completely formulated, explain the phenomenon under consideration: they entail the consequence that the mercury will first drop, then rise. Thus, the event under discussion is explained by subsuming it under general laws, i.e., by showing that it occurred in accordance with those laws, in virtue of the realization of certain specified antecedent conditions.

Consider another illustration. To an observer in a rowboat, that part of an oar which is under water appears to be bent upwards. The phenomenon is explained by means of general laws—mainly the law of refraction and the law that water is an optically denser medium than air—and by reference to certain antecedent conditions—expecially the facts that part of the oar is in the water, part in the air, and that the oar is practically a straight piece of wood. Thus, here again, the question "*Why* does the phenomenon occur?" is construed as meaning "according to what general laws, and by virtue of what antecedent conditions does the phenomenon occur?"

So far, we have considered only the explanation of particular events occurring at a certain time and place. But the question "Why?" may be raised also in regard to general laws. Thus, in our last illustration, the question might be asked: Why does the propagation of light conform to the law of refraction? Classical physics answers in terms of the undulatory theory of light, i.e. by stating that the propagation of light is a wave phenomenon of a certain general type, and that all wave phenomena of that type satisfy the law of refraction. Thus, the explanation of a general regularity consists in subsuming it under another, more comprehensive regularity, under a more general law. Similarly, the validity of Galileo's law for the free fall of bodies near the earth's surface can be explained by deducing it from a more comprehensive set of laws, namely Newton's laws of motion and his law of gravitation, together with some statements about particular facts, namely, about the mass and the radius of the earth.

3. THE BASIC PATTERN OF SCIENTIFIC EXPLANATION. From the preceding sample cases let us now abstract some general characteristics of scientific explanation. We divide an explanation into two major constituents, the *explanandum* and the *explanans*[2]. By the explanandum, we understand the sentence describing the phenomenon to be explained (not that phenomenon itself); by the explanans, the class of those sentences which are adduced to account for the phenomenon. As was noted before, the explanans falls into two subclasses; one of these contains certain sentences $C_1, C_2, \ldots, C_k$ which state specific antecedent conditions; the other is a set of sentences $L_1, L_2, \ldots, L_r$ which represent general laws.

If a proposed explanation is to be sound, its constituents have to satisfy certain conditions of adequacy, which may be divided into logical and empirical conditions. For the following discussion, it will be sufficient to formulate these requirements in a slightly vague manner; in Part III, a more precise restatement of these criteria will be presented.

I. *Logical conditions of adequacy*

(R1) The explanandum must be a logical consequence of the explanans; in other words, the explanandum must be logically deducible from the information contained in the explanans; for otherwise, the explanans would not constitute adequate grounds for the explanandum.

2. These two expressions, derived from the Latin *explanare*, were adopted in preference to the perhaps more customary terms "explicandum" and "explicans" in order to reserve the latter for use in the context of explication of meaning, or analysis. On explication in this sense, cf. Carnap (1945a), p. 513.

(R2)   The explanans must contain general laws, and these must actually be required for the derivation of the explanandum. We shall not make it a necessary condition for a sound explanation, however, that the explanans must contain at least one statement which is not a law; for, to mention just one reason, we would surely want to consider as an explanation the derivation of the general regularities governing the motion of double stars from the laws of celestial mechanics, even though all the statements in the explanans are general laws.

(R3)   The explanans must have empirical content; i.e., it must be capable, at least in principle, of test by experiment or observation. This condition is implicit in (R1); for since the explanandum is assumed to describe some empirical phenomenon, it follows from (R1) that the explanans entails at least one consequence of empirical character, and this fact confers upon it testability and empirical content. But the point deserves special mention because, as will be seen in §4, certain arguments which have been offered as explanations in the natural and in the social sciences violate this requirement.

II. *Empirical condition of adequacy*

(R4)   The sentences constituting the explanans must be true.
       That in a sound explanation, the statements constituting the explanans have to satisfy some condition of factual correctness is obvious. But it might seem more appropriate to stipulate that the explanans has to be highly confirmed by all the relevant evidence available rather than that it should be true. This stipulation, however, leads to awkward consequences. Suppose that a certain phenomenon was explained at an earlier stage of science, by means of an explanans which was well supported by the evidence then at hand, but which has been highly disconfirmed by more recent empirical findings. In such a case, we would have to say that originally the explanatory account was a correct explanation, but that it ceased to be one later, when unfavorable evidence was discovered. This does not appear to accord with sound common usage, which directs us to say that on the basis of the limited initial evidence, the truth of the explanans, and thus the soundness of the explanation, had been quite probable, but that the ampler evidence now available makes it highly probable that the explanans is not true, and hence that the account in question is

not—and never has been—a correct explanation.[3] (A similar point will be made and illustrated, with respect to the requirement of truth for laws, in the beginning of §6.)

Some of the characteristics of an explanation which have been indicated so far may be summarized in the following schema:

$$
\text{Logical deduction}
\left[
\begin{array}{ll}
\left\{
\begin{array}{ll}
C_1, C_2, \ldots, C_k & \text{Statements of antecedent} \\
 & \text{conditions} \\
L_1, L_2, \ldots, L_r & \text{General Laws}
\end{array}
\right\} & \text{Explanans} \\
\hline
\quad\longrightarrow\quad E & \left.
\begin{array}{l}
\text{Description of the} \\
\text{empirical phenomenon} \\
\text{to be explained}
\end{array}
\right\} \text{Explanandum}
\end{array}
\right.
$$

Let us note here that the same formal analysis, including the four necessary conditions, applies to scientific prediction as well as to explanation. The difference between the two is of a pragmatic character. If E is given, i.e. if we know that the phenomenon described by E has occurred, and a suitable set of statements $C_1, C_2, \ldots, C_k, L_1, L_2, \ldots, L_r$ is provided afterwards, we speak of an explanation of the phenomenon in question. If the latter statements are given and E is derived prior to the occurrence of the phenomenon it describes, we speak of a prediction. It may be said, therefore, that an explanation of a particular event is not fully adequate unless its explanans, if taken account of in time, could have served as a basis for predicting the event in question. Consequently, whatever will be said in this article concerning the logical characteristics of explanation or prediction will be applicable to either, even if only one of them should be mentioned.[4]

Many explanations which are customarily offered, especially in prescientific discourse, lack this potential predictive force, however. Thus, we may be told that a car turned over on the road "because" one of its tires blew out while the car was traveling at high speed. Clearly, on the basis of just this information, the accident could not have been predicted, for the explanans provides no explicit general laws by means of which the prediction might be effected, nor does it state adequately the antecedent conditions which would be needed for the

---

3. (Added in 1964.) Requirement (R4) characterizes what might be called a correct or *true explanation*. In an analysis of the logical structure of explanatory arguments, therefore, that requirement may be disregarded. This is, in fact, what is done in section 7, where the concept of *potential explanation* is introduced. On these and related distinctions, see also section 2.1 of the essay "Aspects of Scientific Explanation" in this volume.

4. (Added in 1964.) This claim is examined in much fuller detail, and reasserted with certain qualifications, in sections 2.4 and 3.5 of the essay "Aspects of Scientific Explanation" in this volume.

prediction. The same point may be illustrated by reference to W. S. Jevons's view that every explanation consists in pointing out a resemblance between facts, and that in some cases this process may require no reference to laws at all and "may involve nothing more than a single identity, as when we explain the appearance of shooting stars by showing that they are identical with portions of a comet."[5] But clearly, this identity does not provide an explanation of the phenomenon of shooting stars unless we presuppose the laws governing the development of heat and light as the effect of friction. The observation of similarities has explanatory value only if it involves at least tacit reference to general laws.

In some cases, incomplete explanatory arguments of the kind here illustrated suppress parts of the explanans simply as "obvious"; in other cases, they seem to involve the assumption that while the missing parts are not obvious, the incomplete explanans could at least, with appropriate effort, be so supplemented as to make a strict derivation of the explanandum possible. This assumption may be justifiable in some cases, as when we say that a lump of sugar disappeared "because" it was put into hot tea, but it surely is not satisfied in many other cases. Thus, when certain peculiarities in the work of an artist are explained as outgrowths of a specific type of neurosis, this observation may contain significant clues, but in general it does not afford a sufficient basis for a potential prediction of those peculiarities. In cases of this kind, an incomplete explanation may at best be considered as indicating some positive correlation between the antecedent conditions adduced and the type of phenomenon to be explained, and as pointing out a direction in which further research might be carried on in order to complete the explanatory account.

The type of explanation which has been considered here so far is often referred to as causal explanation.[6] If E describes a particular event, then the antecedent circumstances described in the sentences $C_1, C_2, \ldots, C_k$ may be said jointly to "cause" that event, in the sense that there are certain empirical regularities, expressed by the laws $L_1, L_2, \ldots, L_r$, which imply that whenever conditions of the kind indicated by $C_1, C_2, \ldots, C_k$ occur, an event of the kind described in E will take place. Statements such as $L_1, L_2, \ldots, L_r$, which assert general and unexceptional connections between specified characteristics of events, are customarily called causal, or deterministic, laws. They must be distinguished from the so-called statistical laws which assert that in the long run, an explicitly stated percentage of all cases satisfying a given set of conditions are accompanied by an event of a certain specified kind. Certain cases of scientific explanation

5. (1924) p. 533.
6. (Added in 1964.) Or rather, causal explanation is one variety of the deductive type of explanation here under discussion; see section 2.2 of "Aspects of Scientific Explanation."

involve "subsumption" of the explanandum under a set of laws of which at least some are statistical in character. Analysis of the peculiar logical structure of that type of subsumption involves difficult special problems. The present essay will be restricted to an examination of the deductive type of explanation, which has retained its significance in large segments of contemporary science, and even in some areas where a more adequate account calls for reference to statistical laws.[7]

4. EXPLANATION IN THE NONPHYSICAL SCIENCES. MOTIVATIONAL AND TELEO-LOGICAL APPROACHES. Our characterization of scientific explanation is so far based on a study of cases taken from the physical sciences. But the general principles thus obtained apply also outside this area.[8] Thus, various types of behavior in laboratory animals and in human subjects are explained in psychology by subsumption under laws or even general theories of learning or conditioning; and while frequently the regularities invoked cannot be stated with the same generality and precision as in physics or chemistry, it is clear at least that the general character of those explanations conforms to our earlier characterization.

Let us now consider an illustration involving sociological and economic factors. In the fall of 1946, there occurred at the cotton exchanges of the United States a price drop which was so severe that the exchanges in New York, New

---

7. The account given above of the general characteristics of explanation and prediction in science is by no means novel; it merely summarizes and states explicitly some fundamental points which have been recognized by many scientists and methodologists.

Thus, e.g., Mill says: "An individual fact is said to be explained, by pointing out its cause, that is, by stating the law or laws of causation, of which its production is an instance", and "a law or uniformity in nature is said to be explained, when another law or laws are pointed out, of which that law itself is but a case, and from which it could be deduced." (1858, Book III, Chapter XII, section 1). Similarly, Jevons, whose general characterization of explanation was critically discussed above, stresses that "the most important process of explanation consists in showing that an observed fact is one case of a general law or tendency." (1924, p. 533). Ducasse states the same point as follows: "Explanation essentially consists in the offering of a hypothesis of fact, standing to the fact to be explained as case of antecedent to case of consequent of some already known law of connection." (1925, pp. 150-51). A lucid analysis of the fundamental structure of explanation and prediction was given by Popper in (1935), section 12, and, in an improved version, in his work (1945), especially in Chapter 25 and in note 7 for that chapter.— For a recent characterization of explanation as subsumption under general theories, cf., for example, Hull's concise discussion in (1943a), chapter I. A clear elementary examination of certain aspects of explanation is given in Hospers (1946), and a concise survey of many of the essentials of scientific explanation which are considered in the first two parts of the present study may be found in Feigl (1945), pp. 284 ff.

8. On the subject of explanation in the social sciences, especially in history, cf. also the following publications, which may serve to supplement and amplify the brief discussion to be presented here: Hempel (1942); Popper (1945); White (1943); and the articles *Cause* and *Understanding* in Beard and Hook (1946).

Orleans, and Chicago had to suspend their activities temporarily. In an attempt to explain this occurrence, newspapers traced it back to a large-scale speculator in New Orleans who had feared his holdings were too large and had therefore begun to liquidate his stocks; smaller speculators had then followed his example in a panic and had thus touched off the critical decline. Without attempting to assess the merits of the argument, let us note that the explanation here suggested again involves statements about antecedent conditions and the assumption of general regularities. The former include the facts that the first speculator had large stocks of cotton, that there were smaller speculators with considerable holdings, that there existed the institution of the cotton exchanges with their specific mode of operation, etc. The general regularities referred to are—as often in semi-popular explanations—not explicitly mentioned; but there is obviously implied some form of the law of supply and demand to account for the drop in cotton prices in terms of the greatly increased supply under conditions of practically unchanged demand; besides, reliance is necessary on certain regularities in the behavior of individuals who are trying to preserve or improve their economic position. Such laws cannot be formulated at present with satisfactory precision and generality, and therefore, the suggested explanation is surely incomplete, but its intention is unmistakably to account for the phenomenon by integrating it into a general pattern of economic and socio-psychological regularities.

We turn to an explanatory argument taken from the field of linguistics.[9] In Northern France, there are in use a large variety of words synonymous with the English 'bee', whereas in Southern France, essentially only one such word is in existence. For this discrepancy, the explanation has been suggested that in the Latin epoch, the South of France used the word 'apicula', the North the word 'apis'. The latter, because of a process of phonologic decay in Northern France, became the monosyllabic word 'é'; and monosyllables tend to be eliminated, especially if they contain few consonantic elements, for they are apt to give rise to misunderstandings. Thus, to avoid confusion, other words were selected. But 'apicula', which was reduced to 'abelho', remained clear enough and was retained, and finally it even entered into the standard language, in the form 'abeille'. While the explanation here described is incomplete in the sense characterized in the previous section, it clearly exhibits reference to specific antecedent conditions as well as to general laws.[10]

---

9. The illustration is taken from Bonfante (1946), section 3.

10. While in each of the last two illustrations, certain regularities are unquestionably relied upon in the explanatory argument, it is not possible to argue convincingly that the intended laws, which at present cannot all be stated explicitly, are of a causal rather than a statistical character. It is quite possible that most or all of the regularities which will be discovered

While illustrations of this kind tend to support the view that explanation in biology, psychology, and the social sciences has the same structure as in the physical sciences, the opinion is rather widely held that in many instances, the causal type of explanation is essentially inadequate in fields other than physics and chemistry, and especially in the study of purposive behavior. Let us examine briefly some of the reasons which have been adduced in support of this view.

One of the most familiar among them is the idea that events involving the activities of humans singly or in groups have a peculiar uniqueness and irrepeatability which makes them inaccessible to causal explanation because the latter, with its reliance upon uniformities, presupposes repeatability of the phenomena under consideration. This argument which, incidentally, has also been used in support of the contention that the experimental method is inapplicable in psychology and the social sciences, involves a misunderstanding of the logical character of causal explanation. Every individual event, in the physical sciences no less than in psychology or the social sciences, is unique in the sense that it, with all its peculiar characteristics, does not repeat itself. Nevertheless, individual events may conform to, and thus be explainable by means of, general laws of the causal type. For all that a causal law asserts is that any event of a specified kind, i.e. any event having certain specified characteristics, is accompanied by another event which in turn has certain specified characteristics; for example, that in any event involving friction, heat is developed. And all that is needed for the testability and applicability of such laws is the recurrence of events with the antecedent characteristics, i.e. the repetition of those characteristics, but not of their individual instances. Thus, the argument is inconclusive. It gives occasion, however, to emphasize an important point concerning our earlier analysis: When we spoke of the explanation of a single event, the term "event" referred to the occurrence of some more or less complex characteristic in a specific spatio-temporal location or in a certain individual object, and not to *all* the characteristics of that object, or to all that goes on in that space-time region.

A second argument that should be mentioned here[11] contends that the establishment of scientific generalizations—and thus of explanatory principles—for

---

11. Cf., for example, F. H. Knight's presentation of this argument in (1924), pp. 251-52.

---

as sociology develops will be of a statistical type. Cf., on this point, the suggestive observations in Zilsel (1941), section 8, and (1941a). This issue does not affect, however, the main point we wish to make here, namely that in the social no less than in the physical sciences, subsumption under general regularities is indispensable for the explanation and the theoretical understanding of any phenomenon.

human behavior is impossible because the reactions of an individual in a given situation depend not only upon that situation, but also upon the previous history of the individual. But surely, there is no *a priori* reason why generalizations should not be attainable which take into account this dependence of behavior on the past history of the agent. That indeed the given argument "proves" too much, and is therefore a *non sequitur*, is made evident by the existence of certain physical phenomena, such as magnetic hysteresis and elastic fatigue, in which the magnitude of a specific physical effect depends upon the past history of the system involved, and for which nevertheless certain general regularities have been established.

A third argument insists that the explanation of any phenomenon involving purposive behavior calls for reference to motivations and thus for teleological rather than causal analysis. For example, a fuller statement of the suggested explanation for the break in the cotton prices would have to indicate the large-scale speculator's motivations as one of the factors determining the event in question. Thus, we have to refer to goals sought; and this, so the argument runs, introduces a type of explanation alien to the physical sciences. Unquestionably, many of the—frequently incomplete—explanations which are offered for human actions involve reference to goals and motives; but does this make them essentially different from the causal explanations of physics and chemistry? One difference which suggests itself lies in the circumstance that in motivated behavior, the future appears to affect the present in a manner which is not found in the causal explanations of the physical sciences. But clearly, when the action of a person is motivated, say, by the desire to reach a certain objective, then it is not the as yet unrealized future event of attaining that goal which can be said to determine his present behavior, for indeed the goal may never be actually reached; rather—to put it in crude terms—it is (a) his desire, present before the action, to attain that particular objective, and (b) his belief, likewise present before the action, that such and such a course of action is most likely to have the desired effect. The determining motives and beliefs, therefore, have to be classified among the antecedent conditions of a motivational explanation, and there is no formal difference on this account between motivational and causal explanation.

Neither does the fact that motives are not accessible to direct observation by an outside observer constitute an essential difference between the two kinds of explanation; for the determining factors adduced in physical explanations also are very frequently inaccessible to direct observation. This is the case, for instance, when opposite electric charges are adduced in explanation of the mutual attraction of two metal spheres. The presence of those charges, while eluding direct observation, can be ascertained by various kinds of indirect test, and that is sufficient to guarantee the empirical character of the explanatory statement. Similarly, the presence of certain motivations may be ascertainable only by indirect methods, which may include reference to linguistic utterances of the subject in question, slips of pen or tongue, etc.; but as long as these methods are "operationally determined" with reasonable clarity and precision, there is no essential difference in this respect between motivational explanation and causal explanation in physics.

A potential danger of explanation by motives lies in the fact that the method lends itself to the facile construction of *ex post facto* accounts without predictive force. An action is often explained by attributing it to motives conjectured only after the action has taken place. While this procedure is not in itself objectionable, its soundness, requires that (1) the motivational assumptions in question be capable of test, and (2) that suitable general laws be available to lend explanatory power to the assumed motives. Disregard of these requirements frequently deprives alleged motivational explanations of their cognitive significance.

The explanation of an action in terms of the agent's motives is sometimes considered as a special kind of teleological explanation. As was pointed out above, motivational explanation, if adequately formulated, conforms to the conditions for causal explanation, so that the term "teleological" is a misnomer if it is meant to imply either a non-causal character of the explanation or a peculiar determination of the present by the future. If this is borne in mind, however, the term "teleological" may be viewed, in this context, as referring to causal explanations in which some of the antecedent conditions are motives of the agent whose actions are to be explained.[12]

Teleological explanations of this kind have to be distinguished from a much more sweeping type, which has been claimed by certain schools of thought to be indispensable especially in biology. It consists in explaining characteristics of an organism by reference to certain ends or purposes which the characteristics are said to serve. In contradistinction to the cases examined before, the ends are not assumed here to be consciously or subconsciously pursued by the organism in question. Thus, for the phenomenon of mimicry, the explanation is sometimes offered that it serves the purpose of protecting the animals endowed with it from detection by its pursuers and thus tends to preserve the species. Before teleological hypotheses of this kind can be appraised as to their

---

12. For a detailed logical analysis of the concept of motivation in psychological theory, see Koch (1941). A stimulating discussion of teleological behavior from the standpoint of contemporary physics and biology is contained in the article (1943) by Rosenblueth, Wiener, and Bigelow. The logic of explanation by motivating reasons is examined more fully in section 10 of the essay "Aspects of Scientific Explanation" in the present volume.

potential explanatory power, their meaning has to be clarified. If they are intended somehow to express the idea that the purposes they refer to are inherent in the design of the universe, then clearly they are not capable of empirical test and thus violate the requirement (R3) stated in §3. In certain cases, however, assertions about the purposes of biological characteristics may be translatable into statements in non-teleological terminology which assert that those characteristics function in a specific manner which is essential to keeping the organism alive or to preserving the species.[13] An attempt to state precisely what is meant by this latter assertion—or by the similar one that without those characteristics, and other things being equal, the organism or the species would not survive—encounters considerable difficulties. But these need not be discussed here. For even if we assume that biological statements in teleological form can be adequately translated into descriptive statements about the life-preserving function of certain biological characteristics, it is clear that (1) the use of the concept of purpose is not essential in these contexts, since the term "purpose" can be completely eliminated from the statements in question, and (2) teleological assumptions, while now endowed with empirical content, cannot serve as explanatory principles in the customary contexts. Thus, e.g., the fact that a given species of butterfly displays a particular kind of coloring cannot be inferred from—and therefore cannot be explained by means of—the statement that this type of coloring has the effect of protecting the butterflies from detection by pursuing birds, nor can the presence of red corpuscles in the human blood be inferred from the statement that those corpuscles have a specific function in assimilating oxygen and that this function is essential for the maintenance of life.

One of the reasons for the perseverance of teleological considerations in biology probably lies in the fruitfulness of the teleological approach as a heuristic device: Biological research which was psychologically motivated by a teleological orientation, by an interest in purposes in nature, has frequently led to important results which can be stated in nonteleological terminology and which increase our knowledge of the causal connections between biological phenomena.

Another aspect that lends appeal to teleological considerations is their anthropomorphic character. A teleological explanation tends to make us feel that we really "understand" the phenomenon in question, because it is accounted for in terms of purposes, with which we are familiar from our own experience of purposive behavior. But it is important to distinguish here understanding

---

13. An analysis of teleological statements in biology along these lines may be found in Woodger (1929), especially pp. 432 ff; essentially the same interpretation is advocated by Kaufmann in (1944), Chapter 8.

in the psychological sense of a feeling of empathic familiarity from understanding in the theoretical, or cognitive, sense of exhibiting the phenomenon to be explained as a special case of some general regularity. The frequent insistence that explanation means the reduction of something unfamiliar to ideas or experiences already familiar to us is indeed misleading. For while some scientific explanations do have this psychological effect, it is by no means universal: The free fall of a physical body may well be said to be a more familiar phenomenon than the law of gravitation, by means of which it can be explained; and surely the basic ideas of the theory of relativity will appear to many to be far less familiar than the phenomena for which the theory accounts.

"Familiarity" of the explanans is not only not necessary for a sound explanation, as has just been noted; it is not sufficient either. This is shown by the many cases in which a proposed explanans sounds suggestively familiar, but upon closer inspection proves to be a mere metaphor, or to lack testability, or to include no general laws and therefore to lack explanatory power. A case in point is the neovitalistic attempt to explain biological phenomena by reference to an entelechy or vital force. The crucial point here is not—as is sometimes said—that entelechies cannot be seen or otherwise directly observed; for that is true also of gravitational fields, and yet, reference to such fields is essential in the explanation of various physical phenomena. The decisive difference between the two cases is that the physical explanation provides (1) methods of testing, albeit indirectly, assertions about gravitational fields, and (2) general laws concerning the strength of gravitational fields, and the behavior of objects moving in them. Explanations by entelechies satisfy the analogue of neither of these two conditions. Failure to satisfy the first condition represents a violation of (R3); it renders all statements about entelechies inaccessible to empirical test and thus devoid of empirical meaning. Failure to comply with the second condition involves a violation of (R2). It deprives the concept of entelechy of all explanatory import; for explanatory power never resides in a concept, but always in the general·laws in which it functions. Therefore, notwithstanding the feeling of familiarity it may evoke, the neovitalistic account cannot provide theoretical understanding.

The preceding observations about familiarity and understanding can be applied, in a similar manner, to the view held by some scholars that the explanation, or the understanding, of human actions requires an empathic understanding of the personalities of the agents[14]. This understanding of another person in terms of one's own psychological functioning may prove a useful heuristic device in the search for general psychological principles which might provide

14. For a more detailed discussion of this view on the basis of the general principles outlined above, cf. Zilsel (1941), sections 7 and 8, and Hempel (1942), section 6.

a theoretical explanation; but the existence of empathy on the part of the scientist is neither a necessary nor a sufficient condition for the explanation, or the scientific understanding, of any human action. It is not necessary, for the behavior of psychotics or of people belonging to a culture very different from that of the scientist may sometimes be explainable and predictable in terms of general principles even though the scientist who establishes or applies those principles may not be able to understand his subjects empathically. And empathy is not sufficient to guarantee a sound explanation, for a strong feeling of empathy may exist even in cases where we completely misjudge a given personality. Moroever, as Zilsel has pointed out, empathy leads with ease to incompatible results; thus, when the population of a town has long been subjected to heavy bombing attacks, we can understand, in the empathic sense, that its morale should have broken down completely, but we can understand with the same ease also that it should have developed a defiant spirit of resistance. Arguments of this kind often appear quite convincing; but they are of an *ex post facto* character and lack cognitive significance unless they are supplemented by testable explanatory principles in the form of laws or theories.

Familiarity of the explanans, therefore, no matter whether it is achieved through the use of teleological terminology, through neovitalistic metaphors, or through other means, is no indication of the cognitive import and the predictive force of a proposed explanation. Besides, the extent to which an idea will be considered as familiar varies from person to person and from time to time, and a psychological factor of this kind certainly cannot serve as a standard in assessing the worth of a proposed explanation. The decisive requirement for every sound explanation remains that it subsume the explanandum under general laws.

PART II. ON THE IDEA OF EMERGENCE

5. LEVELS OF EXPLANATION. ANALYSIS OF EMERGENCE. As has been shown above, a phenomenon may be explainable by sets of laws of different degrees of generality. The changing positions of a planet, for example, may be explained by subsumption under Kepler's laws, or by derivation from the far more comprehensive general law of gravitation in combination with the laws of motion, or finally by deduction from the general theory of relativity, which explains—and slightly modifies—the preceding set of laws. Similarly, the expansion of a gas with rising temperature at constant pressure may be explained by means of the Gas Law or by the more comprehensive kinetic theory of heat. The latter explains the Gas Law, and thus indirectly the phenomenon just mentioned, by means of (1) certain assumptions concerning the micro-

behavior of gases (more specifically, the distributions of locations and speeds of the gas molecules) and (2) certain macro–micro principles, which connect such macro–characteristics of a gas as its temperature, pressure and volume with the micro–characteristics just mentioned.

In the sense of these illustrations, a distinction is frequently made between various *levels of explanation*.[15] Subsumption of a phenomenon under general laws directly connecting observable characteristics represents the first level; higher levels require the use of more or less abstract theoretical constructs which function in the context of some comprehensive theory. As the preceding illustrations show, the concept of higher-level explanation covers procedures of rather different character; one of the most important among them consists in explaining a class of phenomena by means of a theory concerning their micro-structure. The kinetic theory of heat, the atomic theory of matter, the electromagnetic as well as the quantum theory of light, and the gene theory of heredity are examples of this method. It is often felt that only the discovery of a micro-theory affords real scientific understanding of any type of pheno-menon, because only it gives us insight into the inner mechanism of the pheno-menon, so to speak. Consequently, classes of events for which no micro-theory was available have frequently been viewed as not actually understood; and concern with the theoretical status of phenomena which are unexplained in this sense may be considered as one of the roots of the doctrine of emergence.

Generally speaking, the concept of *emergence* has been used to characterize certain phemonena as "novel," and this not merely in the psychological sense of being unexpected,[16] but in the theoretical sense of being unexplainable, or unpredictable, on the basis of information concerning the spatial parts or other constituents of the systems in which the phenomena occur, and which in this context are often referred to as "wholes." Thus, e.g., such characteristics of water as its transparence and liquidity at room temperature and atmospheric pressure, or its ability to quench thirst have been considered as emergent on the ground that they could not possibly have been predicted from a knowledge of the properties of its chemical constituents, hydrogen and oxygen. The weight of the compound, on the contrary, has been said not to be emergent because it is a mere "resultant" of its components and could have been pre-dicted by simple addition even before the compound had been formed. The conceptions of explanation and prediction which underly this idea of emergence call for various critical observations, and for corresponding changes in the concept of emergence.

15. For a lucid brief exposition of this idea, see Feigl (1945), pp. 284–88.

16. Concerning the concept of novelty in its logical and psychological meanings, see also Stace (1939).

(1) First, the question whether a given characteristic of a "whole," w, is emergent or not cannot be significantly raised until it has been stated what is to be understood by the parts or constituents of w. The volume of a brick wall, for example, may be inferable by addition from the volumes of its parts if the latter are understood to be the component bricks, but it is not so inferable from the volumes of the molecular components of the wall. Before we can significantly ask whether a characteristic W of an object w is emergent, we shall therefore have to state the intended meaning of the term "part of." This can be done by defining a specific relation Pt and stipulating that those and only those objects which stand in Pt to w count as parts of constituents of w. 'Pt' might be defined as meaning "constituent brick of" (with respect to buildings), or "molecule contained in" (for any physical object), or "chemical element contained in" (with respect to chemical compounds, or with respect to any material object), or "cell of" (with respect to organisms), etc. The term "whole" will be used here without any of its various connotations, merely as referring to any object w to which others stand in the specified relation Pt. In order to emphasize the dependence of the concept of part upon the definition of the relation Pt in each case, we shall sometimes speak of Pt-parts, to refer to parts as determined by the particular relation Pt under consideration.

(2) We turn to a second point of criticism. If a characteristic of a whole is counted as emergent simply if its occurrence cannot be inferred from a knowledge of all the properties of its parts, then, as Grelling has pointed out, no whole can have any emergent characteristics. Thus, to illustrate by reference to our earlier example, the properties of hydrogen include that of forming, if suitably combined with oxygen, a compound which is liquid, transparent, etc. Hence the liquidity, transparence, etc. of water *can* be inferred from certain properties of its chemical constituents. If the concept of emergence is not to be vacuous, therefore, it will be necessary to specify in every case a class G of attributes and to call a characteristic W of an object w emergent relatively to G and Pt if the occurrence of W in w cannot be inferred from a complete characterization of all the Pt-parts with respect to the attributes contained in G, i.e. from a statement which indicates, for every attribute in G, to which of the parts of w it applies. Evidently, the occurrence of a characteristic may be emergent with respect to one class of attributes and not emergent with respect to another. The classes of attributes which the emergentists have in mind, and which are usually not explicitly indicated, will have to be construed as nontrivial, i.e. as not logically entailing the property of each constituent of forming, together with the other constituents, a whole with the characteristics under investigation. Some fairly simple cases of emergence in the sense so far specified arise when the class G is restricted to certain simple properties of the parts, to the exclusion of spatial

or other relations among them. Thus, the electromotive force of a system of several electric batteries cannot be inferred from the electromotive forces of its constituents alone without a description, in terms of relational concepts, of the way in which the batteries are connected with each other.[17]

(3) Finally, the predictability of a given characteristic of an object on the basis of specified information concerning its parts will obviously depend on what general laws or theories are available.[18] Thus, the flow of an electric current in a wire connecting a piece of copper and a piece of zinc which are partly immersed in sulfuric acid is unexplainable, on the basis of information concerning any nontrivial set of attributes of copper, zinc and sulphuric acid, and the particular structure of the system under consideration, unless the theory available contains certain general laws concerning the functioning of batteries, or even more comprehensive principles of physical chemistry. If the theory includes such laws, on the other hand, then the occurrence of the current is predictable. Another illustration, which at the same time provides a good example for the point made under (2) above, is afforded by the optical activity of certain substances. The optical activity of sarco–lactic acid, for example, i.e. the fact that in solution it rotates the plane of polarization of plane-polarized light, cannot be predicted on the basis of the chemical characteristics of its constituent elements; rather, certain facts about the relations of the atoms constituting a molecule of sarco-lactic acid have to be known. The essential point is that the molecule in question contains an asymmetric carbon atom, i.e. one that holds four different atoms or groups, and if this piece of relational information is provided, the optical activity of the solution can be predicted provided that furthermore the theory available for the purpose embodies

17. This observation connects the present discussion with a basic issue in Gestalt theory. Thus, e.g., the insistence that "a whole is more than the sum of its parts" may be construed as referring to characteristics of wholes whose prediction requires knowledge of certain structural relations among the parts. For a further examination of this point, see Grelling and Oppenheim (1937-38) and (1939).

18. Logical analyses of emergence which make reference to the theories available have been propounded by Grelling and recently by Henle (1942). In effect, Henle's definition characterizes a phenomenon as emergent if it cannot be predicted, by means of the theories accepted at the time, on the basis of the data available before its occurrence. In this interpretation of emergence, no reference is made to characteristics of parts or constituents. Henle's concept of predictability differs from the one implicit in our discussion (and made explicit in Part III of this article) in that it implies derivability from the "simplest" hypothesis which can be formed on the basis of the data and theories available at the time. A number of suggestive observations on the idea of emergence and on Henle's analysis of it are presented in Bergmann's article (1944). The idea that the concept of emergence, at least in some of its applications, is meant to refer to unpredictability by means of "simple" laws was advanced also by Grelling in the correspondence mentioned in note (1). Reliance on the notion of simplicity of hypotheses, however, involves considerable difficulties; in fact, no satisfactory definition of that concept is available at present.

the law that the presence of one asymmetric carbon atom in a molecule implies optical activity of the solution; if the theory does not include this micro-macro law, then the phenomenon is emergent with respect to that theory.

An argument is sometimes advanced to the effect that phenomena such as the flow of the current, or the optical activity, in our last examples, are absolutely emergent at least in the sense that they could not possibly have been predicted before they had been observed for the first time; in other words, that the laws requisite for their prediction could not have been arrived at on the basis of information available before their first occurrence.[19] This view is untenable, however. On the strength of data available at a given time, science often establishes generalizations by means of which it can forecast the occurrence of events the like of which have never before been encountered. Thus, generalizations based upon periodicities exhibited by the characteristics of chemical elements then known enabled Mendeleev in 1871 to predict the existence of a certain new element and to state correctly various properties of that element as well as of several of its compounds; the element in question, germanium, was not discovered until 1886. A more recent illustration of the same point is provided by the development of the atomic bomb and the prediction, based on theoretical principles established prior to the event, of its explosion under specified conditions, and of its devastating release of energy.

As Grelling has stressed, the observation that the predictability of the occurrence of any characteristic depends upon the theoretical knowledge available, applies even to those cases in which, in the language of some emergentists, the characteristic of the whole is a mere resultant of the corresponding characteristics of the parts and can be obtained from the latter by addition. Thus, even the weight of a water molecule cannot be derived from the weights of its atomic constituents without the aid of a law which expresses the former as some specific mathematical function of the latter. That this function should be the sum is by no means self-evident; it is an empirical generalization, and at that not a strictly correct one, as relativistic physics has shown.

19. C. D. Broad, who in chapter 2 of his book (1925) gives a clear account and critical discussion of the essentials of emergentism, emphasizes the importance of "laws" of composition in predicting the characteristics of a whole on the basis of those of its parts (*op. cit.,* pp. 61ff.); but he subscribes to the view characterized above and illustrates it specifically by the assertion that "if we want to know the chemical (and many of the physical) properties of a chemical compound, such as silver-chloride, it is absolutely necessary to study samples *of that particular compound.* . . . The essential point is that it would also be useless to study chemical compounds in general and to compare their properties with those of their elements in the hope of discovering a *general* law of composition by which the properties of *any* chemical compound could be foretold when the properties of its separate elements were known." (p. 64) That an achievement of precisely this sort has been possible on the basis of the periodic system of the elements is noted above.

Failure to realize that the question of the predictability of a phenomenon cannot be significantly raised unless the theories available for the prediction have been specified has encouraged the misconception that certain phenomena have a mysterious quality of absolute unexplainability, and that their emergent status has to be accepted with "natural piety," as C. L. Morgan put it. The observations presented in the preceding discussion strip the idea of emergence of these unfounded connotations: emergence of a characteristic is not an ontological trait inherent in some phenomena; rather it is indicative of the scope of our knowledge at a given time; thus it has no absolute, but a relative character; and what is emergent with respect to the theories available today may lose its emergent status tomorrow.

The preceding considerations suggest the following *redefinition of emergence:* The occurrence of a characteristic W in an object w is emergent relative to a theory T, a part relation Pt, and a class G of attributes if that occurrence cannot be deduced by means of T from a characterization of the Pt-parts of w with respect to all the attributes in G.

This formulation explicates the meaning of emergence with respect to *events* of a certain kind, namely the occurrence of some characteristic W in an object w. Frequently, emergence is attributed to *characteristics* rather than to events; this use of the concept of emergence may be interpreted as follows: A characteristic W is emergent relatively to T, Pt. and G if its occurrence in *any* object is emergent in the sense just indicated.

As far as its cognitive content is concerned, the emergentist assertion that the phenomena of life are emergent may now be construed, roughly, as an elliptic formulation of the following statement: Certain specifiable biological phenomena cannot be explained, by means of contemporary physico-chemical theories, on the basis of data concerning the physical and chemical characteristics of the atomic and molecular constituents of organisms. Similarly, the thesis of an emergent status of mind might be taken to assert that present-day physical, chemical, and biological theories do not suffice to explain all psychological phenomena on the basis of data concerning the physical, chemical, and biological characteristics of the cells or of the molecules or atoms constituting the organisms in question. But in this interpretation, the emergent character of biological and psychological phenomena becomes trivial; for the description of various biological phenomena requires terms which are not contained in the vocabulary of present-day physics and chemistry; hence we cannot expect that all specifically biological phenomena are explainable, i.e. deductively inferable, by means of present-day physico-chemical theories on the basis of initial conditions which themselves are described in exclusively physico-chemical terms. In order to obtain a less trivial interpretation of the assertion that the phenomena of life are emergent, we have therefore to include in the explanatory theory of those presumptive laws presently accepted which connect the physico-chemical with the biological "level", i.e., which contain, on the one hand, certain physical and chemical terms, including those required for the description of molecular structures, and on the other hand, certain concepts of biology. An analogous observation applies to the case of psychology. If the assertion that life and mind have an emergent status is interpreted in this sense, then its import can be summarized approximately by the statement that no explanation, in terms of micro-structure theories, is available at present for large classes of phenomena studied in biology and psychology.[20]

Assertions of this type, then, appear to represent the rational core of the doctrine of emergence. In its revised form, the idea of emergence no longer carries with it the connotation of absolute unpredictability—a notion which is objectionable not only because it involves and perpetuates certain logical misunderstandings, but also because, not unlike the ideas of neovitalism, it encourages an attitude of resignation which is stifling for scientific research. No doubt it is this characteristic, together with its theoretical sterility, which accounts for the rejection, by the majority of contemporary scientists, of the classical absolutistic doctrine of emergence.[21]

PART III. LOGICAL ANALYSIS OF LAW AND EXPLANATION

6. PROBLEMS OF THE CONCEPT OF GENERAL LAW. From our general survey of the characteristics of scientific explanation, we now turn to a closer examination of its logical structure. The explanation of a phenomenon, we noted, consists in its subsumption under laws or under a theory. But what is a law, what is a theory? While the meaning of these concepts seems intuitively clear, an attempt to construct adequate explicit definitions for them encounters considerable difficulties. In the present section, some basic problems of the concept of law will be described and analyzed; in the next section, we intend to propose, on the basis of the suggestions thus obtained, definitions of law and of explanation for a formalized model language of a simple logical structue.

20. The following passage from Tolman (1932) may serve to support this interpretation: ". . . 'behavior-acts,' though no doubt in complete one-to-one correspondence with the underlying molecular facts of physics and physiology, have, as 'molar' wholes, certain emergent properties of their own. . . . Further, these molar properties of behavior-acts cannot in the present state of our knowledge, i.e., prior to the working-out of many empirical correlations between behavior and its physiological correlates, be known even inferentially from a mere knowledge of the underlying, molecular, facts of physics and physiology" (*op. cit.*, pp. 7-8). In a similar manner, Hull uses the distinction between molar and molecular theories and points out that theories of the latter type are not at present available in psychology. Cf. (1943a), pp. 19ff.; (1943), p. 275.

21. This attitude of the scientist is voiced, for example, by Hull in (1943a), pp. 24-28.

The concept of law will be construed here so as to apply to true statements only. The apparently plausible alternative procedure of requiring high confirmation rather than truth of a law seems to be inadequate: It would lead to a relativized concept of law, which would be expressed by the phrase "sentence *S* is a law relative to the evidence *E*." This does not accord with the meaning customarily assigned to the concept of law in science and in methodological inquiry. Thus, for example, we would not say that Bode's general formula for the distance of the planets from the sun was a law relative to the astronomical evidence available in the 1770s, when Bode propounded it, and that it ceased to be a law after the discovery of Neptune and the determination of its distance from the sun; rather, we would say that the limited original evidence had given a high probability to the assumption that the formula was a law, whereas more recent additional information reduced that probability so much as to make it it practically certain that Bode's formula is not generally true, and hence not a law.[22]

Apart from being true, a law will have to satisfy a number of additional conditions. These can be studied independently of the factual requirement of truth, for they refer, as it were, to all logically possible laws, no matter whether factually true or false. Adopting a term proposed by Goodman[23], we will say that a sentence is *lawlike* if it has all the characteristics of a general law, with the possible exception of truth. Hence, every law is a lawlike sentence, but not conversely.

Our problem of analyzing the notion of law thus reduces to that of explicating the concept of lawlike sentence. We shall construe the class of lawlike sentences as including analytic general statements, such as 'A rose is a rose', as well as the lawlike sentences of empirical science, which have empirical content.[24] It will not be necessary to require that each lawlike sentence permissible in explanatory contexts be of the second kind; rather, our definition of explanation will be so constructed as to guarantee the factual character of the totality of the laws—though not of every single one of them—which function in an explanation of an empirical fact.

22. The requirement of truth for laws has the consequence that a given empirical statement *S* can never be definitely known to be a law; for the sentence affirming the truth of *S* is tantamount to *S* and is therefore capable only of acquiring a more or less high probability, or degree of confirmation, relative to the experimental evidence available at any given time. On this point, cf. Carnap (1946). For an excellent nontechnical exposition of the semantical concept of truth, which is here invoked, the reader is referred to Tarski (1944).

23. (1947), p. 125.

24. This procedure was suggested by Goodman's approach in (1947). Reichenbach, in a detailed examination of the concept of law, similarly construes his concept of nomological statement as including both analytic and synthetic sentences: cf. (1947). Chapter VIII.

What are the characteristics of lawlike sentences? First of all, lawlike sentences are statements of universal form, such as 'All robins' eggs are greenish-blue', 'All metals are conductors of electricity', 'At constant pressure, any gas expands with increasing temperature'. As these examples illustrate, a lawlike sentence usually is not only of universal, but also of conditional form; it makes an assertion to the effect that universally, if a certain set of conditions, C, is realized, then another specified set of conditions, E, is realized as well. The standard form for the symbolic expression of a lawlike sentence is therefore the universal conditional. However, since any conditional statement can be transformed into a non-conditional one, conditional form will not be considered as essential for a lawlike sentence, while universal character will be held indispensable.

But the requirement of universal form is not sufficient to characterize lawlike sentences. Suppose, for example, that a given basket, b, contains at a certain time t a number of red apples and nothing else.[25] Then the statement

(S_1)   Every apple in basket b at time t is red

is both true and of universal form. Yet the sentence does not qualify as a law; we would refuse, for example, to explain by subsumption under it the fact that a particular apple chosen at random from the basket is red. What distinguishes S_1 from a lawlike sentence? Two points suggest themselves, which will be considered in turn, namely, finite scope, and reference to a specified object.

First, the sentence S_1 makes in effect an assertion about a finite number of objects only, and this seems irreconcilable with the claim to universality which is commonly associated with the notion of law.[26] But are not Kepler's laws considered as lawlike although they refer to a finite set of planets only? And might we not even be willing to consider as lawlike a sentence such as the following?

(S_2)   All the sixteen ice cubes in the freezing tray of this refrigerator
                have a temperature of less than 10 degrees centigrade.

This point might well be granted; but there is an essential difference between S_1, on the one hand, and Kepler's laws, as well as S_2, on the other: The latter,

---

25. The difficulty illustrated by this example was stated concisely by Langford (1941), who referred to it as the problem of distinguishing between universals of fact and causal universals. For further discussion and illustration of this point, see also Chisholm (1946), especially pp. 301f. A systematic analysis of the problem was given by Goodman in (1947), especially part III. While not concerned with the specific point under discussion, the detailed examination of counterfactual conditionals and their relation to laws of nature, in Chapter VIII of Lewis (1946), contains important observations on several of the issues raised in the present section.

26. The view that laws should be construed as not being limited to a finite domain has been expressed, among others, by Popper (1935), section 13 and by Reichenbach (1947), p. 369.

while finite in scope, are known to be consequences of more comprehensive laws whose scope is not limited, while for S_1 this is not the case.

Adopting a procedure recently suggested by Reichenbach[27], we will therefore distinguish between fundamental and derivative laws. A statement will be called a derivative law if it is of universal character and follows from some fundamental laws. The concept of fundamental law requires further clarification; so far, we may say that fundamental laws, and similarly fundamental lawlike sentences, should satisfy a certain condition of nonlimitation of scope.

It would be excessive, however, to deny the status of fundamental lawlike sentence to all statements which, in effect, make an assertion about a finite class of objects only, for that would rule out also a sentence such as 'All robins' eggs are greenish-blue', since presumably the class of all robins' eggs—past, present, and future—is finite. But again, there is an essential difference between this sentence and, say, S_1. It requires empirical knowledge to establish the finiteness of the class of robins' eggs, whereas, when the sentence S_1 is construed in a manner which renders it intuitively unlawlike, the terms 'basket b' and 'apple' are understood so as to imply finiteness of the class of apples in the basket at time t. Thus, so to speak, the meaning of its constitutive terms alone—without additional factual information—entails that S_1 has a finite scope. Fundamental laws, then, will have to be construed so as to satisfy a condition of nonlimited scope; our formulation of that condition however, which refers to what is entailed by "the meaning" of certain expressions, is too vague and will have to be revised later. Let us note in passing that the stipulation here envisaged would bar from the class of fundamental lawlike sentences also such undesirable candidates as 'All uranic objects are spherical', where 'uranic' means the property of being the planet Uranus; indeed, while this sentence has universal form, it fails to satisfy the condition of nonlimited scope.

In our search for a general characterization of lawlike sentences, we now turn to a second clue which is provided by the sentence S_1. In addition to violating the condition of nonlimited scope, that sentence has the peculiarity of making reference to a particular object, the basket b; and this, too, seems to violate the universal character of a law.[28] The restriction which seems indicated here, should again be applied to fundamental lawlike sentences only; for a

27. (1947), p. 361. Our terminology as well as the definitions to be proposed later for the two types of law do not coincide with Reichenbach's, however.

28. In physics, the idea that a law should not refer to any particular object has found its expression in the maxim that the general laws of physics should contain no reference to specific space-time points, and that spatio-temporal coordinates should occur in them only in the form of differences or differentials.

true general statement about the free fall of physical bodies on the moon, while referring to a particular object, would still constitute a law, albeit a derivative one.

It seems reasonable to stipulate, therefore, that a fundamental lawlike sentence must be of universal form and must contain no essential—i.e., uneliminable—occurrences of designations for particular objects. But this is not sufficient; indeed, just at this point, a particularly serious difficulty presents itself. Consider the sentence

(S_3)   Everything that is either an apple in basket b at time t or a sample of ferric oxide is red.

If we use a special expression, say 'x is ferple', as synonymous with 'x is either an apple in b at t or a sample of ferric oxide', then the content of S_3 can be expressed in the form.

(S_4)   Everything that is ferple is red.

The statement thus obtained is of universal form and contains no designations of particular objects, and it also satisfies the condition of nonlimited scope; yet clearly, S_4 can qualify as a fundamental lawlike sentence no more than can S_3.

As long as 'ferple' is a defined term of our language, the difficulty can readily be met by stipulating that after elimination of defined terms, a fundamental lawlike sentence must not contain essential occurrences of designations for particular objects. But this way out is of no avail when 'ferple', or another term of its kind, is a primitive predicate of the language under consideration. This reflection indicates that certain restrictions have to be imposed upon those predicates—i.e., terms for properties or relations—which may occur in fundamental lawlike sentences.[29]

More specifically, the idea suggests itself of permitting a predicate in a fundamental lawlike sentence only if it is purely universal, or, as we shall say, purely qualitative, in character; in other words, if a statement of its meaning does not require reference to any one particular object or spatio-temporal location. Thus, the terms 'soft', 'green', 'warmer than', 'as long as', 'liquid', 'electrically charged', 'female', 'father of', are purely qualitative predicates,

---

29. The point illustrated by the sentences S_3 and S_4 above was made by Goodman, who has also emphasized the need to impose certain restrictions upon the predicates whose occurrence is to be permissible in lawlike sentences. These predicates are essentially the same as those which Goodman calls projectible. Goodman has suggested that the problems of establishing precise criteria for projectibility, of interpreting counterfactual conditionals, and of defining the concept of law are so intimately related as to be virtually aspects of a single problem. Cf. his articles (1946) and 1947). One suggestion for an analysis of projectibility has been made by Carnap in (1947). Goodman's note (1947a) contains critical observations on Carnap's proposals.

while 'taller than the Eiffel Tower', 'medieval', 'lunar', 'arctic', 'Ming' are not.[30]

Exclusion from fundamental lawlike sentences of predicates which are not purely qualitative would at the same time ensure satisfaction of the condition of nonlimited scope; for the meaning of a purely qualitative predicate does not require a finite extension; and indeed, all the sentences considered above which violate the condition of nonlimited scope make explicit or implicit reference to specific objects.

The stipulation just proposed suffers, however, from the vagueness of the concept of purely qualitative predicate. The question whether indication of the meaning of a given predicate in English does or does not require reference to some specific object does not always permit of an unequivocal answer since English as a natural language does not provide explicit definitions or other clear explications of meaning for its terms. It seems therefore reasonable to attempt definition of the concept of law not with respect to English or any other natural language, but rather with respect to a formalized language—let us call it a model language *L*—which is governed by a well-determined system of logical rules, and in which every term either is characterized as primitive or is introduced by an explicit definition in terms of the primitives.

This reference to a well-determined system is customary in logical research and is indeed quite natural in the context of any attempt to develop precise criteria for certain logical distinctions. But it does not by itself suffice to overcome the specific difficulty under discussion. For while it is now readily possible to characterize as not purely qualitative all those among the defined predicates in *L* whose definiens contains an essential occurrence of some individual name, our problem remains open for the primitives of the language, whose meanings are not determined by definitions within the language, but rather by semantical laws of interpretation. For we want to permit the interpretation of the primitives of *L* by means of such attributes as blue, hard, solid, warmer, but not by the properties of being a descendant of Napoleon, or an arctic animal, or a Greek statue; and the difficulty is precisely that of stating rigorous criteria

30. That laws, in addition to being of universal form, must contain only purely universal predicates was argued by Popper (1935, sections 14, 15). Our alternative expression 'purely qualitative predicate' was chosen in analogy to Carnap's term 'purely qualitative property' cf. (1947). The above characterization of purely universal predicates seems preferable to a simpler and perhaps more customary one, to the effect that a statement of the meaning of the predicate must require no reference to particular objects. That formulation might be too restrictive since it could be argued that stating the meaning of such purely qualitative terms as 'blue' or 'hot' requires illustrative reference to some particular object which has the quality in question. The essential point is that no one specific object has to be chosen; any one in the logically unlimited set of blue or of hot objects will do. In explicating the meaning of 'taller than the Eiffel Tower', 'being an apple in basket *b* at time *t*', 'medieval', etc., however, reference has to be made to one specific object or to some one in a limited set of objects.

for the distinction between the permissible and the nonpermissible interpretations. Thus the problem of finding an adequate definition for purely qualitative attributes now arises again; namely for the concepts of the meta-language in which the semantical interpretation of the primitives is formulated. We may postpone an encounter with the difficulty by presupposing formalization of the semantical meta-language, the meta-meta-language, and so forth, but somewhere, we will have to stop at a nonformalized meta-language; and for it, a characterization of purely qualitative predicates will be needed and will present much the same problems as nonformalized English, with which we began. The characterization of a purely qualitative predicate as one whose meaning can be made explicit without reference to any one particular object points to the intended meaning but does not explicate it precisely, and the problem of an adequate definition of purely qualitative predicates remains open.

There can be little doubt, however, that there exists a large number of predicates which would be rather generally recognized as purely qualitative in the sense here pointed out, and as permissible in the formulation of fundamental lawlike sentences; some examples have been given above, and the list could be readily enlarged. When we speak of purely qualitative predicates, we shall henceforth have in mind predicates of this kind.

In the following section, a model language L of a rather simple logical structure will be described, whose primitives will be assumed to be qualitative in the sense just indicated. For this language, the concepts of law and explanation will then be defined in a manner which takes into account the general observations set forth in the present section.

7. DEFINITION OF LAW AND EXPLANATION FOR A MODEL LANGUAGE. Concerning the syntax of our model language L, we make the following assumptions: L has the syntactical structure of the lower functional calculus without the identity sign. In addition to the signs of negation, alternation (disjunction), conjunction, and implication (conditional), and the symbols of universal and existential quantification with respect to individual variables, the vocabulary of L contains individual constants ('a', 'b', . . .), individual variables ('x', 'y', . . .), and predicates of any desired finite degree. The latter may include, in particular, predicates of degree 1 ('P', 'Q', . . .), which express properties of individuals, and predicates of degree 2 ('R', 'S', . . .), which express dyadic relations among individuals.

For simplicity, we assume that all predicates are primitive, i.e., undefined in L, or else that before the criteria subsequently to be developed are applied to a sentence, all defined predicates which it contains are eliminated in favor of primitives.

The syntactical rules for the formation of sentences and for logical inference in L are those of the lower functional calculus. No sentence may contain free variables, so that generality is always expressed by universal quantification.

For later reference, we now define, in purely syntactical terms, a number of auxiliary concepts. In the following definitions, S is always understood to be a sentence in L.

(7.1a) S is formally true (formally false) in L if S (the denial of S) can be proved in L, i.e. by means of the formal rules of logical inference for L. If two sentences are mutually derivable from each other in L, they will be called equivalent.

(7.1b) S is said to be a singular, or alternatively, a molecular sentence if S contains no variables. A singular sentence which contains no statement connectives is also called atomic. Illustrations: The sentences '$R(a, b) \supset [P(a) \cdot \sim Q(a)]$', '$\sim Q(a)$', '$R(a, b)$', '$P(a)$' are all singular, or molecular; the last two are atomic.

(7.1c) S is said to be a generalized sentence if it consists of one or more quantifiers followed by an expression which contains no quantifiers. S is said to be of universal form if it is a generalized sentence and all the quantifiers occurring in it are universal. S is called purely generalized (purely universal) if S is a generalized sentence (is of universal form) and contains no individual constants. S is said to be essentially universal if it is of universal form and not equivalent to a singular sentence. S is called essentially generalized if it is generalized and not equivalent to a singular sentence.

Illustrations: '$(x) [P(x) \supset Q(x)]$', '$(x)R(a, x)$', '$(x)[P(x) \lor P(a)]$',
      '$(x)[P(x) \lor \sim P(x)]$', '$(Ex)[P(x) \cdot \sim Q(x)]$', '$(Ex)(y)[R(a, x) \cdot S(a, y)]$',
are all generalized sentences; the first four are of universal form, the first and fourth are purely universal; the first and second are essentially universal, the third being equivalent to the singular sentence '$P(a)$', and the fourth to '$P(a) \lor \sim P(a)$'. All sentences except the third and fourth are essentially generalized.

Concerning the semantical interpretation of L, we lay down the following two stipulations:

(7.2a) The primitive predicates of L are all purely qualitative.

(7.2b) The universe of discourse of L, i.e., the domain of objects covered by the quantifiers, consists of all physical objects or of all spatio-temporal locations.

A linguistic framework of the kind here characterized is not sufficient for the formulation of scientific theories since it contains no functors and does not provide the means for dealing with real numbers. Besides, the question is open at present whether a constitution system can be constructed in which all of the concepts of empirical science are reduced, by chains of explicit definitions, to a basis of primitives of a purely qualitative character. Nevertheless, we consider it worthwhile to study the problems at hand for the simplified type of language just described because the analysis of law and explanation is far from trivial even for our model language L, and because that analysis sheds light on the logical character of the concepts under investigation also in their application to more complex contexts.

In accordance with the considerations developed in section 6, we now define:

(7.3a) S is a fundamental lawlike sentence in L if S is purely universal; S is a fundamental law in L if S is purely universal and true.

(7.3b) S is a derivative law in L if (1) S is essentially, but not purely, universal and (2) there exists a set of fundamental laws in L which has S as a consequence.

(7.3c) S is a law in L if it is a fundamental or a derivative law in L.

The fundamental laws as here defined obviously include, besides general statements of empirical character, all those statements of purely universal form which are true on purely logical grounds; i.e. those which are formally true in L, such as '$(x)[P(x) \lor \sim P(x)]$', and those whose truth derives exclusively from the interpretation given to its constituents, as is the case with

$$'(x)[P(x) \supset Q(x)]',$$

if 'P' is interpreted as meaning the property of being a father, and 'Q' that of being male. The derivative laws, on the other hand, include neither of these categories; indeed, no fundamental law is also a derivative one.[31]

As the primitives of L are purely qualitative, all the statements of universal form in L also satisfy the requirement of nonlimited scope, and thus it is readily seen that the concept of law as defined above satisfies all the conditions suggested in section 6.[32]

The explanation of a phenomenon may involve generalized sentences which are not of universal form. We shall use the term 'theory' to refer to such sentences, and we define this term by the following chain of definitions:

(7.4a) S is a fundamental theory if S is purely generalized and true.

(7.4b) S is a derivative theory in L if (1) S is essentially, but not purely, generalized and (2) there exists a set of fundamental theories in L which has S as a consequence.

(7.4c) S is a theory in L if it is a fundamental or a derivative theory in L.

By virtue of the above definitions, every law is also a theory, and every theory is true.

---

31. As defined above, fundamental laws include universal conditional statements with vacuous antecedents, such as "All mermaids are brunettes." This point does not appear to lead to undesirable consequences in the definition of explanation to be proposed later. For an illuminating analysis of universal conditionals with vacuous antecedents, see Chapter VIII in Reichenbach (1947).

32. (Added in 1964.) However, Nagel has shown that our definition of the concept of fundamental law is too restrictive; cf. the Postscript to the present essay.

With the help of the concepts thus defined, we will now reformulate more precisely our earlier characterization of scientific explanation with specific reference to our model language L. It will be convenient to state our criteria for a sound explanation in the form of a definition for the expression "the ordered couple of sentences, (T, C), constitutes an explanans for the sentence E." Our analysis will be restricted to the explanation of particular events, i.e., to the case where the explanandum, E, is a singular sentence.[33]

In analogy to the concept of lawlike sentence, which need not satisfy a requirement of truth, we will first introduce an auxiliary concept of potential explanans, which is not subject to a requirement of truth; the notion of explanans will then be defined with the help of this auxiliary concept.—The considerations presented in Part I suggest the following initial stipulations:

(7.5) An ordered couple of sentences, (T, C), constitutes a potential explanans for a singular sentence E only if

(1) T is essentially generalized and C is singular

(2) E is derivable in L from T and C jointly, but not from C alone.

(7.6) An ordered couple of sentences, (T, C), constitutes an explanans for a singular sentence E if and only if

(1) (T, C) is a potential explanans for E

(2) T is a theory and C is true.

(7.6) is an explicit definition of explanation in terms of the concept of potential explanation.[34] On the other hand, (7.5) is not suggested as a definition, but as a statement of necessary conditions of potential explanation. These conditions will presently be shown not to be sufficient, and additional requirements will be discussed by which (7.5) has to be supplemented in order to provide a definition of potential explanation.

---

33. This is not a matter of free choice: The precise rational reconstruction of explanation as applied to general regularities presents peculiar problems for which we can offer no solution at present. The core of the difficulty can be indicated briefly by reference to an example: Kepler's laws, K, may be conjoined with Boyle's law, B, to a stronger law $K \cdot B$; but derivation of K from the latter would not be considered as an explanation of the regularities stated in Kepler's laws; rather, it would be viewed as representing, in effect, a pointless "explanation" of Kepler's laws by themselves. The derivation of Kepler's laws from Newton's laws of motion and of gravitation, on the other hand, would be recognized as a genuine explanation in terms of more comprehensive regularities, or so-called higher-level laws. The problem therefore arises of setting up clear-cut criteria for the distinction of levels of explanation or for a comparison of generalized sentences as to their comprehensiveness. The establishment of adequate criteria for this purpose is as yet an open problem.

34. It is necessary to stipulate, in (7.6) (2), that T be a theory rather than merely that T be true; for as was shown in section 6, the generalized sentences occurring in an explanans have to constitute a theory, and not every essentially generalized sentence which is true is actually a theory, i.e., a consequence of a set of purely generalized true sentences.

Before we turn to this point, some remarks are called for concerning the formulation of (7.5). The analysis presented in Part I suggests that an explanans for a singular sentence consists of a class of generalized sentences and a class of singular ones. In (7.5), the elements of each of these classes separately are assumed to be conjoined to one sentence. This provision will simplify our formulations, and in the case of generalized sentences, it serves an additional purpose: A class of essentially generalized sentences may be equivalent to a singular sentence; thus, the class $\{‘P(a) \lor (x)Q(x)’, ‘P(a) \lor \sim (x)Q(x)’\}$ is equivalent with the sentence '$P(a)$'. Since scientific explanation makes essential use of generalized sentences, sets of laws of this kind have to be ruled out; this is achieved above by combining all the generalized sentences in the explanans into one conjunction, T, and stipulating that T has to be essentially generalized. Again, since scientific explanation makes essential use of generalized sentences E must not be a consequence of C alone: The law of gravitation, combined with the singular sentence 'Mary is blonde and blue-eyed' does not constitute an explanans for 'Mary is blonde'. The last stipulation in (7.5) introduces the requisite restriction and thus prohibits complete self-explanation of the explanandum, i.e., the derivation of E from some singular sentence which has E as a consequence. The same restriction also dispenses with the need for a special requirement to the effect that T has to have factual content if (T, C) is to be a potential explanans for an empirical sentence E. For if E is factual, then, since E is a consequence of T and C jointly, but not of C alone, T must be factual, too.

Our stipulations in (7.5) do not preclude, however, what might be termed partial self-explanation of the explanandum. Consider the sentences $T_1 = $ '$(x)[P(x) \supset Q(x)]$', $C_1 = $ '$R(a, b) \cdot P(a)$', $E_1 = $ '$Q(a) \cdot R(a, b)$'. They satisfy all the requirements laid down in (7.5), but it seems counterintuitive to say that (T_1, C_1) potentially explains E_1, because the occurrence of the component '$R(a, b)$' of C_1 in the sentence E_1 amounts to a partial explanation of the explanandum by itself. Is it not possible to rule out, by an additional stipulation, all those cases in which E shares part of its content with C, i.e. where C and E have a common consequence which is not formally true in L? This stipulation would be tantamount to the requirement that C and E have to be exhaustive alternatives in the sense that their disjunction is formally true, for the content which any two sentences have in common is expressed by their disjunction. The proposed restriction, however, would be very severe. For if E does not share even part of its content with C, then C is altogether unnecessary for the derivation of E from T and C, i.e., E can be inferred from T alone. Therefore, in every potential explanation in which the singular component of the explanans is not dispensable, the explanandum is partly explained by itself. Take, for example, the potential explanation of $E_2 = $ '$Q(a)$' by $T_2 = $ '$(x)[P(x) \supset Q(x)]$' and $C_2 = $ '$P(a)$', which satisfies (7.5), and which surely is intuitively unobjectionable. Its three components may be equivalently expressed by the following sentences:

$$T'_2 = \text{'}(x)[\sim P(x) \text{v} Q(x)]\text{'}; \; C'_2 = \text{'}[P(a) \text{v} Q(a)] \cdot [P(a) \text{v} \sim Q(a)]\text{'};$$
$$E'_2 = \text{'}[P(a) \text{v} Q(a)] \cdot [\sim P(a) \text{v} Q(a)].\text{'}$$

This reformulation shows that part of the content of the explanandum is contained in the content of the singular component of the explanans and is, in this sense, explained by itself.

Our analysis has reached a point here where the customary intuitive idea of explanation becomes too vague to provide further guidance for rational reconstruction. Indeed, the last illustration strongly suggests that there may be no sharp boundary line which separates the intuitively permissible from the counterintuitive types of partial self-explanation; for even the potential explanation just considered, which is acceptable in its original formulation, might be judged unacceptable on intuitive grounds when transformed into the equivalent version given above.

The point illustrated by the last example is stated more explicitly in the following theorem, which we formulate here without proof.

(7.7) *Theorem.* Let (T, C) be a potential explanans for the singular sentence E. Then there exist three singular sentences, E_1, E_2, and C_1 in L such that E is equivalent to the conjunction $E_1 \cdot E_2$, C is equivalent to the conjunction $C_1 \cdot E_1$, and E_2 can be derived in L from T alone.[35]

In more intuitive terms, this means that if we represent the deductive structure of the given potential explanation by the schema $\{T, C\} \rightarrow E$, then this schema can be restated in the form $\{T, C_1 \cdot E_1\} \rightarrow E_1 \cdot E_2$, where E_2 follows from T alone, so that C_1 is entirely unnecessary as a premise; hence, the deductive schema under consideration can be reduced to $\{T, E_1\} \rightarrow E_1 \cdot E_2$, which can be decomposed into the two deductive schemata $\{T\} \rightarrow E_2$ and $\{E_1\} \rightarrow E_1$. The former of these might be called a purely theoretical explanation of E_2 by T, the latter a complete self-explanation of E_1. Theorem (7.7) shows, in other words, that every explanation whose explanandum is a singular sentence can be decomposed into a purely theoretical explanation and a complete self-explanation; and any explanation of this kind in which the singular constituent of the

---

35. In the formulation of the above theorem and subsequently, statement connective symbols are used not only as signs *in* L, but also autonymously in speaking *about* compound expressions of L. Thus, when 'S' and 'T' are names or name variables for sentences in L, their conjunction and disjunction will be designated by '$S \cdot T$' and '$S \text{v} T$', respectively; the conditional which has S as antecedent and T as consequent will be designated by '$S \supset T$', and the negation of S by '$\sim S$'. (Incidentally, this convention has already been used, tacitly, at one place in note 33.)

explanans is not completely unnecessary involves a partial self-explanation of the explanandum.[36]

To prohibit partial self-explanation altogether would therefore mean limiting explanation to purely theoretical explanation. This measure seems too severely restrictive. On the other hand, an attempt to delimit, by some special rule, the permissible degree of self-explanation does not appear to be warranted because, as we saw, customary usage provides no guidance for such a delimitation, and because no systematic advantage seems to be gained by drawing some arbitrary dividing line. For these reasons, we refrain from introducing stipulations to prohibit partial self-explanation.

The conditions laid down in (7.5) fail to preclude yet another unacceptable type of explanatory argument, which is closely related to complete self-explanation, and which will have to be ruled out by an additional stipulation. The point is, briefly, that if we were to accept (7.5) as a definition, rather than merely as a statement of necessary conditions, for potential explanation, then, as a consequence of (7.6), any given particular fact could be explained by means of any true lawlike sentence whatsoever. More explicitly, if E is a true sentence— say, 'Mt. Everest is snowcapped', and T is a law—say, 'All metals are good conductors of heat', then there always exists a true singular sentence C such that E is derivable from T and C, but not from C alone; in other words, such that (7.5) is satisfied. Indeed, let T_s be some arbitrarily chosen particular instance of T, such as 'If the Eiffel Tower is metal, it is a good conductor of heat'. Now since E is true, so is the conditional $T_s \supset E$, and if the latter is chosen as the sentence C, then T, C, E satisfy the conditions laid down in (7.5).

In order to isolate the distinctive characteristic of this specious type of explanation, let us examine an especially simple case of the objectionable kind. Let $T_1 = {}'(x)P(x)'$ and $E_1 = {}'R(a, b)'$; then the sentence $C_1 = {}'P(a) \supset R(a, b)'$ is formed in accordance with the preceding instructions, and T_1, C_1, E_1 satisfy the conditions (7.5). Yet, as the preceding example illustrates, we would not

---

36. The characteristic here referred to as partial self-explanation has to be distinguished from what is sometimes called the circularity of scientific explanation. The latter phrase has been used to cover two entirely different ideas. (a) One of these is the contention that the explanatory principles adduced in accounting for a specific phenomenon are inferred from that phenomenon, so that the entire explanatory process is circular. This belief is false, since general laws cannot be inferred from singular sentences. (b) It has also been argued that in a sound explanation the content of the explanandum is contained in that of the explanans. That is correct since the explanandum is a logical consequence of the explanans; but this peculiarity does not make scientific explanation trivially circular since the general laws occurring in the explanans go far beyond the content of the specific explanandum. For a fuller discussion of the circularity objection, see Feigl (1945), pp. 286 ff, where this issue is dealt with very clearly.

say that (T_1, C_1) constitutes a potential explanans for E_1. The rationale for the verdict may be stated as follows: If the theory T_1 on which the explanation rests, is actually true, then the sentence C_1, which can also be put into the form '$\sim P(a)\mathrm{v}R(a, b)$', can be verified, or shown to be true, only by verifying '$R(a, b)$', i.e., E_1. In this broader sense, E_1 is here explained by itself. And indeed, the peculiarity just pointed out clearly deprives the proposed potential explanation for E_1 of the predictive import which, as was noted in Part I, is essential for scientific explanation: E_1 could not possibly be predicted on the basis of T_1 and C_1 since the truth of C_1 cannot be ascertained in any manner which does not include verification of E_1. (7.5) should therefore be supplemented by a stipulation to the effect that if (T, C) is to be a potential explanans for E, then the assumption that T is true must not imply that verification of C necessitates verification of E.[37]

How can this idea be stated more precisely? Study of an illustration will suggest a definition of verification for molecular sentences. The sentence $M = $ '$[\sim P(a)\cdot Q(a)]\mathrm{v}R(a, b)$' may be verified in two different ways, either by ascertaining the truth of the two sentences '$\sim P(a)$' and '$Q(a)$', which jointly have M as a consequence, or by establishing the truth of the sentence '$R(a, b)$', which again, has M as a consequence. Let us say that S is a basic sentence in L if S is either an atomic sentence or the negation of an atomic sentence in L. Verification of a molecular sentence S may then be defined generally as the establishment of the truth of some class of basic sentences which has S as a consequence. Hence, the intended additional stipulation may be restated: The assumption that T is true must not imply that every class of true basic sentences which has C as a consequence also has E as a consequence.

As brief reflection shows, this stipulation may be expressed in the following form, which avoids reference to truth: T must be compatible in L with at least one class of basic sentences which has C but not E as a consequence; or, equivalently: There must exist at least one class of basic sentences which has C, but neither $\sim T$ nor E as a consequence in L.

If this requirement is met, then surely E cannot be a consequence of C, for otherwise there could be no class of basic sentences which has C but not E as a consequence; hence, supplementation of (7.5) by the new condition renders the second stipulation in (7.5) (2) superfluous. We now define potential explanation as follows:

(7.8) An ordered couple of sentences (T, C), constitutes a potential explanans

37. It is important to distinguish clearly between the following two cases: (a) If T is true then C cannot be true without E being true; and (b) If T is true, C cannot be verified without E being verified. Condition (a) must be satisfied by any potential explanation; the much more restrictive condition (b) must not be satisfied if (T,C) is to be a potential explanans for E.

for a singular sentence E if and only if the following conditions are satisfied:

(1) T is essentially generalized and C is singular

(2) E is derivable in L from T and C jointly

(3) T is compatible with at least one class of basic sentences which has C but not E as a consequence.

The definition of the concept of explanans by means of that of potential explanans as formulated in (7.6) remains unchanged.

In terms of our concept of explanans, we can give the following interpretation to the frequently used phrase "this fact is explainable by means of that theory":

(7.9) A singular sentence E is explainable by a theory T if there exists a singular sentence C such that (T, C) constitutes an explanans for E.

The concept of causal explanation, which has been examined here, is capable of various generalizations. One of these consists in permitting T to include statistical laws. This requires, however, a previous strengthening of the means of expression available in L, or the use of a complex theoretical apparatus in the metalanguage. On the other hand, and independently of the admission of statistical laws among the explanatory principles, we might replace the strictly deductive requirement that E has to be a consequence of T and C jointly by the more liberal inductive one that E has to have a high degree of confirmation relatively to the conjunction of T and C. Both of these extensions of the concept of explanation open important prospects and raise a variety of new problems. In the present essay, however, these issues will not be further pursued.

PART IV. THE SYSTEMATIC POWER OF A THEORY

8. EXPLICATION OF THE CONCEPT OF SYSTEMATIC POWER. Scientific laws and theories have the function of establishing systematic connections among the data of our experience, so as to make possible the derivation of some of those data from others. According as, at the time of the derivation, the derived data are, or are not yet, known to have occurred, the derivation is referred to as explanation or as prediction. Now it seems sometimes possible to compare different theories, at least in an intuitive manner, in regard to their explanatory or predictive powers: Some theories seem powerful in the sense of permitting the derivation of many data from a small amount of initial information; others seem less powerful, demanding comparatively more initial data, or yielding fewer results. Is it possible to give a precise interpretation to comparisons of this kind by defining, in a completely general manner, a numerical measure for the explanatory or predictive power of a theory? In the present section, we shall develop such a definition and examine some of its implications; in the

following section, the definition will be expanded and a general theory of the concept under consideration will be outlined.

Since explanation and prediction have the same logical structure, namely that of a deductive systematization, we shall use the neutral term "systematic power" to refer to the intended concept. As is suggested by the preceding intuitive characterization, the systematic power of a theory T will be reflected in the ratio of the amount of information derivable by means of T to the amount of initial information required for that derivation. This ratio will obviously depend on the particular set of data, or of information, to which T is applied, and we shall therefore relativize our concept accordingly. Our aim, then, is to construct a definition for $s(T, K)$, the systematic power of a theory T with respect to a finite class K of data, or the degree to which T deductively systematizes the information contained in K.

Our concepts will be constructed again with specific reference to the language L. Any singular sentence in L will be said to express a potential datum, and K will accordingly be construed as a finite class of singular sentences.[38] T will be construed in a much broader sense than in the preceding sections; it may be any sentence in L, no matter whether essentially generalized or not. This liberal convention is adopted in the interest of the generality and simplicity of the definitions and theorems now to be developed.

To obtain values between 0 and 1 inclusive, we might now try to identify $s(T, K)$ with the percentage of those sentences in K which are derivable from the remainder by means of T. Thus, if $K_1 = \{$'$P(a)$', '$Q(a)$', '$\sim P(b)$', '$\sim Q(b)$', '$Q(c)$', '$\sim P(d)$'$\}$, and $T_1 = $ '$(x)[P(x) \supset Q(x)]$', then exactly the second and third sentence in K_1 are derivable by means of T_1 from the remainder, in fact from the first and fourth sentence. We might therefore consider setting $s(T_1, K_1) = 2/6 = 1/3$. But then, for the class $K_2 = \{$'$P(a) \cdot Q(a)$', '$\sim P(b) \cdot \sim Q(b)$', '$Q(c)$', '$\sim P(d)$'$\}$, the same T_1 would have the s-value 0, although K_2 contains exactly the same information as K_1; again for yet another formulation of that information, namely, $K_3 = \{$'$P(a) \cdot \sim Q(b)$', '$Q(a) \cdot \sim P(b)$', '$Q(c)$', '$\sim P(d)$'$\}$, T_1 would have the s-value 1/4, and so on. But what we seek is a measure of the degree to which a given theory deductively systematizes a given body of

---

38. As this stipulation shows, the term "datum" is here understood as covering actual as well as potential data. The convention that any singular sentence expresses a potential datum is plausible especially if the primitive predicates of L refer to attributes whose presence or absence in specific instances can be ascertained by direct observation. In this case, each singular sentence in L may be considered as expressing a potential datum in the sense of describing a logically possible state of affairs whose existence might be ascertained by direct observation. The assumption that the primitives of L express directly observable attributes is, however, not essential for the definition and the formal theory of systematic power set forth in sections 8 and 9.

factual information, i.e., a certain content, irrespective of the particular structure and grouping of the sentences in which that content happens to be expressed. We shall therefore make use of a method which represents the content of any singular sentence or class of singular sentences as composed of certain uniquely determined smallest bits of information. By applying our general idea to these bits, we shall obtain a measure for the systematic power of T in K which is independent of the way in which the content of K is formulated. The sentences expressing those smallest bits of information will be called minimal sentences, and an exact formulation of the proposed procedure will be made possible by an explicit definition of this auxiliary concept. To this point we now turn.

If, as will be assumed here, the vocabulary of L contains fixed finite numbers of individual constants and of predicate constants, then only a certain finite number, say n, of different atomic sentences can be formulated in L. By a minimal sentence in L, we will understand a disjunction of any number k ($0 \leqq k \leqq n$) of different atomic sentences and the negations of the $n-k$ remaining ones. Clearly, n atomic sentences determine 2^n minimal sentences. Thus, if a language L_1 contains exactly one individual constant, 'a', and exactly two primitive predicates, 'P' and 'Q', both of degree 1, then L_1 contains two atomic sentences, '$P(a)$' and '$Q(a)$', and four minimal sentences, namely, '$P(a)\mathrm{v}Q(a)$', '$P(a)\mathrm{v}\sim Q(a)$', '$\sim P(a)\mathrm{v}Q(a)$', '$\sim P(a)\mathrm{v}\sim Q(a)$'. If another language, L_2, contains in addition to the vocabulary of L_1 a second individual constant, 'b', and a predicate 'R' of degree 2, then L_2 contains eight atomic sentences and 256 minimal sentences, such as '$P(a)\mathrm{v}\ P(b)\mathrm{v} \sim Q(a)\mathrm{v}\ Q(b)\mathrm{v}\ R(a, a)\mathrm{v}\ R(a, b)\mathrm{v} \sim R(b, a)\mathrm{v} \sim R(b, b)$'.

The term 'minimal sentence' is to indicate that the statements in question are the singular sentences of smallest non-zero content in L, which means that every singular sentence in L which follows from a minimal sentence is either equivalent to that minimal sentence or logically true in L. Minimal sentences do have consequences other than themselves which are not logically true in L, but these are not of singular form; '$(Ex)(P(x)\mathrm{v}Q(x))$' is such a consequence of '$P(a)\mathrm{v}Q(a)$' in L_1 above.

Furthermore, no two minimal sentences have any consequence in common which is not logically, or formally, true in L; in other words, the contents of any two minimal sentences are mutually exclusive.

By virtue of the principles of the sentential calculus, every singular sentence which is not formally true in L can be transformed into a conjunction of uniquely determined minimal sentences; this conjunction will be called the minimal normal form of the sentence. Thus, e.g., in the language L_1 referred to above, the sentences '$P(a)$' and '$Q(a)$' have the minimal normal forms '$[P(a)\mathrm{v}Q(a)]\cdot[P(a)\mathrm{v}\sim Q(a)]$', and '$[P(a)\mathrm{v}Q(a)]\cdot[\sim P(a)\mathrm{v}Q(a)]$', respectively; in L_2, the same sentences have minimal normal forms consisting of 128 conjoined minimal sentences each. If a sentence is formally true in L, its content is zero, and it cannot be represented by a conjunction of minimal sentences. It will be convenient, however, to say that the minimal normal form of a formally true sentence in L is the vacuous conjunction of minimal sentences, which does not contain a single term.

As a consequence of the principle just mentioned, any class of singular sentences which are not all formally true can be represented by a sentence in minimal normal form. The basic idea outlined above for the explication of the concept of systematic power can now be expressed by the following definition:

(8.1) Let T be any sentence in L, and K any finite class of singular sentences in L which are not all formally true. If K' is the class of minimal sentences which occur in the minimal normal form of K, consider all divisions of K' into two mutually exclusive subclasses, K_1' and K_2', such that every sentence in K_2' is derivable from K_1' by means of T. Each division of this kind determines a ratio $n(K_2')/n(K')$, i.e. the number of minimal sentences in K_2' divided by the total number of minimal sentences in K'. Among the values of these ratios, there must be a largest one; $s(T, K)$ is to equal that maximum ratio. (Note that if all the elements of K were formally true, $n(K')$ would be 0 and the above ratio would not be defined.)

Illustration: Let L_1 contain only one individual constant, 'a', and only two predicates, 'P' and 'Q', both of degree 1. In L_1, let $T = $ '$(x)[P(x) \supset Q(x)]$', $K = \{$'$P(a)$', '$Q(a)$'$\}$. Then we have $K' = \{$'$P(a)\mathrm{v}Q(a)$', '$P(a)\mathrm{v} \sim Q(a)$', '$\sim P(a)\mathrm{v}Q(a)$'$\}$. From the subclass K_1' consisting of the first two elements of K'—which together are equivalent to '$P(a)$'—we can derive, by means of T, the sentence '$Q(a)$', and from it, by pure logic, the third element of K'; it constitutes the only element of K_2'. No "better" systematization is possible, hence $s(T, K) = 1/3$.

Our definition leaves open, and is independent of, the question whether for a given K' there might not exist different divisions each of which would yield the maximum value for $n(K_2')/n(K')$. Actually, this can never happen: there exists always exactly one optimal subdivision of a given K'. This fact is a corollary of a general theorem, to which we now turn. It will be noticed that in the last illustration, K_2' can be derived from T alone, without the use of K_1' as a premise; indeed, '$\sim P(a)\mathrm{v}Q(a)$' is but a substitution instance of the sentence '$(x)[\sim P(x)\mathrm{v}Q(x)]$', which is equivalent to T. The theorem now to be formulated, which might appear surprising at first, shows that this observation applies analogously in all other cases.

(8.2) *Theorem.* Let T be any sentence, K' a class of minimal sentences, and K_2' a subclass of K' such that every sentence in K_2' is derivable by means of T

from the class $K_1' = K' - K_2'$.

The proof, in outline, is as follows: Since the contents of any two different minimal sentences are mutually exclusive, so must be the contents of K_1' and K_2', which have not a single minimal sentence in common. But since the sentences of K_2' follow from K_1' and T jointly, they must therefore follow from T alone.

We note the following consequences of our theorem:

(8.2a) *Theorem*. In any class K' of minimal sentences, the largest subclass which is derivable from the remainder by means of a sentence T is identical with the class of those elements in K' which are derivable from T alone.

(8.2b) *Theorem*. Let T be any sentence, K a class of singular sentences which are not all formally true, K' the equivalent class of minimal sentences, and K_t' the class of those among the latter which are derivable from T alone. Then the concept s defined in (8.1) satisfies the following equation:

$$s(T, K) = n(K_t')/n(K')$$

9. SYSTEMATIC POWER AND LOGICAL PROBABILITY OF A THEORY. GENERALIZATION OF THE CONCEPT OF SYSTEMATIC POWER. The concept of systematic power is closely related to that of degree of confirmation, or logical probability, of a theory. A study of this relationship will shed new light on the proposed definition of s, will suggest certain ways of generalizing it, and will finally lead to a general theory of systematic power which is formally analogous to that of logical probability.

The concept of logical probability, or degree of confirmation, is the central concept of inductive logic. Recently, different explicit definitions for this concept have been proposed, for languages of a structure similar to that of our model language, by Carnap[39] and by Helmer, Hempel, and Oppenheim.[40]

While the definition of s proposed in the preceding section rests on the concept of minimal sentence, the basic concept in the construction of a measure for logical probability is that of state description or, as we shall also say, of maximal sentence. A maximal sentence is the dual[41] of a minimal sentence in L; it is a conjunction of k $(0 \leqq k \leqq n)$ different atomic sentences and of the negations

39. Cf. especially (1945), (1945a), (1947).

40. See Helmer and Oppenheim (1945); Hempel and Oppenheim (1945). Certain general aspects of the relationship between the confirmation of a theory and its predictive or systematic success are examined in Hempel (1945), Part II, sections 7 and 8. The definition of s developed in the present essay establishes a quantitative counterpart of what, in that paper, is characterized, in non-numerical terms, as the prediction criterion of confirmation.

41. For a definition and discussion of this concept, see, for example, Church (1942), p. 172.

of the remaining n-k atomic sentences. In a language with n atomic sentences, there exist 2^n state descriptions. Thus, e.g., the language L_1 repeatedly mentioned in §8 contains the following four maximal sentences: '$P(a)\cdot Q(a)$', '$P(a)\cdot\sim Q(a)$', '$\sim P(a)\cdot Q(a)$', '$\sim P(a)\cdot\sim Q(a)$'.

The term "maximal sentence" is to indicate that the sentences in question are the singular sentences of maximum nonuniversal content in L, which means that every singular sentence in L which has a maximal sentence as a consequence is either equivalent with that maximal sentence or formally false in L.

As we saw, every singular sentence can be represented in a conjunctive, or minimal, normal form, i.e., as a conjunction of certain uniquely determined minimal sentences; similarly, every singular sentence can be expressed also in a disjunctive, or maximal, normal form, i.e. as a disjunction of certain uniquely determined maximal sentences. In the language L_1, for example, '$P(a)$' has the minimal normal form '$[P(a)\mathrm{v}Q(a)]\cdot[P(a)\mathrm{v}\sim Q(a)]$' and the maximal normal form '$[P(a)\cdot Q(a)]\mathrm{v}[P(a)\cdot\sim Q(a)]$'; the sentence '$P(a) \supset Q(a)$' has the minimal normal form '$\sim P(a)\mathrm{v}Q(a)$'and the maximal normal form '$[P(a)\cdot Q(a)]\mathrm{v}[\sim P(a)\cdot Q(a)]\mathrm{v}[\sim P(a)\cdot\sim Q(a)]$'; the minimal normal form of a formally true sentence is the vacuous conjunction, while its maximal normal form is the disjunction of all four state descriptions in L_1. The minimal normal form of any formally false sentence is the conjunction of all four minimal sentences in L_1, while its maximal normal form is the vacuous disjunction, as we shall say.

The minimal normal form of a singular sentence is well suited as an indicator of its content, for it represents the sentence as a conjunction of standard components whose contents are minimal and mutually exclusive. The maximal normal form of a sentence is suited as an indicator of its range, that is, intuitively speaking, of the variety of its different possible realizations, or of the variety of those possible states of the world which, if realized, would make the statement true. Indeed, each maximal sentence may be said to describe, as completely as the means of L permit, one possible state of the world; and the state descriptions constituting the maximal normal form of a given singular sentence simply list those among the possible states which would make the sentence true.

Just like the contents of any two different minimal sentences, the ranges of any two maximal sentences are mutually exclusive: no possible state of the world can make two different maximal sentences true because any two maximal sentences are obviously incompatible with each other.[42]

Range and content of a sentence vary inversely. The more a sentence asserts, the smaller the variety of its possible realizations, and conversely. This rela-

42. A more detailed discussion of the concept of range may be found in Carnap (1945), section 2, and in Carnap (1942), sections 18 and 19, where the relation of range and content is examined at length.

tionship is reflected in the fact that the larger the number of constituents in the minimal normal form of a singular sentence, the smaller the number of constituents in its maximal normal form, and conversely. In fact, if the minimal normal form of a singular sentence U contains m_U of the $m = 2^n$ minimal sentences in L, then its maximal normal form contains $l_U = m - m_U$ of the m maximal sentences in L. This is illustrated by our last four examples, where $m = 4$, and $m_U = 2, 1, 0, 4$ respectively.

The preceding observations suggest that the content of any singular sentence U might be measured by the corresponding number m_U or by some magnitude proportional to it. Now it will prove convenient to restrict the values of the content measure function to the interval from 0 to 1, inclusive; and therefore, we define a measure, $g_1(U)$, for the content of any singular sentence in L by the formula

$$(9.1) \qquad g_1(U) = m_U/m$$

To any finite class K of singular sentences, we assign, as a measure $g_1(K)$ of its content, the value $g_1(S)$, where S is the conjunction of the elements of K.

By virtue of this definition, the equation in theorem (8.2b) may be re-written:

$$s(T, K) = g_1(K_t')/g_1(K')$$

Here, K_t' is the class of all those minimal sentences in K' which are consequences of T. In the special case where T is a singular sentence, K_t' is therefore equivalent with TvS, where S is the conjunction of all the elements of K'. Hence, the preceding equation may then be transformed into

$$(9.2) \qquad s(T, S) = g_1(TvS)/g_1(S)$$

This formula holds when T and S are singular sentences, and S is not formally true. It bears a striking resemblance to the general schema for the definition of the logical probability of T in regard to S:

$$(9.3) \qquad p(T, S) = r(T \cdot S)/r(S)$$

Here, $r(U)$ is, for any sentence U in L, a measure of the range of U, T is any sentence in L, and S any sentence in L with $r(S) \neq 0$.

The several specific definitions which have been proposed for the concept of logical probability accord essentially with the pattern exhibited by (9.3),[43] but they differ in their choice of a specific measure function for ranges, i.e. in their

43. In Carnap's theory of logical probability, $p(T, S)$ is defined, for certain cases, as the limit which the function $r(T \cdot S)/r(S)$ assumes under specified conditions, cf. Carnap (1945), p. 75; but we shall refrain here from considering this generalization of that type of definition which is represented by (9.3).

definition of r. One idea which comes to mind is to assign, to any singular sentence U whose maximal normal form contains l_U maximal sentences, the range measure

(9.4) $$r_1(U) = l_U/m$$

which obviously is defined in strict analogy to the content measure g_1 for singular sentences as introduced in (9.1). For every singular sentence U, the two measures add up to unity:

(9.5) $$r_1(U) + g_1(U) = (l_U + m_U)/m = 1$$

As Carnap has shown, however, the range measure r_1 confers upon the corresponding concept of logical probability, i.e., upon the concept p_1 defined by means of it according to the schema (9.3), certain characteristics which are incompatible with the intended meaning of logical probability;[44] and Carnap, as well as Helmer jointly with the present authors, has suggested certain alternative measure functions for ranges, which lead to more satisfactory concepts of probability or of degree of confirmation. While we need not enter into details here, the following general remarks seem indicated to prepare the subsequent discussion.

The function r_1 measures the range of a singular sentence essentially by counting the number of maximal sentences in its maximal normal form; it thus gives equal weight to all maximal sentences (definition (9.1) deals analogously with minimal sentences). The alternative definitions just referred to are based on a different procedure. Carnap, in particular, lays down a rule which assigns a specific weight, i.e. a specific value of r, to each maximal sentence, but these weights are not the same for all maximal sentences. He then defines the range measure of any other singular sentence as the sum of the measures of its constituent maximal sentences. In terms of the function thus obtained—let us call it r_2—Carnap defines the corresponding concept of logical probability, which we shall call p_2, for singular sentences T, S in accordance with the schema (9.3): $p_2(T, S) = r_2(T \cdot S)/r_2(S)$. The definitions of r_2 and p_2 are then extended, by means of certain limiting processes, to the cases where T and S are no longer both singular.[45]

44. (1945), pp. 80–81.

45. The alternative approach suggested by Helmer and the present authors involves use of a range measure function r_I which depends in a specified manner on the empirical information I available; hence, the range measure of any sentence U is determined only if a sentence I, expressing the available empirical information, is given. In terms of this range measure function, the concept of degree of confirmation, dc, can be defined by means of a formula similar to (9.3). The value of $dc(T, S)$ is not defined, however, in certain cases where S is generalized, as has been pointed out by McKinsey (1946); also, the concept dc does not

Now it can readily be seen that just as the function r_1 defined in (9.5) is but one among an infinity of possible range measures, so the analogous function g_1 defined in (9.1) is but one among an infinity of possible content measures; and just as each range measure may serve to define, according to the schema (9.3), a corresponding measure of logical probability, so each content measure function may serve to define, by means of the schema illustrated by (9.2), a corresponding measure of systematic power. The method which suggests itself here for obtaining alternative content measure functions is to choose some suitable range measure r other than r_1 and then to *define* a corresponding content measure g in terms of it by means of the formula

$$(9.6) \qquad\qquad g(U) = 1 - r(U)$$

so that g and r satisfy the analogue to (9.5) by definition. The function g thus defined will lead in turn, via a definition analogous to (9.2), to a corresponding concept s. Let us now consider this procedure a little more closely.

We assume that a function r is given which satisfies the customary requirements for range measures, namely:

(9.7) 1. $r(U)$ is uniquely determined for all sentences U in L.
      2. $0 \leqq r(U) \leqq 1$ for every sentence U in L.
      3. $r(U) = 1$ if the sentence U is formally true in L and thus has universal range.
      4. $r(U_1 \vee U_2) = r(U_1) + r(U_2)$ for any two sentences U_1, U_2 whose ranges are mutually exclusive, i.e., whose conjunction is formally false.

In terms of the given range measure let the corresponding content measure g be defined by means of (9.6). Then g can readily be shown to satisfy the following conditions:

(9.8) 1. $g(U)$ is uniquely determined for all sentences U in L.
      2. $0 \leqq g(U) \leqq$ for 1 every sentence U in L.
      3. $g(U) = 1$ if the sentence U is formally false in L and thus has universal content.
      4. $g(U_1 \cdot U_2) = g(U_1) + g(U_2)$ for any two sentences U_1, U_2 whose contents are mutually exclusive, i.e., whose disjunction is formally true.

---

satisfy all the theorems of elementary probability theory (cf. the discussion of this point in the first two articles mentioned in note 40); therefore, the degree of confirmation of a theory relative to given evidence is not a probability in the strict sense of the word. On the other hand, the definition of dc here referred to has certain metholodogically desirable features, and it might therefore be of interest to construct a related concept of systematic power by means of the range measure function r_l. In the present paper, however, this question will not be pursued.

In analogy to (9.2), we next define, by means of g, a corresponding function s:

(9.9) $$s(T, S) = g(T \vee S)/g(S)$$

This function is determined for every sentence T, and for every sentence S with $g(S) \neq 0$, whereas the definition of systematic power given in §8 was restricted to those cases where S is singular and not formally true. Finally, our range measure r determines a corresponding probability function by virtue of the definition

(9.10) $$p(T, S) = r(T \cdot S)/r(S)$$

This formula determines the function p for any sentence T, and for any sentence S with $r(S) \neq 0$.

In this manner, every range measure r which satisfies (9.7) determines uniquely a corresponding content measure g which satisfies (9.8), a corresponding function s, defined by (9.9), and a corresponding function p, defined by (9.10). As a consequence of (9.7) and (9.10), the function p can be shown to satisfy the elementary laws of probability theory, especially those listed in (9.12) below; and by virtue of these, it is finally possible to establish a very simple relationship which obtains, for any given range measure r, between the corresponding concepts $p(T, S)$ and $s(T, S)$. Indeed, we have

$$
\begin{aligned}
(9.11) \quad s(T, S) &= g(T \vee S)/g(S) \\
&= [1 - r(T \vee S)]/[1 - r(S)] \\
&= r[\sim (T \vee S)]/r(\sim S) \\
&= r(\sim T \cdot \sim S)/r(\sim S) \\
&= p(\sim T, \sim S)
\end{aligned}
$$

We now list, without proof, some theorems concerning p and s which follow from our assumptions and definitions; they hold in all cases where the values of p and s referred to exist, i.e., where the r-value of the second argument of p, and the g-value of the second arguments of s, is not 0.

(9.12) (1) a. $\qquad\qquad\qquad 0 \leqq p(T, S) \leqq 1$

   b. $\qquad\qquad\qquad 0 \leqq s(T, S) \leqq 1$

(2) a. $\qquad\qquad\qquad p(\sim T, S) = 1 - p(T, S)$

   b. $\qquad\qquad\qquad s(\sim T, S) = 1 - s(T, S)$

(3) a. $p(T_1 \vee T_2, S) = p(T_1, S) + p(T_2, S) - p(T_1 \cdot T_2, S)$

   b. $s(T_1 \cdot T_2, S) = s(T_1, S) + s(T_2, S) - s(T_1 \vee T_2, S)$

(4) a. $p(T_1 \cdot T_2, S) = p(T_1, S) \cdot p(T_2, T_1 \cdot S)$

   b. $s(T_1 \vee T_2, S) = s(T_1, S) \cdot s(T_2, T_1 \vee S)$

In the above grouping, these theorems exemplify the relationship of dual correspondence which obtains between p and s. A general characterization of this correspondence is given in the following theorem, which can be proved on the basis of (9.11), and which is stated here in a slightly informal manner in order to avoid the tedium of lengthy formulations.

(9.13) *Dualism theorem.* From any demonstrable general formula expressing an equality or an inequality concerning p, a demonstrable formula concerning s is obtained if 'p' is replaced, throughout, by 's', and '·' and 'v' are exchanged for each other. The same exchange, and replacement of 's' by 'p', conversely transforms any theorem expressing an equality or an inequality concerning s into a theorem about p.

We began our analysis of the systematic power of a theory in regard to a class of data by interpreting this concept, in §8, as a measure of the optimum ratio of those among the given data which are derivable from the remainder by means of the theory. Systematic elaboration of this idea has led to the definition, in the present section, of a more general concept of systematic power, which proved to be the dual counterpart of the concept of logical probability. This extension of our original interpretation yields a simpler and more comprehensive theory than would have been attainable on the basis of our initial definition.

But the theory of systematic power, in its narrower as well as in its generalized version, is, just like the theory of logical probability, purely formal in character, and a significant application of either theory in epistemology or the methodology of science requires the solution of certain fundamental problems which concern the logical structure of the language of science and the interpretation of its concepts. One urgent desideratum here is the further elucidation of the requirement of purely qualitative primitives in the language of science; another crucial problem is that of choosing, among an infinity of formal possibilities, an adequate range measure r. The complexity and difficulty of the issues which arise in these contexts has been brought to light by recent investigations[46]; it can only be hoped that recent advances in formal theory will soon be followed by progress in solving those open problems and thus clarifying the conditions for a sound application of the theories of logical probability and of systematic power.

REFERENCES

Beard, Charles A., and Sidney Hook, "Problems of Terminology in Historical Writing." Chapter IV of *Theory and Practice in Historical Study: A Report of the Committee on Historiography.* New York, Social Science Research Council, 1946.

Bergmann, Gustav, "Holism, Historicism, and Emergence," *Philosophy of Science,* 11 (1944), 209-21.

46. Cf. especially Goodman (1946), (1947), (1947a) and Carnap (1947).

Bonfante, G., "Semantics, Language." An article in P. L. Harriman, ed., *The Encyclopedia of Psychology*. New York, 1946.

Broad, C. D., *The Mind and its Place in Nature*. New York, 1925.

Carnap, Rudolf, *Introduction to Semantics*. Cambridge, Mass., 1942.

Carnap, Rudolf, "On Inductive Logic," *Philosophy of Science*, 12 (1945), 72-97.

Carnap, Rudolf, "The Two Concepts of Probability," *Philosophy and Phenomenological Research*, 5 (1945), 513-32.

Carnap, Rudolf, "Remarks on Induction and Truth," *Philosophy and Phenomenological Research*, 6 (1946), 590-602.

Carnap, Rudolf, "On the Application of Inductive Logic," *Philosophy and Phenomenological Research*, 8 (1947), 133-47.

Chisholm, Roderick M., "The Contrary-to-Fact Conditional," *Mind*, 55 (1946), 289-307.

Church, Alonzo, "Logic, formal," in Dagobert D. Runes, ed. *The Dictionary of Philosophy*. New York, 1942.

Ducasse, C. J., "Explanation, Mechanism, and Teleology," *The Journal of Philosophy*, 22 (1925), 150-55.

Feigl, Herbert, "Operationism and Scientific Method," *Psychological Review*, 52 (1945), 250-59 and 284-88.

Goodman, Nelson, "A Query on Confirmation," *The Journal of Philosophy*, 43 (1946), 383-85.

Goodman, Nelson, "The Problem of Counterfactual Conditionals," *The Journal of Philosophy*, 44 (1947), 113-28.

Goodman, Nelson, "On Infirmities of Confirmation Theory," *Philosophy and Phenomenological Research*, 8 (1947), 149-51.

Grelling, Kurt and Paul Oppenheim, "Der Gestaltbegriff im Lichte der neuen Logik," *Erkenntnis*, 7 (1937-38), 211-25 and 357-59.

Grelling, Kurt and Paul Oppenheim, "Logical Analysis of Gestalt as 'Functional Whole'". Preprinted for distribution at Fifth Internat. Congress for the Unity of Science, Cambridge, Mass., 1939.

Helmer, Olaf and Paul Oppenheim, "A Syntactical Definition of Probability and of Degree of Confirmation," *The Journal of Symbolic Logic*, 10 (1945), 25-60.

Hempel, Carl G., "The Function of General Laws in History." *The Journal of Philosophy*, 39 (1942), 35-48. (Reprinted in this volume).

Hempel, Carl, G., "Studies in the Logic of Confirmation," *Mind*, 54 (1945); Part I: pp. 1-26, Part II: pp. 97-121. (Reprinted in this volume).

Hempel, Carl G. and Paul Oppenheim, "A Definition of Degree of Confirmation," *Philosophy of Science*, 12 (1945), 98-115.

Henle, Paul, "The Status of Emergence," *The Journal of Philosophy*, 39 (1942), 486-93.

Hospers, John, "On Explanation," *The Journal of Philosophy*, 43 (1946), 337-56.

Hull, Clark L., "The Problem of Intervening Variables in Molar Behavior Theory," *Psychological Review*, 50 (1943), 273-91.

Hull, Clark, L., *Principles of Behavior*. New York, 1943.

Jevons, W. Stanley, *The Principles of Science*. London, 1924 (1st ed. 1874).

Kaufmann, Felix, *Methodology of the Social Sciences*. New York, 1944.

Knight, Frank H., "The Limitations of Scientific Method in Economics," in R. Tugwell, ed., *The Trend of Economics*. New York, 1924.

Koch, Sigmund, "The Logical Character of the Motivation Concept," *Psychological Review*, 48 (1941); Part I: pp. 15-38, Part II: pp. 127-154.

Langford, C. H., Review in *The Journal of Symbolic Logic*, 6 (1941), pp. 67-68.

Lewis, C. I., *An Analysis of Knowledge and Valuation*. La Salle, Ill., 1946.

McKinsey, J. C. C., Review of Helmer and Oppenheim (1945). *Mathematical Reviews*, 7 (1946), 45.

Mill, John Stuart, *A System of Logic*. New York, 1858.

Morgan, C. Lloyd, *Emergent Evolution*. New York, 1923.

Morgan, C. Lloyd, *The Emergence of Novelty*. New York, 1933.

Popper, Karl, *Logik der Forschung*. Wien, 1935.

Popper, Karl, *The Open Society and its Enemies*. London, 1945.

Reichenbach, Hans, *Elements of Symbolic Logic*. New York, 1947.

Rosenblueth, A., N. Wiener and J. Bigelow, "Behavior, Purpose, and Teleology," *Philosophy of Science*, 10 (1943), 18-24.

Stace, W. T., "Novelty, Indeterminism and Emergence," *Philosophical Review*, 48 (1939), 296-310.

Tarski, Alfred, "The Semantical Conception of Truth, and the Foundations of Semantics," *Philosophy and Phenomenological Research*, 4 (1944), 341-76.

Tolman, Edward Chase, *Purposive Behavior in Animals and Men*. New York, 1932.

White, Morton G., "Historical Explanation." *Mind*, 52 (1943), 212-29.

Woodger, J. H., *Biological Principles*. New York, 1929.

Zilsel, Edgar, *Problems of Empiricism*. Chicago, 1941.

Zilsel, Edgar, "Physics and the Problem of Historico-Sociological Laws," *Philosophy of Science*, 8 (1941), 567-79.

STUDIES IN THE
LOGIC OF EXPLANATION

The preceding essay has been widely discussed in the philosophical literature. Most of the discussion has been concerned with the general conception, set forth in Part I, of explanation by deductive subsumption under laws or theoretical principles. Indeed, some commentators seem to attribute to me the the view that all adequate scientific explanations must be of this type, despite the fact that in the final paragraphs of sections 3 and 7 of the essay, as well as in section 5.3 of the earlier article "The Function of General Laws in History," another type of explanation is acknowledged, which invokes probabilistic-statistical laws. The logic of such explanation is not, however, further explored in either of those two articles; an attempt to fill this gap is made in section 3 of the essay "Aspects of Scientific Explanation" in the present volume. That essay also incorporates my responses to some of the stimulating comments and criticisms that have been directed at the two earlier studies.

In this Postscript, I will limit myself to surveying certain shortcomings of the ideas developed in Part III of the preceding essay.

(1) As E. Nagel has rightly pointed out,[1] the definition (7.3b) of the concept of derivative law is too restrictive; for, contrary to the intention indicated in section 6, it bars such laws as Galileo's and Kepler's from the status of derivative laws. This is so because those generalizations cannot be derived from the fundamental Newtonian laws of mechanics and of gravitation alone—which, in effect, would have to be done solely by substituting constant terms for variables occurring in the latter. Actually, the derivation requires additional

---

1. E. Nagel, *The Structure of Science*. New York, 1961, p. 58.

premises which do not have the character of fundamental laws; in the case of Galileo's law, for example, these include statements specifying the mass and the radius of the earth. (In fact, even with the help of such additional premises, Galileo's and Kepler's laws cannot strictly be derived from the Newtonian principles; they are only approximations of statements that are so derivable. However, this point, which is discussed further in section 2 of "Aspects of Scientific Explanation," clearly does not diminish the force of Nagel's argument.)

Nagel notes further that if the definition (7.3b) were modified so as to countenance the use of additional non-lawlike premises, then certain unfit candidates would be qualified as derivative laws. Indeed, this would be true, for example, of the sentence 'Every apple now in this basket is red', which is deducible from the (putative) law 'All Winesap apples are red' in conjunction with the premise 'Every apple now in this basket is a Winesap.' Nagel illustrates his point by the sentence 'All screws in Smith's car are rusty', which is deducible from the law 'All iron exposed to oxygen rusts', in conjunction with suitable particular premises.

What bars generalizations like the two just mentioned from the status of potential laws appears to be their limited scope: each seems to pertain to only a finite number of objects. This observation suggests that the requirement of nonlimitation of scope, which in section 6 was imposed on fundamental lawlike sentences, should be extended to derivative lawlike sentences as well. And indeed, Nagel requires that lawlike sentences in general should be "unrestricted universals," i.e., that their "scope of predication" must not fall into "a fixed spatial region or a particular period of time."[2] But on this formulation of the intended requirement, it may happen that a given sentence is disqualified whereas another, logically equivalent one is not. For example, the two restricted universals just considered are logically equivalent to the following generalizations, whose scopes of predication clearly do satisfy Nagel's condition: 'Anything that is not red is not an apple in this basket' and 'Any object that is nonrusty is not a screw in Smith's car'.

This difficulty is avoided if the scope requirement is given the following form: Except for purely logical truths (which are equivalent to '$Pa \vee \sim Pa$'), lawlike statements must not have a finite scope in the sense of being logically equivalent to some finite conjunction of singular sentences about particular cases (as in 'apple a is red and apple b is red and apple c is red'); or, more precisely and briefly: they must be essentially universal. Evidently, if a sentence satisfies this condition then so does any logical equivalent of it.

2. *Op. cit.*, p. 59.

This condition, which the definitions (7.3a) and (7.3b) do in fact impose upon fundamental and derivative lawlike sentences, is discussed more fully in section 2.1 of "Aspects of Scientific Explanation." But while clearly a necessary condition for lawlike sentences, it is too weak fully to avoid the difficulty pointed out by Nagel. In fact, it does not rule out the two undesirable generalizations just considered: neither of these can be equivalently transformed into a finite conjunction of singular sentences about particular apples or screws, for the sentences do not even indicate how many apples there are in the basket or how many screws in Smith's car; and even less do they provide a list of names for the individual objects referred to, as would be required for the transformation. Hence it remains an important desideratum to find a satisfactory version of the scope condition which requires more of a lawlike sentence than that it must be essentially universal.

(2) I now turn to a shortcoming of the definition (7.8) of a potential explanans. That definition, as I realized a number of years ago, is much too inclusive; for, in a sense presently to be illustrated, it countenances the explanation of any particular fact by itself and makes it possible to generate a potentially explanatory theory for any given particular fact from any essentially generalized sentence. Consider, for example, the argument

$$
(2a) \qquad \frac{\begin{array}{l}(x)Px \\ Qa\end{array}}{Qa} \quad \text{or briefly} \quad \frac{\begin{array}{l}T \\ C\end{array}}{C}
$$

It has the form of a complete self-explanation and is therefore ruled out by condition (3) in definition (7.8). But its explanans can be equivalently restated in a form which is acceptable under (7.8), and which yields the following argument:

$$
(2b) \qquad \frac{\begin{array}{l}(x)(Px \cdot Qa) \\ Qa \vee \sim Qa\end{array}}{Qa} \quad \text{or briefly} \quad \frac{\begin{array}{l}T' \\ C'\end{array}}{C}
$$

This argument clearly satisfies conditions (1) and (2) in (7.8). But it also satisfies condition (3); for T' is compatible with the class containing the basic sentence 'Pb' as its only element; and that class has C' but not C as a logical consequence.

This flaw can be eliminated by limiting T in definition (7.8) to purely generalized sentences. However, this is a highly undesirable restriction, for the definition was also intended to cover explanation by means of derivative laws and theories.

(3) But even if one were willing to pay this price, the modified version of (7.8) would still have quite unacceptable consequences. This has been brought to light in an incisive critical study by Eberle, Kaplan, and Montague,[3] which shows that virtually any fundamental theory yields an explanation in the sense of (7.8) for virtually any particular fact. The authors establish this by proving five theorems, each of which exhibits such explainability relations for some large class of cases in which the theory would normally be regarded as irrelevant to the fact to be explained.

The first of those theorems, for example, is this: Let T be a fundamental law and E a true singular sentence, neither of which is logically provable in the language L, and, furthermore, let the two sentences have no predicates in common—so that, intuitively speaking, T deals with a subject matter totally different from that of E. Then, granting only the availability of an adequate supply of further individual constants and predicates in L, there is a fundamental law T' which is logically derivable from T and by which E is explainable in the sense of definition (7.9). For example, let T be '$(x)Fx$' and E be 'Ha'; then consider the sentence

$$T' : (x)\,(y)[Fx \lor (Gy \supset Hy)]$$

It is of purely universal form and is derivable from T and thus is true since by hypothesis T is a law and therefore true. Hence, T' is a fundamental law. Next, consider the sentence

$$C : (Fb \lor \sim Ga) \supset Ha$$

This sentence is singular and is a consequence of E and thus is true, since by hypothesis, E is true. And as can now readily be verified, (T', C) forms a potential explanans (and indeed a true one) for E in the sense of (7.8).

I am happy to be able to say in conclusion that it is possible to modify the the definitions (7.8) and (7.9) so as to forestall these disabling consequences. One method has been pointed out by one of the authors of the critical study just discussed, D. Kaplan.[4] An alternative modification has been devised by J. Kim.[5]

The crucial part of Kim's revision is a requirement to be added to those specified in (7.8), to the following effect: Let C be put into a complete conjunctive normal form in those atomic sentences which occur essentially in C; then none of the conjuncts of that normal form must be logically derivable from

3. R. Eberle, D. Kaplan, and R. Montague, "Hempel and Oppenheim on Explanation", *Philosophy of Science* 28 (1961), pp. 418-28.

4. D. Kaplan, "Explanation Revisited," *Philosophy of Science* 28 (1961), pp. 429-36.

5. J. Kim, "Discussion: On the Logical Conditions of Deductive Explanation," *Philosophy of Science* 30 (1963), pp. 286-91.

E. In our illustration of the first of the five critical theorems, this requirement is violated; for 'Ha' logically implies, in fact, every one of the conjuncts of the complete conjunctive normal form of '$(Fb \ v \sim Ga) \supset Ha$', namely, '$Fb \ v \ Ga \ v \ Ha$', '$\sim Fb \ v \ Ga \ v \ Ha$', and '$\sim Fb \ v \sim Ga \ v \ Ha$'. Kim shows generally that his additional requirement blocks the proofs offered by Eberle, Kaplan, and Montague for the five theorems that "trivialize" the definitions (7.8) and (7.9). However, it would be desirable to ascertain more clearly to what extent the additional requirement is justifiable, not on the *ad hoc* ground that it blocks those proofs, but in terms of the rationale of scientific explanation.

Kaplan approaches the problem by formulating three very plausible requirements of adequacy for any analysis of the deductive type of explanation here to be explicated. He then shows that the analysis proposed in Part III does not satisfy those requirements jointly, and that the difficulties exhibited in the five trivializing theorems are linked to this shortcoming. Finally, he revises the definitions offered in Part III so that they meet the requirements of adequacy and avoid the difficulties we have been discussing. For the details of this illuminating contribution, the reader will have to consult Kaplan's article.

11. THE LOGIC OF

FUNCTIONAL ANALYSIS

1. INTRODUCTION

E MPIRICAL SCIENCE, in all its major branches, seeks not only to *describe* the phenomena in the world of our experience, but also to *explain* or *understand* them. While this is widely recognized, it is often held, however, that there exist fundamental differences between the explanatory *methods* appropriate to the different fields of empirical science. In the physical sciences, according to this view, all explanation is achieved ultimately by reference to causal or correlational antecedents; whereas in psychology and the social and historical disciplines—and, according to some, even in biology—the establishment of causal or correlational connections, while desirable and important, is not sufficient. Proper understanding of the phenomena studied in these fields is held to require other types of explanation.

One of the explanatory methods that have been developed for this purpose is that of functional analysis, which has found extensive use in biology, psychology sociology, and anthropology. This procedure raises problems of considerable interest for the comparative methodology of empirical science. The present essay is an attempt to clarify some of these problems; its object is to examine the logical structure of functional analysis and its explanatory and predictive significance by means of a confrontation with the principal characteristics of the explanatory procedures used in the physical sciences. We begin therefore with a brief examination of the latter.

This article is reprinted with some changes by permission from Llewellyn Gross, Editor, *Symposium on Sociological Theory.* New York: Harper & Row, 1959.

2. NOMOLOGICAL EXPLANATION: DEDUCTIVE AND INDUCTIVE

In a beaker filled to the brim with water at room temperature, there floats a chunk of ice which partly extends above the surface. As the ice gradually melts, one might expect the water in the beaker to overflow. Actually the water level remains unchanged. How is this to be explained? The key to an answer is provided by Archimedes' principle, according to which a solid body floating in a liquid displaces a volume of liquid which has the same weight as the body itself. Hence the chunk of ice has the same weight as the volume of water its submerged portion displaces. Since melting does not affect the weights involved, the water into which the ice turns has the same weight as the ice itself, and hence, the same weight as the water initially displaced by the submerged portion of the ice. Having the same weight, it also has the same volume as the displaced water; hence the melting ice yields a volume of water that suffices exactly to fill the space initially occupied by the submerged part of the ice. Therefore, the water level remains unchanged.

This account (which deliberately disregards certain effects of small magnitude) is an example of an argument intended to explain a given event. Like any explanatory argument, it falls into two parts, which will be called the *explanans* and the *explanandum*.[1] The latter is the statement, or set of statements, describing the phenomenon to be explained; the former is the statement, or set of statements, adduced to provide an explanation. In our illustration, the explanandum states that at the end of the process, the beaker contains only water, with its surface at the same level as at the beginning. To explain this, the explanans adduces, first of all, certain laws of physics; among them, Archimedes' principle; laws to the effect that at temperatures above 0°C. and atmospheric pressure, a body of ice turns into a body of water having the same weight; and the law that, at any fixed temperature and pressure, amounts of water that are equal in weight are also equal in volume.

---

1. These terms are given preference over the more familiar words 'explicans' and 'explicandum,' in order to reserve the latter for use in the context of philosophical explication in the technical sense proposed by R. Carnap; see, for example, his *Logical Foundations of Probability* (Chicago: University of Chicago Press, 1950), secs. 1-3. The terms 'explanans' and 'explanandum' were introduced, for this reason, in an earlier article: Carl G. Hempel and P. Oppenheim, "Studies in the Logic of Explanation," *Philosophy of Science*, 15 (1948), pp. 135-75 (reprinted in the present volume). While that article does not deal explicitly with inductive explanation, its first four sections contain various further considerations on deductive explanation that are relevant to the present study. For a careful critical examination of some points of detail discussed in the earlier article, such as especially the relation between explanation and prediction, see the essay by I. Scheffler, "Explanation, Prediction, and Abstraction," *The British Journal for the Philosophy of Science*, 7 (1957), pp. 293-309, which also contains some interesting comments bearing on functional analysis.

In addition to these laws, the explanans contains a second group of statements; these describe certain particular circumstances which, in the experiment, precede the outcome to be explained; such as the facts that at the beginning, there is a chunk of ice floating in a beaker filled with water; that the water is at room temperature; and that the beaker is surrounded by air at the same temperature and remains undisturbed until the end of the experiment.

The explanatory import of the whole argument lies in showing that the outcome described in the explanandum was to be expected in view of the antecedent circumstances and the general laws listed in the explanans. More precisely, the explanation may be construed as an argument in which the explanandum is deduced from the explanans. Our example then illustrates what we will call explanation by deductive subsumption under general laws, or briefly, *deductive-nomological explanation*. The general form of such an explanation is given by the following schema:

$$(2.1) \qquad \left. \begin{array}{l} L_1, L_2, \ldots, L_m \\ \\ C_1, C_2, \ldots, C_n \end{array} \right\} \text{Explanans}$$

$$\overline{\qquad E \qquad} \qquad \text{Explanandum}$$

Here, $L_1, L_2, \ldots, L_m$ are general laws and $C_1, C_2, \ldots, C_n$ are statements of particular fact; the horizontal line separating the conclusion E from the premises indicates that the former follows logically from the latter.

In our example, the phenomenon to be explained is a particular event that takes place at a certain place and time. But the method of deductive subsumption under general laws lends itself also to the explanation of what might be called "general facts" or uniformities, such as those expressed by laws of nature. For example, the question why Galileo's law holds for physical bodies falling freely near the earth's surface can be answered by showing that the law refers to a special case of accelerated motion under gravitational attraction, and that it can be deduced from the general laws for such motion (namely, Newton's laws of motion and of gravitation) by applying these to the special case where two bodies are involved, one of them the earth and the other the falling object, and where the distance between their centers of gravity equals the length of the earth's radius. Thus, an explanation of the regularities expressed by Galileo's law can be achieved by deducing the latter from the Newtonian laws and from statements specifying the mass and the radius of the earth; the latter two yield the value of the constant acceleration of free fall near the earth.

It might be helpful to mention one further illustration of the role of deductive-nomological explanation in accounting for particular facts as well as for general uniformities or laws. The occurrence of a rainbow on a given occasion can be deductively explained by reference to (1) certain particular determining conditions, such as the presence of raindrops in the air, sunlight falling on these drops, the observer facing away from the sun, etc., and (2) certain general laws, especially those of optical reflection, refraction, and dispersion. The fact that these laws hold can be explained in turn by deduction from the more comprehensive principles of, say, the electromagnetic theory of light.

Thus, the method of deductive-nomological explanation accounts for a particular event by subsuming it under general laws in the manner represented by the schema (2.1); and it can similarly serve to explain the fact that a given law holds by showing that the latter is subsumable, in the same fashion, under more comprehensive laws or theoretical principles. In fact, one of the main objectives of a theory (such as, say, the electromagnetic theory of light) is precisely to provide a set of principles—often expressed in terms of "hypothetical," not directly observable, entities (such as electric and magnetic field vectors) —which will deductively account for a group of antecedently established "empirical generalizations" (such as the laws of rectilinear propagation, reflection, and refraction of light). Frequently, a theoretical explanation will show that the empirical generalizations hold only approximately. For example, the application of Newtonian theory to free fall near the earth yields a law that is like Galileo's except that the acceleration of the fall is seen not to be strictly constant, but to vary slightly with geographical location, altitude above sea level, and certain other factors.

The general laws or theoretical principles that serve to account for empirical generalizations may in turn be deductively subsumable under even more comprehensive principles; for example, Newton's theory of gravitation can be subsumed, as an approximation, under that of the general theory of relativity. Obviously, this explanatory hierarchy has to end at some point. Thus, at any time in the development of empirical science, there will be certain facts which, at that time, are not explainable; these include the most comprehensive general laws and theoretical principles then known and, of course, many empirical generalizations and particular facts for which no explanatory principles are available at the time. But this does not imply that certain facts are intrinsically unexplainable and thus must remain unexplained forever: any particular fact as yet unexplainable, and any general principle, however comprehensive, may subsequently be found to be explainable by subsumption under even more inclusive principles.

Causal explanation is a special type of deductive nomological explanation; for a certain event or set of events can be said to have caused a specified "effect" only if there are general laws connecting the former with the latter in such a way that, given a description of the antecedent events, the occurrence of the effect can be deduced with the help of the laws. For example, the explanation of the lengthening of a given iron bar as having been caused by an increase in its temperature amounts to an argument of the form (2.1) whose explanans includes (a) statements specifying the initial length of the bar and indicating that the bar is made of iron and that its temperature was raised, (b) a law pertaining to the increase in the length of any iron bar with rising temperature.[2]

Not every deductive-nomological explanation is a causal explanation, however. For example, the regularities expressed by Newton's laws of motion and of gravitation cannot properly be said to *cause* the free fall of bodies near the earth's surface to satisfy Galileo's laws.

Now we must consider another type of explanation, which again accounts for a given phenomenon by reference to general laws, but in a manner which does not fit the deductive pattern (2.1). When little Henry catches the mumps, this might be explained by pointing out that he contracted the diesase from a friend with whom he played for several hours just a day before the latter was confined with a severe case of mumps. The particular antecedent factors here invoked are Henry's exposure and, let us assume, the fact that Henry had not had the mumps before. But to connect these with the event to be explained, we cannot adduce a general law to the effect that under the conditions just mentioned, the exposed person invariably contracts the mumps: what can be asserted is only that the disease will be transmitted with high statistical probability. Again, when a neurotic trait in an adult is psychoanalytically explained by reference to critical childhood experiences, the argument explicitly or implicitly claims that the case at hand is but an exemplification of certain general laws governing the development of neuroses. But surely, whatever specific laws of this kind might be adduced at present can purport, at the very best, to express probabilistic trends rather than deterministic uniformities: they may be construed as *laws of statistical form*, or briefly as *statistical laws*, to the effect that, given the childhood experiences in question—plus, presumably, certain particular environmental conditions in later life—there is such and such a statistical probability that a specified kind of neurosis will develop. Such

---

2. An explanation by means of laws which are causal in the technical sense of theoretical physics also has the form (2.1) of a deductive-nomological explanation. In this case, the laws invoked must meet certain conditions as to mathematical form, and $C_1, C_2, \ldots, C_n$ express so-called boundary conditions. For a fuller account of the concepts of causal law and of causality as understood in theoretical physics, see, for example, H. Margenau, *The Nature of Physical Reality* (New York: McGraw-Hill Book Company, Inc., 1950), Chapter 19; or Ph. Frank, *Philosophy of Science* (Englewood Cliffs, N. J.: Prentice-Hall, Inc., 1957), Chapters 11, 12.

statistical laws differ in form from strictly universal laws of the kind mentioned in our earlier examples of explanatory arguments. In the simplest case, a *law of strictly universal form*, or briefly, a *universal law*, is a statement to the effect that in *all* cases satisfying certain antecedent conditions A (e.g., heating of a gas under constant pressure), an event of a specified kind B (e.g., an increase in the volume of the gas) will occur; whereas a law of statistical form asserts that the probability for conditions A to be accompanied by an event of kind B has some specific value p.

Explanatory arguments which, in the manner just illustrated, account for a phenomenon by reference to statistical laws are not of the strictly deductive type (2.1). For example, the explanans consisting of information about Henry's exposure to the mumps and of a statistical law about the transmission of this disease does not logically imply the conclusion that Henry catches the mumps; it does not make that conclusion necessary, but, as we might say, more or less probable, depending upon the probability specified by the statistical laws. An argument of this kind, then, accounts for a phenomenon by showing that its occurrence is highly probable in view of certain particular facts and statistical laws specified in the explanans. An account of this type will be called an *explanation by inductive subsumption under statistical laws*, or briefly, an *inductive explanation*.

Closer analysis shows that inductive explanation differs from its deductive counterpart in several important respects;[3] but for the purposes of the following discussion, our sketchy account of explanation by statistical laws will suffice.

The two types of explanation we have distinguished will both be said to be varieties of *nomological explanation;* for either of them accounts for a given phenomenon by "subsuming it under laws," i.e., by showing that its occurrence could have been inferred—either deductively or with a high probability—by applying certain laws of universal or of statistical form to specified antecedent circumstances. Thus, a nomological explanation shows that we might in fact have *predicted* the phenomenon at hand, either deductively or with a high probability, if, at an earlier time, we had taken cognizance of the facts stated in the explanans.

But the predictive power of a nomological explanation goes much farther than this: precisely because its explanans contains general laws, it permits

---

3. For details, see section 3 of the essay "Aspects of Scientific Explanation" in this volume. Some stimulating comments on explanation by means of statistical laws will be found in S. E. Gluck, "Do Statistical Laws Have Explanatory Efficacy?" *Philosophy of Science*, 22 (1955), 34–38. For a much fuller analysis of the logic of statistical inference, see R. B. Braithwaite, *Scientific Explanation* (Cambridge: Cambridge University Press, 1953), chapters V, VI, VII. For a study of the logic of inductive inference in general, Carnap's *Logical Foundations of Probability, op. cit.*, is of great importance.

predictions concerning occurrences other than that referred to in the explanandum. In fact, such predictions provide a means of testing the empirical soundness of the explanans. For example, the laws invoked in a deductive explanation of the form (2.1) imply that the kind of event described in E will recur whenever and wherever circumstances of the kind described by C_1, $C_2, \ldots, C_n$ are realized; e.g., when the experiment with ice floating in water is repeated, the outcome will be the same. In addition, the laws will yield predictions as to what is going to happen under certain specifiable conditions which differ from those mentioned in $C_1, C_2, \ldots, C_n$. For example, the laws invoked in our illustration also yield the prediction that if a chunk of ice were floating in a beaker filled to the brim with concentrated brine, which has a greater specific gravity than water, some of the liquid would overflow as the ice was melting. Again, the Newtonian laws of motion and of gravitation, which may be used to explain various aspects of planetary motion, have predictive consequences for a variety of totally different phenomena, such as free fall near the earth, the motion of a pendulum, the tides, and many others.

This kind of account of further phenomena which is made possible by a nomological explanation is not limited to future events; it may refer to the past as well. For example, given certain information about the present locations and velocities of the celestial bodies involved, the principles of Newtonian mechanics and of optics yield not only predictions about future solar and lunar eclipses, but also "postdictions," or "retrodictions," about past ones. Analogously, the statistical laws of radioactive decay, which can function in various kinds of predictions, also lend themselves to retrodictive use; for example, in the dating, by means of the radiocarbon method, of a bow or an ax handle found in an archaeological site.

A proposed explanation is scientifically acceptable only if its explanans is capable of empirical test, i.e., roughly speaking, if it is possible to infer from it certain statements whose truth can be checked by means of suitable observational or experimental procedures. The predictive and postdictive implications of the laws invoked in a nomological explanation clearly afford an opportunity for empirical tests; the more extensive and varied the set of implications that have been borne out by empirical investigation, the better established will be the explanatory principles in question.

3. THE BASIC PATTERN OF FUNCTIONAL ANALYSIS

Historically speaking, functional analysis is a modification of teleological explanation, i.e., of explanation not by reference to causes which "bring about" the event in question, but by reference to ends which determine its course. Intuitively, it seems quite plausible that a teleological approach might be required for an adequate understanding of purposive and other goal-directed behavior; and teleological explanation has always had its advocates in this context. The trouble with the idea is that in its more traditional forms, it fails to meet the minimum scientific requirement of empirical testability. The neovitalistic idea of entelechy or of vital force is a case in point. It is meant to provide an explanation for various characteristically biological phenomena, such as regeneration and regulation, which according to neovitalism cannot be explained by physical and chemical laws alone. Entelechies are conceived as goal-directed nonphysical agents which affect the course of physiological events in such a way as to restore an organism to a more or less normal state after a disturbance has occurred. However, this conception is stated in essentially metaphorical terms: no testable set of statements is provided (i) to specify the circumstances in which an entelechy will supervene as an agent directing the course of events otherwise governed by physical and chemical laws, and (ii) to indicate precisely what observable effects the action of an entelechy will have in such a case. And since neovitalism thus fails to state general laws as to when and how entelechies act, it cannot explain any biological phenomena; it can give us no grounds to expect a given phenomenon, no reasons to say: "Now we see that the phenomenon had to occur." It yields neither predictions nor retrodictions: the attribution of a biological phenomenon to the supervention of an entelechy has no testable implications at all. This theoretical defect can be thrown into relief by contrasting the idea of entelechy with that of a magnetic field generated by an electric current, which may be invoked to explain the deflection of a magnetic needle. A magnetic field is not directly observable any more than an entelechy; but the concept is governed by strictly specifiable laws concerning the strength and direction, at any point, of the magnetic field produced by a current flowing through a given wire, and by other laws determining the effect of such a field upon a magnetic needle in the magnetic field on the earth. And it is these laws which, by their predictive and retrodictive import, confer explanatory power upon the concept of magnetic field. Teleological accounts referring to entelechies are thus seen to be pseudo-explanations. Functional analysis, as will be seen, though often formulated in teleological terms, need not appeal to such problematic entities and has a definitely empirical core.

The kind of phenomenon that a functional analysis[4] is invoked to explain

---

4. For the account of functional analysis presented in this section, I have obtained much stimulation and information from the illuminating essay "Manifest and Latent Functions" in R. K. Merton's book, *Social Theory and Social Structure* (New York: The Free Press; revised and enlarged edition, 1957), 19-84. Each of the passages from this work which is referred to in the present essay may also be found in the first edition (1949), on a page with approximately the same number.

is typically some recurrent activity or some behavior pattern in an individual or a group, such as a physiological mechanism, a neurotic trait, a culture pattern or a social institution. And the principal objective of the analysis is to exhibit the contribution which the behavior pattern makes to the preservation or the development of the individual or the group in which it occurs. Thus, functional analysis seeks to understand a behavior pattern or a sociocultural institution by determining the role it plays in keeping the given system in proper working order or maintaining it as a going concern.

By way of a simple and schematized illustration, consider first the statement:

(3.1) The heartbeat in vertebrates has the function of circulating blood through the organism.

Before examining the possibilities of its explanatory use, we should ask ourselves: What does the statement *mean?* What is being asserted by this attribution of function? It might be held that all the information conveyed by a sentence such as (3.1) can be expressed just as well by substituting the word "effect" for the word "function." But this construal would oblige us to assent also to the statement:

(3.2) The heartbeat has the function of producing heart sounds; for the heartbeat has that effect.

Yet a proponent of functional analysis would refuse to assert (3.2), on the ground that heart sounds are an effect of the heartbeat which is of no importance to the functioning of the organism; whereas the circulation of the blood effects the transportation of nutriment to, and the removal of waste from, various parts of the organism—a process that is indispensable if the organism is to remain in proper working order, and indeed if it is to stay alive. Thus understood, the import of the functional statement (3.1) might be summarized as follows:

(3.3) The heartbeat has the effect of circulating the blood, and this ensures the satisfaction of certain conditions (supply of nutriment and removal of waste) which are necessary for the proper working of the organism.

We should notice next that the heart will perform the function here attributed to it only if certain conditions are met by the organism and by its environment. For example, circulation will fail if there is a rupture of the aorta; the blood can carry oxygen only if the environment affords an adequate supply of oxygen and the lungs are in proper condition; it will remove certain kinds of waste only if the kidneys are reasonably healthy; and so forth. Most of the conditions that would have to be specified here are usually left unmentioned, partly no doubt because they are assumed to be satisfied as a matter of course in situations in which the organism normally finds itself. But in part, the omission reflects lack of relevant knowledge, for an explicit specification of the relevant conditions would require a theory in which (*a*) the possible states of organisms and of their environments could be characterized by the values of certain physicochemical or perhaps biological "variables of state," and in which (b) the fundamental theoretical principles would permit the determination of that range of internal and external conditions within which the pulsations of the heart would perform the function referred to above.[5] At present, a general theory of this kind, or even one that could deal in this fashion with some particular class of organisms, is unavailable, of course.

Also, a full restatement of (3.1) in the manner of (3.3) calls for criteria of what constitutes "proper working," "normal functioning," and the like, of the organism at hand; for the function of a given trait is here construed in terms of its causal relevance to the satisfaction of certain necessary conditions of proper working or survival of the organism. Here again, the requisite criteria are often left unspecified—an aspect of functional analysis whose serious implications will be considered later (in section 5).

The considerations here outlined suggest the following schematic characterization of a functional analysis:

(3.4) *Basic pattern of a functional analysis:* The object of the analysis is some "item" *i*, which is a relatively persistent trait or disposition (e.g., the beating of the heart) occurring in a system *s* (e.g., the body of a living vertebrate); and the analysis aims to show that *s* is in a state, or internal condition, c_i and in an environment representing certain external conditions c_e such that under conditions c_i and c_e (jointly to be referred to as *c*) the trait *i* has effects which satisfy some "need" or "functional requirement" of *s*, i.e., a condition *n* which is necessary for the system's remaining in adequate, or effective, or proper, working order.

Let us briefly consider some examples of this type of analysis in psychology and in sociological and anthropological studies. In psychology, it is especially psychoanalysis which shows a strong functional orientation. One clear instance is Freud's functional characterization of the role of symptom formation. In *The Problem of Anxiety*, Freud expresses himself as favoring a conception according to which "all symptom formation would be brought about solely in order to avoid anxiety; the symptoms bind the psychic energy which otherwise would be discharged as anxiety."[6] In support of this view, Freud points out that if an agoraphobic who has usually been accompanied when going out is left alone in the street, he will suffer an attack of anxiety, as will the compulsion neurotic, who, having touched something, is prevented from washing

5. For a fuller statement and further development of this point, see the essay "A Formalization of Functionalism" in E. Nagel, *Logic Without Metaphysics* (New York; The Free Press, 1957), 247-83. Part I of that study offers a detailed analysis of Mertons' essay mentioned in Note 4.

6. S. Freud, *The Problem of Anxiety* (Transl. by H. A. Bunker. New York: Psychoanalytic Quarterly Press, and W. W. Norton & Company, Inc., 1936), p. 111.

his hands. "It is clear, therefore, that the stipulation of being accompanied and the compulsion to wash has as their purpose, and also their result, the averting of an outbreak of anxiety."[7] In this account, which is put in strongly teleological terms, the system *s* is the individual under consideration; *i* his agoraphobic or compulsive behavior pattern; *n* the binding of anxiety, which is necessary to avert a serious psychological crisis that would make it impossible for the individual to function adequately.

In anthropology and sociology the object of functional analysis is, in Merton's words, "a *standardized* (i.e., patterned and repetitive) item, such as social roles, institutional patterns, social processes, cultural pattern, culturally patterned emotions, social norms, group organization, social structure, devices for social control, *etc.*"[8] Here, as in psychology and biology, the function, i.e., the stabilizing or adjusting effect, of the item under study may be one not consciously sought (and indeed, it might not even be consciously recognized) by the agents; in this case, Merton speaks of *latent* functions—in contradistinction to *manifest* functions, i.e., those stabilizing objective effects which are intended by participants in the system.[9] Thus, e.g., the rain-making ceremonials of the Hopi fail to achieve their manifest meteorological objective, but they "may fulfill the latent function of reinforcing the group identity by providing a periodic occasion on which the scattered members of a group assemble to engage in a common activity."[10]

Radcliffe-Brown's functional analysis of the totemic rites of certain Australian tribes illustrates the same point:

> To discover the social function of the totemic rites we have to consider the whole body of cosmological ideas of which each rite is a partial expression. I believe that it is possible to show that the social structure of an Australian tribe is connected in a very special way with these cosmological ideas and that the maintenance of its continuity depends on keeping them alive, by their regular expression in myth and rite.
>
> Thus, any satisfactory study of the totemic rites of Australia must be based not simply on the consideration of their ostensible purpose . . . , but on the discovery of their meaning and of their social function.[11]

7. *Ibid.*, p. 112.

8. Merton, *op. cit.*, p. 50 (Author's italics).

9. *Ibid.*, p. 51. Merton defines manifest functions as those which are both intended and recognized, and latent functions as those which are neither intended nor recognized, But this characterization allows for functions which are neither manifest nor latent; e.g., those which are recognized though not intended. It would seem to be more in keeping with Merton's intentions, therefore, to base the distinction simply on whether or not the stabilizing effect of the given item was deliberately sought.

10. *Ibid.*, pp. 64–65.

11. A. R. Radcliffe-Brown, *Structure and Function in Primitive Society* (London: Cohen and West Ltd., 1952), 145.

Malinowski attributes important latent functions to religion and to magic: he argues that religious faith establishes and enhances mental attitudes such as reverence for tradition, harmony with environment, and confidence and courage in critical situations and at the prospect of death—attitudes which, embodied and maintained by cult and ceremonial, have "an immense biological value." He points out that magic, by providing man with certain ready-made rituals, techniques, and beliefs, enables him "to maintain his poise and his mental integrity in fits of anger, in the throes of hate, of unrequited love, of despair and anxiety. The function of magic is to ritualize man's optimism, to enhance his faith in the victory of hope over fear."[12]

There will soon be occasion to add to the preceding examples from psychoanalysis and anthropology some instances of functional analysis in sociology. To illustrate the general character of the procedure, however, the cases mentioned so far will suffice: they all exhibit the basic pattern outlined in (3.4). From our examination of the form of functional analysis we now turn to an appraisal of its significance as a mode of explanation.

4. THE EXPLANATORY IMPORT OF FUNCTIONAL ANALYSIS

Functional analysis is widely considered as achieving an *explanation* of the "items" whose functions it studies. Malinowski, for example, says of the functional analysis of culture that it "aims at the explanation of anthropological facts at all levels of development by their function . . ."[13] and he adds, in the same context: "To explain any item of culture, material or moral, means to indicate its functional place within an institution, . . ."[14] At another place, Malinowski speaks of the "functional explanation of art, recreation, and public ceremonials."[15]

Radcliffe-Brown, too, considers functional analysis as an explanatory

---

12. B. Malinowski, *Magic, Science and Religion, and Other Essays* (Garden City, N.Y.: Doubleday Anchor Books, 1954), p. 90. For an illuminating comparison of Malinowski's views on the functions of magic and religion with those advanced by Radcliffe-Brown, see G. C. Homans, *The Human Group* (New York: Harcourt, Brace & World, Inc., 1950), 321 ff. (Note also Homan's general comments on "the functional theory," *ibid.*, pp. 268-72.) This issue and other aspects of functional analysis in anthropology are critically examined in the following article, which confronts some specific applications of the method with programmatic declarations by its proponents: Leon J. Goldstein, "The Logic of Explanation in Malinowskian Anthropology," *Philosophy of Science*, 24 (1957), 156-66.

13. B. Malinowski, "Anthropology," *Encyclopaedia Britannica*, First Supplementary volume (London and New York: The Encyclopaedia Britannica, Inc., 1926), 132.

14. *Ibid.*, p. 139.

15. B. Malinowski, *A Scientific Theory of Culture, and Other Essays* (Chapel Hill: University of North Carolina Press, 1944), 174.

method, though not as the only one suited for the social sciences: "Similarly one 'explanation' of a social system will be its history, where we know it— the detailed account of how it came to be what it is and where it is. Another 'explanation' of the same system is obtained by showing (as the functionalists attempt to do) that is it a special exemplification of laws of social physiology or social functioning. The two kinds of explanation do not conflict, but supplement one another."[16]

Apart from illustrating the attribution of explanatory import to functional analysis, this passage is of interest because it stresses that a functional analysis has to rely on general laws. This is shown also in our schematic characterization (3.4): the statements that i, in the specified setting c, has effects that satisfy n, and that n is a necessary condition for the proper functioning of the system, both involve general laws. For a statement of causal connection this is well known; and the assertion that a condition n constitutes a functional prerequisite for a state of some specified kind (such as proper functioning) is tantamount to the statement of a law to the effect that whenever condition n fails to be satisfied, the state in question fails to occur. Thus, explanation by functional analysis requires reference to laws.[17]

What explanatory import may properly be claimed for functional analysis? Suppose, then, that we are interested in explaining the occurrence of a trait i in

---

16. Radcliffe-Brown, *op. cit.*, p. 186. For an analysis of the idea of historic-genetic explanation, referred to in this passage, see section 7 of the essay "Aspects of Scientific Explanation", in this volume.

17. Malinowski, at one place in his writings, endorses a pronouncement which might appear to be at variance with this conclusion: "Description cannot be separated from explanation, since in the words of a great physicist, 'explanation in nothing but condensed description'." (Malinowski, "Anthropology," *op. cit.*, p. 132.) He seems to be referring here to the views of Ernst Mach or of Pierre Duhem, who took a similar position on this point. Mach conceived the basic objective of science as the brief and economic description of recurrent phenomena and considered laws as a highly efficient way of compressing, as it were, the description of an infinitude of potential particular occurrences into a simple and compact formula. But, thus understood, the statement approvingly quoted by Malinowski is, of course, entirely compatible with our point about the relevance of laws for functional explanation.

Besides, a law can be called a description only in a Pickwickian sense. For even so simple a generalization as "All vertebrates have hearts" does not describe any particular individual, such as Rin-Tin-Tin, as being a vertebrate and having a heart; rather, it asserts of Rin-Tin-Tin and of any other object, whether vertebrate or not—that *if* it is a vertebrate *then* it has a heart. Thus, the generalization has the import of an indefinite set of conditional statements about particular objects. In addition, a law might be said to imply statements about "potential events" which never actually take place. The gas law, for example, implies that if a given body of gas were to be heated under constant pressure at time t, its volume would increase. But if in fact the gas is not heated at t this statement can hardly be said to be a description of any particular event.

a system s (at a certain time t), and that the following functional analysis is offered:

    (a) At t, s functions adequately in a setting of kind c (characterized by specific internal and external conditions)

    (b) s functions adequately in a setting of kind c only if a certain necessary condition, n, is satisfied

(4.1)

    (c) If trait i were present in s then, as an effect, condition n would be satisfied

    (d) (Hence), at t, trait i is present in s

For the moment, let us leave aside the question as to what precisely is meant by statements of the types (a) and (b), and especially by the phrase "s functions adequately"; these matters will be examined in section 5. Right now, we will concern ourselves only with the *logic* of the argument; i.e., we will ask whether (d) formally follows from (a), (b), (c), just as in a deductive-nomological explanation the explanandum follows from the explanans. The answer is obviously in the negative, for, to put it pedantically, the argument (4.1) involves the fallacy of affirming the consequent in regard to premise (c). More explicitly, the statement (d) could be validly inferred if (c) asserted that *only* the presence of trait i could effect satisfaction of condition n. As it is, we can infer merely that condition n must be satisfied in some way or other at time t; for otherwise by reason of (b), the system s could not be functioning adequately in its setting, in contradiction to what (a) asserts. But it might well be that the occurrence of any one of a number of alternative items would suffice no less than the occurrence of i to satisfy requirement n, in which case the account provided by the premises of (4.1) simply fails to explain why the trait i rather than one of its alternatives is present in s at t.

As has just been noted, this objection would not apply if premise (c) could be replaced by the statement that requirement n can be met *only* by the presence of trait i. And indeed, some instances of functional analysis seem to include the claim that the specific item under analysis is, in this sense, functionally indispensable for the satisfaction of n. For example, Malinowski makes this claim for magic when he asserts that "magic fulfills an indispensable function within culture. It satisfies a definite need which cannot be satisfied by any other factors of primitive civilization," and again when he says about magic that "without its power and guidance early man could not have mastered his practical difficulties as he has done, nor could man have advanced to the higher stages of culture. Hence the universal occurrence of magic in primitive societies and its enormous sway. Hence we do find magic an invariable adjunct of all important activities."[18]

---

18. Malinowski, "Anthropology," *op. cit.*, p. 136; and *Magic, Science and Religion, and Other Essays, op. cit.*, p. 90. (Note the explanatory claim implicit in the use of the word "hence.")

However, the assumption of functional indispensability for a given item is highly questionable on empirical grounds: in all concrete cases of application, there do seem to exist alternatives. For example, the binding of anxiety in a given subject might be effected by an alternative symptom, as the experience of psychiatrists seems to confirm. Similarly, the function of the rain dance might be subserved by some other group ceremonial. And interestingly, Malinowski himself, in another context, invokes "the principle of limited possibilities, first laid down by Goldenweiser. Given a definite cultural need, the means of its satisfaction are small in number, and therefore the cultural arrangement which comes into being in response to the need is determined within narrow limits."[19] This principle obviously involves at least a moderate liberalization of the conception that every cultural item is functionally indispensable. But even so, it may still be too restrictive. At any rate, sociologists such as Parsons and Merton have assumed the existence of "functional equivalents" for certain cultural items; and Merton, in his general analysis of functionalism, has insisted that the conception of the functional indispensability of cultural items be replaced explicitly by the assumption of "functional alternatives, or functional equivalents, or functional substitutes."[20] This idea, incidentally, has an interesting parallel in the "principle of multiple solutions" for adaptational problems in evolution. This principle, which has been emphasized by functionally oriented biologists, states that for a given functional problem (such as that of perception of light) there are usually a variety of possible solutions, and many of these are actually used by different—and often closely related—groups of organisms.[21]

It should be noted here that, in any case of functional analysis, the question whether there are functional equivalents to a given item i has a definite meaning only if the internal and external conditions c in (4.1) are clearly specified. Otherwise, any proposed alternative to i, say i', could be denied the status of a functional equivalent on the ground that, being different from i, the item i' would have certain effects on the internal state and the environment of s which would not be brought about by i; and that therefore, if i' rather than i were realized, s would not be functioning in the same internal and external situation. Suppose, for example, that the system of magic of a given primitive

19. B. Malinowski, "Culture," *Encyclopedia of the Social Sciences*, IV (New York: The Macmillan Company, 1931), 626.

20. Merton, *op. cit.*, p. 34. Cf. also T. Parsons, *Essays in Sociological Theory, Pure and Applied* (New York: The Free Press, 1949), 58. For an interesting attempt to establish the existence of functional alternatives in a specific case, see R. D. Schwartz, "Functional alternatives to inequality," *American Sociological Review*, 20 (1955), 424-30.

21. See G. G. Simpson, *The Meaning of Evolution* (New Haven: Yale University Press, 1949), 164 ff., 190, 342-43; and G. G. Simpson, C. S. Pittendrigh, L. H. Tiffany, *Life* (New York: Harcourt, Brace & World, Inc., 1957), 437.

group were replaced by an extension of its rational technology plus some modification of its religion, and that the group were to continue as a going concern. Would this establish the existence of a functional equivalent to the original system of magic? A negative answer might be defended on the ground that as a result of adopting the modified pattern, the group had changed so strongly in regard to some of its basic characteristics (i.e., its internal state, as characterized by c_i, had been so strongly modified) that it was not the original kind of primitive group any more; and that there simply was no functional equivalent to magic which would leave all the "essential" features of the group unimpaired. Consistent use of this type of argument would safeguard the postulate of the functional indispensability of every cultural item against any conceivable empirical disconfirmation—but at the cost of turning it from an empirical hypothesis into a covert definitional truth.

That unilluminating procedure certainly must be eschewed. But what can a functional analysis in the general manner of (4.1) establish if the possibility of functional equivalents of i is not thus ruled out by definitional fiat?[22] Let I be the class of all those items which are empirically sufficient for n under the circumstances indicated in (4.1), so that an item j will be included in I just in case its realization in system s under conditions of kind c would be empirically sufficient to ensure the satisfaction of requirement n. (The qualification 'empirically' is to indicate that the satisfaction of n by j must be a matter of empirical fact and not just of pure logic. This proviso excludes from I trivial items, such as n itself.) The class I will then be a class of functional equivalents in the sense mentioned above. Let us now replace premise (c) in (4.1) by the following statement:

(c') I is the class of all empirically sufficient conditions for the fulfillment of requirement n in the context determined by system s in setting c.

What the premises (a), (b), and (c') enable us to infer is then at best this:

(4.2) Some one of the items included in class I is present in system s at time t

But this conclusion offers no grounds for expecting the occurrence of any particular item from I rather than of one of its functional equivalents. And strictly, even the weak conclusion (4.2) is warranted only on the further premise that the class I is not empty, i.e., that there is at least one item whose occurrence would, by law, ensure satisfaction of n.

Thus, functional analysis surely does not account in the manner of a deductive argument for the presence of the particular item i that it is meant to explain. Perhaps, then, it could more adequately be construed as an inductive argument which exhibits the occurrence of i as highly probable under the circumstances

<hr>

22. (Added in 1964.) The balance of this section has been revised to remedy a flaw in the original version, called to my attention by Professor John R. Gregg.

described in the premises? Might it not be possible, for example, to add to the premises of (4.1) a further statement to the effect that the functional prerequisite n can be met only by i and by a few specifiable functional alternatives? And might not these premises make the presence of i highly probable? This course is hardly promising, for in most, if not all, concrete cases it would be impossible to specify with any precision the range of alternative behavior patterns, institutions, customs, or the like that would suffice to meet a given functional prerequisite or need. And even if that range could be characterized, there is no satisfactory method in sight for dividing it into some finite number of cases and assigning a probability to each of these.

Suppose, for example, that Malinowski's general view of the function of magic is correct: how are we to determine, when trying to explain the system of magic of a given group, all the different systems of magic and alternative cultural patterns which would satisfy the same functional requirements for the group as does the actually existing system of magic? And how are we to ascribe probabilities of occurrence to each of these potential functional equivalents? Clearly, there is no satisfactory way of answering these questions, and practitioners of functional analysis do not claim to achieve their explanation in this extremely problematic fashion.

Nor is it any help to construe the general laws implicit in the statements (*b*) and (*c*) in (4.1) as statistical rather than strictly universal in form, i.e., as expressing connections that are very probable, but do not hold universally; for the premises thus obtained again would not preclude functional alternatives of i (each of which would make satisfaction of n highly probable), and thus the basic difficulty would remain: the premises taken jointly could still not be said to make the presence just of i highly probable.

In sum then, the information typically provided by a functional analysis of an item i affords neither deductively nor inductively adequate grounds for expecting i rather than one of its alternatives. The impression that a functional analysis does provide such grounds, and thus explains the occurrence of i, is no doubt at least partly due to the benefit of hindsight: when we seek to explain an item i, we presumably know already that i has occurred.

As was noted a moment ago, however, functional analysis might be construed as a deductive explanation with a very weak explanandum, thus:

(4.3)

(*a*)   At time t, system s functions adequately in a setting of kind c

(*b*) s functions adequately in a setting of kind c only if requirement n is satisfied

(*c'*) I is the class of empirically sufficient conditions for n, in the context determined by s and c; and I is not empty

(*d'*)   Some one of the items included in I is present in s at t

This kind of inference is rather trivial, however, except when we have additional knowledge about the items contained in class I. Suppose for example that at time t, a certain dog (system s) is in good health in a "normal" kind of setting c which precludes the use of such devices as artificial hearts, lungs, and kidneys. Suppose further that in a setting of kind c, the dog can be in good health only if his blood circulates properly (condition n). Then schema (4.3) leads in effect only to the conclusion that in some way or other, the blood is being kept circulating properly in the dog at t—hardly a very illuminating result. If however, we have additional knowledge of the ways in which the blood may be kept circulating under the circumstances and if we know, for example, that the only feature that would ensure proper circulation (the only item in class I) is a properly working heart, then we may draw the much more specific conclusion that at t the dog has a properly working heart. But if we make explicit the further knowledge here used by expressing it as an additional premise, then our argument can be restated in the form (4.1), except that premise (c) has been replaced by the statement that i is the *only* trait by which n can be satisfied in setting c; and, as was pointed out above, the conclusion (d) of (4.1) does follow in this case.

In general, however, additional knowledge of the kind here referred to is not available, and the explanatory import of functional analysis is then limited to the precarious role schematized in (4.3).

5. THE PREDICTIVE IMPORT OF FUNCTIONAL ANALYSIS

We noted earlier the predictive significance of nomological explanation; now we will ask whether functional analysis can be put to predictive use.

First of all, the preceding discussion shows that the information which is typically provided by a functional analysis yields at best premises of the forms (a), (b), (c) in (4.1); and these afford no adequate basis for the deductive or inductive prediction of a sentence of the form (d) in (4.1). Thus, functional analysis no more enables us to predict than it enables us to explain the occurrence of a particular one of the items by which a given functional requirement can be met.

Second, even the much less ambitious explanatory schema (4.3) cannot readily be put to predictive use; for the derivation of the weak conclusion (e) relies on the premise (a); and if we wish to infer (e) with respect to some future time t, that premise is not available, for we do not know whether s will or will not be functioning adequately at that time. For example, consider a person developing increasingly severe anxieties, and suppose that a necessary condition for his adequate functioning is that his anxiety be bound by neurotic symptoms, or be overcome by other means. Can we predict that one or another of the modes of "adjustment" in the class *I* thus roughly characterized will actually come to pass? Clearly not, for we do not know whether the person in question will in fact continue to function adequately or will suffer some more or less serious breakdown, perhaps to the point of self-destruction.

It is of interest to note here that a somewhat similar limitation exists also for the predictive use of nomological explanations, even in the most advanced branches of science. For example, if we are to predict, by means of the laws of classical mechanics, the state in which a given mechanical system will be at a specified future time t, it does not suffice to know the state of the system at some earlier time t_0, say the present; we also need information about the boundary conditions during the time interval from t_0 to t, i.e., about the external influences affecting the system during that time. Similarly, the "prediction," in our first example, that the water level in the beaker will remain unchanged as the ice melts assumes that the temperature of the surrounding air will remain constant, let us say, and that there will be no disturbing influences such as an earthquake or a person upsetting the beaker. Again when we predict for an object dropped from the top of the Empire State Building that it will strike the ground about eight seconds later, we assume that during the period of its fall, the object is acted upon by no forces other than the gravitational attraction of the earth. In a full and explicit formulation then, nomological predictions such as these would have to include among their premises statements specifying the boundary conditions obtaining from t_0 up to the time t to which the prediction refers. This shows that even the laws and theories of the physical sciences do not actually enable us to predict certain aspects of the future exclusively on the basis of certain aspects of the present: the prediction also requires certain assumptions about the future. But in many cases of nomological prediction, there are good inductive grounds, available at t_0, for the assumption that during the time interval in question the system under study will be practically "closed," i.e., not subject to significant outside interference (this case is illustrated, for example, by the prediction of eclipses) or that the boundary conditions will be of a specified kind—a situation illustrated by predictions of events occurring under experimentally controlled conditions.

The predictive use of (4.3) likewise requires a premise concerning the future, namely (*a*); but there is often considerable uncertainty as to whether (*a*) will in fact prove to be true. Furthermore, if in a particular instance there should be good inductive grounds for considering (*a*) as true, the forecast yielded by (4.3) is still rather weak; for the argument then leads from the inductively warranted assumption that the system will be properly functioning at t to the "prediction" that a certain condition n, which is empirically necessary for such functioning, will be satisfied at t in some way or other.

The need to include assumptions about the future among the premises of predictive arguments can be avoided, in nomological predictions as well as in those based on functional analysis, if we are satisfied with predictive conclusions which are not categorical, but only conditional, or hypothetical, in character. For example, (4.3) may be replaced by the following argument, in which premise (*a*) is avoided at the price of conditionalizing the conclusion:

> (*b*) System *s* functions adequately in a setting of kind *c* only if condition *n* is satisfied

(5·1) (*c'*) *I* is the class of empirically sufficient conditions for *n* in the context determined by *s* and *c*; and *I* is not empty

> (*d"*) If *s* functions adequately in a setting of kind *c* at time *t*, then some one of the items in class *I* is present in *s* at *t*

This possibility deserves mention because it seems that at least some of the claims made by advocates of functional analysis may be construed as asserting no more than that functional analysis permits such conditional predictions. This may be the intent, for example, of Malinowski's claim: "If such [a functional] analysis discloses to us that, taking an individual culture as a coherent whole, we can state a number of general determinants to which it has to conform, we shall be able to produce a number of predictive statements as guides for field-research, as yardsticks for comparative treatment, and as common measures in the process of cultural adaptation and change."[23] The statements specifying the determinants in question would presumably take the form of premises of type (*b*); and the "predictive statements" would then be hypothetical.

Many of the predictions and generalizations made in the context of functional analysis, however, do not have this conditional form. They proceed from a statement of a functional prerequisite or need to the categorical assertion of the occurrence of some trait, institution, or other item presumably sufficient to meet the requirement in question. Consider, for example, Sait's functional explanation of the emergence of the political boss: "Leadership is necessary; and *since* it does not develop readily within the constitutional framework, the boss provides it in a crude and irresponsible form from the outside."[24] Or take Merton's characterization of one function of the political machine: referring to various specific ways in which the political machine can serve the interests of business, he concludes, "These 'needs' of business, as presently constituted, are not adequately provided for by conventional and culturally approved social structures; *consequently*, the extra-legal but more-or-less efficient organization

23. Malinowski, *A Scientific Theory of Culture, and Other Essays, op. cit.*, p. 38.

24. E. M. Sait, "Machine, Political," *Encyclopedia of the Social Sciences*, IX (New York: The Macmillan Company, 1933), p. 659. (Italics supplied.)

of the political machine comes to provide these services."[25] Each of these arguments, which are rather typical of the functionalist approach, is an inference from the existence of a certain functional prerequisite to the categorical assertion that the prerequisite will be satisfied in some way. What is the basis of the inferential claims suggested by the words, 'since' and 'consequently' in the passages just quoted? When we say that *since* the ice cube was put into warm water it melted; or that the current was turned on, and *consequently*, the ammeter in the circuit responded, these inferences can be explicated and justified by reference to certain general laws of which the particular cases at hand are simply special instances; and the logic of the inferences can be exhibited by putting them into the form of the schema (2.1). Similarly, each of the two functionalist arguments under consideration clearly seems to presuppose a general principle to the effect that, within certain limits of tolerance or adaptability, a system of the kind under analysis will—either invariably or with high probability—satisfy, by developing appropriate traits, the various functional requirements (necessary conditions for its continued adequate operation) that may arise from changes in its internal state or in its environment. Any assertion of this kind, no matter whether of strictly universal or of statistical form, will be called a (*general*) *hypothesis of self-regulation*.

Unless functional analyses of the kind just illustrated are construed as implicitly proposing or invoking suitable hypotheses of self-regulation, it remains quite unclear what connections the expressions 'since,' 'consequently,' and others of the same character are meant to indicate, and how the existence of those connections in a given case is to be objectively established.

Conversely, if a precise hypothesis of self-regulation for systems of a specified kind is set forth, then it becomes possible to explain, and to predict categorically, the satisfaction of certain functional requirements simply on the basis of information concerning antecedent needs; and the hypothesis can then be objectively tested by an empirical check of its predictions. Take, for example, the statement that if a hydra is cut into several pieces, most of these will grow into complete hydras again. This statement may be considered as a hypothesis concerning a specific kind of self-regulation in a particular kind of biological system. It can clearly be used for explanatory and predictive purposes, and indeed the success of the predictions it yields confirms it to a high degree.

We see, then, that whenever functional analysis is to serve as a basis for categorical prediction or for generalizations of the type quoted from Sait and from Merton, it is of crucial importance to establish appropriate hypotheses of self-regulation in an objectively testable form.

---

25. Merton, *op. cit.*, p. 76. (Italics supplied.)

The functionalist literature does contain some explicitly formulated general-izations of the kind here referred to. Merton, for example, after citing the passage from Sait quoted above, comments thus: "Put in more generalized terms, *the functional deficiencies of the official structure generate an alternative (un-official) structure to fulfill existing needs somewhat more effectively.*"[26] This statement seems clearly intended to make explicit a hypothesis of self-regulation that might be said to underlie Sait's specific analysis and to provide the rationale for his 'since'. Another hypothesis of this kind is suggested by Radcliffe-Brown: "it may be that we should say that . . . a society that is thrown into a condition of functional disunity or inconsistency . . . will not die, except in such com-paratively rare instances as an Australian tribe overwhelmed by the white man's destructive force, but will continue to struggle toward . . . some kind of social health. . . ."[27]

But, as was briefly suggested above, a formulation proposed as a hypothesis of self-regulation can serve as a basis for explanation or prediction only if it is sufficiently definite to permit objective empirical test. And indeed many of the leading representatives of functional analysis have expressed their concern to develop hypotheses and theories which meet this requirement. Malinowski, for example, in his essay significantly entitled "A Scientific Theory of Culture," insists that "each scientific theory must start from and lead to observation. It must be inductive and it must be verifiable by experience. In other words, it must refer to human experiences which can be defined, which are public, that is, accessible to any and every observer, and which are recurrent, hence fraught with inductive generalizations, that is, predictive."[28] Similarly, Murray and Kluckhohn have this to say about the basic objective of their functionally oriented theory, and indeed about any scientific "formulation," of personality: "the general purposes of formulation are three: (1) to *explain* past and present events; (2) to *predict* future events (the conditions being specified); and (3) to serve, if required, as a basis for the selection of effective measures of *control.*"[29]

Unfortunately, however, the formulations offered in the context of con-crete functional analyses quite often fall short of these general standards. Among the various ways in which those conditions may be violated, two call for special consideration because of their pervasiveness and central importance in functional analysis. They will be referred to as (i) *inadequate specification of scope*, and

26. Merton, *op. cit.*, p. 73. (Author's italics.)

27. Radcliffe-Brown, *op. cit.*, p. 183.

28. Malinowski, *A Scientific Theory of Culture, and Other Essays, op. cit.*, p. 67.

29. Henry A. Murray and Clyde Kluckhohn, "Outline of a Conception of Personality," in Clyde Kluckhohn and Henry A. Murray, eds., *Personality in Nature, Society, and Culture* (New York: Knopf, 1950), pp. 3-32; quotation from p. 7; authors' italics.

(ii) *nonempirical use of functionalist key terms* (such as 'need,' 'functional require-ment,' 'adaptation,' and others). We will consider these two defects in turn: the former in the balance of the present section, the latter in the next.

Inadequate specification of scope consists in failure to indicate clearly the kind of system to which the hypothesis refers, or the range of situations (the limits of tolerance) within which those systems are claimed to develop traits that will satisfy their functional requirements. Merton's formulation, for exam-ple, does not specify the class of social systems and of situations to which the proposed generalization is meant to apply; as it stands, therefore, it cannot be put to an empirical test or to any predictive use.

The generalization tentatively set forth by Radcliffe-Brown has a similar shortcoming. Ostensibly, it refers to any society whatever, but the conditions under which social survival is claimed to occur are qualified by a highly indefinite "except" clause, which precludes the possibility of any reasonably clear-cut test. The clause might even be used to protect the proposed generalization against any conceivable disconfirmation: If a particular social group should "die," this very fact might be held to show that the disruptive forces were as overwhelming as in the case of the Australian tribe mentioned by Radcliffe-Brown. Systematic use of this methodological strategy would, of course, turn the hypothesis into a covert tautology. This would ensure its truth, but at the price of depriving it of empirical content: thus construed, the hypothesis can yield no explanation or prediction whatever.

A similar comment is applicable to the following pronouncement by Malinowski, in which we italicize the dubious qualifying clause: "When we consider any culture *which is not on the point of breaking down or completely disrupted, but which is a normal going concern*, we find that need and response are directly related and tuned up to each other."[30]

To be sure, Radcliffe-Brown's and Malinowski's formulations do not *have to* be construed as covert tautologies, and their authors no doubt intended them as empirical assertions; but, in this case, the vagueness of the qualifying clauses still deprives them of the status of definite empirical hypotheses that might be used for explanation or prediction.

6. THE EMPIRICAL IMPORT OF FUNCTIONALIST TERMS AND HYPOTHESES

A second flaw that may vitiate the scientific role of a proposed hypotheses of self-regulation consists in using key terms of functional analysis, such as

---

30. Malinowski, *A Scientific Theory of Culture, and Other Essays, op. cit.*, p. 94.

'need' and 'adequate (proper) functioning'[31] in a nonempirical manner, i.e., without giving them a clear "operational definition," or more generally, without specifying objective criteria of application for them.[32] If functionalist terms are used in this manner, then the sentences containing them have no clear empirical meaning; they lead to no specific predictions and thus cannot be put to an objective test; nor, of course, can they be used for explanatory purposes.

A consideration of this point is all the more important here because the functionalist key terms occur not only in hypotheses of self-regulation, but also in functionalist sentences of various other kinds, such as those of the types (a), (b), and (d'') in (4.1), (4.3), and (5.1). Nonempirical use of functionalist terms may, therefore, bar sentences of these various kinds from the status of scientific hypotheses. We turn now to some examples.

Consider first the terms 'functional prerequisite' and 'need,' which are used as more or less synonymous in the functionalist literature, and which serve to define the term 'function' itself. "Embedded in every functional analysis is some conception, tacit or expressed, of the functional requirements of the system under observation",[33] and indeed, "a definition [of function] is provided by showing that human institutions, as well as partial activities within these, are related to primary, that is, biological, or derived, that is, cultural needs. Function means, therefore, always the satisfaction of a need. . . ."[34]

How is this concept of need defined? Malinowski gives an explicit answer: "By need, then, I understand the system of conditions in the human organism, in the cultural setting, and in the relation of both to the natural environment, which are sufficient and necessary for the survival of group and organism."[35] This definition sounds clear and straightforward; yet it is not even quite in accord with Malinowski's own use of the concept of need. For he distinguishes,

31. In accordance with a practice followed widely in contemporary logic, we will understand by terms certain kinds of words or other linguistic expressions, and we will say that a term expresses or signifies a concept. For example, we will say that the term 'need' signifies the concept of need. As this illustration shows, we refer to, or mention, a linguistic expression by using a name for it which is formed by simply enclosing the expression in single quotes.

32. A general discussion of the nature and significance of "operational" criteria of application for the terms used in empirical science, and references to further literature on the subject, may be found in C. G. Hempel, *Fundamentals of Concept Formation in Empirical Science* (University of Chicago Press, 1952), sections 5-8; and in the symposium papers on the present state of operationalism by G. Bergmann, P. W. Bridgman, A. Grunbaum, C. G. Hempel, R. B. Lindsay, H. Margenau, and R. J. Seeger, which form chapter II of Philipp G. Frank, ed., *The Validation of Scientific Theories* (Boston: The Beacon Press, 1956).

33. Merton, *op. cit.*, p. 52.

34. Malinowski, *A Scientific Theory of Culture, and other Essays, op. cit.*, p. 159.

35. Malinowski, *ibid.*, p. 90.

very plausibly, a considerable number of different needs, which fall into two major groups: primary biological needs and derivative cultural ones; the latter include "technological, economic, legal, and even magical, religious, or ethical"[36] needs. But if every single one of these needs did actually represent not only a necessary condition of survival but also a sufficient one, then clearly the satisfaction of just one need would suffice to ensure survival, and the other needs could not constitute necessary conditions of survival at all. It seems reasonable to assume, therefore, that what Malinowski intended was to construe the needs of a group as a set of conditions which are individually necessary and jointly sufficient for its survival.[37]

However, this correction of a minor logical flaw does not remedy a more serious defect of Malinowski's definition, which lies in the deceptive appearance of clarity of the phrase "survival of group and organism." In reference to a biological organism, the term 'survival' has a fairly clear meaning, though even here, there is need for further clarification. For when we speak of biological needs or requirements—e.g., the minimum daily requirements, for human adults, of various vitamins and minerals—we construe these, not as conditions of just the barest survival but as conditions of persistence in, or return to, a "normal," or "healthy" state, or to a state in which the system is a "properly functioning whole." For the sake of objective testability of functionalist hypotheses, it is essential, therefore, that definitions of needs or functional prerequisites be supplemented by reasonably clear and objectively applicable criteria of what is to be considered a healthy state or a normal working order of the systems under consideration; and that the vague and sweeping notion of survival then be construed in the relativized sense of survival in a healthy state as specified. Otherwise, there is definite danger that different investigators will use the concept of functional prerequisite—and hence also that of function—in different ways, and with valuational overtones corresponding to their diverse conceptions of what are the most "essential" characteristics of "genuine" survival for a system of the kind under consideration.

Functional analyses in psychology, sociology, and anthropology are even

---

36. Malinowski, *ibid.*, p. 172; see also *ibid.*, pp. 91 ff.

37. In some of his statements Malinowski discards, by implication, even the notion of function as satisfaction of a condition that is at least *necessary* for the survival of group or organism. For example, in the essay containing the two passages just quoted in the text, Malinowski comments as follows on the function of some complex cultural achievements: "Take the airplane, the submarine, or the steam engine. Obviously, man does not need to fly, nor yet to keep company with fishes, and move about within a medium for which he is neither anatomically adjusted nor physiologically prepared. In defining, therefore, the function of any of those contrivances, we can not predicate the true course of their appearance in any terms of metaphysical necessity." (*Ibid.*, pp. 118–19.)

more urgently in need of objective empirical criteria of the kind here referred to; for the characterization of needs as necessary conditions of psychological or emotional survival for an individual, or of survival of a group is so vague as to permit, and indeed invite, quite diverse subjective interpretations.

Some authors characterize the concept of functional prerequisite or the concept of function without making use of the term 'survival' with its misleading appearance of clarity. Merton, for example, states: "*Functions* are those observed consequences which make for the adaptation or adjustment of a given system; and *dysfunctions*, those observed consequences which lessen the adaptation or adjustment of the system."[38] And Radcliffe-Brown characterizes the function of an item as its contribution to the maintenance of a certain kind of unity of a social system, "which we may speak of as a functional unity. We may define it as a condition in which all parts of the social system work together with a sufficient degree of harmony or internal consistency, i.e., without producing persistent conflicts which can neither be resolved nor regulated."[39] But like the definitions in terms of survival, these alternative characterizations, though suggestive, are far from giving clear empirical meanings to the key terms of functional analysis. The concepts of adjustment and adaptation, for example, require specification of some standard; otherwise, they have no definite meaning and are in danger of being used tautologically or else subjectively, with valuational overtones.

Tautological use could be based on construing *any* response of a given system as an adjustment, in which case it becomes a trivial truth that any system will adjust itself to any set of circumstances. Some instances of functional analysis seem to come dangerously close to this procedure, as is illustrated by the following assertion: "Thus we are provided with an explanation of suicide and of numerous other apparently antibiological effects as so many forms of relief from intolerable suffering. Suicide does not have *adaptive* (survival) value but it does have *adjustive* value for the organism. Suicide is *functional* because it abolishes painful tension."[40]

Or consider Merton's formulation of one of the assumptions of functional analysis: ". . . when *the net balance of the aggregate of consequences* of an existing social structure is clearly dysfunctional, there develops a strong and insistent pressure for change."[41] In the absence of clear empirical criteria of adaptation and thus of dysfunction, it is possible to treat this formulation as a covert tautology and thus to render it immune to empirical disconfirmation. Merton

38. .Merton, *op. cit.*, p. 51. (Author's italics.)
39. Radcliffe-Brown, *op. cit.*, p. 181.
40. Murray and Kluckhohn, *op. cit.*, p. 15 (Author's italics.)
41. Merton, *op. cit.*, p. 40.

is quite aware of such danger: in another context he remarks that the notion of functional requirements of a given system "remains one of the cloudiest and empirically most debatable concepts in functional theory. As utilized by sociologists, the concept of functional requirement tends to be tautological or *ex post facto*."[42] Similar warnings against tautological use and against *ad hoc* generalizations about functional prerequisites have been voiced by other writers, such as Malinowski[43] and Parsons.[44]

In the absence of empirical criteria of adjustment or adaptation, there is also the danger of each investigator's projecting into those concepts (and thus also into the concept of function) his own ethical standards of what would constitute a "proper" or "good" adjustment of a given system—a danger which has been pointed out very clearly by Levy.[45] This procedure would obviously deprive functionalist hypotheses of the status of precise objectively testable scientific assertions. And, as Merton notes, "If theory is to be productive, it must be sufficiently *precise* to be *determinate*. Precision is an integral element of the criterion of *testability*."[46]

It is essential, then, for functional analysis as a scientific procedure that its key concepts be explicitly construed as relative to some standard of survival or adjustment. This standard has to be specified for each functional analysis, and it will usually vary from case to case. In the functional study of a given system *s*, the standard would be indicated by specifying a certain class or range *R* of possible states of *s*, with the understanding that *s* is to be considered as "surviving in proper working order," or as "adjusting properly under changing conditions" just in case *s* remains in, or upon disturbance returns to, some state within the range *R*. A need, or functional requirement, of system *s* relative to *R* is then a necessary condition for the system's remaining in, or returning to, a state in *R;* and the function, relative to *R*, of an item *i* in *s* consists in *i*'s effecting the satisfaction of some such functional requirement.

In the field of biology, Sommerhoff's analysis of adaptation, appropriateness, and related concepts, is an excellent illustration of a formal study in which the relativization of the central functionalist concepts is entirely explicit.[47] The

42. Merton, *op. cit.*, p. 52.

43. See, for example, Malinowski, *A Scientific Theory of Culture, and Other Essays, op. cit.*, pp. 169-70; but also compare this with pp. 118-19 of the same work.

44. See, for example, T. Parsons, *The Social System* (New York: The Free Press, 1951), 29, n. 4.

45. Marion J. Levy, Jr., *The Structure of Society* (Princeton: Princeton University Press, 1952), 76ff.

46. R. K. Merton, "The Bearing of Sociological Theory on Empirical Research" in Merton, *Social Theory and Social Structure, op. cit.*, pp. 85-101; quotation from 98. (Author's italics)

47. See G. Sommerhoff, *Analytical Biology* (New York: Oxford University Press, 1950).

need of such relativization is made clear also by Nagel, who points out that "the claim that a given change is functional or dysfunctional must be understood as being relative to a specified G (or sets of G's)"[48], where the G's are traits whose preservation serves as the defining standard of adjustment or survival. In sociology, Levy's analysis of the structure of society[49] clearly construes the functionalist key concepts as relative in the sense just outlined.

Only if the key concepts of functional analysis are thus relativized can hypotheses involving them have the status of determinate and objectively testable assumptions or assertions; only then can those hypotheses enter significantly into arguments such as those schematized in (4.1), (4.3), and (5.1).

But although such relativization may give definite empirical content to the functionalist hypotheses that serve as premises or conclusions in those arguments, it leaves the explanatory and predictive import of the latter as limited as we found it in sections 4 and 5; for our verdict on the logical force of those arguments depended solely on their formal structure and not on the meaning of their premises and conclusions.

It remains true, therefore, even for a properly relativized version of functional analysis, that its explanatory force is rather limited; in particular, it does not provide an explanation of why a particular item i rather than some functional equivalent of it occurs in system s. And the predictive significance of functional analysis is practically nil—except in those cases where suitable hypotheses of self-regulation can be established. Such a hypothesis would be to the effect that within a specified range C of circumstances, a given system s (or: any system of a certain kind S, of which s is an instance) is self-regulating relative to a specified range R of states; i.e., that after a disturbance which moves s into a state outside R, but which does not shift the internal and external circumstances of s out of the specified range C, the system s will return to a state in R. A system satisfying a hypothesis of this kind might be called *self-regulating with respect to* R.

Biological systems offer many illustrations of such self-regulation. For example, we mentioned earlier the regenerative ability of a hydra. Consider the case, then, where a more or less large segment of the animal is removed and the rest grows into a complete hydra again. The class R here consists of those states in which the hydra is complete; the characterization of range C

48. Nagel, "A Formalization of Functionalism," *op. cit.*, p. 269. See also the concluding paragraph of the same essay (pp. 282-83).

49. Levy speaks of eufunction and dysfunction of a unit (i.e., a system) and characterizes these concepts as relative to "the unit as defined." He points out that relativization is necessary "because it is to the definition of the unit that one must turn to determine whether or not 'adaptation or adjustment' making for the persistence or lack of persistence of the unit is taking place." (Levy, *ibid.*, pp. 77-78).

would have to include (i) a specification of the temperature and the chemical composition of the water in which a hydra will perform its regenerative feat (clearly, this will not be just one unique composition, but a class of different ones: the concentrations of various salts, for example, will each be allowed to take some value within a specified, and perhaps narrow, range; the same will hold of the temperature of the water); and (ii) a statement as to the kind and size of segment that may be removed without preventing regeneration.

It will no doubt be one of the most important tasks of functional analysis in psychology and the social sciences to ascertain to what extent such phenomena of self-regulation can be found, and can be represented by corresponding laws.

7. FUNCTIONAL ANALYSIS AND TELEOLOGY

Whatever specific laws might be discovered by research along these lines, the kind of explanation and prediction made possible by them does not differ in its logical character from that of the physical sciences.

It is true that hypotheses of self-regulation, which would be the results of successful functionalist research, appear to have a teleological character since they assert that within specified conditions systems of some particular kind will tend toward a state within the class R, which thus assumes the appearance of a final cause determining the behavior of the system.

But, first of all, it would be simply untenable to say of a system s which is self-regulating with respect to R that the future event of its return to (a state in) R is a "final cause" which determines its present behavior. For even if s is self-regulating with respect to R and if it has been shifted into a state outside R, the future event of its return to R may never come about: in the process of its return toward R, s may be exposed to further disturbances, which may fall outside the permissible range C and lead to the destruction of s. For example, in a hydra that has just had a tentacle removed, certain regenerative processes will promptly set in; but these cannot be explained teleologically by reference to a final cause consisting in the future event of the hydra being complete again. For that event may never actually come about since in the process of regeneration, and before its completion, the hydra may suffer new, and irreparably severe, damage, and may die. Thus, what accounts for the present changes of a self-regulating system s is not the "future event" of s being in R, but rather the *present disposition* of s to return to R; and it is this disposition that is expressed by the hypothesis of self-regulation governing the system s.

Whatever teleological character may be attributed to a functionalist explanation or prediction invoking (properly relativized) hypotheses of self-regulation lies merely in the circumstance that such hypotheses assert a tendency of certain systems to maintain, or return to, a certain kind of state. But such laws attributing, as it were, a characteristic goal-directed behavior to systems of specified kinds are by no means alien to physics and chemistry. On the contrary, it is these latter fields which provide the most adequately understood instances of self-regulating systems and corresponding laws. For example, a liquid in a vessel will return to a state of equilibrium, with its surface horizontal, after a mechanical disturbance; an elastic band, after being stretched (within certain limits), will return to its original shape when it is released. Various systems controlled by negative feedback devices, such as a steam engine whose speed is regulated by a governor, or a homing torpedo, or a plane guided by an automatic pilot, show, within specifiable limits, self-regulation with respect to some particular class of states.

In all of these cases, the laws of self-regulation exhibited by the systems in question are capable of explanation by subsumption under general laws of a more obviously causal form. But this is not even essential, for the laws of self-regulation themselves are causal in the broad sense of asserting that for systems of a specified kind, any one of a class of different "initial states" (any one of the permissible states of disturbance) will lead to the same kind of final state. Indeed as our earlier formulations show, functionalist hypotheses, including those of self-regulation, can be expressed without the use of any teleological phraseology at all.[50]

There are, then, no systematic grounds for attributing to functional analysis a character *sui generis* not found in the hypotheses and theories of the natural sciences and in the explanations and predictions based on them. Yet, psychologically, the idea of function often remains closely associated with that of purpose, and some functionalist writing has no doubt encouraged this association, by using a phraseology which attributes to the self-regulatory behavior of a given system practically the character of a purposeful action. For example, Freud, speaking of the relation of neurotic symptoms to anxiety, uses strongly teleological language when he says that "the symptoms are created in order to remove or rescue the ego from the situation of danger";[51] the quotations given in section 3 provide further illustrations. Some instructive examples of sociological and anthropological writings which confound the concepts of function

---

50. For illuminating discussions of further issues concerning "teleological explanation," especially with respect to self-regulating systems, see R. B. Braithwaite, *Scientific Explanation* (Cambridge: Cambridge University Press, 1953), chapter X; and E. Nagel, "Teleological Explanation and Teleological Systems" in S. Ratner, ed., *Vision and Action: Essays in Honor of Horace Kallen on His Seventieth Birthday* (New Brunswick, N.J.: Rutgers University Press, 1953); reprinted in H. Feigl and M. Brodbeck, eds., *Readings in the Philosophy of Science* (New York: Appleton-Century-Crofts, Inc., 1953).

51. Freud, *op. cit.*, p. 112.

and purpose are listed by Merton, who is very explicit and emphatic in rejecting this practice.[52]

It seems likely that precisely this psychological association of the concept of function with that of purpose, though systematically unwarranted, accounts to a large extent for the appeal and the apparent plausibility of functional analysis as a mode of explanation; for it seems to enable us to "understand" self-regulatory phenomena of all kinds in terms of purposes or motives, in much the same way in which we "understand" our own purposive behavior and that of others. Now, explanation by reference to motives, objectives, or the like may be perfectly legitimate in the case of purposive behavior and its effects. An explanation of this kind would be causal in character, listing among the causal antecedents of the given action, or of its outcome, certain purposes or motives on the part of the agent, as well as his beliefs as to the best means available to him for attaining his objectives. This kind of information about purposes and beliefs might even serve as a starting point in explaining a self-regulatory feature in a human artifact. For example, in an attempt to account for the presence of the governor in a steam engine, it may be quite reasonable to refer to the purpose its inventor intended it to serve, to his beliefs concerning matters of physics, and to the technological facilities available to him. Such an account, it should be noted, might conceivably give a probabilistic explanation for the presence of the governor, but it would not explain why it functioned as a speed-regulating safety device: to explain this latter fact, we would have to refer to the construction of the machine and to the laws of physics, not to the intensions and beliefs of the designer. (An explanation by reference to motives and beliefs can be given as well for certain items which do not, in fact, function as intended; e.g., some superstitious practices, unsuccessful flying machines, ineffective economic policies, etc.). Furthermore—and is this the crucial point in our context—for most of the self-regulatory phenomena that come within the purview of functional analysis, the attribution of purposes is an illegitimate transfer of the concept of purpose from its domain of significant applicability to a much wider domain, where it is devoid of objective empirical import. In the context of purposive behavior of individuals or groups, there are various methods of testing whether the assumed motives or purposes are indeed present in a given situation; interviewing the agents in question might be one rather direct way, and there are various alternative "operational" procedures of a more indirect character. Hence, explanatory hypotheses in terms of purposes are here capable of reasonably objective test. But such empirical criteria are lacking in other cases of self-regulating systems, and the attribution of purposes

52. Merton, "Manifest and Latent Functions," *op. cit.*, pp. 23–25, 60ff.

to them has therefore no scientific meaning. Yet, it tends to encourage the illusion that a profound understanding is achieved, that we gain insight into the nature of these processes by likening them to a type of behavior with which we are thoroughly familiar from daily experience. Consider, for example, the law of "adaptation to an obvious end" set forth by the sociologist L. Gumplowicz with the claim that it holds both in the natural and the social domains. For the latter, it asserts that "every social growth, every social entity, serves a definite end, however much its worth and morality may be questioned. For the universal law of adaptation signifies simply that no expenditure of effort, no change of condition, is purposeless on any domain of phenomena. Hence, the inherent reasonableness of all social facts and conditions must be conceded."[53] There is a strong suggestion here that the alleged law enables us to understand social dynamics in close analogy to purposive behavior aimed at the achievement of some end. Yet that law is completely devoid of empirical meaning since no empirical interpretation has been given to such key terms as 'end,' 'purposeless', and 'inherent reasonableness' for the contexts to which it is applied. The "law" asserts nothing whatever, therefore, and cannot possibly explain any social (or other) phenomena.

Gumplowicz's book antedates the writings of Malinowski and other leading functionalists by several decades, and certainly these more recent writers have been more cautious and sophisticated in stating their ideas. Yet, there are certain quite central assertions in the newer functionalist literature which are definitely reminiscent of Gumplowicz's formulation in that they suggest an understanding of functional phenomena in the image of deliberate purposive behavior or of systems working in accordance with a preconceived design. The following statements might illustrate this point: "[Culture] is a system of objects, activities, and attitudes in which every part exists as a means to an end,"[54] and "The functional view of culture insists therefore upon the principle that in every type of civilization, every custom, material object, idea and belief fulfills some vital function, has some task to accomplish, represents an indispensable part within a working whole."[55] These statements express what Merton, in a critical discussion, calls the postulate of universal functionalism.[56] Merton qualifies this postulate as premature;[57] the discussion presented in the previous section shows that, in the absence of a clear empirical interpre-

---

53. L. Gumplowicz, *The Outlines of Sociology;* translated by F. W. Moore (Philadelphia: American Academy of Policical and Social Science, 1899), pp. 79–80.
54. Malinowski, *A Scientific Theory of Culture, and Other Essays, op. cit.,* p. 150.
55. Malinowski, "Anthrolopogy," *op. cit.,* p. 133.
56. Merton, "Manifest and Latent Functions," *op. cit.,* pp. 30ff.
57. *Ibid.,* p. 31.

tation of the functionalist key terms, it is even less than that, namely, empirically vacuous. Yet formulations of this kind may evoke a sense of insight and understanding by likening sociocultural developments to purposive behavior and in this sense reducing them to phenomena with which we feel thoroughly familiar. But scientific explanation and understanding are not simply a reduction to the familiar: otherwise, science would not seek to explain familiar phenomena at all; besides, the most significant advances in our scientific understanding of the world are often achieved by means of new theories which, like quantum theory, assume some quite unfamiliar kinds of objects or processes which cannot be directly observed, and which sometimes are endowed with strange and even seemingly paradoxical characteristics. A class of phenomena has been scientifically understood to the extent that they can be fitted into a testable, and adequately confirmed, theory or a system of laws; and the merits of functional analysis will eventually have to be judged by its ability to lead to this kind of understanding.

8. THE HEURISTIC ROLE OF FUNCTIONAL ANALYSIS

The preceding considerations suggest that what is often called "functionalism" is best viewed, not as a body of doctrine or theory advancing tremendously general principles such as the principle of universal functionalism, but rather as a program for research guided by certain heuristic maxims or "working hypotheses." The idea of universal functionalism, for example, which becomes untenable when formulated as a sweeping empirical law or theoretical principle, might more profitably be construed as expressing a directive for inquiry, namely to search for specific self-regulatory aspects of social and other systems and to examine the ways in which various traits of a system might contribute to its particular mode of self-regulation (A similar construal as heuristic maxims for empirical research might be put upon the "general axioms of functionalism" suggested by Malinowski, and considered by him as demonstrated by all the pertinent empirical evidence.[58])

In biology, for example, the contribution of the functionalist approach does not consist in the sweeping assertion that all traits of any organism satisfy some need and thus serve some function; in this generality, the claim is apt to be either meaningless or covertly tautologous or empirically false (depending on whether the concept of need is given no clear empirical interpretation at all, or is handled in a tautologizing fashion, or is given a specific empirical interpretation). Instead, functional studies in biology have been aimed at showing, for example, how in different species, specific homeostatic and regenerative processes contribute to the maintenance and development of the

58. Malinowski, *A Scientific Theory of Culture, and Other Essays, op. cit.*, p. 150.

living organism; and they have gone on (i) to examine more and more precisely the nature and limits of those processes (this amounts basically to establishing various specific empirical hypotheses or laws of self-regulation), and (ii) to explore the underlying physiological or physicochemical mechanisms, and the laws governing them, in an effort to achieve a more thorough theoretical understanding of the phenomena at hand.[59] Similar trends exist in the study of functional aspects of psychological processes, including, for example, symptom formation in neurosis.[60]

Functional analysis in psychology and in the social sciences no less than in biology may thus be conceived, at least ideally, as a program of inquiry aimed at determining the respects and the degrees in which various systems are self-regulating in the sense here indicated. This conception is clearly reflected in Nagel's essay, "A Formalization of Functionalism,"[61] which develops an analytic scheme inspired by, and similar to, Sommerhoff's formal analysis of self-regulation in biology[62] and uses it to exhibit and clarify the structure of functional analysis, especially in sociology and anthropology.

The functionalist mode of approach has proved illuminating, suggestive, and fruitful in many contexts. If the advantages it has to offer are to be reaped in full, it seems desirable and indeed necessary to pursue the investigation of specific functional relationships to the point where they can be expressed in terms of reasonably precise and objectively testable hypotheses. At least initially, these hypotheses will likely be of quite limited scope. But this would simply parallel the present situation in biology, where the kinds of self-regulation, and the uniformities they exhibit, vary from species to species. Eventually, such "empirical generalizations" of limited scope might provide a basis for a more general theory of self-regulating systems. To what extent these objectives can be reached cannot be decided in *a priori* fashion by logical analysis or philosophical reflection: the answer has to be found by intensive and rigorous scientific research.

59. An account of this kind of approach to homeostatic processes in the human body will be found in Walter B. Cannon, *The Wisdom of the Body* (New York: W. W. Norton & Company, Inc.; revised edition 1939).

60. See, for example, J. Dollard and N. E. Miller, *Personality and Psychotherapy* (New York: McGraw-Hill Book Company, Inc., 1950), chapter XI, "How Symptoms are Learned," and note particularly pp. 165–66.

61. Nagel, "A Formalization of Functionalism," *op. cit.* See also the more general discussion of functional analysis included in Nagel's paper, "Concept and Theory Formation in the Social Sciences," in *Science, Language, and Human Rights;* American Philosophical Association, Eastern Division, Volume 1 (Philadelphia: University of Pennsylvania Press, 1952), pp. 43–64. Reprinted in J. L. Jarrett and S. M. McMurrin, eds., *Contemporary Philosophy* (New York: Henry Holt & Co., Inc., 1954).

62. Sommerhoff, *op. cit.*

ASPECTS OF

SCIENTIFIC EXPLANATION

CONTENTS

1. INTRODUCTION

Among the many factors that have prompted and sustained inquiry in the diverse fields of empirical science, two enduring human concerns have provided the principal stimulus for man's scientific efforts.

One of them is of a practical nature. Man wants not only to survive in the world, but also to improve his strategic position in it. This makes it important for him to find reliable ways of foreseeing changes in his environment and, if possible, controlling them to his advantage. The formulation of laws and theories that permit the prediction of future occurrences are among the proudest achievements of empirical science; and the extent to which they answer man's quest for foresight and control is indicated by the vast scope of their practical applications, which range from astronomic predictions to meteorological, demographic, and economic forecasts, and from physico-chemical and biological technology to psychological and social control.

The second basic motive for man's scientific quest is independent of such practical concerns; it lies in his sheer intellectual curiosity, in his deep and persistent desire to know and to understand himself and his world. So strong, indeed, is this urge that in the absence of more reliable knowledge, myths are often invoked to fill the gap. But in time, many such myths give way to scientific conceptions of the what and the why of empirical phenomena.

What is the nature of the explanations empirical science can provide? What understanding of empirical phenomena do they convey? This essay attempts to shed light on these questions by examining in some detail the form and the function of some of the major types of explanatory account that have been advanced in different areas of empirical science.

The terms 'empirical science' and 'scientific explanation' will here be understood to refer to the entire field of empirical inquiry, including the natural and the social sciences as well as historical research. This broad use of the two terms is not intended to prejudge the question of the logical and methodological

---

This essay has not previously appeared in print. It includes, however, some passages from the following articles:

"Deductive-Nomological vs. Statistical Explanation," *Minnesota Studies in the Philosophy of Science*, Vol. III, edited by Herbert Feigl and Grover Maxwell. University of Minnesota Press, Minneapolis. Copyright 1962 by the University of Minnesota.—Excerpts reprinted by permission of the publisher.

"Explanation in Science and in History," R. Colodny (ed.) *Frontiers of Science and Philosophy*, Pittsburgh: University of Pittsburgh Press, 1962; pp. 9-33. Excerpts reprinted by permission of the publisher.

"Rational Action," from *Proceedings and Addresses of the American Philosophical Association*, Vol. 35 (1961-62), pp. 5-23. Yellow Springs, Ohio: The Antioch Press, 1962. Excerpts reprinted by permission of the American Philosophical Association.

similarities and differences between different areas of empirical inquiry, except for indicating that the procedures used in those different areas will be taken to conform to certain basic standards of objectivity. According to these standards, hypotheses and theories—including those invoked for explanatory purposes—must be capable of test by reference to publicly ascertainable evidence, and their acceptance is always subject to the proviso that they may have to be abandoned if adverse evidence or more adequate hypotheses or theories should be found.

A scientific explanation may be regarded as an answer to a why-question, such as: 'Why do the planets move in elliptical orbits with the sun at one focus?', 'Why does the moon look much larger when it is near the horizon than when it is high in the sky?', 'Why did the television apparatus on Ranger VI fail?', 'Why are children of blue-eyed parents always blue-eyed?', 'Why did Hitler go to war against Russia?'. There are other modes of formulating what we will call *explanation-seeking questions:* we might ask what caused the failure of the television apparatus on Ranger VI, or what led Hitler to his fateful decision. But a why-question always provides an adequate, if perhaps sometimes awkward, standard phrasing.

Sometimes the subject matter of an explanation, or the *explanandum,* is indicated by a noun, as when we ask for an explanation of the aurora borealis. It is important to realize that this kind of phrasing has a clear meaning only in so far as it can be restated in terms of why-questions. Thus, in the context of an explanation, the aurora borealis must be taken to be characterized by certain distinctive general features, each of them describable by a that-clause, for example: that it is normally found only in fairly high northern latitudes; that it occurs intermittently; that sunspot maxima, with their eleven-year cycle, are regularly accompanied by maxima in the frequency and brightness of aurora borealis displays; that an aurora shows characteristic spectral lines of rare atmospheric gases, and so on. And to ask for an explanation of the aurora borealis is to request an explanation of *why* auroral displays occur in the fashion indicated and *why* they have physical characteristics such as those just mentioned. Indeed, requests for an explanation of the aurora borealis, of the tides, of solar eclipses in general or of some individual solar eclipse in particular, or of a given influenza epidemic, and the like have a clear meaning only if it is understood what aspects of the phenomenon in question are to be explained; and in that case the explanatory problem can again be expressed in the form 'Why is it the case that p?', where the place of 'p' is occupied by an empirical statement specifying the explanandum. Questions of this type will be called *explanation-seeking why-questions.*

Not all why-questions call for explanations, however. Some of them solicit reasons in support of an assertion. Thus, statements such as 'Hurricane Delila will veer out into the Atlantic', 'He must have died of a heart attack', 'Plato would have disliked Stravinsky's music' might be met with the question 'Why should this be so?', which seeks to elicit, not an explanation, but evidence or grounds or reasons in support of the given assertion. Questions of this kind will be called *reason-seeking* or *epistemic*. To put them into the form 'Why should it be the case that *p*?' is misleading; their intent is more adequately conveyed by a phrasing such as 'Why should it be believed that *p*?' or 'What reasons are there for believing that *p*?'.

An explanation-seeking why-question normally presupposes that the statement occupying the place of '*p*' is true, and asks for an explanation of the presumptive fact, event, or state of affairs described by it; an epistemic why-question does not presuppose the truth of the corresponding statement, but on the contrary, solicits reasons for believing it true. An appropriate answer to the former will therefore offer an explanation of a presumptive empirical phenomenon; whereas an appropriate answer to the latter will offer validating or justifying grounds in support of a statement. Despite these differences in presuppositions and objectives, there are also important connections between the two kinds of question; in particular, as will be argued later (in sections 2.4 and 3.5), any adequate answer to an explanation-seeking question 'Why is it the case that *p*?' must also provide a potential answer to the corresponding epistemic question 'What grounds are there for believing that *p*?'

In the discussion that follows, I will first distinguish two basic types of scientific explanation, deductive-nomological and inductive-statistical, each characterized by a schematic "model"; and I will examine certain logical and methodological questions to which these models give rise, including a number of objections that have been raised against them. Following this, I propose to assess the significance and adequacy of the basic conceptions inherent in those models by exploring the extent to which they can serve to analyze the structure and to illuminate the rationale of different kinds of explanation offered in empirical science.

2. DEDUCTIVE-NOMOLOGICAL EXPLANATION

2.1 FUNDAMENTALS: D-N EXPLANATION AND THE CONCEPT OF LAW. In his book, *How We Think,*[1] John Dewey describes a phenomenon he observed one day while washing dishes. Having removed some glass tumblers from the hot suds and placed them upside down on a plate, he noticed that soap bubbles emerged from under the tumbler's rims, grew for a while, came to a standstill

---

1. Dewey (1910), chap. VI.

and finally receded into the tumblers. Why did this happen? Dewey outlines an explanation to this effect: Transferring the tumblers to the plate, he had trapped cool air in them; that air was gradually warmed by the glass, which initially had the temperature of the hot suds. This led to an increase in the volume of the trapped air, and thus to an expansion of the soap film that had formed between the plate and the tumblers' rims. But gradually, the glass cooled off, and so did the air inside, and as a result, the soap bubbles receded.

The explanation here outlined may be regarded as an argument to the effect that the phenomenon to be explained, *the explanandum phenomenon*, was to be expected in virtue of certain explanatory facts. These fall into two groups: (i) particular facts and (ii) uniformities expressible by means of general laws. The first group includes facts such as these: the tumblers had been immersed in soap suds of a temperature considerably higher than that of the surrounding air; they were put, upside down, on a plate on which a puddle of soapy water had formed that provided a connecting soap film, and so on. The second group of explanatory facts would be expressed by the gas laws and by various other laws concerning the exchange of heat between bodies of different temperature, the elastic behavior of soap bubbles, and so on. While some of these laws are only hinted at by such phrasings as 'the warming of the trapped air led to an increase in its pressure', and others are not referred to even in this oblique fashion, they are clearly presupposed in the claim that certain stages in the process yielded others as their results. If we imagine the various explicit or tacit explanatory assumptions to be fully stated, then the explanation may be conceived as a deductive argument of the form

$$(\text{D-N}) \qquad \left.\begin{array}{c} C, C_2, \ldots, C_k \\[2mm] L_1, L_2, \ldots, L_r \end{array}\right\} \text{Explanans } S$$

$$\frac{}{E \qquad\qquad \text{Explanandum-sentence}}$$

Here, $C_1, C_2, \ldots, C_k$ are sentences describing the particular facts invoked; $L_1, L_2, \ldots, L_r$ are the general laws on which the explanation rests. Jointly these sentences will be said to form the *explanans* S, where S may be thought of alternatively as the set of the explanatory sentences or as their conjunction. The conclusion E of the argument is a sentence describing the explanandum-phenomenon; I will call E the explanandum-sentence or explanandum-statement; the word 'explanandum' alone will be used to refer either to the explanandum-phenomenon or to the explanandum-sentence: the context will show which is meant.

The kind of explanation whose logical structure is suggested by the schema

(D-N) will be called *deductive-nomological explanation* or D-N *explanation* for short; for it effects a deductive subsumption of the explanandum under principles that have the character of general laws. Thus a D-N explanation answers the question '*Why* did the explanandum-phenomenon occur?' by showing that the phenomenon resulted from certain particular circumstances, specified in $C_1, C_2, \ldots, C_k$, in accordance with the laws $L_1, L_2, \ldots, L_r$. By pointing this out, the argument shows that, given the particular circumstances and the laws in question, the occurrence of the phenomenon *was to be expected;* and it is in this sense that the explanation enables us to *understand why* the phenomenon occurred.[2]

In a D-N explanation, then, the explanandum is a logical consequence of the explanans. Furthermore, reliance on general laws is essential to a D-N explanation; it is in virtue of such laws that the particular facts cited in the explanans possess explanatory relevance to the explanandum phenomenon. Thus, in the case of Dewey's soap bubbles, the gradual warming of the cool air trapped under the hot tumblers would constitute a mere accidental antecedent rather than an explanatory factor for the growth of the bubbles, if it were not for the gas laws, which connect the two events. But what if the explanandum sentence E in an argument of the form (D-N) is a logical consequence of the sentences $C_1, C_2, \ldots, C_k$ alone? Then, surely, no empirical laws are *required* to deduce E from the explanans; and any laws included in the latter are gratuitous, dispensable premises. Quite so; but in this case, the argument would not count as an explanation. For example, the argument:

The soap bubbles first expanded and then receded

The soap bubbles first expanded

2. A general conception of scientific explanation as involving a deductive subsumption under general laws was espoused, though not always clearly stated, by various thinkers in the past, and has been advocated by several recent or contemporary writers, among them N. R. Campbell [(1920), (1921)], who developed the idea in considerable detail. In a textbook published in 1934, the conception was concisely stated as follows: "Scientific explanation consists in subsuming under some rule or law which expresses an invariant character of a group of events, the particular events it is said to explain. Laws themselves may be explained, and in the same manner, by showing that they are consequences of more comprehensive theories." (Cohen and Nagel 1934, p. 397.) Popper has set forth this construal of explanation in several of his publications; *cf.* the note at the end of section 3 in Hempel and Oppenheim (1948). His earliest statement appears in section 12 of his book (1935), of which his work (1959) is an expanded English version. His book (1962) contains further observations on scientific explanation. For some additional references to other proponents of the general idea, see Donagan (1957), footnote 2; Scriven (1959), footnote 3. However, as will be shown in section 3, deductive subsumption under general laws does not constitute the only form of scientific explanation.

though deductively valid, clearly cannot qualify as an explanation of why the bubbles first expanded. The same remark applies to all other cases of this kind. A D-N explanation will have to contain, in its explanans, some general laws that are *required* for the deduction of the explanandum, i.e. whose deletion would make the argument invalid.

If the explanans of a given D-N explanation is true, i.e. if the conjunction of its constituent sentences is true, we will call the *explanation true;* a true explanation, of course, has a true explanandum as well. Next, let us call a *D-N explanation more or less strongly supported or confirmed* by a given body of evidence according as its explanans is more or less strongly confirmed by the given evidence. (One factor to be considered in appraising the empirical soundness of a given explanation will be the extent to which its explanans is supported by the total relevant evidence available.) Finally, by a *potential D-N explanation*, let us understand any argument that has the character of a D-N explanation except that the sentences constituting its explanans need not be true. In a potential D-N explanation, therefore, $L_1, L_2, \ldots, L_r$ will be what Goodman has called *lawlike sentences*, i.e. sentences that are like laws except for possibly being false. Sentences of this kind will also be referred to as *nomic* or *nomological*. We use the notion of a potential explanation, for example, when we ask whether a novel and as yet untested law or theory would provide an explanation for some empirical phenomenon; or when we say that the phlogiston theory, though now discarded, afforded an explanation for certain aspects of combustion.[3] Strictly speaking, only true lawlike statements can count as laws—one would hardly want to speak of false laws of nature. But for convenience I will occasionally use the term 'law' without implying that the sentence in question is true, as in fact, I have done already in the preceding sentence.

The characterization of laws as true lawlike sentences raises the important and intriguing problem of giving a clear characterization of lawlike sentences without, in turn, using the concept of law. This problem has proved to be highly recalcitrant, and I will make here only a few observations on certain aspects of it that are relevant also to the analysis of scientific explanation.

Lawlike sentences can have many different logical forms. Some paradigms of nomic sentences, such as 'All gases expand when heated under constant pressure' may be construed as having the simple universal conditional form $(x)(Fx \supset Gx)'$; others involve universal as well as existential generalization,

---

3. The explanatory role of the phlogiston theory is described in Conant (1951), pp. 164–71. The concept of potential explanation was introduced in Hempel and Oppenheim (1948), section 7. The concept of lawlike sentence, in the sense here indicated, is due to Goodman (1947).

as does the sentence 'For every chemical compound there exists a range of temperatures and pressures at which the compound is liquid'; many of the lawlike sentences and theoretical principles of the physical sciences assert more or less complex mathematical relationships between different quantitative variables.[4]

But lawlike sentences cannot be characterized in terms of their form alone. For example, not all sentences of the simple universal conditional form just mentioned are lawlike; hence, even if true, they are not laws. The sentences 'All members of the Greenbury School Board for 1964 are bald' and 'All pears in this basket are sweet' illustrate this point. Goodman[5] has pointed out a characteristic that distinguishes laws from such nonlaws: The former can, whereas the latter cannot, sustain counterfactual and subjunctive conditional statements. Thus the law about the expansion of gases can serve to support statements such as 'If the oxygen in this cylinder had been heated (were heated) under constant pressure then it would have expanded (would expand)'; whereas the statement about the School Board lends no support at all to the subjunctive conditional 'If Robert Crocker were a member of the Greenbury School Board for 1964 then he would be bald'.

We might add that the two kinds of sentence differ analogously in explanatory power. The gas law, in combination with suitable particular data, such as that the oxygen in the cylinder was heated under constant pressure, can serve to explain why the volume of the gas increased; but the statement about the School Board, analogously combined with a statement such as 'Harry Smith is a member of the Greenbury School Board for 1964' cannot explain why Harry Smith is bald.

But though these observations shed light on the concept of lawlikeness they afford no satisfactory explication of it; for one of them presupposes an understanding of counterfactual and of subjunctive conditional statements, which present notorious philosophical difficulties; the other makes use of the idea of explanation to clarify the concept of a lawlike statement; and we are

---

4. When Scriven speaks of "the deductive model, with its syllogistic form, where no student of elementary logic could fail to complete the inference, given the premise" (1959, p. 462), he imposes upon the model an entirely unwarranted oversimplified construal; for the schema (D-N) clearly allows for the use of highly complex general laws of the kind specified in the text above; and where there occur in the explanans, the explanandum cannot, of course, be deduced by syllogistic methods.

5. Goodman (1955), p. 25; for certain qualifications, *cf. ibid.*, p. 118.

here trying conversely to characterize a certain type of explanation with the help of concepts which include that of lawlike statement.

Now, our examples of non-lawlike sentences share a characteristic that might seem to afford a criterion for the distinction we seek to draw; namely, each of them applies to only a finite number of individual cases or instances. Must not a general law be conceived as admitting of indefinitely many instances?

Surely a lawlike sentence must not be *logically* limited to a finite number of instances: it must not be logically equivalent to a finite conjunction of singular sentences, or, briefly, it must be of *essentially generalized form*. Thus, the sentence 'Every element of the class consisting of the objects *a*, *b*, and *c* has the property *P*' is not lawlike; for it is logically equivalent to the conjunction '$Pa \cdot Pb \cdot Pc$', and clearly a sentence of this kind cannot support counterfactual conditionals or provide explanations.[6]

But our two earlier nonlawlike generalizations are not ruled out by this condition: they are not logically equivalent to corresponding finite conjunctions since they do not state specifically who are the members of the School Board, or what particular pears are in the basket. Should we, then, deny lawlike status also to any general sentence which—by empirical accident, so to speak—has only a finite number of instances? This would surely be ill-advised. Suppose, for example, that from the basic laws of celestial mechanics a general statement is derived concerning the relative motion of the components of a double star in the special case where those components are of exactly equal mass. Is this statement to be termed a law only if it has been established that there exist at least two (or perhaps more) instances of this special kind of double star? Or consider the general statement, derivable from Newton's laws of gravitation and of motion, which deals, in a manner similar to Galileo's law, with the free fall of physical bodies near the surface of a spherical mass having the same density as the Earth, but twice its radius. Should this statement not be called a law unless it had been shown to have several instances—even though it is a logical consequence of a set of laws with many instances?

6. In such references to "the form" of a sentence, there lurks another difficulty: that form is clearly determined only if the sentence is expressed in a formalized language. An English sentence such as 'This object is soluble in water' may be construed as a singular sentence of the form 'Pa', but alternatively also as a sentence of generalized form stating that if at any time the object is put into any (sufficiently large) body of water, it will dissolve. (This will be elaborated further in section 2.3.1.) Our remark about a sentence of the form 'For all x, if x is a, b, or c, then x has property P' might be stated more circumspectly by saying that that kind of sentence is not a law *in terms of P*; it cannot serve to explain the occurrence of P in any particular case; nor can it support counterfactual or subjunctive conditionals about particular occurrences of P.

Besides, there appears to be only an inessential "difference in degree" between a general statement that happens to have just one instance and another which happens to have two or some other finite number. But, then, how many instances would a law be required to have? To insist on some particular finite number would be arbitrary; and the requirement of an infinite number of actual instances would raise obvious difficulties. Clearly, the concept of scientific law cannot reasonably be subjected to any condition concerning the number of instances, except for the requirement barring logical equivalence with singular statements.

Besides, we should note that the concept, presupposed in the preceding discussion, of a "case" or an "instance" of a general statement is by no means as clear as it might seem. Consider, for example, general statements of the form, 'All objects with the property F also have the property G', or briefly 'All F are G'. It seems natural to accept the criterion that a particular object i is an instance of such a statement if and only if i has the property F and the property G, or briefly, if i is both F and G. This would imply that if there are no objects with the property F at all, the general statement has no instances. Yet, the statement is logically equivalent with 'All non-G are non-F', which, under the contemplated criterion, may well have instances even if there are no F. Thus, the general statement, 'All unicorns feed on clover' would have no instance, but its equivalent 'Anything that does not feed on clover is not a unicorn' would have many—perhaps infinitely many—instances. An analogous remark might well be true of the law mentioned earlier concerning double stars whose components have equal mass. Hence, the contemplated criterion of instantiation, which seems quite obvious at first, has the consequence that of two logically equivalent general statements, one may have no instances, the other, infinitely many. But this makes the criterion unacceptable since such equivalent sentences express the same law and thus should be instantiated by the same objects.

For laws of the simple kind just considered, the following alternative definition of instantiation will suffice to assign the same instances to equivalent statements: an object i is an instance of the statement 'All F are G' if and only if it is not the case that i is F but not G. However, for laws of more complex logical form, the concept of instance raises further problems.[7] But these

---

7. These difficulties concerning the intuitive idea of instantiation of a general law are closely related to the paradoxes of confirmation set forth in Hempel (1945). The inadequacy of the initially contemplated intuitive criterion is further illustrated by the following consequence: The sentence 'All F are G' is logically equivalent to 'Anything that is F but not G is both G and not G'; and on the criterion in question, this sentence clearly cannot have any instances—even if 'All F are G' is true and is instantiated by infinitely many objects that are both F and G. Our modified criterion of instantiation avoids this difficulty: the sets of instances, thus construed, of any two logically equivalent universally quantified sentences in one variable are identical.

need not be pursued here, for I am not proposing that a law must satisfy certain minimum conditions concerning the number of its instances.

There is yet another common trait of our non-lawlike generalizations that seems to hold promise as a criterion for the distinction here under discussion: they contain terms, such as 'this basket' and 'the Greenbury School Board for 1964', which directly or indirectly refer to particular objects, persons, or places; whereas the terms occurring in Newton's laws or in the gas laws involve no such reference. In an earlier article on the subject, Oppenheim and I suggested, therefore, that the constituent predicates of what we called fundamental law-like sentences must all be such that the specification of their meaning requires no reference to any one particular object or location.[8] We noted, however, that this characterization still is not satisfactory for purposes of explication because the idea of "the meaning" of a given term is itself far from being clear.

Besides, reference to particular individuals does not always deprive a general statement of explanatory power, as is illustrated by Galileo's law for free fall, whose full formulation makes reference to the earth. Now it is true that, with qualifications soon to be stated, Galileo's law may be regarded as derivable from the laws of Newtonian theory, which have the character of fundamental lawlike sentences, so that an explanation based on Galileo's law can also be effected by means of fundamental laws. But it certainly cannot be taken for granted that all other laws mentioning particular individuals can similarly be derived from fundamental laws.

Goodman, in a searching exploration of the concept of law, has argued that, in contrast to non-lawlike generalizations, lawlike sentences are capable of being supported by observed instances and hence of being "projected" from examined to unexamined cases; and he has argued further that the relative "projectibiltiy" of generalizations is determined primarily by the relative "entrenchment" of their constituent predicates, i.e. by the extent to which those predicates have been used in previously projected generalizations.[9] Thus, terms, like 'member of the Greenbury School Board for 1964' and 'pear in this basket' would be disqualified, for the purposes of formulating lawlike sentences, on the ground that they lack adequate entrenchment.

8. Hempel and Oppenheim (1948), section 6. "Specification of meaning" might be conceived as effected by definition or perhaps by weaker means, such as Carnap's reduction sentences. See Carnap (1938) and, for more details, (1936-37). The distinction thus attempted between those terms which in some way refer to particular individuals and those which do not is closely akin to the distinction made by Popper, in section 14 of (1935) and (1959), between individual concepts, "in the definition of which proper names (or equivalent signs) are indispensable," and universal concepts, for which this is not the case.

9. For details, and for further considerations that affect projectibility, see Goodman (1955), especially chapters III and IV.

But while Goodman's criterion thus succeeds in barring from the class of lawlike sentences such generalizations as our two examples, the class of lawlike sentences it delimits still seems too inclusive for our purposes. For according to Goodman, the "entrenchment of a predicate results from the actual projection not merely of that predicate alone but also of all predicates coextensive with it. In a sense, not the word itself but the class it selects is what becomes entrenched . . ."[10] Hence, replacing a predicate in a lawlike sentence by a coextensive one should yield a lawlike sentence again. Is this generally the case? Suppose that the hypothesis h: '$(x)(Px \supset Qx)$' is lawlike, but that as a matter of empirical fact there happen to be just three elements in the class selected by 'P', namely a, b, and c. Then 'Px' is coextensive with '$x = a$ v $x = b$ v $x = c$.' Replacement of 'Px' by this expression, however, turns h into the sentence '$(x)[(x=a$ v $x=b$ v $x=c) \supset Qx]$', which, being logically equivalent with '$Qa \cdot Qb \cdot Qc$', is not lawlike on our understanding that a lawlike sentence must be of essentially generalized form, so as to be able to serve in an explanatory role. Our conception of lawlikeness differs at this point from that envisaged by Goodman, who introduces the notion principally in an effort to establish a dividing line between sentences that are confirmable by their instances and those that are not.[11] It may not be necessary to require of the former that they be of essentially general form, and Goodman does not impose this requirement on lawlike sentences. For laws, however, that are to function in an explanatory capacity, the requirement seems to me indispensable.

Though the preceding discussion has not led to a fully satisfactory general characterization of lawlike sentences and thus of laws, it will, I hope, have clarified to some extent the sense in which those concepts will be understood in the present study.[12]

The examples we have considered so far illustrate the deductive explanation of particular occurrences by means of empirical laws. But empirical science raises the question "Why?" also in regard to the uniformities expressed by such laws and often answers it, again, by means of a deductive-nomological explanation, in which the uniformity in question is subsumed under more inclusive laws or under theoretical principles. For example, the questions of why freely falling bodies move in accordance with Galileo's law and why the motion of the planets exhibit the uniformities expressed by Kepler's laws are answered by showing that these laws are but special consequences of the Newtonian laws of gravitation and of motion. Similarly, the uniformities

10. Goodman (1955), pp. 95-96.

11. On this distinction, see the Postscript to the article "Studies in the Logic of Confirmation" in this volume.

12. For further discussions of the problems here referred to see Braithwaite (1953), chap. IX and Nagel (1961), chap. 4.

expressed by the laws of geometrical optics, such as those of the rectilinear propagation of light and of reflection and refraction, are accounted for by subsumption under the principles of wave optics. For brevity, an explanation of a uniformity expressed by a law will sometimes be elliptically referred to as an explanation of the law in question.

It should be noted, however, that in the illustrations just mentioned, the theory invoked does not, strictly speaking, imply the presumptive general laws to be explained; rather, it implies that those laws hold only within a limited range, and even there, only approximately. Thus, Newton's law of gravitation implies that the acceleration of a freely falling body is not constant, as Galileo's law asserts, but undergoes a very slight but steady increase as the body approaches the ground. But while, strictly speaking, Newton's law contradicts Galileo's, it shows that the latter is almost exactly satisfied in free fall over short distances. In slightly greater detail, we might say that the Newtonian theory of gravitation and of motion implies its own laws concerning free fall under various circumstances. According to one of these, the acceleration of a small object falling freely toward a homogeneous spherical body varies inversely as the square of its distance from the center of the sphere, and thus increases in the course of the fall; and the uniformity expressed by this law is explained in a strictly deductive sense by the Newtonian theory. But when conjoined with the assumption that the earth is a homogeneous sphere of specified mass and radius, the law in question implies that for free fall over short distances near the surface of the earth, Galileo's law holds to a high degree of approximation; in this sense, the theory might be said to provide an *approximative D-N explanation* of Galileo's law.

Again, in the case of planetary motion, the Newtonian theory implies that since a planet is subject to gravitational attraction not only from the Sun, but also from the other planets, its orbit will not be exactly elliptical, but will show certain perturbations. Hence, as Duhem[13] noted, Newton's law of gravitation, far from being an inductive generalization based on Kepler's laws, is, strictly speaking, incompatible with them. One of its important credentials is precisely the fact that it enables the astronomer to compute the deviations of the planets from the elliptic orbits Kepler had assigned to them.

A similar relation obtains between the principles of wave optics and the laws of geometrical optics. For example, the former calls for a diffractive "bending" of light around obstacles—a phenomenon ruled out by the con-

___
13. See Duhem (1906), pp. 312 ff. Duhem's remarks on this subject are included in those excerpts from P. P. Wiener's translation of Duhem's work that are reprinted in Feigl and Brodbeck (1953). The point has recently been re-emphasized by several writers, among them Popper (1957a), pp. 29-34, and Feyerabend (1962), pp. 46-48.

ception of light as composed of rays traveling in straight lines. But in analogy to the preceding illustration, the wave-theoretical account implies that the laws of rectilinear propagation, of reflection, and of refraction as formulated in geometrical optics are satisfied to a very high degree of approximation within a limited range of cases, including those which provided experimental support for the laws in their original formulation.

In general, an explanation based on theoretical principles will both broaden and deepen our understanding of the empirical phenomena concerned. It will achieve an increase in breadth because the theory will usually cover a wider range of occurrences than do the empirical laws previously established. For example, Newton's theory of gravitation and of motion governs free fall not only on the earth, but also on other celestial bodies; and not only planetary motions, but also the relative motion of double stars, the orbits of comets and of artificial satellites, the movements of pendulums, certain aspects of the tides, and many other phenomena. And a theoretical explanation deepens our understanding for at least two reasons. First, it reveals the different regularities exhibited by a variety of phenomena, such as those just mentioned in reference to Newton's theory, as manifestations of a few basic laws. Secondly, as we noted, the generalizations previously accepted as correct statements of empirical regularities will usually appear as approximations only of certain lawlike statements implied by the explanatory theory, and to be very nearly satisfied only within a certain limited range. And in so far as tests of the laws in their earlier formulation were confined to cases in that range, the theoretical account also indicates why those laws, though not generally true, should have been found confirmed.

When a scientific theory is superseded by another in the sense in which classical mechanics and electrodynamics were superseded by the special theory of relativity, then the succeeding theory will generally have a wider explanatory range, including phenomena the earlier theory could not account for; and it will as a rule provide approximative explanations for the empirical laws implied by its predecessor. Thus, special relativity theory implies that the laws of the classical theory are very nearly satisfied in cases involving motion only at velocities which are small compared to that of light.

The general conception of explanation by deductive subsumption under general laws or theoretical principles, as it has been outlined in this section, will be called the *deductive nomological-model*, or the *D-N model of explanation;* the laws invoked in such an explanation will also be referred to, in William Dray's suggestive phrase, as *covering laws*.[14] Unlike Dray, however, I will not

---

14. For Dray's use of the terms 'covering law' and 'covering law model', see Dray (1957), and also (1963), p. 106.

refer to the D-N model as the covering-law model, for I will subsequently introduce a second basic model of scientific explanation which also relies on covering laws, but which is not of deductive-nomological form. The term 'covering-law model' will then serve to refer to both of those models.

As the schema (D-N) plainly indicates, a deductive-nomological explanation is not conceived as invoking only one covering law; and our illustrations show how indeed many different laws may be invoked in explaining one phenomenon. A purely logical point should be noted here, however. If an explanation is of the form (D-N), then the laws $L_1, L_2, \ldots, L_r$ invoked in its explanans logically imply a law L^* which by itself would suffice to explain the explanandum event by reference to the particular conditions noted in the sentences $C_1, C_2, \ldots, C_k$. This law L^* is to the effect that whenever conditions of the kind described in the sentences $C_1, C_2, \ldots, C_k$ are realized then an event of the kind described by the explanandum-sentence occurs.[15] Consider an example: A chunk of ice floats in a large beaker of water at room temperature. Since the ice extends above the surface, one might expect the water level to rise as the ice melts; actually, it remains unchanged. Briefly, this can be explained as follows: According to Archimedes' principle, a solid body floating in a liquid displaces a volume of liquid that has the same weight as the body itself. Hence, the chunk of ice has the same weight as the water displaced by its submerged portion. Since melting does not change the weight, the ice turns into a mass of water of the same weight, and hence also of the same volume, as the water initially displaced by its submerged portion; consequently, the water level remains unchanged. The laws on which this account is based include Archimedes' principle, a law concerning the melting of ice at room temperature; the principle of the conservation of mass; and so on. None of these laws mentions the particular glass of water or the particular piece of ice with which the explanation is concerned. Hence the laws imply not only that as this particular piece of ice melts in this particular glass, the water level remains unchanged, but rather the general statement L^* that under the same *kind* of circumstance, i.e., when any piece of ice floats in water in any glass at room temperature, the same *kind* of phenomenon will occur, i.e., the water level will remain unchanged. The law L^* will usually be "weaker" than the laws $L_1, L_2, \ldots, L_r$; i.e., while being logically implied by the conjunction of those laws, it will not, in general, imply that conjunction. Thus, in our illustration one of the original explanatory laws applies also to the floating of a piece of marble on mercury or of a boat on water, whereas L^* deals only with the case of ice floating on water. But clearly, L^* in conjunction with $C_1, C_2, \ldots, C_k$ logically implies E and could indeed be used to

---

15. This was noted already in Hempel (1942), section 2.1.

explain, in this context, the event described by E. We might therefore refer to L^* as a *minimal covering law* implicit in a given D-N explanation.[16] But while such laws might be used for explanatory purposes, the D-N model by no means restricts deductive-nomological explanations to the use of minimal laws. Indeed such a restriction would fail to do justice to one important objective of scientific inquiry, namely, that of establishing laws and theories of broad scope, under which narrower generalizations may then be subsumed as special cases or as close approximations of such.[17]

2.2 CAUSAL EXPLANATION AND THE D-N MODEL. An explanation of a particular occurrence is often conceived as pointing out what "caused" it. Thus, the initial expansion of the soap bubbles described by John Dewey might be said to have been caused by the warming of the air caught in the tumblers. But causal attributions of this kind presuppose appropriate laws, such as that under

16. The problem of formulating a precise definition of this notion need not detain us: it can be solved only by reference to some formalized language, and for our purposes the rough characterization here given will suffice. Incidentally, the notion of "the number of laws" invoked in a given explanation is not as clear as it might seem, for one law may sometimes be quite plausibly rewritten as a conjunction of two or more, and, conversely, several laws may sometimes be plausibly conjoined into one. But again, it is not necessary for us to pursue this problem.

17. In a recent essay, Feyerabend has criticized the deductive model of explanation for leading "to the demand. . . that all successful theories in a given domain must be mutually consistent" (1962, p. 30), or, more fully, that "only such theories are admissible (for explanation and prediction) in a given domain which either *contain* the theories already used in this domain, or are at least *consistent* with them" (1962, p. 44, italics the author's). Feyerabend rightly argues that this demand conflicts with actual scientific procedure and is unsound on methodological grounds. But he is completely mistaken in his allegation—for which he offers no support—that the conception of explanation by deductive subsumption under general laws or theoretical principles entails the incriminated methodological maxim. Indeed, the D-N model of explanation concerns simply the relation between explanans and explanandum and implies nothing whatever about the compatibility of different explanatory principles that might be accepted successively in a given field of empirical science. In particular, it does not imply that a new explanatory theory may be accepted only on condition that it be logically compatible with those previously accepted. One and the same phenomenon, or set of phenomena, may be deductively subsumable under different, and logically incompatible, laws or theories. To illustrate this schematically: the fact that three objects a, b, c, each of which has the property P, also have the property Q could be deductively accounted for by the hypothesis H_1 that all and only P's are Q's, and alternatively by the hypothesis H_2 that all P's and also some non-P's are Q's; i.e., the explanandum-sentence '$Qa.Qb.Qc$' can be deduced from '$Pa.Pb.Pc$' in conjunction with either H_1 or H_2, although H_1 and H_2 are logically incompatible. Thus a "new" explanatory theory for a given class of phenomena may deductively account for those phenomena even though it is logically incompatible with an earlier theory which also deductively accounts for them. But the conflicting theories cannot both be true, and it may well be that the earlier theory is false. Hence the maxim criticized by Feyerabend is indeed unsound. But this observation does not affect the D-N model of explanation, which does not imply that maxim at all.

constant pressure the volume of a gas increases as its temperature rises. And by virtue of thus presupposing general laws which connect "cause" and "effect," causal explanation conforms to the D-N model. Let me briefly amplify and substantiate this remark.

Consider first the explanatory use of what may be called *general* statements of causal connection: these are to the effect that an event of some *kind A* (e.g., motion of a magnet through a closed wire loop) causes an event of a certain other *kind, B* (e.g., flow of an electric current in the wire). Without entering into a more detailed analysis, we may say that in the simplest case a statement of this type affirms a law to the effect that whenever an event of kind *A* takes place then there occurs, at the same location or at a specifiable different one, a corresponding event of kind *B*. This construal fits, for example, the statements that motion of a magnet causes the flow of a current in a neighboring wire loop, and that raising the temperature of a gas under constant pressure increases its volume. Many general statements of causal connection call for a more complex analysis, however. Thus, the statement that in a mammal, stoppage of the heart will cause death presupposes certain "standard" conditions that are not explicitly stated, but that are surely meant to preclude, for example, the use of a heart-lung machine. "To say that *X* causes *Y* is to say that under proper conditions, an *X* will be followed by a *Y*," as Scriven[18] puts it. When this kind of causal locution is used, there usually is some understanding of what "proper" or "standard" background conditions are presupposed in the given context. But to the extent that those conditions remain indeterminate, a general statement of causal connection amounts at best to the vague claim that *there are* certain further unspecified background conditions whose explicit mention in the given statement would yield a truly general law connecting the "cause" and the "effect" in question.

Next, consider statements of causal connections between individual events. Take, for example, the assertion that the expansion and subsequent shrinkage of Dewey's soap bubbles were *caused* by a rise and subsequent drop of the temperature of the air trapped in the tumblers. Clearly, those temperature changes afford the requisite explanation only in conjunction with certain other conditions, such as the presence of a soap film, practically constant temperature and pressure of the air outside the glasses, and so on. Accordingly, in the context of explanation, a "cause" must be allowed to be a more or less complex set of circumstances and events, which might be described by a set of statements $C_1, C_2, \ldots, C_k$. And, as is suggested by the principle "Same cause, same effect," the assertion that those circumstances jointly caused a given event implies that

18. Scriven (1958), p. 185.

whenever and wherever circumstances of the kind in question occur, an event of the kind to be explained takes place. Thus the causal explanation implicitly claims that there are general laws—let us say, $L_1, L_2, \ldots, L_r$—in virtue of which the occurrence of the causal antecedents mentioned in $C_1, C_2, \ldots, C_k$ is a sufficient condition for the occurrence of the explanandum event. This relation between causal factors and effect is reflected in our schema (D-N): causal explanation is, at least implicitly, deductive-nomological.

Let me restate the point in more general terms. When an individual event b is said to have been caused by another individual event a, then surely the claim is implied that whenever "the same cause" is realized, "the same effect" will occur. But this claim cannot be taken to mean that whenever a recurs then so does b; for a and b are individual events at particular spatiotemporal locations and thus occur only once. Rather, a and b must be viewed as particular events of certain *kinds* (such as heating or cooling of a gas, expansion or shrinking of a gas) of which there may be further instances. And the law tacitly implied by the assertion that b, as an event of kind B, was caused by a as an event of kind A is a general statement of causal connection to the effect that, under suitable circumstances, an instance of A is invariably accompanied by an instance of B. In most causal explanations the requisite circumstances are not fully stated; the import of the claim that b was caused by a may then be suggested by the following approximate formulation: Event b was in fact preceded by event a in circumstances which, though not fully specified, were of such a kind that an occurrence of an event of kind A under such circumstances is universally followed by an event of kind B. For example, the statement that the burning (event of kind B) of a particular haystack was caused by a lighted cigarette dropped into the hay (particular event of kind A) asserts, first of all, that the latter event did take place; but a burning cigarette will set a haystack on fire only if certain further conditions are satisfied, which cannot at present be fully stated; and thus, the causal attribution at hand implies secondly that further conditions of a not fully specified kind were realized, under which an event of kind A is invariably followed by an event of kind B.

To the extent that a statement of individual causation leaves the relevant antecedent conditions, and thus also the requisite explanatory laws, indefinite it is like a note saying that there is a treasure hidden somewhere. Its significance and utility will increase as the location of the treasure is more narrowly circumscribed, as the relevant conditions and the corresponding covering laws are made increasingly explicit. In some cases, this can be done quite satisfactorily; the covering-law structure then emerges, and the statement of individual causal connection becomes amenable to test. When, on the other hand, the relevant conditions or laws remain largely indefinite, a statement of causal connection is rather in the nature of a program, or of a sketch, for an explanation in terms of causal laws; it might also be viewed as a "working hypothesis" which may prove its worth by giving new, and fruitful, direction to further research.

The view here taken of statements of individual causation might be further clarified by some comments on the thesis that "when one asserts that X causes Y one is certainly committed to the generalization that an identical cause would produce an identical effect, but this in no way commits one to any necessity for producing laws not involving the term 'identical,' which justify this claim. Producing laws is one way, not necessarily more conclusive, and usually less easy than other ways of supporting the causal statement.... (The idea of individual causation has, I think, this not inconsiderable basis.)"[19] Two questions must be clearly distinguished here, namely (i) what is being claimed by the statement that X causes Y (where, in the case of "individual causation," X and Y are individual events), and in particular, whether asserting it commits one to a generalization, and (ii) what kind of evidence would support the causal statement, and in particular, whether support can be provided only by producing generalizations in the form of laws.

Concerning the first question, I have argued that the given causal statement must be taken to claim by implication that an appropriate law or set of laws holds by virtue of which X causes Y. But, as noted earlier, the laws in question *cannot* be expressed by saying that an identical cause would produce an identical effect; for if X and Y are individual events with specific spatiotemporal locations, the recurrence of a cause identical with X, or of an effect identical with Y, is logically impossible. Rather, the general claim implied by the statement of individual causation that X caused Y is of the kind suggested in our discussion of the assertion that individual event a, as an instance of A, caused individual event b, as an instance of B.

We turn now to the second question. In certain cases, such as that of the soap bubbles observed by Dewey, some of the laws connecting the individual events X and Y may be explicitly stateable; and then, it may be possible to secure supporting evidence for them by appropriate experiments or observations. Hence, while the statement of individual causal connection implicitly *claims* the existence of underlying laws, the claim may well be *supported* by evidence consisting of particular confirming instances rather than of general laws. In other cases, when the nomological claim implicit in a causal statement is merely to the effect that *there are* relevant factors and suitable laws connecting X and Y, it may be possible to lend some credibility to this claim by showing

19. Scriven (1958), p. 194.

that under certain conditions, an event of kind X is at least very frequently accompanied by an event of kind Y: this might justify the working hypothesis that the background conditions could be further narrowed down in a way that would eventually yield a strictly causal connection. It is this kind of statistical evidence, for example, that is adduced in support of such claims as that cigarette smoking is "a cause of" or "a causative factor in" cancer of the lungs. In this case, the supposed causal laws cannot at present be explicitly stated. Thus, the nomological claim implied by this causal conjecture is of the existential type; it has the character of a working hypothesis for further research. The statistical evidence adduced lends support to the hypothesis and suggests further investigation, aimed at determining more precisely the conditions under which smoking will lead to cancer of the lungs.

The best examples of explanations conforming to the D-N model are based on physical theories of deterministic character. Briefly, a deterministic theory deals with the changes of "state" in physical systems of some specified kind. The state of such a system at any given time is characterized by the values assumed at that time by certain quantitative characteristics of the system, the so-called variables of state; and the laws specified by such a theory for the changes of state are deterministic in the sense that, given the state of the system at any one time, they determine its state at any other, earlier or later, time. For example, classical mechanics offers a deterministic theory for a system of point masses (or, practically, bodies that are small in relation to their distances) which move under the influence of their mutual gravitational attraction alone. The state of such a system at a given time is defined as determined by the positions and momenta of its component bodies at that time and does not include other aspects that might undergo change, such as the color or the chemical constitution of the moving bodies. The theory provides a set of laws—essentially, the Newtonian laws of gravitation and of motion—which, given the positions and momenta of the elements of such a system at any one time, mathematically determine their positions and momenta at any other time. In particular, those laws make it possible to offer a D-N explanation of the system's being in a certain state at a given time, by specifying, in the sentences $C_1, C_2, \ldots, C_k$ of the schema (D-N), the state of the system at some earlier time. The theory here referred to has been applied, for example, in accounting for the motions of planets and comets, and for solar and lunar eclipses.

In the explanatory or predictive use of a deterministic theory, then, the notion of a cause as a more or less narrowly circumscribed antecedent event has been replaced by that of some antecedent state of the total system, which provides the "initial conditions" for the computation, by means of the theory, of the later state that is to be explained. If the system is not isolated, i.e., if relevant outside influences act upon the system during the period of time from the initial state invoked to the state to be explained, then the particular circumstances that must be stated in the explanans include also those outside influences; and it is these "boundary conditions" in conjunction with the "initial" conditions which replace the everyday notion of cause, and which are specified by the statements $C_1, C_2, \ldots, C_k$ in the schematic representation (D–N) of deductive-nomological explanation.[20]

Causal explanation in its various degrees of explicitness and precision is not, however, the only mode of explanation on which the D–N model has a bearing. For example, the explanation of a general law by deductive subsumption under theoretical principles is clearly not an explanation by causes. But even when used to account for individual events, D–N explanations are not always causal. For example, the fact that a given simple pendulum takes two seconds to complete one full swing might be explained by pointing out that its length is 100 centimeters, and that the period t (in seconds), of any simple pendulum is connected with its length l (in centimeters) by the law that $t = 2\pi\sqrt{l/g}$, where g is the acceleration of free fall. This law expresses a mathematical relationship between the length and the period (which is a quantitative dispositional characteristic) of the pendulum at one and the same time; laws of this kind, of which the laws of Boyle and of Charles, as well as Ohm's law are other examples, are sometimes called *laws of coexistence*, in contradistinction to *laws of succession*, which concern temporal changes in a system. These latter include, for example, Galileo's law and the laws for the changes of state in systems covered by a deterministic theory. Causal explanation by reference to antecedent events clearly presupposes laws of succession; in the case of the pendulum, where only a law of coexistence is invoked, one surely would not say that the pendulum's having a period of two seconds was *caused* by the fact that it had a length of 100 centimeters.

One further point deserves notice here. The law for the simple pendulum makes it possible not only to infer the period of a pendulum from its length, but also conversely to infer its length from its period; in either case, the inference is of the form (D–N). Yet a sentence stating the length of a given pendulum, in conjunction with the law, will be much more readily regarded as explaining the pendulum's period than a sentence stating the period, in conjunction with the law, would be considered as explaining the pendulum's length. This distinction appears to reflect the idea that we might change the length of the

---

20. For more detailed accounts of the notions of causality and of deterministic theory and deterministic system, see, for example, Feigl (1953); Frank (1957), chapters 11 and 12; Margenau (1950), chapter 19; Nagel (1961), pp. 73–78 and chapters 7 and 10.

pendulum at will and thus control its period as a "dependent variable," whereas the reverse procedure does not seem possible.[21] This conception is questionable, however; for we can also change the period of a given pendulum at will, namely, by changing its length. It cannot validly be argued that in the first case we have a change of length independently of a change of the period, for if the location of the pendulum remains fixed, then its length cannot be changed without also changing the period. In cases such as this, the common-sense conception of explanation appears to provide no clear grounds on which to decide whether a given argument that deductively subsumes an occurrence under laws is to qualify as an explanation.

In the instance just considered, a particular fact was explained, not by causal antecedents but by reference to another contemporaneous fact. It might even be argued that sometimes a particular event can be satisfactorily explained by reference to subsequent occurrences. Consider, for example, a beam of light that travels from a point A in one optical medium to a point B in another, which borders upon the first along a plane. Then, according to Fermat's principle of least time, the beam will follow a path that makes the traveling time from A to B a minimum as compared with alternative paths available. Which path this is will depend on the refractive indices of the two media; we will assume that these are given. Suppose now that the path from A to B determined by Fermat's principle passes through an intermediate point C. Then this fact may be said to be D-N explainable by means of Fermat's law in conjunction with the relevant data concerning the optical media and the information that the light traveled from A to B. But its "arrival at B," which thus serves as one of the explanatory factors, occurs only after the event to be explained, namely, the beam's passing through C.

Any uneasiness at explaining an event by reference to factors that include later occurrences might spring from the idea that explanations of the more familiar sort, such as our earlier examples, seem to exhibit the explanandum event as having been brought about by earlier occurrences; whereas no event can be said to have been brought about by factors some of which were not even realized at the time of its occurrence. Perhaps this idea also seems to cast doubt upon purported explanations by reference to simultaneous circumstances. But, while such considerations may well make our earlier examples of explanation, and all causal explanations, seem more natural or plausible, it is not clear what precise construal could be given to the notion of factors "bringing about" a given event, and what reason there would be for denying

21. In this connection, *cf.* the discussion of causal statements as recipes for producing a given effect, in Gasking (1955).

the status of explanation to all accounts invoking occurrences that temporally succeed the event to be explained.[22]

2.3 THE ROLE OF LAWS IN EXPLANATION. The D-N model, as we have seen, assigns to laws or theoretical principles the role of indispensable premises in explanatory arguments. I will now consider some alternative conceptions of the role of laws in explanation.

2.3.1. *The Conception of Laws as Inference Rules.* One recently influential view construes laws and theoretical principles as inference rules in accordance with which particular statements of empirical fact may be inferred from other such statements.

Thus Schlick once held the view, for which he gave credit to Wittgenstein, that "basically a natural law does not have the logical character of a 'proposition' but represents 'a direction for the formulation of propositions'."[23] Schlick espoused this idea largely because he held at the time that a genuine statement must be capable of strict verification by particular experiential findings—a requirement evidently not met by general laws, which pertain to indefinitely many particular cases. But the requirement of strict verifiability for sentences that are to qualify as empirically significant has long since been abandoned as too restrictive,[24] and it surely constitutes no good reason for construing laws as rules rather than as statements.

In a somewhat different vein, Ryle has characterized law statements as statements which are true or false, but which characteristically function as inference licenses authorizing inferential moves from the assertion of some factual statements to the assertion of others.[25] This conception has influenced the views of several other writers on the role of laws in scientific and historical explanation. Dray, for example, has offered some interesting considerations in support of it with special reference to historical explanation. He points out that since an explanation of a concrete historical event will usually have to take into account a large set of relevant factors, the corresponding covering law may well be so highly qualified as to possess only one single, instance namely, the

22. For further observations on this issue, cf. Scheffler (1957).

23. Schlick (1931), p. 190 of English translation. See also the discussion of this idea by Toulmin, who accepts it with certain qualifications (1953, pp. 90-105), and who develops, in a somewhat similar spirit, an extensive analogy between physical theories and maps (1953, chapter 4). For illuminating comments on Toulmin's views, and on the problem in general, see Nagel's review of Toulmin's book in *Mind* 63, pp. 403-12 (1954), reprinted in Nagel (1956), pp. 303-15.

24. For details, see the essay "Empiricist Criteria of Cognitive Significance: Problems and Changes," in this volume.

25. Cf. Ryle (1949), pp. 121-123 and Ryle (1950).

occurrence it explains. But under these circumstances, Dray questions the propriety of applying the term 'law', whose ordinary use "has 'other cases' built right into it."[26] He holds, therefore, that though, when offering the explanation 'E because $C_1, C_2, \ldots, C_n$', the historian "commits himself to the truth of the covering general statement, 'If $C_1 \ldots C_n$ then E', . . . the statement thus elicited . . . is surely nothing more than a formulation of the *principle of the historian's inference* when he says that from the set of factors specified, a result of this kind could reasonably be predicted. The historian's inference may be said to be *in accordance with* this principle. But it is quite another matter to say that his explanation entails a corresponding *empirical law*."[27] Dray conceives of such principles of inference as being "general hypotheticals" of the form 'if p then q'; and he holds that "to claim simply that a 'general hypothetical' lurks implicitly in the historian's explanation is to claim *considerably less* than covering law theorists generally do"; for if the general hypothetical is construed as an inference license in Ryle's sense, then "to say that the historian's explanation commits him to the covering 'law' is merely to say that it commits him . . . . to reasoning in a similar way in any further cases *which may turn up*, since he claims universal validity for the corresponding argument, 'p so q'."[28]

But surely, to claim universal validity for this argument scheme is to assert by implication, the general statement 'Whenever p and q', and vice versa: there is no difference in the strength of the claims, but only in the mode of expressing them. And if the general statement has only one instance, then so does the corresponding rule, and one might with equal justice question the propriety of qualifying the latter as a principle of inference, on the ground that the idea of such a principle or rule, no less than the idea of a law, carries with it a suggestion of generality.

In his remarks on the number of instances of a law, Dray seems to view a historical explanation as using only one general hypothetical, namely, in effect, a "minimum covering law" of the kind mentioned earlier. As a rule, however, an explanation will rely on a more or less comprehensive set of laws, each of which has many instances, and of which the narrower covering law is simply a highly specific consequence. But suppose that a given explanation does rely on just one highly specific generalization that has only one instance. Can that generalization be qualified as a law? Our discussion in section 2.1 bears on this question, and it will suffice to add here only a few brief remarks. Suppose that an attempt were made to explain Hitler's decision to invade Russia by means of the generalization 'Anyone exactly like Hitler in all respects, and facing

26. Dray (1957), p. 40.
27. Dray (1957), p. 39. Italics the author's.
28. Dray (1957), p. 41. Italics supplied.

exactly the same circumstances, decides to invade Russia'. This clearly affords no explanation because the general statement invoked is equivalent to the sentence 'Hitler decided to invade Russia', which is not a general sentence at all, and which simply restates the explanandum; for being exactly like Hitler in all respects is the same thing as being identical with Hitler. Thus, the proposed generalization is nonlawlike because it is not essentially generalized.

But a general statement—such as one of the highly specific covering laws envisaged by Dray—may well have only one instance without being logically equivalent to a singular sentence. This feature, as we noted earlier, would not deprive the generalization of lawlike status and potential explanatory power.

The arguments here briefly considered, then, do not lend much support to the conception of laws and theoretical principles as rules or principles of inference. On the other hand, there are some considerations which clearly militate against this construal.

First, in the writings of scientists, laws and theoretical principles are treated as statements. For example, general statements are used in conjunction with singular statements about particular facts to serve as *premises* from which other statements about particular facts are inferred; similarly, statements of general form, such as laws of narrower scope, often appear as *conclusions* derived from more comprehensive laws. Again, general laws or theoretical principles are accepted or rejected on the basis of empirical tests in much the same way as statements of particular facts, such as those concerning the constitution of the earth's interior, for example.

Indeed—and this brings us to a second difficulty—the distinction here presupposed between singular sentences on the one hand and general sentences on the other has no precise meaning in reference to statements formulated in a natural language. For example, the statement that the earth is a sphere may be regarded as a singular sentence of the form 'Se', which assigns to a particular object, the earth, a certain property, sphericity. But it may also be construed as a general statement, e.g., as asserting that there is a point in the interior of the earth from which all the points on its surface have the same distance. Similarly, the statement that a given crystal of salt is soluble in water may be construed as a singular statement ascribing solubility to a particular object, or, alternatively, as a statement of general character, asserting or implying that the given crystal will dissolve at any time upon being put into water.

A precise distinction of the kind here in question can be drawn if (i) the statements to be classified are expressed in a suitably formalized language that provides for quantificational notation, and (ii) every extra-logical term of the language is characterized either as primitive or as defined, each defined term possessing a unique definition in terms of primitives. A sentence of such a language may then be said to be essentially singular if it is logically equivalent to a sentence containing no defined terms and no quantifiers; all other sentences will be essentially general. The sentence 'The earth is spherical' will then be essentially singular if, for example, both 'the earth' and 'spherical' count as primitive terms of the language in which our statements are formulated; it will be essentially general if, for example, 'spherical' is defined by an expression containing one or more noneliminable quantifiers.

But even if we assume that a precise dividing line between singular and general statements has been drawn in this or a similar manner, the proposal to construe general statements as inference rules connecting singular statements still faces another, more serious difficulty: the formulation of law statements as inference rules proves difficult, if not impossible, and the resulting system of rules is awkward, to say the least. To be sure, a statement of the simple form 'All F are G', or '(x) $(Fx \supset Gx)$', where 'F' and 'G' are primitive predicates in the sense just explained, might be replaced by a rule licensing inferential transition from any sentence of the form 'Fi' (which is singular, i.e., quantifier-free) to the corresponding sentence of the form 'Gi'. But scientific explanations are often based on laws of a more complex structure; and for these, recasting in the form of inference rules connecting singular statements becomes problematic. Take the law, for example, that every metal has a specific melting point (at atmospheric pressure); i.e., that for every metal there exists a temperature T such that at any lower temperature and at no higher temperature the metal is solid at atmospheric pressure. The corresponding inference rule could not be construed as authorizing the transition from any sentence of the form 'i is a metal' to the sentence 'there is a temperature T such that at any lower temperature, but at no higher one, i is solid at atmospheric pressure'; for the conclusion thus obtained is not a sentence of singular form, but a statement involving both existential and universal quantifiers. Indeed, the subclauses 'at any temperature below T, i is solid' and 'at any temperature above T, i is nonsolid' have themselves the universal form of a law, and the general conception here under discussion would therefore seem to require that they in turn be construed as inference rules rather than as statements. But in the given context, this is not possible since they are qualified by the existential-quantifier phrase 'there is a temperature T such that. . . .'. In sum, the given law cannot be construed as tantamount to a rule establishing certain inferential connections among singular sentences. This is not to say that the law permits no such inferences: indeed, with its help (i.e., using it as an additional premise), we can infer from the statement 'this key is metal and is not liquid at 80°C and atmospheric pressure' further descriptive statements to the effect that the key won't be liquid at 74°C, 30°C, and other specific temperatures below 80°C, at atmospheric pressure. But these and similar inferential connections among singular statements which are mediated by the given law clearly do not exhaust its content; for, as we noted, the law also establishes connections, for example, between singular sentences ('i is a metal') and quantified ones ('there is a temperature T such that. . . .').

It may even happen that of two or more laws of complex form, none taken by itself establishes any inferential connections among singular sentences, whereas jointly they do. For example, two sentences of the form '(x) $[Fx \supset (\exists y) Rxy]$' and '$(x)[(\exists y)(Rxy) \supset Gx]$' jointly permit the inference from 'Fi' to 'Gi'; but, individually, neither of them establishes any connection among singular sentences. Thus, the totality of inferential transitions among singular sentences that are made possible by a set of laws or theoretical principles may far exceed the (logical- or class-) sum of the inferential connections established, among the same singular sentences, by the laws or theoretical principles individually. Hence, if one were to insist on construing scientific laws and theoretical principles as extralogical inference rules, licensing certain transitions among singular sentences, then one would have to do so, not for each of the laws and theoretical principles individually, but at once for the entire set of laws and principles assumed in a given context. No doubt the simplest way of doing this would be to formulate just one extralogical rule, authorizing all and only those transitions among singular statements which can be effected by using only purely logical rules of inference and by treating the laws and theoretical principles "as if" they were statements capable of functioning as additional premises in deductive arguments. But to adopt this rule would be simply to pay lip service to the construal of laws as rules rather than as statements.[29]

In sum, then, there is serious doubt, on purely logical grounds, whether *all* laws and theoretical principles can be adequately construed as inference rules. And even in the cases where this is possible, the preceding considerations

---

29. It is of interest to note here that Carnap, in his theory of logical syntax, explicitly provides for the possibility of constructing languages with extralogical rules of inference; see Carnap (1937), section 51. He calls the latter physical rules or P-rules. But he does not claim that all general laws or theoretical principles can be construed as such rules; and he emphasizes that the extent to which P-rules are to be countenanced in constructing a language will be a matter of convenience. For example, if we use P-rules, then the discovery of empirical phenomena that "conflict" with our previously accepted theories may oblige us to alter the rules of inference, and thus the entire formal structure, of our scientific language; whereas in the absence of P-rules, only a modification of some previously accepted theoretical statements is called for. W. Sellars (1953), (1958), also has advocated the admission of material rules of inference in connection with his analysis of subjunctive conditionals.

For a lucid survey and critical appraisal of various reasons that have been adduced in support of construing general laws as inference rules see Alexander (1958).

suggest that it would be simpler and more helpful, for a clarification of the issues with which we are here concerned, to construe general laws and theoretical principles as statements: hence this course will be followed from here on.

2.3.2 *The Conception of Laws as Role-Justifying Grounds for Explanations.* Another conception that would normally preclude the mention of laws in an explanation has been set forth by Scriven,[30] who argues that in so far as laws are relevant to an explanation, they will usually function as "role-justifying grounds" for it. This conception doubtless reflects the view that, as Ryle has put it, "Explanations are not arguments but statements. They are true or false."[31] Explanations might then take the form '*q* because *p*', where the '*p*'-clause mentions particular facts but no laws; and the kind of explanation represented as an argument in our schema (D-N) would be expressed by a statement of the form '*E* because $C_1, C_2, \ldots, C_k$.' The citation of laws is appropriate, according to Scriven, not in response to the question 'Why *q*?', which '*q* because *p*' serves to answer, but rather in response to the quite different question as to the grounds on which the facts mentioned in the '*p*'-clause may be claimed to explain the facts referred to in the '*q*'-clause. To include the relevant laws in the statement of the explanation itself would be, according to Scriven, to confound the statement of an explanation with a statement of its grounds.

Now it is quite true that in ordinary discourse and also in scientific contexts, a question of the form 'Why did such-and-such an event happen?' is often answered by a because-statement that cites only certain particular facts—even in cases where the relevant laws could be stated. The explanation statement 'The ice cube melted because it was floating in water at room temperature' is an example. But as this sentence equally illustrates, an explanation as ordinarily formulated will often mention only some of a larger set of particular facts which jointly could explain the occurrence in question. It will forego mention of other factors, which are taken for granted, such as that the water as well as the surrounding air remained approximately at room temperature for an adequate time. Hence, in order to justify attributing an explanatory role to the facts actually specified, one would have to cite here not only certain laws, but also the relevant particulars that had not been explicitly mentioned among the explanatory facts. Thus it is not clear why only laws should be singled out for the function of role-justification.[32] And if statements of particular fact were equally allowed to serve as role-justifying grounds in explanations, then the distinction between explanatory facts and role-justifying grounds would become obscure and arbitrary.

30. Scriven (1959), especially section 3.1.
31. Ryle (1950), p. 330.
32. The same point has been made by Alexander (1958, section I).

Scriven goes beyond relegating explanatory laws to the place of role-justifying grounds: He holds that we can sometimes be quite certain of a given explanation without being able to justify it by reference to any laws; in his own words, "certain evidence is adequate to guarantee certain explanations without the benefit of deduction from laws."[33] One of his examples is this:

> As you reach for the dictionary, your knee catches the edge of the table and thus turns over the ink-bottle, the contents of which proceed to run over the table's edge and ruin the carpet. If you are subsequently asked to explain how the carpet was damaged you have a complete explanation. You did it, by knocking over the ink. The certainty of this explanation is primeval. It has absolutely nothing to do with your knowledge of the relevant laws of physics; a cave-man could supply the same account and be quite as certain of it. . . . If you were asked to produce the role-justifying grounds for your explanation, what could you do? *You could not produce any true universal hypothesis* in which the antecedent was identifiably present (i.e., which avoids such terms as "knock hard enough"), and the consequent is the effect to be explained.[34]

At best, Scriven continues, one could offer a vague generalization to the effect that if you knock a table hard enough, it will cause an ink-bottle not too securely placed on it to spill over provided that there is enough ink in it. But this needs tightening in many ways, and, Scriven claims, it cannot be turned into a true universal hypothesis which, for the example in question, would "save the deductive model." In particular, physics cannot be expected to yield such a hypothesis, for "the explanation has become not one whit more certain since the laws of elasticity and inertia were discovered."[35]

Undeniably, in our everyday pursuits and also in scientific discussions, we often offer or accept explanatory accounts of the sort illustrated by Scriven's example. But an analytic study of explanation cannot content itself with simply registering this fact: it must treat it as material for analysis; it must seek to clarify what is *claimed* by an explanatory statement of this sort, and how the claim might be *supported*. And, at least to the first question, Scriven offers no explicit answer. He does not tell us just what, on his construal, is asserted by the given law-free explanation; and it remains unclear, therefore, precisely what claim he regards as having primeval certainty, for cave-man and modern physicist alike. Presumably the explanation he has in mind would be expressed by a statement roughly to the effect that the carpet was stained with ink because the table was knocked. But, surely, this statement claims by implication that the antecedent circumstances invoked were of a kind which generally yields effects of the sort to be explained. Indeed, it is just this implicit claim

33. Scriven (1959), p. 456.
34. *Loc. cit.*, italics the author's.
35. *Loc. cit.*

of covering uniform connections which distinguishes the causal attribution here made from a mere sequential narrative to the effect that first the table was knocked, then the bottle tipped over, and finally the ink dripped on the rug. Now, in a case such as the spilling of the ink, we feel familiar, at least in a general manner, with the relevant uniform connections even though we may not be able to state them precisely, and thus we are willing to take them for granted without explicit mention. On the other hand, there are various conceivable, particular antecedents any one of which might, by virtue of roughly the same general uniformities, account for the tipping over of the ink bottle: I might have knocked the table, the cat might have pushed the ink bottle, the curtain might have brushed against the bottle in a breeze, and so forth. Thus, the question of how the ink spot got on the rug will usually be aimed at eliciting information about the particular antecedents that led to the damage; and it might seem, therefore, that an explanation need have nothing to do with uniformities or laws. But this appearance surely does not refute the view that any particular explanatory claim made in terms of antecedent circumstances still presupposes suitable covering laws.

This brings us to a crucial question posed by Scriven's argument. Is it possible to specify, in the given case, a set of laws which would actually provide role-justification, by enabling us to deduce the explanandum, given the information about the antecedent explanatory events? The question cannot be answered unequivocally because it is too vague. Assuming that the explanatory statement takes the form 'q because p', we have not been told precisely what takes the places of 'p' and of 'q' in the case of the overturned ink bottle. If, for example, the 'p'-statement were taken to include the information that a full, uncorked, ink bottle was in fact knocked over, and if the 'q'-statement reported merely that the ink leaked out, then some elementary laws in the mechanics of fluids might well provide adequate nomological support for the explanatory statement. If, by contrast, the 'q'-statement is taken to specify, not only that the ink spilled out, but also that it produced a stain of specified size and shape on the rug, then, to be sure, no laws are known that would permit the inference from the 'p'-statement (in any plausible construal) to this 'q'-statement. But, just for this reason, an account of the sort suggested by Scriven's example would not be regarded as explaining the size or the shape of the ink stain at all.

No doubt, the explanatory claim envisaged by Scriven lies between these extremes and is roughly to the effect that the rug was stained because the table, with an open bottle of ink standing on it, was caught and lifted by my knee. This claim might be paraphrased by saying that there are laws connecting the presence of an ink stain on the rug with certain antecedent circumstances, which include an open bottle of ink standing on the table, and the fact that the table's edge was lifted. And there seems to be no reason to doubt the possibility of adducing or establishing a gradually expanding set of laws which would afford an increasingly accurate and detailed explanation of the phenomenon at hand.

We might say, in agreement with Scriven, that these laws would lend support or justification to the given because-statement. But we should note also that an expansion of the set of supporting laws will normally call for a corresponding expansion of the set of antecedent circumstances which have to be taken into account, and thus, strictly, for a modification of the explanatory because-statement itself.

Furthermore, the task of establishing the statements, whether of laws or of particular facts, which may thus be invoked in support of a because-statement comes clearly within the domain of scientific inquiry; hence it cannot reasonably be argued that progress in physical or chemical research has no significance for the explanation at hand. Thus Scriven's cave man, or perhaps a child, might well assume that when any opaque liquid is poured on any kind of textile it will soak in and produce a stain; which would lead him to expect a stain when mercury is dropped on a rug or when ink is poured on a specially treated nonstaining textile. And if his explanation or understanding of the ink stain on the rug presupposes that assumption then it would plainly be far from primevally certain: it would be false.

In sum then, the claim that the cave man could explain the staining of the rug with the same "certainty" as a modern scientist loses its initial striking plausibility when we ask ourselves precisely what the explanation would assert and what it would imply, and when we make sure it is not simply taken to be a narration of selected stages in the process concerned. An explanation may well be put into the form of a sequential narrative, but it will explain only if it at least tacitly presupposes certain nomic connections between the different stages cited. Such "genetic" explanations will be examined more closely later in this essay.

In the preceding discussion we have construed an explanatory statement of the form 'q because p' as an assertion to this effect: p is (or was) the case, and there are laws (not explicitly specified) such that the statement that q is (or was) the case follows logically from those laws taken in conjunction with the statement of p and perhaps other statements, which specify antecedents not included in p but tacitly presupposed in the explanation. In his discussion of the explanatory role of laws, Scriven considers the closely related idea that when we are able to specify the cause of a particular event such as the staining of the rug, "we are in a position to judge, not that certain specifiable laws apply, but that *some* laws must apply." And he objects that "it is *very* odd to say this rather than that we can sometimes be quite sure of causal statements even when we do not know any relevant laws. This capacity for identifying causes is learnt, is better developed in some people than in others, can be tested, and is the basis for what we call *judgments*."[36]

But this surely is no telling objection. For first of all, if the thesis is to have a clear meaning we need to know exactly what is meant by 'identifying the cause of a particular event', and how, accordingly, the capacity for identifying causes may be tested: and Scriven does not provide this information.

Secondly, the conception that a statement of the form '*q* because *p*' asserts, by implication, the existence of certain covering laws is by no means incompatible with the view that people may have a capacity for causal judgment even when they are unable to specify suitable covering laws or to explicate the notion of cause they are using. Consider a parallel: An experienced carpenter or gardener may have a capacity for judging very accurately the size of the area enclosed by a given circular line without being able to give an analytic definition of the area of a circle in terms of the convergent series formed by the areas of certain inscribed or circumscribed polygons. But this surely would not justify the claim that therefore, at least in the specific cases accessible to the judgments of skilled craftsmen, the mathematical analysis of the concept of the area of a circle is irrelevant or does not apply. Similarly a physician, a garage mechanic, or an electrician may have a remarkable capacity for judging what causes trouble in a particular case without always being able to adduce general laws supporting the diagnosis, and indeed without even believing that the latter presupposes the existence of such laws. But this acknowledgment does not warrant the conclusion that it is impossible or inappropriate to construe the causal statements in question as making reference to, or at least implying the existence of, corresponding laws.

Even the way in which causal statements based on such practical "judgment" are tested and substantiated indicates that they make, at least implicitly, a claim of general character. Thus, the assertion that a certain therapeutic measure caused improvement in a given case would require corroboration by similar results in similar cases, so as to rule out the possibility of a mere coincidence as contradistinguished from a causal connection.

But, since explanatory accounts are often formulated as 'because'-statements, should we not at least introduce a further model, which construes explanations as statements of the form '*q* because *p*' rather than as arguments? To characterize a certain type of explanation simply as having that form would surely be

36. *Loc. cit.*, italics the author's.

insufficient: the chief task of the contemplated model would be to clarify the meaning of the word 'because' in explanatory contexts, and this requires further analysis. To claim that we can sometimes proffer explanations of the form '*q* because *p*' with complete certainty, or that they can be guaranteed by suitable kinds of evidence without the benefit of laws, is to sidestep this issue; indeed, the claim cannot even be assessed independently of an analysis of the explanatory use of the word 'because'. The paraphrasing of because-statements suggested above is rather vague and no doubt capable of improvement, but at least it seems to me correct in exhibiting the assumption of lawlike connections implicit in such explanatory formulations.

2.4 EXPLANATION AS POTENTIALLY PREDICTIVE. Because of its essential reliance on laws and theoretical principles, D-N explanation may be expected to show a close affinity to scientific prediction; for laws and theoretical principles, making general claims, range also over cases not as yet examined and have definite implications for them.

The affinity in question is vividly illustrated in the fourth part of the *Dialogues Concerning Two New Sciences*. Here, Galileo develops his laws for the motion of projectiles and deduces from them the corollary that if projectiles are fired from the same point with equal initial velocity, but different elevations, the maximum range will be attained when the elevation is 45°. Then, Galileo has Sagredo remark: "From accounts given by gunners, I was already aware of the fact that in the use of cannon and mortars, the maximum range. . . is obtained when the elevation is 45°. . .; but to understand why this happens far outweighs the mere information obtained by the testimony of others or even by repeated experiment."[37] The reasoning that affords such understanding can readily be put into the form (D-N); it amounts to a deduction, by logical and mathematical means, of the corollary from a set of premises that contains (i) the fundamental laws of Galileo's theory for the motion of projectiles and (ii) particular statements specifying that all the missiles considered are fired from the same place with the same initial velocity. Clearly, then, the phenomenon previously noted by the gunners is here *explained*, and thus *understood*, by showing that its occurrence was to be expected under the specified circumstances in view of certain general laws set forth in Galileo's theory. And Galileo himself points with obvious pride to the *predictions* that may in like fashion be obtained by deduction from his laws; the latter imply "what has perhaps never been observed in experience, namely, that of other shots those which exceed or fall short of 45° by equal amounts have equal ranges." Thus, the explanation

37. Galilei (1946), p. 265.

afforded by Galileo's theory "prepares the mind to understand and ascertain other facts without need of recourse to experiment,"[38] namely, by deductive subsumption under the laws on which the explanation is based.

Checking the predictions thus derived from the general laws or theoretical principles invoked in an explanation is an important way of testing those "covering" generalizations, and a favorable outcome may lend strong support to them. Consider, for example, the explanation offered by Torricelli for a fact that had intrigued his teacher Galileo; namely, that a lift pump drawing water from a well will not raise the water more than about 34 feet above the surface of the well.[39] To account for this, Torricelli advanced the idea that the air above the water has weight and thus exerts pressure on the water in the well, forcing it up the pump barrel when the piston is raised, for there is no air inside to balance the outside pressure. On this assumption the water can rise only to the point where its pressure on the surface of the well equals the pressure of the outside air on that surface, and the latter will therefore equal that of a water column about 34 feet high.

The explanatory force of this account hinges on the conception that the earth is surrounded by a "sea of air" that conforms to the basic laws governing the equilibrium of liquids in communicating vessels. And because Torricelli's explanation presupposed such general laws it yielded predictions concerning as yet unexamined phenomena. One of these was that if the water were replaced by mercury, whose specific gravity is about 14 times that of water, the air should counterbalance a column about 34/14 feet, or somewhat less than $2\frac{1}{2}$ feet, in length. This prediction was confirmed by Torricelli in the classic experiment that bears his name. In addition, the proposed explanation implies that at increasing altitudes above sea level, the length of the mercury column supported by air pressure should decrease because the weight of the counterbalancing air decreases. A careful test of this prediction was performed at the suggestion of Pascal only a few years after Torricelli had offered his explanation: Pascal's brother-in-law carried a mercury barometer (i.e., essentially a mercury column counterbalanced by the air pressure) to the top of the Puy-de-Dôme, measuring the length of the column at various elevations during the ascent and again during the descent; the readings were in splendid accord with the prediction.[40]

The inferences by which such predictions are obtained are again of deductive-

---

38. *Loc. cit.*

39. The following account is based on the presentation of this case in Conant (1951), chapter 4.

40. Pascal's own account and appraisal of the "great experiment" is reprinted in English translation in Moulton and Schifferes (1945), pp. 145-53.

nomological form: The premises comprise the explanatory laws in question (in our last example, especially Torricelli's hypothesis) and certain statements of particular fact (e.g., that a barometer of such and such construction will be carried to the top of a mountain). Let us refer to predictive arguments of the form (D-N) as D-N predictions. In empirical science many predictive arguments are of this kind. Among the most striking examples are forecasts, based on the principles of celestial mechanics and of optics, concerning the relative positions of the Sun, the Moon, and the planets at a given time, and concerning solar and lunar eclipses.

It may be well to stress here that while the principles of classical mechanics or other deterministic laws or theories afford the basis for very impressive D-N explanations and predictions, the additional premises required for this purpose must provide not only a specification of the state of the system at some time t_0 earlier than the time t_1 for which the state of the system is to be inferred, but also a statement of the boundary conditions prevailing between t_0 and t_1; these specify the external influences acting upon the system during the time interval in question. For certain purposes in astronomy the disturbing influence of celestial objects other than those explicitly considered may be neglected as insignificant, and the system under consideration may be treated as "isolated"; but this should not lead us to overlook the fact that even those exemplars of deductive-nomological prediction do not enable us to forecast future events strictly on the basis of information about the present: the predictive argument also requires certain premises concerning the future—e.g., absence of disturbing influences, such as a collision of Mars with an unexpected comet; and the temporal scope of these boundary conditions must extend up to the very time of occurrence of the predicted event. The assertion therefore that laws and theories of deterministic form enable us to predict certain aspects of the future from information about the present has to be taken with a grain of salt. Analogous remarks apply to deductive-nomological explanation.

Since in a fully stated D-N explanation of a particular event the explanans logically implies the explanandum, we say may that the explanatory argument might have been used for a deductive prediction of the explanandum-event *if* the laws and the particular facts adduced in its explanans had been known and taken into account at a suitable earlier time. In this sense, a D-N explanation is a potential D-N prediction.

This point was made already in an earlier article by Oppenheim and myself,[41] where we added that scientific explanation (of the deductive-nomological kind) differs from scientific prediction not in logical structure, but in certain

41. Hempel and Oppenheim (1948), section 3.

pragmatic respects. In one case, the event described in the conclusion is known to have occurred, and suitable statements of general law and particular fact are sought to account for it; in the other, the latter statements are given and the statement about the event in question is derived from them before the time of its presumptive occurrence. This conception, which has sometimes been referred to as the *thesis of the structural identity* (or of the symmetry) *of explanation and prediction*, has recently been questioned by several writers. A consideration of some of their arguments may help to shed further light on the issuse involved.

To begin with, some writers[42] have noted that what is usually called a prediction is not an argument but a sentence. More precisely, as Scheffler has pointed out, it is a sentence-token, i.e., a concrete utterance or inscription of a sentence purporting to describe some event that is to occur after the production of the token.[43] This is certainly so. But in empirical science predictive sentences are normally established on the basis of available information by means of arguments that may be deductive or inductive in character; and the thesis under discussion should be understood, of course, to refer to explanatory and predictive *arguments*.

Thus construed, *the thesis of structural identity amounts to* the conjunction of *two sub-theses*, namely (i) that *every adequate explanation is potentially a prediction* in the sense indicated above; (ii) that conversely *every adequate prediction is potentially an explanation*. I will now examine a number of objections that have been raised against the thesis, dealing first with those which, in effect, concern the first sub-thesis, and then with those concerning the second sub-thesis. I will argue that the first sub-thesis is sound, whereas the second one is indeed open to question. Though the following considerations are concerned principally with D-N explanation, some of them are applicable to other types of explanation as well. The adequacy of the structural identity thesis for the case of statistical explanation will be examined in detail in section 3.5.

The first sub-thesis, as has already been noted, is an almost trivial truth in the case of D-N explanation, since here the explanans logically implies the explanandum. But it is supported also by a more general principle, which applies to other types of explanation as well, and which expresses, I would submit, a general *condition of adequacy for any rationally acceptable explanation of a particular event*. That condition is the following: Any rationally acceptable answer to the question 'Why did event X occur?' must offer information

---

42. See Scheffler (1957), section 1 and (1963), Part I, sections 3 and 4; Scriven (1962), p. 177.

43. *Cf.* Scheffler (1957), section 1. For a more detailed study of explanation and prediction in the light of the type-token distinction, see Kim (1962).

which shows that X was to be expected—if not definitely, as in the case of D-N explanation, then at least with reasonable probability. Thus, the explanatory information must provide good grounds for believing that X did in fact occur; otherwise, that information would give us no adequate reason for saying: "That explains it—that does show why X occurred." And an explanatory account that satisfies this condition constitutes, of course, a potential prediction in the sense that it could have served to predict the occurrence of X (deductively or with more or less high probability) if the information contained in the explanans had been available at a suitable earlier time.

The condition of adequacy just stated can be extended, in an obvious manner, to explanations concerned, not with individual events, but with empirical uniformities expressed by putative laws. But such explanations cannot well be spoken of as potential *predictions* since law-statements purport to express timeless uniformities and thus make no reference to any particular time, whether past, present, or future.[44]

It will hardly be necessary to emphasize that it is not, of course, the *purpose* of an explanation to provide grounds in support of the explanandum-statement; for, as was noted in the first section of this essay, a request for an explanation normally *presupposes* that the explanandum-statement is true. The point of the preceding remarks is rather that an adequate explanation cannot help providing information which, if properly established, also provides grounds in support of the explanandum-statement. In the terminology of section 1, we may say that an adequate answer to an explanation-seeking why-question is always also a potential answer to the corresponding epistemic why-question.

The converse, however, does not hold; the condition of adequacy is necessary but not sufficient for an acceptable explanation. For example, certain empirical findings may give excellent grounds for the belief that the orientation of the earth's magnetic field shows diurnal and secular variations, without in the least explaining why. Similarly, a set of experimental data may strongly *support* the assumption that the electric resistence of metals increases with their temperature or that a certain chemical inhibits the growth of cancer cells, without providing any *explanation* for these presumptive empirical regularities. The predictive inferences here involved are inductive rather than deductive; but what bars them from the status of potential explanations is not their inductive character (in section 3, we will deal with inductive arguments that afford perfectly good scientific explanations), but the fact that they invoke no laws or theoretical principles, no explanatory statements that make a general claim. Reliance on general principles, while perhaps not indispensable for

---

44. This point is made, for example, by Scriven (1962), pp. 179ff.

prediction, is required in any explanation: such principles alone can give to whatever particular circumstances may be adduced the status of explanatory factors for the event to be explained.

Some of the objections recently raised against the thesis of the structural identity of explanation and prediction concern in effect the first of its two sub-theses, which has now been presented in some detail: the claim that any adequate explanatory argument is also potentially predictive. I will consider three objections to the effect that there are certain perfectly satisfactory explanations that do not constitute potential predictions.

Scriven has argued that the occurrence of an event X is sometimes quite adequately explained by means of a "proposition of the form 'The only cause of X is A' . . . for example, 'The only cause of paresis is syphilis';" this proposition enables us to explain why a certain patient has paresis by pointing out that he previously suffered from syphilis. And this explanation holds good, according to Scriven, even though only quite a small percentage of syphilitic patients develop paresis, so that "we must, on the evidence [that a given person has syphilis], still predict that [paresis] will *not* occur."[45] But if it does occur, then the principle that the only cause of paresis is syphilis can "provide and guarantee our explanation" in terms of antecedent syphilitic infection.[46] Thus we have here a presumptive explanation which indeed is not adequate as a potential prediction. But precisely because paresis is such a rare sequel of syphilis, prior syphilitic infection surely cannot by itself provide an adequate explanation for it. A condition that is nomically necessary for the occurrence of an event does not, in general, explain it; or else we would be able to explain a man's winning the first prize in the Irish sweepstakes by pointing out that

---

45. Scriven (1959a), p. 480, italics the author's.

46. *Loc. cit.* Barker has argued analogously that "it can be correct to speak of explanation in many cases where specific prediction is not possible. Thus, for instance, if the patient shows all the symptoms of pneumonia, sickens and dies, I can then explain his death—I know what killed him—but I could not have definitely predicted in advance that he was going to die; for usually pneumonia fails to be fatal." (1961, p. 271). This argument seems to me open to questions similar to those just raised in reference to Scriven's illustration. First of all, it is not clear just what would be claimed by the assertion that pneumonia killed the patient. Surely the mere information that the patient had pneumonia does not suffice to explain his death, precisely because in most cases pneumonia is not fatal. And if the explanans is taken to state that the patient was suffering from very severe pneumonia (and perhaps that he was elderly or weak) then it may well provide a basis at least for a probabilistic explanation of the patient's death—but in this case it obviously also permits prediction of his death with the same probability. For some further observations on Barker's argument, see the comments by Feyerabend and by Rudner, and Barker's rejoinders, in Feigl and Maxwell (1961), pp. 278-85. A detailed critical discussion that sheds further light on Scriven's paresis example will be found in Grünbaum (1963) and (1963a), chapter 9; see also Scriven's rejoinder (1963).

he had previously bought a ticket, and that only a person who owns a ticket can win the first prize.

A second argument which, like Scriven's, has considerable initial plausibility has been advanced by Toulmin[47] by reference to "Darwin's theory, explaining the origin of species by variation and natural selection. No scientist has ever used this theory to foretell the coming-into-existence of creatures of a novel species, still less verified his forecast. Yet many competent scientists have accepted Darwin's theory as having great explanatory power." In examining this argument, let me distinguish what might be called the *story* of evolution from the *theory* of the underlying mechanisms of mutation and natural selection. The story of evolution, as a hypothesis about the gradual development of various types of organisms, and about the subsequent extinction of many of these, has the character of a hypothetical historical narrative *describing* the putative stages of the evolutionary process; it is the associated theory which provides what *explanatory insight* we have into this process. The story of evolution might tell us, for example, that at a certain stage in the process dinosaurs made their appearance and that, so much later, they died out. Such a narrative account does not, of course, explain why the various kinds of dinosaurs with their distinctive characteristics came into existence, nor does it explain why they became extinct. Indeed even the associated theory of mutation and natural selection does not answer the first of these questions, though it might be held to shed some light on the latter. Yet, even to account for the extinction of the dinosaurs, we need a vast array of additional hypotheses about their physical and biological environment and about the species with which they had to compete for survival. But if we have hypotheses of this kind that are specific enough to provide, in combination with the theory of natural selection, at least a probabilistic explanation for the extinction of the dinosaurs, then clearly the explanans adduced is also qualified as a basis for a potential probabilistic prediction. The undeniably great persuasiveness of Toulmin's argument would seem to derive from two sources, a widespread tendency to regard the basically descriptive story of evolution as explaining the various states of the process, and a similarly widespread tendency to overestimate the extent to which even the theory of mutation and natural selection can account for the details of the evolutionary sequence.

I now turn to a third objection to the claim that an adequate explanation is also a potential prediction. It is based on the observation that sometimes the only ground we have for asserting some essential statement in the explanans lies

---

47. Toulmin (1961), pp. 24–25. Scriven (1959a) and Barker (1961) have offered arguments in the same vein. For a critical discussion of Scriven's version, see Grünbaum (1963) and (1963a), chapter 9.

in the knowledge that the explanandum event did in fact occur. In such cases, the explanatory argument clearly could not have been used to predict that event. Consider one of Scriven's examples.[48] Suppose that a man has killed his wife whom he knew to have been unfaithful to him, and that his action is explained as the result of intense jealousy. The fact that the man was jealous might well have been ascertainable before the deed, but to explain the latter, we need to know that his jealousy was intense enough to drive him to murder; and this we can know only after the deed has actually been committed. Here then, the occurrence of the explanandum event provides the only grounds we have for asserting one important part of the explanans; the explanandum event could not therefore have been predicted by means of the explanatory argument. In another example,[49] Scriven considers an explanation to the effect that the collapse of a bridge was caused by metal fatigue. This account, he argues, might be supported by pointing out that the failure could have been caused only by an excessive load, by external damage, or by metal fatigue, and that the first two factors were not present in the case at hand, whereas there is evidence of metal fatigue. *Given the information that the bridge did in fact collapse*, this would establish not only that metal fatigue was at fault but that it was strong enough to cause the failure. While Scriven's notion of "the only possible cause" of a given event surely requires further elucidation, his example does afford another illustration of an explanatory account one of whose constituent hypotheses is supported only by the occurrence of the event to be explained—so that the latter could not have been predicted by means of the explanatory argument.

However, the point thus illustrated does not affect at all the conditional thesis that an adequate explanatory argument must be such that it could have served to predict the explanandum event *if* the information included in the explanans had been known and taken into account before the occurrence of that event. What Scriven's cases show is that sometimes we do not know independently of the occurrence of the explanandum event that all the conditions listed in the explanans are realized. However, this means only that in such cases our conditional thesis is counterfactual, i.e., that its if-clause is not satisfied, but not that the thesis itself is false. Moreover, Scriven's argument does not even show that in the kind of case he mentions it is logically or nomologically impossible (impossible by reason of the laws of logic or the laws of nature) for us to know the critical explanatory factor before, or independently of, the occurrence of the explanandum-event; the impossibility appears to be rather a practical and perhaps temporary one, reflecting present limitations of knowledge or technology.

48. Scriven (1959), pp. 468–69.
49. Scriven (1962), pp. 181–87.

But while it thus leaves our thesis unaffected, Scriven's observation is of methodological interest in its own right: it shows that sometimes an event is explained by means of hypotheses for some of which the fact of its occurrence affords the only available evidential support. This may happen, as we saw, when one of the explanatory hypotheses states that a certain relevant factor was strong enough to bring about the event in question; but the observation applies also to other cases. Thus the explanation, outlined in section 2.1, of the appearance and initial growth of the soap bubbles, includes in its explanans the assumption that a soap film had formed between the plate and the rims of the tumblers; and practically the only evidence available in support of this explanatory assumption is the fact that soap bubbles did emerge from under the tumblers. Or consider the explanation of the characteristic dark lines in the absorption spectrum of a particular star. The key assumption in the explanans is that the star's atmosphere contains certain elements, such as hydrogen, helium, and calcium, whose atoms absorb radiation of the wave lengths corresponding to the dark lines; the explanation relies, of course, on many other assumptions, including the optical theory that forms the basis for spectroscopy, and the assumption that the apparatus used is a properly constructed spectroscope. But while these latter explanans statements are capable of independent test and corroboration, it may well be that the only evidence available in support of the key explanatory hypothesis is the occurrence of the very lines whose appearance in the spectrum the argument serves to explain. Strictly speaking, the explanandum event here provides support for the key explanatory hypothesis only by virtue of the background theory, which connects the presence of certain elements in the atmosphere of a star with the appearance of corresponding absorption lines in its spectrum. Thus, the information that the explanandum event has occurred does not by itself support the explanatory hypothesis in question, but it constitutes, as we might say, an essential part of the only evidence available in support of that hypothesis.

Explanations of the kind here considered may be schematically characterized as arguments of the form (D-N) in which the information or assumption that E is true provides an indispensable part of the only available evidential support for one of the explanans statements, say, C_1. Let us call such explanations *self-evidencing*. It might be held that the actual occurrence of the explanandum event always provides some slight additional support even for an explanans whose constituent sentences have been accepted on the basis of independent evidence, and that in this sense every D-N explanation with true explanandum is in some measure self-evidencing; but we will apply this appellation to an explanatory account only if, at the time of its presentation, the occurrence of the explanandum event provides the only evidence, or an indispensable part of the only evidence, available in support of some of the explanans-statements.

An explanatory argument of the form (D-N) which is self-evidencing is not for that reason circular or pointless. To be sure, if the same argument were adduced in support of the assertion that the explanandum-event did occur (or, that E is true), then it would be open to the charge of epistemic circularity. If the argument is to achieve its objective then all the grounds it adduces in support of E—i.e., C_1, C_2, ..., C_k; $L_1, L_2, ..., L_r$—would have to be established independently of E; and this condition is violated here since the only ground we have for believing or asserting C_1 includes the assumption that E is true. But when the same argument is used for explanatory purposes it does not claim to establish that E is true; that is *presupposed* by the question 'Why did the event described by E occur?'. Nor need a self-evidencing explanation involve an explanatory circle. The information that the explanandum event has occurred is not included in the explanans (so that the occurrence of the event is not "explained by itself"); rather it serves, quite outside the explanatory context, as evidence supporting one of the explanans statements. Thus, an acceptable self-evidencing explanation benefits, as it were, by the wisdom of hindsight derived from the information that the explanandum event has occurred, but it does not misuse that information so as to produce a circular explanation.

An explanation that is self-evidencing may for that reason rest on a poorly supported explanans and may therefore have no strong claim to empirical soundness. But even this is not inevitable. In the case of the absorption spectrum of a star, for example, the previously accepted background information, including the relevant theories, may indicate that the dark lines observed occur *only* if the specified elements are present in the star's atmosphere; and then the explanandum, in conjunction with the background information, lends very strong support to the crucial explanatory hypothesis.

The notion of a self-evidencing explanation can, I think, shed some further light on the puzzle illustrated by the explanation of paresis in terms of antecedent syphilitic infection. Consider another illustration. Some cases of skin cancer are attributed to intensive ultraviolet irradiation. But this factor very often does not lead to cancer, so that the information that a person has been exposed to such radiation does not permit the prediction of cancer. Is that information alone nevertheless sufficient to explain the development of skin cancer when it does follow intensive irradiation? No doubt, an explanation will often be formulated so as to mention only the antecedent irradiation; but the underlying rationale surely must be more complex. Leaving aside the important quantitative aspects of the problem, the crucial point in that rationale can, I suggest, be schematically stated as follows: Some, though by no means all, individuals have the disposition to develop skin cancer upon exposure to strong ultraviolet irradiation; let us call these radiation-sensitive. Now, in the case of explanation, we know that the given individual was exposed to strong radiation (C_1) and did develop cancer of the skin in the affected area (E). But jointly, these two pieces of information lend support to the assumption that the individual is radiation-sensitive (C_2)—an hypothesis that is not supported in the case of prediction, where C_1 is available, but not E. And the two statements C_1 and C_2 (in combination with the general statement that sensitive individuals will develop skin cancer when exposed to intensive radiation) do provide an adequate explanans for E. If the explanation is thus construed as invoking C_2 in addition to C_1, it is seen to be self-evidencing, but also to possess an explanans which would provide an adequate basis for prediction if C_2 could be known in advance. That is impossible, of course, as long as the only available test for radiation-sensitivity consists in checking whether an individual does develop skin cancer upon intensive irradiation. But, clearly, it is conceivable that other, independent, tests of radiation-sensitivity might be found and then C_2 might well be established independently of, and even prior to, the occurrence of the event described by E.

In discussing the structural identity of explanation and prediction, I have so far considered only the first of the two sub-theses distinguished earlier, namely, the claim that every adequate explanation is also a potential prediction. I have argued that the objections raised against this claim fall short of their mark, and that the first sub-thesis is sound and can indeed serve as a necessary condition of adequacy for any explicitly stated, rationally acceptable explanation.

I turn now to the second sub-thesis, namely, that every adequate predictive argument also affords a potential explanation. This claim is open to question even in the case of certain predictive arguments that are of deductive-nomological character, as the following example illustrates. One of the early symptoms of measles is the appearance of small whitish spots, known as Koplik spots, on the mucous linings of the cheeks. The statement, L, that the appearance of Koplik spots is always followed by the later manifestations of the measles might therefore be taken to be a law, and it might then be used as a premise in D-N arguments with a second premise of the form 'Patient i has Koplik spots at time t', and with a conclusion stating that i subsequently shows the later manifestations of the measles. An argument of this type is adequate for predictive purposes, but its explanatory adequacy might be questioned. We would not want to say, for example, that i had developed high fever and other symptoms of the measles because he had previously had Koplik spots.

Yet this case—and others similar to it—does not constitute a decisive objection against the second sub-thesis. For the reluctance to regard the appearance of Koplik spots as explanatory may well reflect doubts as to whether, as a matter of universal law, those spots are always followed by the later manifestations of measles. Perhaps a local inoculation with a small amount of measles virus would produce the spots without leading to a full-blown case of the measles. If this were so, the appearance of the spots would still afford a usually reliable basis for predicting the occurrence of further symptoms, since exceptional conditions of the kind just mentioned would be extremely rare; but the generalization that Koplik spots are always followed by later symptoms of the measles would not express a law and thus could not properly support a corresponding D-N explanation.

The objection just considered concerns the explanatory potential of predictive arguments of the form (D-N). But the second sub-thesis, in its general form, which is not limited to D-N predictions, has further been challenged, particularly by Scheffler and by Scriven,[50] on the ground that there are other kinds of predictive argument that are adequate for scientific prediction, yet not for explanation. Specifically, as Scheffler notes, a scientific prediction may be based on a finite set of data which includes no laws and which would have no explanatory force. For example, a finite set of data obtained in an extensive test of the hypothesis that the electric resistance of metals increases with their temperature may afford good support for that hypothesis and may thus provide an acceptable basis for the prediction that in an as yet unexamined instance, a rise in temperature in a metal conductor will be accompanied by an increase in resistance. But if this event then actually occurs, the test data clearly do not provide an explanation for it. Similarly, a list of the results obtained in a long series of tossings of a given coin may provide a good basis for predicting the percentage of Heads and Tails to be expected in the next 1000 tossings of the same coin; but again, that list of data provides no explanation for the subsequent results. Cases like these raise the question of whether there are not sound modes of scientific prediction that proceed from particulars to particulars without benefit of general laws such as seem to be required for any adequate explanation. Now, the predictive arguments just considered are not deductive but probabilistic in character; and the role of probabilistic inference for explanation and prediction will be considered more fully in section 3 of this essay. But in regard to the second sub-thesis of the structural identity claim, let us note this much here: the predictions in our illustrations proceed from an observed sample of a population to another, as yet unobserved one; and on some current theories

50. See Scheffler (1957), p. 296 and (1963), p. 42; Scriven (1959a), p. 480.

of probabilistic inference such arguments do not depend upon the assumption of general empirical laws. According to Carnap's theory of inductive logic,[51] for example, such inferences are possible on purely logical grounds; the information about the given sample confers a definite logical probability upon any proposed prediction concerning an as yet unobserved sample. On the other hand, certain statistical theories of probabilistic inference eschew the notion of purely logical probabilities and qualify predictions of the kind here considered as sound only on the further assumption that the selection of individual cases from the total population has the character of a random experiment with certain general statistical characteristics. But that assumption, when explicitly spelled out, has the form of a general law of statistic-probabilistic form; hence, the predictions are effected by means of covering laws after all. And though these laws do not have the strictly universal character of those invoked in D-N explanations and predictions, they can serve in an explanatory capacity as well. Thus construed, even the predictions here under discussion turn out to be (incompletely formulated) potential explanations.

The basic questions at issue between these different conceptions of probabilistic inference are still the subject of debate and research, and this essay is not the place to attempt a fuller appraisal of the opposing views. The second sub-thesis of the structural identity claim for explanation and prediction will therefore be regarded here as an open question.

3. STATISTICAL EXPLANATION

3.1 LAWS OF STATISTICAL FORM. We now turn our attention to explanations based on nomological statements of a kind we have not so far considered, which have come to play an increasingly important role in empirical science. I will refer to them as *laws or theoretical principles of statistic-probabilistic form*, or as *statistical laws*, for short.

Most of our discussion will be concerned with the explanatory use of statistical laws of a very simple kind; we will call them *laws of basic statistical form*. These are statements to the effect that the statistical probability for an event of kind F to be also of kind G is r, or that

$$p(G,F) = r$$

for short. Broadly speaking, this statement asserts that in the long run the proportion of those instances of F which are also instances of G is approximately r. (A fuller account will be given in section 3.3.)

For example, the statement that the rolling of a given slightly irregular die

---

51. Carnap (1950), section 110.

(event of kind F) yields an ace (event of kind G) with a probability of .15, i.e., in about 15 per cent of all cases in the long run, has this basic statistical form. And so does the law that the half-life of radon is 3.82 days, i.e., that the statistical probability for a radon atom to disintegrate during any given period of 3.82 days is 1/2, which means, roughly, that of a sample of radon containing a large number of atoms, very close to one half of the atoms decay within 3.82 days.

Laws of basic statistical form may be regarded as less stringent counterparts of laws that have the universal conditional form

$$(x)\,(F\,x\,\supset G\,x)$$

asserting that any instance of F is an instance of G, as for example: 'Any gas expands when heated under constant pressure'. Indeed, the two kinds of law share an important feature, which is symptomatic of their nomological character: both make general claims concerning a class of cases that might be said to be potentially infinite. As we noted earlier, a statement which is logically equivalent to a finite conjunction of singular sentences, and which in this sense makes a claim concerning only a finite class of cases, does not qualify as a law and lacks the explanatory force of a nomological statement. Lawlike sentences, whether true or false, are not just conveniently telescoped summaries of finite sets of data concerning particular instances.

For example, the law that gases expand when heated under constant pressure is not tantamount to the statement that in all instances that have so far been observed, or perhaps in all instances that have so far occurred, an increase in the temperature of a gas under constant pressure has been accompanied by an increase in volume. Rather it asserts that a growth in volume is associated with the heating of a gas under constant pressure in *any* case, whether past, present, or future, and whether actually observed or not. It even implies counterfactual and subjunctive conditionals to the effect that if a given body of gas had been heated or were to be heated under constant pressure, its volume would have increased, or would increase, as well.

Similarly, the probabilistic laws of genetics or of radioactive decay are not tantamount to descriptive reports of the frequencies with which some kind of phenomenon has been found to occur in a finite class of observed cases: they assert certain peculiar, namely probabilistic, modes of connection between potentially infinite classes of occurrences. In a statistical law of basic form, as contradistinguished from a statistical description specifying relative frequencies in some finite set, the "reference class" F is not assumed to be finite. Indeed, we might say that a law of the form '$p\,(G,F) = r$' refers not only to all actual instances of F, but, so to speak, to the class of all its potential instances. Suppose, for example, that we are given a homogeneous regular tetrahedron whose faces are marked 'I', 'II', 'III', 'IV'. We might then assert that the probability of obtaining a III, i.e., of the tetrahedron's coming to rest on that face upon being tossed out of a dice box, is 1/4. But, while this assertion says something about the frequency with which a III is obtained as a result of rolling the tetrahedron, it cannot be construed as simply specifying that frequency for the class of all tosses which are, in fact, ever performed with the tetrahedron. For we might well maintain our hypothesis even if we were informed that the tetrahedron would actually be tossed only a few times throughout its existence, and in this case, our probability statement would surely not be meant to assert that exactly, or even nearly, one-fourth of those tosses would yield the result III. Moreover, our statement would be perfectly meaningful and might, indeed, be well supported (e.g., by results obtained with similar tetrahedra or with other homogeneous bodies in the form of regular solids) even if the given tetrahedron happened to be destroyed without ever having been tossed at all. What the probability statement attributes to the tetrahedron is, therefore, not the frequency with which the result III is obtained in actual past or future rollings, but a certain *disposition*, namely, the disposition to yield the result III in about one out of four cases, in the long run. This disposition might be characterized by means of a subjunctive conditional phrase: if the tetrahedron were to be tossed a large number of times, it would yield the result III in about one-fourth of the cases.[1] Implications in the form of counterfactual and subjective conditionals are thus hallmarks of lawlike statements both of strictly universal and of statistical form.

As for the distinction between lawlike sentences of strictly universal form and those of probabilistic or statistical form, it is sometimes thought that statements asserting strictly universal connections, such as Galileo's law or Newton's law of gravitation, rest, after all, only on a finite and thus inevitably incomplete body of evidence; that, therefore, they may well have as yet

---

1. Carnap (1951-54, pp. 190-92) has argued in a similar vein that the statistical probability of rolling an ace with a given die is a physical characteristic, which he also calls "the probability state" of the die, and that the relative frequency with which rollings of the die yield an ace is a symptom of that state, much as the expansion of the mercury column in a thermometer is a symptom of its temperature state.

The dispositional construal I have outlined for the concept of statistical probability appears to be in close accord also with the "propensity interpretation" advocated by Popper. The latter "differs from the purely statistical or frequency interpretation only in this—that it considers the probability as a characteristic property of the experimental arrangement rather than as a property of a sequence"; the property in question is explicitly construed as *dispositional*. (Popper 1957, pp. 67-68). See also the discussion of this paper in Körner (1957), pp. 78-89, *passim*. However, the currently available statements of the propensity interpretation are all rather brief; a fuller presentation is to be given in a forthcoming book by Popper.

undetected exceptions; and that accordingly they, too, should be qualified as only probabilistic. But this argument confounds the claim made by a given statement with the evidence available in support of it. On the latter score, all empirical statements are only more or less well supported by the relevant evidence at our disposal; or, in the parlance of some theorists, they have a more or less high logical or inductive probability conferred upon them by that evidence. But the distinction between lawlike statements of strictly universal form and those of probabilistic form pertains, not to the evidential support of the statements in question, but to the claims made by them: roughly speaking, the former attribute (truly or falsely) a certain characteristic to all members of a certain class; the latter, to a specified proportion of its members.

Even if all the supposedly universal laws of empirical science should eventually come to be regarded as reflections of underlying statistical uniformities—an interpretation that the kinetic theory of matter gives to the classical laws of thermodynamics, for example—even then the distinction between the two types of law and the corresponding explanations is not wiped out: in fact, it is presupposed in the very formulation of the conjecture.

Nor is a statement of the universal conditional form

$$(x)(F x \supset G x)$$

logically equivalent to the corresponding statement of the basic statistical form

$$p (G, F) = 1$$

for, as will be shown more fully in section 3.3, the latter asserts only that it is practically certain that in a large number of instances of F, almost all are instances of G; hence the probability statement may be true even if the corresponding statement of strictly universal form is false.

So far, we have dealt only with statistical laws of basic form. Let us now say more generally that *a statement has the form of a statistical law*, or is of probabilistic-statistical character, if it is formulated in terms of statistical probabilities, i.e., if it contains (nonvacuously) the term 'statistical probability' or some notational equivalent, or a term—such as 'half-life'—which is defined by means of statistical probabilities.

Take, for example, the statement that when two coins are flipped simultaneously, the face shown by one is independent of that shown by the other. This amounts to saying that the probability for the second coin to show heads when the first shows heads is the same as when the first shows tails; and vice versa. Generally, assertions of statistical independence have the form of statistical laws, though they are not of basic statistical form. Similarly, a statement asserting a statistical dependence or "aftereffect" has the form of a statistical law; for example, the statement that in any given area the probability for a day to be cloudy when it follows a cloudy day is greater than when it follows a noncloudy day. Still other laws of statistical form are formulated in terms of mean values of certain variables, such as the mean kinetic energy and the mean free path of the molecules in a gas; the notion of mean value here invoked is defined by reference to statistical probabilities.

By a *statistical explanation*, let us now understand any explanation that makes essential use of at least one law or theoretical principle of statistical form. In the following subsections, we will examine the logical structure of such explanations. We will find that there are two logically different types of statistical explanation. One of them amounts, basically, to the deductive subsumption of a narrower statistical uniformity under more comprehensive ones: I will call it *deductive-statistical explanation*. The other involves the subsumption, in a peculiar nondeductive sense, of a particular occurrence under statistical laws; for reasons to be given later, it will be called *inductive-statistical explanation*.

3.2 DEDUCTIVE-STATISTICAL EXPLANATION. It is an instance of the so-called gambler's fallacy to assume that when several successive tossings of a fair coin have yielded heads, the next toss will more probably yield tails than heads. Why this is not the case can be explained by means of two hypotheses that have the form of statistical laws. The first is that the random experiment of flipping a fair coin yields heads with a statistical probability of 1/2. The second hypothesis is that the outcomes of different tossings of the coin are statistically independent, so that the probability of any specified sequence of outcomes—such as heads twice, then tails, then heads, then tails three times—equals the product of the probabilities of the constituent single outcomes. These two hypothesis in terms of statistical probabilities imply *deductively* that the probability for heads to come up after a long sequence of heads is still 1/2.

Certain statistical explanations offered in science are of the same deductive character, though often quite complex mathematically. Consider, for example, the hypothesis that for the atoms of every radioactive substance there is a characteristic probability of disintegrating during a given unit time interval, circumstances. This complex statistical hypothesis explains, by deductive implication, various other statistical aspects of radioactive decay, among them, the following: Suppose that the decay of individual atoms of some radioactive substance is recorded by means of the scintillations produced upon a sensitive screen by the alpha particles emitted by the disintegrating atoms. Then the time intervals separating successive scintillations will vary considerably in length, but intervals of different lengths will occur with different statistical probabilities. Specifically, if the mean time interval between successive scintillations is s seconds, then the probability for two successive scintillations to be separated by more than $n \cdot s$ seconds is $(1/e)^n$, where e is the base of the natural logarithms.[2]

Explanations of the kind here illustrated will be called *deductive-statistical explanations*, or *D-S explanations*. They involve the deduction of a statement in the form of a statistical law from an explanans that contains indispensably at least one law or theoretical principle of statistical form. The deduction is effected by means of the mathematical theory of statistical probability, which makes it possible to calculate certain derivative probabilities (those referred to in the explanandum) on the basis of other probabilities (specified in the explanans) which have been empirically ascertained or hypothetically assumed. What a D-S explanation accounts for is thus always a general uniformity expressed by a presumptive law of statistical form.

Ultimately, however, statistical laws are meant to be applied to particular occurrences and to establish explanatory and predictive connections among them. In the next subsection, we will examine the statistical explanation of particular events. Our discussion will be limited to the case where the explanatory statistical laws are of basic form: this will suffice to exhibit the basic logical differences between the statistical and the deductive-nomological explanation of individual occurrences.

3.3 INDUCTIVE-STATISTICAL EXPLANATION. As an explanation of why patient John Jones recovered from a streptococcus infection, we might be told that Jones had been given penicillin. But if we try to amplify this explanatory claim by indicating a general connection between penicillin treatment and the subsiding of a streptococcus infection we cannot justifiably invoke a general law to the effect that in all cases of such infection, administration of penicillin will lead to recovery. What can be asserted, and what surely is taken for granted here, is only that penicillin will effect a cure in a high percentage of cases, or with a high statistical probability. This statement has the general character of a law of statistical form, and while the probability value is not specified, the statement indicates that it is high. But in contrast to the cases of deductive-nomological and deductive-statistical explanation, the explanans consisting of this statistical law together with the statement that the patient did receive penicillin obviously does not imply the explanandum statement, 'the patient

2. *Cf.* Mises (1939), pp. 272-78, where both the empirical findings and the explanatory argument are presented. This book also contains many other illustrations of what is here called deductive-statistical explanation.

recovered', with deductive certainty, but only, as we might say, with high likelihood, or near-certainty. Briefly, then, the explanation amounts to this argument:

(3a) The particular case of illness of John Jones—let us call it j—was an instance of severe streptococcal infection (Sj) which was treated with large doses of penicillin (Pj); and the statistical probability p (R, $S \cdot P$) of recovery in cases where S and P are present is close to 1; hence, the case was practically certain to end in recovery (Rj).

This 'argument might invite the following schematization:

(3b)
$$\frac{p\ (R,\ S \cdot P) \text{ is close to } 1}{Sj \cdot Pj}$$
(Therefore:) It is practically certain (very likely) that Rj

In the literature on inductive inference, arguments thus based on statistical hypotheses have often been construed as having this form or a similar one. On this construal, the conclusion characteristically contains a modal qualifier such as 'almost certainly', 'with high probability', 'very likely', etc. But the conception of arguments having this character is untenable. For phrases of the form 'it is practically certain that p' or 'It is very likely that p', where the place of 'p' is taken by some statement, are not complete self-contained sentences that can be qualified as either true or false. The statement that takes the place of 'p'—for example, 'Rj'—is either true or false, quite independently of whatever relevant evidence may be available, but it can be qualified as more or less likely, probable, certain, or the like only *relative to some body of evidence*. One and the same statement, such as 'Rj', will be certain, very likely, not very likely, highly unlikely, and so forth, depending upon what evidence is considered. The phrase 'it is almost certain that Rj' taken by itself is therefore neither true nor false; and it cannot be inferred from the premises specified in (3b) nor from any other statements.

The confusion underlying the schematization (3b) might be further illuminated by considering its analogue for the case of deductive arguments. The force of a deductive inference, such as that from 'all F are G' and 'a is F' to 'a is G', is sometimes indicated by saying that if the premises are true, then the conclusion is necessarily true or is certain to be true—a phrasing that might suggest the schematization

All F are G
a is F
_____
(Therefore:) It is necessary (certain) that a is G.

But clearly the given premises—which might be, for example, 'all men are mortal' and 'Socrates is a man'—do not establish the sentence '*a* is *G*' ('Socrates is mortal') as a necessary or certain truth. The certainty referred to in the informal paraphrase of the argument is relational: the statement '*a* is *G*' is certain, or necessary, *relative to the specified premises*; i.e., their truth will guarantee its truth—which means nothing more than that '*a* is *G*' is a logical consequence of those premises.

Analogously, to present our statistical explanation in the manner of schema (3b) is to misconstrue the function of the words 'almost certain' or 'very likely' as they occur in the formal wording of the explanation. Those words clearly must be taken to indicate that on the evidence provided by the explanans, or relative to that evidence, the explanandum is practically certain or very likely, i.e., that

(3c) 'Rj' is practically certain (very likely) relative to the explanans containing the sentences '$p (R, S \cdot P)$ is close to 1' and '$Sj \cdot Pj$'.[3]

The explanatory argument misrepresented by (3b) might therefore suitably be schematized as follows:

$$
(3d) \quad \begin{array}{l} p (R, S \cdot P) \text{ is close to 1} \\ Sj \cdot Pj \\ \hline\hline \\ Rj \end{array} = \text{[makes practically certain (very likely)]}
$$

In this schema, the double line separating the "premises" from the "conclusion" is to signify that the relation of the former to the latter is not that of deductive implication but that of inductive support, the strength of which is indicated in square brackets.[4,5]

3. Phrases such as 'It is almost certain (very likely) that *j* recovers', even when given the relational construal here suggested, are ostensibly concerned with relations between propositions, such as those expressed by the sentences forming the conclusion and the premises of an argument. For the purpose of the present discussion, however, involvement with propositions can be avoided by construing the phrases in question as expressing logical relations between corresponding *sentences*, e.g., the conclusion-sentence and the premise-sentence of an argument. This construal, which underlies the formulation of (3c), will be adopted in this essay, though for the sake of convenience we may occasionally use a paraphrase.

4. In the familiar schematization of deductive arguments, with a single line separating the premises from the conclusion, no explicit distinction is made between a weaker and a stronger claim, either of which might be intended; namely (i) that the premises logically imply the conclusion and (ii) that, in addition, the premises are true. In the case of our probabilistic argument, (3c) expresses a weaker claim, analogous to (i), whereas (3d) may be taken to express a "proffered explanation" (the term is borrowed from Scheffler, (1957), section 1) in which, in addition, the explanatory premises are—however tentatively—asserted as true.

5. The considerations here outlined concerning the use of terms like 'probably' and 'certainly' as modal qualifiers of individual statements seem to me to militate also against

(continued overleaf)

Our schematization thus reflects explicitly the understanding that 'almost certain', 'very likely', 'practically impossible' and similar expressions often used in the phrasing of probabilistic arguments, including explanations, do not stand for properties possessed by certain propositions or the corresponding sentences, but for relations that some sentences bear to others. According to this understanding, the notion of the explanans of (3d) making the explanandum almost certain or very likely is but a special case of the idea of a given statement or set of statements—let us call it the grounds or the evidence *e*—conferring more or less strong inductive support or confirmation or credibility upon some statement *h*. To clarify and systematically to elaborate the idea here sketchily characterized is, of course, the objective of various theories of inductive reason-

the notion of categorical probability statement that C. I. Lewis sets forth in the following passage (italics the author's):

Just as 'If *D* then (certainly) *P*, and *D* is the fact,' leads to the categorical consequence, 'Therefore (certainly) *P*'; so too, 'If *D* then probably *P*, and *D* is the fact', leads to a categorical consequence expressed by 'It is probable that *P*'. And this conclusion is not merely the statement over again of the probability relation between '*P*' and '*D*'; any more than 'Therefore (certainly) *P*' is the statement over again of 'If *D* then (certainly) *P*'. 'If the barometer is high, tomorrow will probably be fair; and the barometer *is* high', categorically assures something expressed by 'Tomorrow will probably be fair'. This probability is still relative to the grounds of judgment; but if these grounds are actual, and contain all the available evidence which is pertinent, then it is not only categorical but may fairly be called *the* probability of the event in question. (1946, p. 319).

This position seems to me to be open to just those objections suggested in the main text. If '*P*' is a statement, then the expressions 'certainly *P*' and 'probably *P*' as envisaged in the quoted passage are not statements. If we ask how one would go about trying to ascertain whether they were true, we realize that we are entirely at a loss unless and until a reference set of statements or assumptions has been specified relative to which *P* may then be found to be certain, or to be highly probable, or neither. The expressions in question, then, are essentially incomplete; they are elliptic formulations of relational statements; neither of them can be the conclusion of an inference. However plausible Lewis's suggestion may seem, there is no analogue in inductive logic to *modus ponens*, or the "rule of detachment," of deductive logic, which, given the information that '*D*', and also 'if *D* then *P*', are true statements, authorizes us to detach the consequent '*P*' in the conditional premise and to assert it as a self-contained statement which must then be true as well.

At the end of the quoted passage, Lewis suggests the important idea that 'probably *P*' might be taken to mean that the total relevant evidence available at the time confers high probability upon *P*. But even this statement is relational in that it tacitly refers to some unspecified time, and, besides, his general notion of a categorical probability statement as a conclusion of an argument is not made dependent on the assumption that the premises of the argument include all the relevant evidence available.

It must be stressed, however, that elsewhere in his discussion, Lewis emphasizes the relativity of (logical) probability, and, thus, the very characteristic that rules out the conception of categorical probability statements.

Similar objections apply, I think, to Toulmin's construal of probabilistic arguments; *cf.* Toulmin (1958) and the discussion in Hempel (1960), sections 1-3.

ing. It is still a matter of debate to what extent clear criteria and a precise theory for the concept at issue can be developed. Several attempts have been made to formulate rigorous logical theories for a concept of inductive support that admits of numerical or nonnumerical gradations in strength: two outstanding examples of such efforts are Keynes's theory of probability and, especially, Carnap's impressive system of inductive logic.[6] In the latter, the degree to which a sentence, or hypothesis, h is confirmed by an evidence sentence e is represented by a function $c(h,e)$, whose values lie in the interval from 0 to 1 inclusive, and which satisfies all the basic principles of abstract probability theory; $c(h,e)$ is therefore also referred to as the *logical or inductive probability* of h on e. This concept of inductive probability as a quantitative logical relation between statements must be sharply distinguished from the concept of statistical probability as a quantitative empirical relation between kinds or classes of events. The two concepts have a common formal structure, however, in virtue of which both of them qualify as probabilities: both are defined, in their respective formal theories, in terms of nonnegative additive set functions whose values range from 0 to 1. Carnap's theory provides an explicit definition of $c(h,e)$ for the case where the sentences h and e belong to one or another of certain relatively simple kinds of formalized language; the extension of his approach to languages whose logical apparatus would be adequate for the formulation of advanced scientific theories is as yet an open problem.

But, independently of the extent to which the relation of the explanandum to the explanans can be analyzed in terms of Carnap's quantitative concept of inductive probability, probabilistic explanations must be viewed as inductive in the broad sense here adumbrated. To refer to the general notion of inductive support as capable of gradations, without commitment to any one particular theory of inductive support or confirmation, we will use the phrase '*(degree of) inductive support of h relative to e*'.[7]

Explanations of particular facts or events by means of statistic-probabilistic laws thus present themselves as arguments that are *inductive* or *probabilistic* in the sense that the explanans confers upon the explanandum a more or less high degree of inductive support or of logical (inductive) probability; they

6. See Keynes (1921); of Carnap's numerous writings on the subject, *cf.* especially (1945), (1950), (1952), (1962).

7. Some recent attempts to give precise explications of this general notion have led to concepts that do not have all the formal characteristics of a probability function. One such construal is presented in Helmer and Oppenheim (1945) and, less technically, in Hempel and Oppenheim (1945). Another is the concept of degree of factual support propounded and theoretically developed in Kemeny and Oppenheim (1952). For a suggestive distinction and comparison of different concepts of evidence, see Rescher (1958).

will therefore be called *inductive-statistical explanations*, or *I-S explanations*. Explanations, such as (3d), in which the statistical laws invoked are of basic form, will also be called *I-S explanations of basic form*.

I will now try to show that the inductive construal here suggested for the statistical explanation of particular facts is called for also by the empirical interpretation that probabilistic laws have received in recent versions of the theory of statistical probability and its applications.

The mathematical theory of statistical probability is intended to provide a theoretical account of the statistical aspects of repeatable processes of a certain kind, which are referred to as random processes or random experiments. Roughly, a random experiment is a kind of process or event which can be repeated indefinitely by man or by nature, and which yields in each case one out of a certain finite or infinite set of "results" or "outcomes" in such a way that while the outcomes vary from case to case in an irregular and unpredictable manner, the relative frequencies with which the different outcomes occur tend to become more or less constant as the number of performances increases. The flipping of a coin, with heads and tails as the possible outcomes, is a familiar example of a random experiment.

The theory of probability offers a "mathematical model" of the general mathematical properties and interrelations of the long-run frequencies associated with the outcomes of random experiments.

In the model, each of the different "possible outcomes" assigned to a given random experiment F is represented by a set G, which may be thought of as the set of those performances of the experiment that yield the outcome in question, while F may be viewed as the set of all performances of the random experiment. The probability of obtaining an outcome of a given kind G as a result of performing an experiment of kind F is then represented as a measure, $p_F(G)$, of the size of set G in relation to set F.

The postulates of the mathematical theory specify that p_F is a nonnegative additive set function whose maximum value is 1, i.e., for every possible outcome G of F, $p_F(G) \geqslant 0$; if G_1, G_2 are mutually exclusive outcomes of F, then $p_F(G_1 \vee G_2) = p_F(G_1) + p_F(G_2)$; and $p_F(F) = 1$. These stipulations permit the proof of the theorems of elementary probability theory; to deal with experiments that admit of infinitely many different outcomes, the requirement of additivity is suitably extended to infinite sequences of mutually exclusive outcome sets G_1, G_2, G_3, ...

The resulting abstract theory is applied to empirical subject matter by means of an interpretation that relates statements in terms of probabilities as set-measures to statements about long-run relative frequencies associated with the outcomes of random experiments. I will now state this interpretation in a formulation which is essentially that given by Cramér.[8] For convenience, the notation 'P_F (G)' will henceforth be replaced by '$p(G,F)$'.

(3e) *Frequency interpretation of statistical probability.* Let F be a given kind of random experiment and G a possible result of it; then the statement that $p(G, F) = r$ means that in a long series of repetitions of F, it is practically certain that the relative frequency of the result G will be approximately equal to r.

Cramér also states two corrollaries of this interpretation which refer to those cases where r differs very little from 0 or from 1; they are of special interest for our further discussion of probabilistic explanation. I will therefore note them here, again following Cramér's formulation in its essentials.[9]

(3e.1) If $1 - p(G,F) < \varepsilon$, where ε is some very small positive number, then if random experiment F is performed one single time, it is practically certain that the result G will occur.

(3e.2) If $p(G,F) < \varepsilon$, where ε is some very small positive number, then if random experiment F is performed one single time, it is practically certain that result G will not occur.

As the frequency interpretation here formulated makes use of such vague phrases as 'a long series', 'practically certain', 'approximately equal', and the like, it clearly does not provide a precise definition of statistical probabilities in terms of observable relative frequencies. But some vagueness appears to be inevitable if the mathematical calculus of probability is to serve as a theoretical representation of the mathematical relations among empirically ascertained relative frequencies which remain only approximately constant when the observed sample increases.[10]

---

8. See Cramér (1946), pp. 148–49. Cramér's book includes a detailed discussion of the foundations of statistical probability theory and its applications. Similar formulations of the frequency interpretation have been given by earlier representatives of this measure-theoretical conception of statistical probability; for example, by Kolmogoroff (1933, p. 4).

9. For (3e.1), see Cramér (1946), p. 150; for (3e.2), see Cramér (1946), p. 149 and the very similar formulation in Kolmogoroff (1933), p. 4.

10. In certain forms of the mathematical theory, the statistical probability of a given outcome is explicitly defined, namely, as the limit of the relative frequency of that outcome in an infinite series of performances of the pertinent random experiment. Two important variants of this approach were developed by Mises, *cf.* (1931), (1939) and by Reichenbach, *cf.* (1949). But infinite series of performances are not realizable or observable, and the limit-definition of statistical probability thus provides no criteria for the application of that concept to observable empirical subject matter. In this respect the limit-construal of probability is an idealized theoretical concept, and criteria for its empirical application will again have to involve some vague terms of the kind resorted to in (3c) and its corollaries. In particular, a statement specifying the limit of the relative frequency of the result G in an infinite sequence of performances of random experiment F has no deductive implications concerning the frequency of G in any finite set of performances, however large it may be. The relation between

(continued overleaf)

Of particular interest for an analysis of I-S explanation, however, is the fact that the phrase 'it is practically certain that' occurs in the general statement (3e) of the statistical interpretation and that its two special corollaries (3e.1) and (3e.2) still contain that phrase, though they manage to avoid the vague expressions 'a long series of repetitions' and 'approximately equal'. The function of the words 'it is practically certain that' is clear: they indicate that the logical connection between statistical probability statements and the empirical frequency statements associated with them is inductive rather than deductive. This point can be made more explicit by restating (3e) as follows: The information that $p(G,F) = r$ and that S is a set of n performances of F, where n is a large number, confers near-certainty (high inductive support) upon the statement that the number of those performances in S whose outcome is G is approximately $n \cdot r$. The two corollaries admit of an analogous construal. Thus, (3e.1) may be restated as follows: The information that $1-p(G,F) < \varepsilon$ (where ε is a small positive number) and that individual event i is a performance of random experiment F (or that Fi, for short) lends strong inductive support to the statement that i yields outcome G, or that Gi, for short. Or, in a slightly different phrasing: 'Gi' is practically certain relative to the two sentences '$p(G,F)$ is very close to 1' and 'Fi'. This last version has the same form as (3c); thus, in giving an inductive construal to the explanatory import of probabilistic laws in the manner illustrated by (3d), we are in basic accord with the empirical interpretation given to probabilistic laws in the contemporary theory of statistical probability.[11]

In our example concerning recovery from a streptococcus infection, the statistical law invoked did not specify a definite numerical value for the probability of effecting recovery by means of penicillin. Now we will consider a simple case of I-S explanation in which the relevant probability statement is quite specific. Let the experiment D (more exactly, an experiment of kind D) consist in drawing, with subsequent replacement, a ball from an urn containing 999 white balls and one black, all of the same size and material. We might then accept the statistical hypothesis that with respect to the outcomes "white ball"

---

11. However, the representatives of current statistical probability theory do not, in general, take explicit notice of the inductive character of their statistical interpretation of probability statements. Even less do they attempt to analyze the inductive concept of practical certainty, which clearly falls outside the mathematical theory that is their principal concern.

---

probability statements thus construed and the corresponding statements about relative frequencies in finite runs must therefore again be viewed as inductive.

For a concise account of the limit conception of statistical probability and a lucid discussion of some of its difficulties, see Nagel (1939), especially sections 4 and 7.

and "black ball," D is a random experiment in which the probability of obtaining a white ball is $p(W,D)=.999$. According to the statistical interpretation, this is a hypothesis susceptible of test by reference to finite statistical samples, but for our present purposes, we need not consider the grounds we might have for accepting the hypothesis; for we are concerned only with its explanatory use. Our rule (3e.1) suggests that the hypothesis might indeed be used to explain probabilistically the results of certain individual drawings from the urn, i.e., the results of certain performances of D. Suppose, for example, that a particular drawing, d, produces a white ball. Since $p(W,D)$ differs from 1 by less than, say, .0011, which is quite a small amount, rule (3e.1) suggests the following explanatory argument in analogy to (3d):

$$(3f) \quad \frac{\begin{array}{c} 1 - p(W,D) < .0011 \\ Dd \end{array}}{Wd} \text{ [makes practically certain]}$$

Again, the explanans here does not logically imply the explanandum; and the argument does not show that, assuming the truth of the statements adduced in the explanans, the explanandum phenomenon was to be expected "with certainty." Rather, the argument may be said to show that on the information provided by the explanans, the explanandum event was to be expected with "practical" certainty, or with very high likelihood.

Carnap's conception of inductive logic suggests that the vague phrase 'makes practically certain', which appears between brackets in (3f), might be replaced by a more definite quantitative one. This would call for an extension of Carnap's theory to languages in which statistical probability statements can be formulated. While the logical apparatus of the languages covered by Carnap's published work is not rich enough for this purpose,[12] it seems clear that in cases of the simple kind exemplified by (3f), the numerical value of the logical probability should equal that of the corresponding statistical probability. For example, the information that with statistical probability .999, a drawing from the urn will produce a white ball, and that the particular event d is a drawing from the urn, should confer a logical probability of .999 upon the "conclusion" that the ball produced by d is white. More generally, this rule may be stated as follows:

(3.g) If e is the statement '$(p(G,F)=r) \cdot F b$', and h is '$G b$', then $c(h, e)=r$.

This rule is in keeping with the conception, set forth by Carnap, of logical probability as a fair betting quotient for a bet on h on the basis of e. It accords

12. According to a personal communication from Professor Carnap, his system has by now been extended in that direction.

equally with Carnap's view that the logical probability on evidence e of the hypothesis that a particular case b will have a specified property M may be regarded as an estimate, based on e, of the relative frequency of M in any class K of cases on which the evidence e does not report. Indeed, Carnap adds that the logical probability of 'Mb' on e may in certain cases be considered as an estimate of the statistical probability of M.[13] If, therefore, e actually contains the information that the statistical probability of M is r, then the estimate, on e, of that statistical probability, and thus of the logical probability of 'Mb' on e, should clearly be r as well.

And just as the rule (3e.1) provides the logical rationale for statistical explanations such as (3f), so our rule (3g) provides the rationale for a similar kind of probabilistic explanation, which invokes quantitatively definite statistical laws and which may be schematized as follows:

$$\text{(3h)} \quad \frac{\begin{array}{l} p(G,F) = r \\ F\,i \end{array}}{G\,i} = [r]$$

An explanatory argument of this form would serve to account for the fact that a given individual case i exhibits the characteristic G by pointing out that i is a case of F; that the statistical probability for an F to exhibit characteristic G is r; and that, according to rule (3g), this explanatory information confers the logical probability r upon the explanandum statement. I will refer to r also as the probability *associated with* the explanation. Of course, an argument of this kind will count as explanatory only if the number r is fairly close to 1. But it seems impossible, without being arbitrary, to designate any particular number, say .8, as the minimum value of the probability r permissible in an explanation.

In our example, the probabilistic explanation of the drawing of a white ball may now be put into the form (3h) as follows:

$$\text{(3i)} \quad \frac{\begin{array}{l} p(W,D) = .999 \\ D\,d \end{array}}{W\,d} = [.999]$$

Now, it is often said that probabilistic laws can serve to account for statistical aspects of large samples, but surely can explain nothing about an individual case. Examples like the following might seem to bear out this contention. The law that the flipping of a regular coin yields heads with the probability $1/2$

13. Carnap (1950), pp. 168-75.

clearly does not enable us to explain why a particular flipping produced heads; whereas the same law (plus the assumption that the results of different flippings are statistically independent of each other) may be used to account for the fact that the number of heads obtained in a particular series of 10,000 flippings fell between 4,900 and 5,100; for this outcome has a probability exceeding .95. But if we count this outcome as explained because of the high probability the explanans confers upon it, then clearly we must also grant explanatory status to arguments such as (3i) whose explanans makes it highly probably that the given outcome will occur if the relevant random experiment is performed just once.

It is also sometimes thought that because probabilistic arguments are not logically conclusive they cannot serve to explain; for even if the explanans is true, it is still possible that the explanandum phenomenon might not have come about;[14] in the case of (3i), for example, drawing *d* might have produced a black ball despite the high probability for a white one to be drawn. But this objection to the idea of probabilistic explanation rests on a too restrictive conception of scientific explanation; for many important explanatory accounts offered by empirical science make quite explicit use of statistical laws which, in conjunction with the rest of the explanatory information adduced, make the explanandum no more than highly probable.

For example, by means of Mendelian genetic principles it can be shown to be highly probable that in a random sample taken from a population of pea plants each of whose parent plants represents a cross of a pure white-flowered and a pure red-flowered strain, approximately 75 per cent of the plants will have red flowers and the rest, white ones. This argument, which may be used for explanatory or for predictive purposes, is inductive-statistical; what it explains or predicts are the approximate percentages of red- and white-flowered plants in the sample. The "premises" by reference to which the specified percentages are shown to be highly probable include (1) the pertinent laws of genetics, some of which have statistical, others strictly universal form; and (2) information of the kind mentioned above about the genetic make-up of the parent generation of the plants from which the sample is taken. The genetic principles of strictly universal form include the laws that the colors in question are tied to specific genes, that the red gene is dominant over the white one,

---

14. Thus Scriven (1959, p. 467), says that "statistical statements are too weak—they abandon the hold on the individual case. . . . An event can rattle around inside a network of statistical laws." Dray (1963, p. 119), expresses a similar view. These observations are quite correct if they are simply meant to say that statistical laws have no deductive implications concerning particular events, but they are misleading if they are used to suggest that statistical laws can have no explanatory significance for particular occurrences.

and various other general laws concerning the transmission, by genes, of the colors in question—or, perhaps, of a broader set of gene-linked traits. Among the statistical generalizations invoked is the hypothesis that the four possible combinations of color-determining genes—WW, WR, RW, RR—are statistically equiprobable in their occurrence in the offspring of two plants of the hybrid generation.

Let us now examine somewhat more closely an explanatory use of the law for radioactive decay of radon, which states that this element has a half-life of 3.82 days. This law may be invoked for a statistical explanation of the fact that within 7.64 days, a particular sample consisting of 10 milligrams of radon was reduced, by radioactive decay, to a residual amount falling somewhere within the interval from 2.4 to 2.6 milligrams; it could similarly be used for predicting a particular outcome of this kind. The gist of the explanatory and predictive arguments is this: The statement giving the half-life of radon conveys two statistical laws, (i) the statistical probability for an atom of radon to undergo radioactive decay within a period of 3.82 days is 1/2, and (ii) the decay of different radon atoms constitutes statistically independent events. One further premise used is the statement that the number of atoms in 10 milligrams of radon is enormously large (in excess of 10^{19}). As mathematical probability theory shows, the two laws in conjunction with this last statement imply deductively that the statistical probability is exceedingly high that the mass of the radon atoms surviving after 7.64 days will not deviate from 2.5 milligrams by more than .1 milligrams, i.e., that it will fall within the specified interval. More explicitly, the consequence deducible from the two statistical laws in conjunction with the information on the large number of atoms involved is another statistical law to this effect: The statistical probability is very high that the random experiment F of letting 10 milligrams of radon decay for 7.68 days will yield an outcome of kind G, namely a residual amount of radon whose mass falls within the interval from 2.4 to 2.6 milligrams. Indeed, the probability is so high that, according to the interpretation (9.2b), if the experiment F is performed just one single time, it is "practically certain" that the outcome will be of kind G. In this sense, it is rational on the basis of the given information to expect the outcome G to occur as the result of a single performance of F. Also in this sense, the information concerning the half-life of radon and the large number of atoms involved in an experiment of kind F affords a statistical explanation or prediction of the occurrence of G in a particular performance of the experiment.

By way of another illustration, take the problem of explaining certain quantitative aspects of the Brownian movement displayed by small particles suspended in a liquid—a phenomenon qualitatively explained as resulting from the irregular impacts, upon the suspended particles, of the surrounding molecules in thermal agitation. From assumptions based on the probabilistic principles of the kinetic theory of heat, Einstein derived a law to the effect that the mean displacement of such particles is proportional to the square root of the elapsed time.[15] But the theoretical definition of the mean displacement is formulated in terms of the statistical probabilities of the various possible displacements, and Einstein's law is therefore probabilistic in character. Hence it does not logically imply definite values for the average displacement exhibited by finite numbers of particles. But the law makes it highly probable, in the sense discussed above, that the average displacements in finite samples will be very nearly proportional to the square root of the elapsed time—and this has indeed been found to be the case. Thus, Einstein's law provides a probabilistic explanation for observed aspects of Brownian movement.

As is illustrated by these examples and by others that will be considered soon, accounts in terms of statistical laws or theories thus play a very important role in science. Rather than deny them explanatory status on the ground that nonrealization of the explanandum is compatible with the explanans, we have to acknowledge that they constitute explanations of a distinct logical character, reflecting, we might say, a different sense of the word 'because'. Mises expresses this point of view when, contemplating recent changes in the notion of causality, he anticipates that "people will gradually come to be satisfied by causal statements of this kind: It is *because* the die was loaded that the 'six' shows more frequently (but we do not know what the next number will be); or: *Because* the vacuum was heightened and the voltage increased, the radiation became more intense (but we do not know the precise number of scintillations that will occur in the next minute)."[16] This passage clearly refers to statistical explanation in the sense here under consideration; it sets forth what might be called a statistical-probabilistic concept of "because," in contradistinction to a strictly deterministic one, which would correspond to deductive-nomological explanation.

Our discussion of the statistical explanation of particular occurrences has so far been concerned to exhibit its inductive character. In the next subsection, we will consider a further important characteristic which sets I-S explanation sharply apart from its deductive counterparts.

---

15. For details, and for a full account of some experimental tests of this formula, see Svedberg (1912), pp. 89 ff. The basic ideas of the probabilistic explanation of some other quantitative aspects of Brownian movement are lucidly presented in Mises (1939), pp. 259–68.

16. Mises (1951), p. 188, italics the author's.

3.4 The Ambiguity of inductive-Statistical Explanation and the Requirement of Maximal Specificity.

3.4.1. *The Problem of Explanatory Ambiguity.* Consider once more the explanation (3d) of recovery in the particular case j of John Jones's illness. The statistical law there invoked claims recovery in response to penicillin only for a high percentage of streptococcal infections, but not for all of them; and in fact, certain streptococcus strains are resistant to penicillin. Let us say that an occurrence, e.g., a particular case of illness, has the property S^* (or belongs to the class S^*) if it is an instance of infection with a penicillin-resistant streptococcus strain. Then the probability of recovery among randomly chosen instances of S^* which are treated with penicillin will be quite small, i.e., $p(R, S^*{\cdot}P)$ will be close to 0 and the probability of non-recovery, $p(\overline{R}, S^*{\cdot}P)$ will be close to 1. But suppose now that Jones's illness is in fact a streptococcal infection of the penicillin-resistant variety, and consider the following argument:

$$\text{(3k)} \quad \frac{\begin{array}{c} p(\overline{R}, S^*{\cdot}P) \text{ is close to 1} \\ S^*j \,.\, Pj \end{array}}{\overline{R}\,j} \quad \text{[makes practically certain]}$$

This "rival" argument has the same form as (3d), and on our assumptions, its premises are true, just like those of (3d). Yet its conclusion is the contradictory of the conclusion of (3d).

Or suppose that Jones is an octogenarian with a weak heart, and that in this group, S^{**}, the probability of recovery from a streptococcus infection in response to penicillin treatment, $p(R, S^{**}{\cdot}P)$, is quite small. Then, there is the following rival argument to (3d), which presents Jones's nonrecovery as practically certain in the light of premises which are true:

$$\text{(3l)} \quad \frac{\begin{array}{c} p(\overline{R}, S^{**}{\cdot}P) \text{ is close to 1} \\ S^{**}j \cdot Pj \end{array}}{\overline{R}\,j} \quad \text{[makes practically certain]}$$

The peculiar logical phenomenon here illustrated will be called the *ambiguity of inductive-statistical explanation* or, briefly, of *statistical explanation*. This ambiguity derives from the fact that a given individual event (e.g., Jones's illness) will often be obtainable by random selection from any one of several "reference classes" (such as $S{\cdot}P$, S^*P, $S^{**}P$), with respect to which the kind of occurrence (e.g., R) instantiated by the given event has very different statistical probabilities. Hence, for a proposed probabilistic explanation with true explanans which confers near-certainty upon a particular event, there will often exist a rival argument of the same probabilistic form and with equally true premises which confers near-certainty upon the nonoccurrence of the same event. And any statistical explanation for the occurrence of an event must seem suspect if there is the possibility of a logically and empirically equally sound probabilistic account for its nonoccurrence. *This predicament has no analogue in the case of deductive explanation*; for if the premises of a proposed deductive explanation are true then so is its conclusion; and its contradictory, being false, cannot be a logical consequence of a rival set of premises that are equally true.

Here is another example of the ambiguity of I-S explanation: Upon expressing surprise at finding the weather in Stanford warm and sunny on a date as autumnal as November 27, I might be told, by way of explanation, that this was rather to be expected because the probability of warm and sunny weather (W) on a November day in Stanford (N) is, say, .95. Schematically, this account would take the following form, where 'n' stands for 'November 27':

$$p\,(W,N) = .95$$

(3m)
$$\frac{Nn}{Wn} \quad [.95]$$

But suppose it happens to be the case that the day before, November 26, was cold and rainy, and that the probability for the immediate successors (S) of cold and rainy days in Stanford to be warm and sunny is .2; then the account (3m) has a rival in the following argument which, by reference to equally true premises, presents it as fairly certain that November 27 is not warm and sunny:

$$p\,(\overline{W}, S) = .8$$

(3n)
$$\frac{Sn}{\overline{W}n} \quad [.8]$$

In this form, the problem of ambiguity concerns I-S arguments whose premises are in fact true, no matter whether we are aware of this or not. But, as will now be shown, the problem has a variant that concerns explanations whose explanans statements, no matter whether in fact true or not, are *asserted or accepted* by empirical science at the time when the explanation is proffered or contemplated. This variant will be called *the problem of the epistemic ambiguity of statistical explanation*, since it refers to what is presumed to be known in science rather than to what, perhaps unknown to anyone, is in fact the case.

Let K_t be the class of all statements asserted or accepted by empirical science at time t. This class then represents the total scientific information, or "scientific knowledge" at time t. The word 'knowledge' is here used in the sense in which we commonly speak of the scientific knowledge at a given time. It is not meant to convey the claim that the elements of K_t are true, and hence neither that they are definitely known to be true. No such claim can justifiably be made for any of the statements established by empirical science; and the basic standards of scientific inquiry demand that an empirical statement, however well supported, be accepted and thus admitted to membership in K_t only tentatively, i.e., with the understanding that the privilege may be withdrawn if unfavorable evidence should be discovered. The membership of K_t therefore changes in the course of time; for as a result of continuing research, new statements are admitted into that class; others may come to be discredited and dropped. Henceforth, the class of accepted statements will be referred to simply as K when specific reference to the time in question is not required. We will assume that K is logically consistent and that it is closed under logical implication, i.e., that it contains every statement that is logically implied by any of its subsets.

The *epistemic ambiguity of I-S explanation* can now be characterized as follows: The total set K of accepted scientific statements contains different subsets of statements which can be used as premises in arguments of the probabilistic form just considered, and which confer high probabilities on logically contradictory "conclusions." Our earlier examples (3k), (3l) and (3m), (3n) illustrate this point if we assume that the premises of those arguments all belong to K rather than that they are all true. If one of two such rival arguments with premises in K is proposed as an explanation of an event considered, or acknowledged, in science to have occurred, then the conclusion of the argument, i.e., the explanandum statement, will accordingly belong to K as well. And since K is consistent, the conclusion of the rival argument will not belong to K. Nonetheless it is disquieting that we should be able to say: No matter whether we are informed that the event in question (e.g., warm and sunny weather on November 27 in Stanford) did occur or that it did not occur, we can produce an explanation of the reported outcome in either case; and an explanation, moreover, whose premises are scientifically established statements that confer a high logical probability upon the reported outcome.

This epistemic ambiguity, again, has no analogue for deductive explanation; for since K is logically consistent, it cannot contain premise-sets that imply logically contradictory conclusions.

Epistemic ambiguity also bedevils the predictive use of statistical arguments. Here, it has the alarming aspect of presenting us with two rival arguments whose premises are scientifically well established, but one of which characterizes a contemplated future occurrence as practically certain, whereas the other characterizes it as practically impossible. Which of such conflicting arguments, if any, are rationally to be relied on for explanation or for prediction?

3.4.2 *The Requirement of Maximal Specificity and the Epistemic Relativity of Inductive-Statistical Explanation.* Our illustrations of explanatory ambiguity suggest that a decision on the acceptability of a proposed probabilistic explanation or prediction will have to be made in the light of all the relevant information at our disposal. This is indicated also by a general principle whose importance for inductive reasoning has been acknowledged, if not always very explicitly, by many writers, and which has recently been strongly emphasized by Carnap, who calls it *the requirement of total evidence.* Carnap formulates it as follows: "in the application of inductive logic to a given knowledge situation, the total evidence available must be taken as basis for determining the degree of confirmation."[17] Using only a part of the total evidence is permissible if the balance of the evidence is irrelevant to the inductive "conclusion," i.e., if on the partial evidence alone, the conclusion has the same confirmation, or logical probability, as on the total evidence.[18]

The requirement of total evidence is not a postulate nor a theorem of inductive logic; it is not concerned with the formal validity of inductive arguments. Rather, as Carnap has stressed, it is a maxim for the *application* of inductive logic; we might say that it states a necessary condition of rationality of any such application in a given "knowledge situation," which we will think of as represented by the set K of all statements accepted in the situation.

But in what manner should the basic idea of this requirement be brought to bear upon probabilistic explanation? Surely we should not insist that the explanans must contain all and only the empirical information available at the time. Not *all* the available information, because otherwise all probabilistic explanations acceptable at time t would have to have the same explanans, K_t; and not *only* the available information, because a proffered explanation may

17. Carnap (1950), p. 211.

The requirement is suggested, for example, in the passage from Lewis (1946) quoted in note 5 for this section. Similarly Williams speaks of "the most fundamental of all rules of probability logic, that 'the' probability of any proposition is its probability in relation to the known premises and them only." (Williams, 1947, p. 72).

I am greatly indebted to Professor Carnap for having pointed out to me in 1945, when I first noticed the ambiguity of probabilistic arguments, that this was but one of several apparent paradoxes of inductive logic that result from disregard of the requirement of total evidence.

Barker (1957), pp. 70–78, has given a lucid independent presentation of the basic ambiguity of probabilistic arguments, and a skeptical appraisal of the requirement of total evidence as a means of dealing with the problem. However, I will presently suggest a way of remedying the ambiguity of probabilistic explanation with the help of a rather severely modified version of the requirement of total evidence. It will be called the requirement of maximal specificity, and is not open to the same criticism.

18. *Cf.* Carnap (1950), p. 211 and p. 494.

meet the intent of the requirement in not overlooking any relevant information available, and may nevertheless invoke some explanans statements which have not as yet been sufficiently tested to be included in K_t.

The extent to which the requirement of total evidence should be imposed upon statistical explanations is suggested by considerations such as the following. A proffered explanation of Jones's recovery based on the information that Jones had a streptococcal infection and was treated with penicillin, and that the statistical probability for recovery in such cases is very high is unacceptable if K includes the further information that Jones's streptococci were resistant to penicillin, or that Jones was an octogenarian with a weak heart, and that in these reference classes the probability of recovery is small. Indeed, one would want an acceptable explanation to be based on a statistical probability statement pertaining to the narrowest reference class of which, according to our total information, the particular occurrence under consideration is a member. Thus, if K tells us not only that Jones had a streptococcus infection and was treated with penicillin, but also that he was an octogenarian with a weak heart (and if K provides no information more specific than that) then we would require that an acceptable explanation of Jones's response to the treatment be based on a statistical law stating the probability of that response in the narrowest reference class to which our total information assigns Jones's illness, i.e., the class of streptococcal infections suffered by octogenarians with weak hearts.[19]

Let me amplify this suggestion by reference to our earlier example concerning the use of the law that the half-life of radon is 3.82 days in accounting for the fact that the residual amount of radon to which a sample of 10 milligrams was reduced in 7.64 days was within the range from 2.4 to 2.6 milligrams. According to present scientific knowledge, the rate of decay of a radioactive element depends solely upon its atomic structure as characterized by its atomic number and its mass number, and it is thus unaffected by the age of the sample and by such factors as temperature, pressure, magnetic and electric forces, and chemical interactions. Thus, by specifying the half-life of radon as well as the initial mass of the sample and the time interval in question, the explanans takes into account all the available information that is relevant to

---

19. This idea is closely related to one used by Reichenbach (cf. (1949), section 72) in an attempt to show that it is possible to assign probabilities to individual events within the framework of a strictly statistical conception of probability. Reichenbach proposed that the probability of a single event, such as the safe completion of a particular scheduled flight of a given commercial plane, be construed as the statistical probability which the *kind* of event considered (safe completion of a flight) possesses within the narrowest reference class to which the given case (the specified flight of the given plane) belongs, and for which reliable statistical information is available (for example, the class of scheduled flights undertaken so far by planes of the line to which the given plane belongs, and under weather conditions similar to those prevailing at the time of the flight in question).

appraising the probability of the given outcome by means of statistical laws. To state the point somewhat differently: Under the circumstances here assumed, our total information K assigns the case under study first of all to the reference class say F_1, of cases where a 10 milligram sample of radon is allowed to decay for 7.64 days; and the half-life law for radon assigns a very high probability, within F_1, to the "outcome," say G, consisting in the fact that the residual mass of radon lies between 2.4 and 2.6 milligrams. Suppose now that K also contains information about the temperature of the given sample, the pressure and relative humidity under which it is kept, the surrounding electric and magnetic conditions, and so forth, so that K assigns the given case to a reference class much narrower than F_1, let us say, $F_1 F_2 F_3 \ldots F_n$. Now the theory of radioactive decay, which is equally included in K, tells us that the statistical probability of G within this narrower class is the same as within G. For this reason, it suffices in our explanation to rely on the probability $p(G,F_1)$.

Let us note, however, that "knowledge situations" are conceivable in which the same argument would not be an acceptable explanation. Suppose, for example, that in the case of the radon sample under study, the amount remaining one hour before the end of the 7.64 day period happens to have been measured and found to be 2.7 milligrams, and thus markedly in excess of 2.6 milligrams—an occurrence which, considering the decay law for radon, is highly improbable, but not impossible. That finding, which then forms part of the total evidence K, assigns the particular case at hand to a reference class, say F^*, within which, according to the decay law for radon, the outcome G is highly improbable since it would require a quite unusual spurt in the decay of the given sample to reduce the 2.7 milligrams, within the one final hour of the test, to an amount falling between 2.4 and 2.6 milligrams. Hence, the additional information here considered may not be disregarded, and an explanation of the observed outcome will be acceptable only if it takes account of the probability of G in the narrower reference class, i.e., $p(G,F_1 F^*)$. (The theory of radioactive decay implies that this probability equals $p(G,F^*)$, so that as a consequence the membership of the given case in F_1 need not be explicitly taken into account.)

The requirement suggested by the preceding considerations can now be stated more explicitly; we will call it the *requirement of maximal specificity for inductive-statistical explanations*. Consider a proposed explanation of the basic statistical form

$$
(3o) \qquad \begin{array}{c} p(G,F) = r \\ Fb \\ \hline Gb \end{array} [r]
$$

Let s be the conjunction of the premises, and, if K is the set of all statements accepted at the given time, let k be a sentence that is logically equivalent to K (in the sense that k is implied by K and in turn implies every sentence in K). Then, to be rationally acceptable in the knowledge situation represented by K, the proposed explanation (3o) must meet the following condition (the requirement of maximal specificity): If $s \cdot k$ implies[20] that b belongs to a class F_1, and that F_1 is a subclass of F, then $s \cdot k$ must also imply a statement specifying the statistical probability of G in F_1, say

$$p(G, F_1) = r_1$$

Here, r_1 must equal r unless the probability statement just cited is simply a theorem of mathematical probability theory.

The qualifying unless-clause here appended is quite proper, and its omission would result in undesirable consequences. It is proper because theorems of pure mathematical probability theory cannot provide an explanation of empirical subject matter. They may therefore be discounted when we inquire whether $s \cdot k$ might not give us statistical laws specifying the probability of G in reference classes narrower than F. And the omission of the clause would prove troublesome, for if (3o) is proffered as an explanation, then it is presumably accepted as a fact that Gb; hence 'Gb' belongs to K. Thus K assigns b to the narrower class $F \cdot G$, and concerning the probability of G in that class, $s \cdot k$ trivially implies the statement that $p(G, F \cdot G) = 1$, which is simply a consequence of the measure-theoretical postulates for statistical probability. Since $s \cdot k$ thus implies a more specific probability statement for G than that invoked in (3o), the requirement of maximal specificity would be violated by (3o)—and analogously by any proffered statistical explanation of an event that we take to have occurred—were it not for the unless-clause, which, in effect, disqualifies the notion that the statement '$p(G, F \cdot G) = 1$' affords a more appropriate law to account for the presumed fact that Gb.

The requirement of maximal specificity, then, is here tentatively put forward as characterizing the extent to which the requirement of total evidence properly applies to inductive-statistical explanations. The general idea thus suggested comes to this: In formulating or appraising an I-S explanation, we should take into account all that information provided by K which is of potential *explanatory* relevance to the explanandum event; i.e., all pertinent statistical laws, and such

---

20. Reference to $s \cdot k$ rather than to k is called for because, as was noted earlier, we do not construe the condition here under discussion as requiring that all the explanans statements invoked be scientifically accepted at the time in question, and thus be included in the corresponding class K.

particular facts as might be connected, by the statistical laws, with the explanandum event.[21]

The requirement of maximal specificity disposes of the problem of epistemic ambiguity; for it is readily seen that of two rival statistical arguments with high associated probabilities and with premises that all belong to K, at least one violates the requirement of maximum specificity. Indeed, let

$$\frac{\begin{array}{c} p\ (G,F) = r_1 \\ F\,b \end{array}}{G\,b}\ [r_1] \quad \text{and} \quad \frac{\begin{array}{c} p(\overline{G}, H) = r_2 \\ H\,b \end{array}}{\overline{G}\,b}\ [r_2]$$

be the arguments in question, with r_1 and r_2 close to 1. Then, since K contains the premises of both arguments, it assigns b to both F and H and hence to $F \cdot H$. Hence if both arguments satisfy the requirement of maximal specificity, K must imply that

$$p(G, F \cdot H) = p(G, F) = r_1$$
$$p(\overline{G}, F \cdot H) = p(\overline{G}, H) = r_2$$

But
$$p(G, F \cdot H) + p(\overline{G}, F \cdot H) = 1$$

Hence
$$r_1 + r_2 = 1$$

and this is an arithmetic falsehood, since r_1 and r_2 are both close to 1; hence it cannot be implied by the consistent class K.

Thus, for I-S explanations that meet the requirement of maximal specificity the problem of epistemic ambiguity no longer arises. We are *never* in a position to say: No matter whether this particular event did or did not occur, we can produce an acceptable explanation of either outcome; and an explanation, moreover, whose premises are scientifically accepted statements which confer a high logical probability upon the given outcome.

21. By its reliance on this general idea, and specifically on the requirement of maximal specificity, the method here suggested for eliminating the epistemic ambiguity of statistical explanation differs substantially from the way in which I attempted in an earlier study (Hempel, 1962, especially section 10) to deal with the same problem. In that study, which did not distinguish explicitly between the two types of explanatory ambiguity characterized earlier in this section, I applied the requirement of total evidence to statistical explanations in a manner which presupposed that the explanans of any acceptable explanation belongs to the class K, and which then demanded that the probability which the explanans confers upon the explanandum be equal to that which the total evidence, K, imparts to the explanandum. The reasons why this approach seems unsatisfactory to me are suggested by the arguments set forth in the present section. Note in particular that, if strictly enforced, the requirement of total evidence would preclude the possibility of any significant statistical explanation for events whose occurrence is regarded as an established fact in science; for any sentence describing such an occurrence is logically implied by K and thus trivially has the logical probability 1 relative to K.

While the problem of epistemic ambiguity has thus been resolved, ambiguity in the first sense discussed in this section remains unaffected by our requirement; i.e., it remains the case that for a given statistical argument with true premises and a high associated probability, there may exist a rival one with equally true premises and with a high associated probability, whose conclusion contradicts that of the first argument. And though the set K of statements accepted at any time never includes all statements that are in fact true (and no doubt many that are false), it is perfectly possible that K should contain the premises of two such conflicting arguments; but as we have seen, at least one of the latter will fail to be rationally acceptable because it violates the requirement of maximal specificity.

The preceding considerations show that *the concept of statistical explanation for particular events is essentially relative to a given knowledge situation as represented by a class K of accepted statements*. Indeed, the requirement of maximal specificity makes explicit and unavoidable reference to such a class, and it thus serves to characterize the concept of "I-S explanation relative to the knowledge situation represented by K." We will refer to this characteristic as the *epistemic relativity of statistical explanation*.

It might seem that the concept of deductive explanation possesses the same kind of relativity, since whether a proposed D-N or D-S account is acceptable will depend not only on whether it is deductively valid and makes essential use of the proper type of general law, but also on whether its premises are well supported by the relevant evidence at hand. Quite so; and this condition of empirical confirmation applies equally to statistical explanations that are to be acceptable in a given knowledge situation. But the epistemic relativity that the requirement of maximal specificity implies for I-S explanations is of quite a different kind and has no analogue for D-N explanations. For the specificity requirement is not concerned with the evidential support that the total evidence K affords for the explanans statements: it does not demand that the latter be included in K, nor even that K supply supporting evidence for them. It rather concerns what may be called the concept of a *potential* statistical explanation. For it stipulates that no matter how much evidential support there may be for the explanans, a proposed I-S explanation is not acceptable if its potential explanatory force with respect to the specified explanandum is vitiated by statistical laws which are included in K but not in the explanans, and which might permit the production of rival statistical arguments. As we have seen, this danger never arises for deductive explanations. Hence, these are not subject to any such restrictive condition, and the notion of a potential deductive explanation (as contradistinguished from a deductive explanation with well-confirmed explanans) requires no relativization with respect to K.

As a consequence, we can significantly speak of true D-N and D-S explanations: they are those potential D-N and D-S explanations whose premises (and hence also conclusions) are true—no matter whether this happens to be known or believed, and thus no matter whether the premises are included in K. But this idea has no significant analogue for I-S explanation since, as we have seen, the concept of potential statistical explanation requires relativization with respect to K.

3.4.3 *Discrete State Systems and Explanatory Ambiguity.* In a lucid and instructive article, Rescher[22] has shown that physical systems of a particular kind, which he calls discrete state systems, afford excellent illustrations of deductive and probabilistic explanation and prediction, and that a closer examination of such systems can shed a good deal of light on the logical structure, the scope, and the interrelations of those procedures. I propose to show that a study of those systems also confronts one with the problem of explanatory ambiguity and supports the solution here suggested.

By a *discrete state system*, or a DS system for short, Rescher understands a physical system which at any moment is in one of several possible states, $S_1, S_2, \ldots$, each of whose occurrences occupies a finite, though perhaps very brief, period of time; for the purpose at hand, the number of possible states for a DS system is taken to be finite. The succession of states exhibited by a DS system is governed by a set of laws, each of which may be deterministic or probabilistic (statistical). A deterministic law has the form 'State S_i is always immediately followed by state S_j'; a probabilistic law has the form 'The statistical probability for (an occurrence of) state S_i to be immediately followed by (an occurrence of) state S_j is r_{ij}.' A DS system of this kind can be characterized by means of the matrix of all the transition probabilities r_{ij}.

There are various physical examples of DS systems; among them Rescher mentions an electronic digital computer; an atom of a radioactive element in its successive states of decay; and—given a suitably schematized mode of description—a particle in Brownian motion. A ball rolling down a Galton Board[23] is yet another DS system; its state at a given time being represented by the number of pins that separate it horizontally from the vertical center line of the board.

A potential probabilistic explanation (of a momentary state of a DS system) is defined by Rescher as an argument whose conclusion is of the form 'the state of the system in time-interval t is S_i', or '$st(t) = S_i$' for short, and whose premises consist of the laws governing the system and of a set of statements specifying the states exhibited by the system during certain other time intervals,

22. Rescher (1963).
23. For a discussion of this process, see Mises (1939), pp. 237-40.

$t_1, t_2, \ldots, t_n$, all of which are different from t.[24] The argument may be "probabilistic, either in the strong sense. . . that $st(t) = S_i$ is (conditionally) *more likely than not*, or in the weak sense . . . that $st(t) = S_i$ is (conditionally) *more likely than st(t)* $= S_j$ for any $j \neq i$."[25] Finally, "A potentially explanatory argument becomes an *(actual) explanation* if its premises are actually or probably true."[26]

To see that probabilistic explanation thus construed again is plagued by ambiguity, consider a DS system capable of just three states, S_1, S_2, S_3, with transition probabilities as specified in the following schema:

	S_1	S_2	S_3
S_1	0	.99	.01
S_2	0	0	1
S_3	1	0	0

Thus, the probability of S_1 being immediately followed by S_1 is 0; by S_2, .99; by S_3, .01; and so forth.

Alternatively, DS systems can be characterized by what Rescher calls transition-diagrams. In our case, the diagram takes the following form:

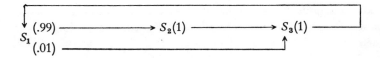

As is readily seen, the transition laws here indicated imply the following two derivative laws:

(L_1)   The probability for the two-period successor of S_1 to be S_3 is $.99 \times 1 = .99$.

(L_2)   The probability for the immediate successor of S_3 to be again S_3 is 0.

Suppose now that in two particular successive time intervals t_1 and t_2, our

24. Rescher does not require of a potential explanation—as he does of a potential prediction, which is otherwise characterized in the same manner—that the time intervals t_1, t_2, ..., t_n must all precede t. As a result, every potential prediction is a potential explanation, but not conversely. His reason for this construal will be examined in section 3.5.

25. Rescher (1963), p. 330, italics the author's. The concept of conditional likelihood here invoked is not further clarified; but it evidently is meant to represent the likelihood which the conclusion of the explanatory argument possesses relative to, or conditional upon, the premises. In this case, likelihoods would have the general character of logical probabilities; and Rescher does seem to operate with them in accordance with the conception reflected by our schema (3h), where the "likelihood" in question is specified in square brackets next to the double line separating the conclusion from the premises.

26. Rescher (1963), p. 329, italics the author's.

system exhibits the states S_1 and S_3 respectively; i.e. that the following statements are true:

(C₁) $st(t_1) = S_1$

(C₂) $st(t_2) = S_3$

Then C_1 jointly with L_1 provides the premises for a probabilistic argument which gives the "likelihood" .99 to the conclusion that in the time interval t_3 immediately following t_2, the system is in state S_3; i.e., that $st(t_3) = S_3$. But C_2 jointly with L_2 analogously gives the likelihood 1 to the conclusion that $st(t_3) \neq S_3$. On our assumptions, the premises invoked in these conflicting arguments are true; hence the arguments constitute strong probabilistic explanations, in Rescher's sense, of the occurrence and of the nonoccurrence of S_3 during time interval t_3; and both are actual explanations in Rescher's sense since all the explanatory premises are true. Thus we have explanatory ambiguity in the first of our two senses. That ambiguity in the second, epistemic, sense is present as well is clear when we consider that on our assumptions, all the premises invoked may of course belong to the class K of statements that are accepted at the time.[27]

To preclude this untenable consequence, Rescher's definitions of probabilistic explanation and prediction must be supplemented by a suitable additional requirement. In our example, the first of the two competing arguments would clearly be rejected on the ground that it disregards some relevant information. But this is precisely the verdict of the requirement of maximal specificity. For in our illustration, we may assume that the class K includes the information conveyed by C_1, C_2, L_1, and L_2; but that K contains no more specific information which would imply a probability assignment, on empirical grounds, to the sentence '$st(t_3) = S_3$'. The first of the two probabilistic arguments violates the requirement of maximal specificity, since it takes into account only that the state of the system at t_1 is S_1, although K tells us further that the occurrence of S_1 at t_1 is directly followed by an occurrence of S_3, and that for an occurrence of S_1 that is followed by an occurrence of S_3 the probability of having S_3 as a two-period successor is 0. (For L_2 tells us quite generally that the probability for an occurrence of S_3 no matter what its predecessor may be—to be followed by an occurrence of S_3 is 0.) Hence only the second of the two rival arguments is acceptable under the requirement of maximal specificity.

---

27. The same ambiguity would jeopardize the predictive use of these arguments: though both based on accepted (and indeed, true) premises, they lead to contradictory predictions about the state of the system during t_3.

3.5 PREDICTIVE ASPECTS OF STATISTICAL EXPLANATION. Can it be maintained that an inductive-statistical explanation of a particular event, much like a deductive-nomological one, constitutes a potential prediction of that event?

If the statement describing the occurrence in question is included in the class K of accepted statements, then the question of predicting the event clearly cannot arise in the knowledge situation represented by K. Let us therefore put our problem into this form: Suppose that an argument of the type (3o) meets the requirement of maximum specificity relative to K and that its explanans is well confirmed by K; would it then be acceptable as a predictive argument in the knowledge situation characterized by K? The answer will depend, of course, on the conditions we think a statistical argument has to satisfy if it is to be rationally acceptable for predictive purposes in a given knowledge situation. Let us briefly consider this question.

Rationality clearly demands that in forming expectations concerning future occurrences we take into account all the relevant information available at the time: this is the gist of the requirement of total evidence. But how is this requirement to be construed more specifically? If a general definition and theory of logical, or inductive, probability is available, the condition comes to this: the probability conferred upon the conclusion of the predictive argument by the premises alone should equal the probability imparted to it by the total evidence K; in that case, the balance of the total evidence is justifiably disregarded in the argument, for its addition to the premises would not change the probability of the conclusion. At present, no definition and theory of inductive probability is available which is sufficiently comprehensive to be applicable to all the kinds of inductive argument that would have to be considered. If such a definition should be constructed—for example, by generalizing Carnap's approach—it might turn out that a statistical argument whose premises are well supported by K, and which does satisfy the requirement of maximal specificity, still does not strictly meet the requirement of total evidence in the precise quantitative form under consideration. For example, let K consist of the premises of (3o) and the further statement 'Hd', then, though intuitively this latter statement is entirely irrelevant to the conclusion 'Gb', it is conceivable that the logical probability, in the sense here assumed, of 'Gb' relative to K should differ from the logical probability r of 'Gb' relative to the premises of (3o) alone. Or suppose that K consists of the statements '$p(G,F) = .9$', '$p(G,H) = .1$', '$p(G,F \cdot H) = .85$', 'Fb', 'Hb'; then a statistical argument with the last three of these statements as premises and 'Gb' as conclusion satisfies the requirement of maximal specificity relative to K. Yet again, the logical probability of 'Gb' relative to K might differ from the logical probability, .85, of 'Gb' relative to the set of the three premise-statements.

In the absence of a suitable general definition of logical probability, however, it seems quite clear that the predictive argument just considered would indeed by regarded as rationally acceptable in the knowledge situation represented by K; the statistical law specifying the probability of G in $F \cdot H$ would count as overriding the laws specifying the probability of G relative to F and to H, respectively. Similarly, an argument of the type (3o) whose premises are well substantiated and which conforms to the requirement of maximum specificity would surely be regarded as a rational way of forming expectations concerning the event described by the conclusion. And in general, predictive arguments in science which are based on probabilistic laws appear to be governed by the requirement of maximum specificity and the requirement of adequate confirmation for the premises. To the extent thus indicated, then, an argument that constitutes an acceptable statistical explanation relative to K also forms an acceptable potential prediction relative to K.

Hanson[28] has put forward an interesting view of the relation between explanatory and predictive arguments in science, which gives me an occasion as well as an opportunity to amplify the general position just outlined, and to argue further in its support.

According to Hanson, the view that an adequate explanation also affords a potential prediction conforms well to the character of the explanations and predictions made possible by Newtonian classical mechanics, which is deterministic in character; but it is quite inappropriate in reference to quantum theory, which is fundamentally nondeterministic. More specifically, Hanson holds that the laws of quantum theory do not permit the *prediction* of any individual quantum phenomenon P, such as the emission of a beta-particle by a radioactive substance, but that "P can be completely *explained* ex post facto; one can understand fully just what kind of event occurred, in terms of the well-established laws of . . . quantum theory. . . . These laws give the *meaning* of 'explaining single microevents'."[29]

It is indeed the case that because of their purely statistical character, the laws of radioactive decay permit the prediction of events such as the emission of beta-particles by disintegrating atoms only with probability and not with deductive-nomological definiteness for an individual occurrence. But for exactly the same reason, those laws permit only a probabilistic explanation of a particular emission P rather than a "complete" explanation "ex post facto," as Hanson puts it. For if, as the phrase "ex post facto" might seem to suggest, the information that P has occurred were included in the explanans, the

---

28. Hanson (1959) and (1963), chapter 2.
29. Hanson (1959), p. 354, italics the author's; similarly in Hanson (1963), p. 29.

resulting account would be unilluminatingly circular: surely Hanson does not mean that. And if the explanans contains only statements about antecedent conditions, plus the statistical laws of radioactive decay, then it can show at best that the occurrence of P was highly probable; but this affords only an inductive-statistical explanation, which has the same logical form as the probabilistic, i.e., inductive-statistical, prediction of P.[30]

In the context of his argument, Hanson puts forward another assertion, namely: "Every prediction, if inferentially respectable, must possess a corresponding postdiction."[31] By a postdiction, Hanson means "simply the logical reversal of a prediction": a prediction proceeds "from initial conditions through boundary conditions to a statement about some future event x," and a postdiction consists "in inferring from a statement about some present event x, through the boundary conditions, back to already *known* initial conditions."[32] But Hanson's thesis is incorrect, as is shown by the following counter-example. Consider a discrete state system whose three possible states, S_1, S_2, S_3, are linked by the following laws: S_1 as well as S_2 is always followed by S_3; S_3 is followed, with a probability of .5, by S_1 and with the same probability by S_2. The corresponding transition diagram is this:

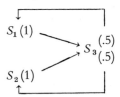

Then the information that in time-interval t_5 the system is in S_2 permits the deductive-nomological, and thus clearly "inferentially respectable" prediction that during t_6, the system will be in S_3; but no corresponding postdiction is possible from the latter information to the former.[33]

In conclusion, I wish to consider an argument put forward by Rescher as to the relation between explanation and prediction. The gist of it can most

30. For comments in a similar vein, see Henson (1963); *cf.* also the critical response in Feyerabend (1964).

31. Hanson (1963), p. 193, *cf.* also p. 40. Hanson goes on to say: "This is part of Hempel's thesis, and it is sound, necessarily" (*Ibid.*). Actually, I have argued *against* this thesis, which is true of predictions based on deterministic theories, but not true in general. See Hempel (1962), pp. 114–15.

32. Hanson (1963), p. 193, italics the author's.

33. On this point, see also Grünbaum (1963), p. 76. Grünbaum's article presents a detailed discussion of the structural identity of explanation and prediction and examines a variety of objections to this idea.

simply be stated by particular reference to Rescher's study of discrete state systems, which we considered in section 3.4. On Rescher's definition, an argument explaining the state of such a system in time interval t may refer, in the explanans, to the states exhibited by the system at certain other times, which may be earlier or later than t; whereas an argument predicting the state at t is required to refer only to preceding states. As a consequence of these definitional stipulations, "it follows that whenever a prediction . . . is given, so *a fortiori* is an explanation," but not conversely. "For our defining conditions for prediction . . . in effect add to the conditions for explanation . . . certain added restrictions of a temporal character."[34]

In defense of imposing that additional requirement on prediction, Rescher argues, in effect, as follows: Suppose that the premises of a proposed argument predicting the state of the system at t include a statement specifying the state of that system for some later time interval t_1. Then, since the argument is predictive, t is later than "the present," t_N, and hence so is t_1. Now there are two possibilities. Either (i) the premise pertaining to t_1 can itself be inferred, by means of laws, from past states of the system: then the given predictive argument can evidently be replaced by one that infers the state at t, with the help of laws, solely from past states, so that the restrictive requirement is met; or (ii) the explanatory premise about t_1 cannot be inferred from statements about past states: then "we do not actually have a proper prediction at all —for we are basing our 'predictive' argument on a premise which cannot be justified in terms of *available* information."[35]

But as the reference to justificatory evidence indicates, this consideration has no bearing on the thesis that an explanatory argument is potentially also a predictive one, i.e., that it could have been used to derive a predictive sentence concerning the state of the system at t if the statements forming the explanans had been formulated and used as premises before t. To be sure, we would normally ask for an explanation of a given state only after its occurrence, i.e., in our case, after t;[36] and it is true, as the argument points out, that we may then be able to support the critical premise by evidence that was not available before t. But the empirical support for the premises has no bearing on the structural relationships between explanatory and predictive arguments; nor, I think, do considerations based on it afford good grounds for imposing a restrictive formal condition upon predictive inferences.

34. Rescher (1963), p. 329.
35. Rescher (1963), p. 333, italics the author's.
36. Indeed, by parity of reasoning, Rescher would seem obliged to say that the argument considered in our example, one of whose premises refers to t_1, is not a proper explanation either, if it is presented before t_1 (though after t), for it then rests on a premise that is not justified by available evidence.

It should also be remembered that, as was noted in section 2.4, even the most perfect cases of scientific prediction normally make use of some statements about the future that are not inferred by law from information about the past. Thus, the prediction of the positions of the planets at a given time on the basis of the requisite data concerning their locations and momenta a month earlier requires an assumption concerning the boundary conditions during the intervening time interval, normally to the effect that there will be no outside interference with the system. And though this is not inferred by law from other particulars, the arguments presupposing those boundary conditions are not regarded as therefore affording no proper predictions at all.

Finally, we might note with Scheffler that we may sometimes reasonably speak of explaining a future event, and that indeed, in some cases, one and the same argument may be considered as predicting a certain event and explaining it; as, for example, when the question 'Why will the sun rise tomorrow?' is answered by offering some appropriate astronomical information.[37] For this reason, too, it seems inadvisable to impose different formal requirements upon explanatory and predictive arguments.

3.6 THE NONCONJUNCTIVENESS OF INDUCTIVE-STATISTICAL EXPLANATION. Inductive-statistical explanation differs from its deductive counterparts in yet another important respect. When a given explanans deductively accounts for each of several explananda, then it also deductively accounts for their conjunction; but the analogue for I-S explanation does not generally hold because an explanans that confers high probability on each of several explananda may confer a very low probability on their conjunction. In this sense, then, *I-S explanation, in contrast to deductive explanation, is non-conjunctive*.

Consider, for example, the random experiment F of flipping a fair coin ten times in succession. Each performance of this experiment will yield, as its outcome, one of the $2^{10} = 1024$ different possible sequences of 10 individual results each of which is either heads or tails. Let $O_1, O_2, \ldots, O_{1024}$ be the different possible kinds of outcome thus characterized. Then, according to the standard statistical hypothesis—let us call it S—for this kind of experiment, the probability of obtaining heads by flipping the coin is 1/2, and the results of different flippings are statistically independent of each other. It follows therefore deductively that the statistical probability of obtaining outcome O_k as a result of performing F is $p(O_k, F) = 1/1024$, and the probability of getting a result other than O_k is $p(\overline{O_k}, F) = 1-1/1024 = 1023/1024$, for any one of the different possible outcomes O_k.

37. Scheffler (1957), p. 300.

Suppose now that a particular performance, f, of F has yielded O_{500} as its outcome: $O_{500}(f)$. This result can also be described by saying that f did not yield any of the other possible outcomes:

$$\overline{O}_1(f) \cdot \overline{O}_2(f) \ldots \overline{O}_{499}(f) \cdot \overline{O}_{501}(f) \cdot \ldots \cdot \overline{O}_{1024}(f)$$

Now, our statistical hypothesis S in conjunction with the information that f was a particular performance of F, i.e., that $F(f)$, provides an I-S explanation with high associated probability for (the facts described by) each of the 1023 sentences here conjoined as follows:

$$\frac{\begin{array}{l} p(\overline{O}_k, F) = 1023/1024 \\ F(f) \end{array}}{\overline{O}_k(f)} \qquad [1023/1024]$$

The requirement of maximal specificity is satisfied by these accounts since for such further information about the particular experiment f as may be available to us under the circumstances, S may be taken to imply that it does not affect the probability of O_k. But though S in combination with the information that $F(f)$ thus confers a high probability on each of the 1023 conjoined statements just listed, it assigns the very low probability of 1/1024 to their conjunction, which is tantamount to the statement '$O_{500}(f)$'; For we have

$$\frac{\begin{array}{l} p(O_{500}, F) = 1/1024 \\ F(f) \end{array}}{O_{500}(f)} \qquad [1/1024]$$

Thus, while S together with '$F(f)$' provides an I-S explanation with high associated probability for (the facts described by) any of the 1023 sentences cited above, it does not do so for (the facts described by) their conjunction.[38]

This nonconjunctiveness of I-S explanation thus springs from the fact that one and the same set of sentences may confirm to a very high degree each of n alternative statements while confirming with similar strength the negation of their conjunction. This fact, in turn, is rooted in the general multiplication theorem for probabilities, which implies that the probability of the conjunction of two items (i.e., characteristics or sentences, according as statistical or logical probabilities are concerned) is, in general, less than the probability of either item taken by itself. Hence, once the connection between explanans and explanandum in the statistical explanation of particular phenomena is viewed as

38. For another illustration, *cf.* Hempel (1962), p. 165.

inductive, nonconjunctiveness presents itself as an inevitable aspect of it, and thus as one of the fundamental characteristics that set I-S explanation apart from its deductive counterparts.

4. THE CONCEPTS OF COVERING-LAW EXPLANATION AS EXPLICATORY MODELS

4.1 GENERAL CHARACTER AND INTENT OF THE MODELS. We have by now distinguished three basic types of scientific explanative: deductive-nomological, inductive-statistical, and deductive-statistical. The first of these is often referred to as the covering-law model or the deductive model of explanation, but since the other two types also involve reference to covering laws, and since one of them is deductive as well, we will call the first more specifically the *deductive-nomological model;* analogously, we will speak of the others as the *inductive-statistical* and the *deductive statistical models of explanation.*

As is made clear by our earlier discussions, these models are not meant to describe how working scientists actually formulate their explanatory accounts. Their purpose is rather to indicate in reasonably precise terms the logical structure and the rationale of various ways in which empirical science answers explanation-seeking why-questions. The construction of our models therefore involves some measure of abstraction and of logical schematization.

In these respects, our concepts of explanation resemble the concept, or concepts, of mathematical proof (within a given mathematical theory) as construed in metamathematics. Let us note the principal points of resemblance.

In either case, the models seek to explicate the use and function of certain "explicandum" terms—'proof' and its cognates in one case, 'explanation' and its cognates in the other. However, the models are selective; they are not meant to illuminate all the different customary uses of the terms in question, but only certain special ones. Thus, metamathematical proof theory is concerned only with the notion of proof in mathematics. To put the theory forward is not to deny that there are other contexts in which we speak of proofs and proving, nor is it to assert that the metamathematical concepts are relevant to those contexts.

Similarly, to put forward the covering-law models of scientific explanation is not to deny that there are other contexts in which we speak of explanation, nor is it to assert that the corresponding uses of the word 'explain' conform to one or another of our models. Obviously, those models are not intended to reflect the various senses of 'explain' that are involved when we speak of explaining the rules of a contest, explaining the meaning of a cuneiform inscription or of a complex legal clause or of a passage in a symbolist poem, explaining how to bake Sacher torte or how to repair a radio. Explicating the concept of scientific explanation is not the same thing as writing an entry on the word 'explain' for the *Oxford English Dictionary*. Hence to deplore, as one critic does, the "hopelessness" of the deductive-nomological model on the ground that it does not fit the case of explaining or understanding the rules of Hanoverian succession[1] is simply to miss the intent of the model. And it is the height of irrelevance to point out that the deductive-nomological model presupposes that explanations are formulated in a "descriptive language," whereas "there are clearly cases where we can explain without language, e.g., when we explain to the mechanic in a Yugoslav garage what has gone wrong with the car."[2] This is like objecting to a metamathematical definition of proof on the ground that it does not fit the use of the word 'proof' in 'the proof of the pudding is in the eating', nor in '86 proof Scotch'. Wordless gesticulation intended to indicate to a Yugoslav mechanic what is wrong with the car indeed does not qualify as scientific explanation according to any of our models; but that is as it should be, for a construal of scientific explanation that did admit this case would thereby show itself to be seriously inadequate.

In support of the idea that all these different uses of the word 'explain' should be encompassed by an adequate analysis of explanation, Scriven has argued that they all have the same "logical function," about which he remarks: "the request for an explanation presupposes that *something* is understood, and a complete answer is one that relates the object of inquiry to the realm of under-standing in some comprehensible and appropriate way. What this way is varies from subject matter to subject matter. . . ; but the *logical function* of explanation . . . is the same in each field."[3] But while the opening remark of this passage may well apply to many different kinds of explanation, neither it nor the rest of Scriven's remarks on the subject concern what could properly be called a *logical* aspect of explanation. Indeed, such expressions as 'realm of understanding' and 'comprehensible' do not belong to the vocabulary of logic, for they refer to the psychological or pragmatic aspects of explanation. We will consider these aspects in the next section and will see that when construed as observations about the pragmatics rather than the logic of expla-nation, characterizations such as Scriven's are quite relevant.

But the different ways of explaining contemplated by Scriven certainly cannot be said to have the same logical function. For, first, even the linguistic

---

1. Scriven (1959), p. 452.

2. Scriven (1962), p. 192. That such objections are irrelevant has been stressed also by Brodbeck (1962), p. 240. Some perceptive and stimulating comments on this issue and on other aspects of "the quarrel about historical explanation" will be found in Weingartner's article (1961).

3. Scriven (1962), p. 202, Italics the author's.

means which serve to indicate the subject matter of different kinds of explanation are of different logical character. For example, when an explanation is to indicate the "meaning" of a literary passage, a symbol, a work of art, and the like, the explanandum will be specified by means of a *noun-phrase* ('the ampersand sign', 'the first sentence of Genesis', 'the swastika'); whereas explanations of the kind we have been considering are concerned with facts, occurrences, events, uniformities—any one of which is properly characterized by means of a *sentence* (which appears as the explanandum-sentence in our schemata). Secondly, the problem of specifying meanings and that of stating the "causes" of an occurrence or perhaps the reasons for which an action was done surely are of different logical character; and the adequacy of the solutions proposed in each case must be judged by quite different criteria. The differences between the tasks to be accomplished by these and other kinds of explanation lie, in fact, precisely in differences between the logical structure of the corresponding kinds of explanation.

From the selectiveness of explicatory models of proof and of explanation let us now turn to another common feature. Metamathematical proof theory is not intended to give a descriptive account of how mathematicians formulate their proofs. Indeed the formulations that mathematicians actually offer will usually depart to some extent from that called for by rigorous and, as it were, "ideal" metamathematical standards. Yet those standards may be said to exhibit the logical structure and the rationale of mathematical demonstration and to provide criteria for the critical appraisal of particular proofs that might be proposed.

A proposed proof may then be found to depart from a given theoretical standard only in inessential ways; for example, by omitting as obvious certain intermediate steps in the argument; or by failing to mention certain premises, which are taken to be understood, and which can be specified explicitly if the need should arise. In such cases, we might say that the proof is *elliptically formulated*. On the other hand, the shortcomings may be crucial, as in the various proofs of the postulate of the parallels on the basis of the other postulates of Euclidean geometry.

In addition to providing standards for critical appraisal, the construction of rigorous concepts of mathematical proof has permitted the development of a powerful theory which has yielded far-reaching and often quite unexpected results concerning provability, decidability, and definability in mathematical systems of specified kinds.

Analytic models of scientific explanation, I think, can serve similar purposes, if on a much more modest scale. As for the possibility of general systematic developments, we might mention, for example, the results established by

Ramsey and by Craig[4] concerning the role and the possible dispensability, in the context of scientific explanation, of principles ostensibly referring to unobservable "theoretical" entities. These results, and whatever insight they convey into the logic of scientific procedure, could be achieved only by reference to a precisely formulated, and to some extent schematic, conception of scientific explanation.

4.2 VARIETIES OF EXPLANATORY INCOMPLETENESS

4.2.1 *Elliptic Formulation.* Like a proposed mathematical proof, a proposed explanation may be *elliptically formulated.* When we explain, for example, that a lump of butter melted because it was put into a hot frying pan, or that a small rainbow appeared in the spray of a lawn sprinkler because sunlight was reflected and refracted in the water droplets, we may be said to be offering elliptic versions of D-N explanations. Accounts of this kind forego mention of certain laws or particular facts that are tacitly taken for granted, and whose explicit inclusion in the explanans would yield a complete D-N argument. An elliptically formulated explanation may be said to be *incomplete*, but in a rather harmless sense.

4.2.2 *Partial Explanation.* Often, however, explanatory accounts exhibit a more serious kind of incompleteness. Here, the statements actually included in the explanans, even when supplemented by those which may reasonably be assumed to have been tacitly taken for granted in the given context, account for the specified explanandum only partially, in a sense I will try to indicate by an illustration.

In his *Psychopathology of Everyday Life*, Freud offers this description and explanation of a slip of the pen:

> On a sheet of paper containing principally short daily notes of business interest, I found, to my surprise, the incorrect date "Thursday, October 20th," bracketed under the correct date of the month of September. It was not difficult to explain this anticipation as the expression of a wish. A few days before, I had returned fresh from my vacation and felt ready for any amount of professional work, but as yet, there were few patients. On my arrival, I had found a letter from a patient announcing her arrival on the twentieth of October. As I wrote the same date in September, I may certainly have thought, "X ought to be here already; what a pity about that whole month!" and with this thought, I pushed the current date a month ahead.[5]

Clearly, this formulation of the intended explanation is elliptical in the

4. See Ramsey (1931), pp. 212-15, 231; and Craig (1956). *Cf.* also the discussion of these results in Hempel (1958), section 9.

5. Freud (1951), p. 64.

sense considered a moment ago; for it does not mention any laws or theoretical principles in virtue of which the subconscious wish, and the other particular circumstances referred to, could be held to explain the slip in question. However, the theoretical ideas that Freud proposes for the interpretation of such lapses strongly suggest that his explanation is governed by a general hypothesis to the effect that when a person has a strong, though perhaps subconscious, wish, then if he commits a slip of pen, tongue, or memory, the slip will take a form in which it expresses, and perhaps symbolically fulfills, that wish.

Even this vague statement is no doubt more definite than what Freud would have been willing to assert; and perhaps, despite Freud's deterministic leanings, it would be more appropriate to conceive of the key hypothesis as being of statistical form, and to regard the proposed explanation as probabilistic. But for the sake of the argument, let us take the hypothesis as stated and incorporate it into the explanans, together with particular statements to the effect that Freud did have the subconscious wish he mentions, and that in fact he was going to commit a slip of the pen. Even then, the resulting explanans enables us to infer only that the slip would take *some form or other* that would express, and perhaps symbolically fulfill, Freud's subconscious wish; but the explanans does not imply that the slip would take the specific form of writing "Thursday, October 20," on the calendar, next to the corresponding date for September.

But inasmuch as the class, say F, of slips taking this latter form is a proper subclass of the class, say W, of those slips of the pen which in some way express and perhaps symbolically fulfill the specified wish, we might say that the explanandum as described by Freud—i.e., that he made a slip falling into the class F—is explained at least in part by this account, which places the slip into the wider class W. Arguments of this kind might be called *partial explanations*. Many of the explanatory accounts offered in the literature of psychoanalysis[6] and of historiography are at most partial explanations in this sense: the explanans does not account for the explanandum-phenomenon in the specificity with which it is characterized by the explanandum-sentence, and thus, the explanatory force of the argument is less than what it claims or appears to be.

I think it is important and illuminating to distinguish such partial explanations, however widely they may be offered and accepted, and however fruitful and suggestive they may prove, from what might be called *deductively complete explanations*, i.e., those in which the explanandum as stated is logically implied by the explanans; for the latter do, whereas the former do not, account for the explanandum phenomenon in the specificity with which the explanandum

6. This holds true, I think, for the many, often highly suggestive, explanatory analyses included in Freud's *Psychopathology of Everyday Life*.

sentence describes it.[7] An explanation that conforms to the D-N model is, therefore, automatically complete in this sense; and a partial explanation as we have characterized it always falls short of being a D-N explanation.

In a statistical explanation, the explanans does not logically imply the explanandum. Are we then to qualify all such explanations as incomplete? Dray raises this question when he asks whether "an event can be *completely* explained (although perhaps in a different sense) without subsuming it under a universal law licensing its deduction, and consequently without showing that it had to happen."[8] The answer that statistical explanations are deductively incomplete would be an uninteresting truism. As is suggested by Dray's clause "although perhaps in a different sense", we are, rather, faced with the question whether the notion of explanatory completeness, which so far has been defined only in reference to proposed D-N explanations, might reasonably be broadened so as to become applicable also within the domain of probabilistic explanation. It seems inadvisable to construct an extended concept of explanatory completeness in such a way as to qualify all statistical explanations as incomplete. For this qualification carries with it connotations of a deficiency, and surely, we cannot regard statistical explanations simply as unsuccessful D-N explanations: they constitute an important type of explanation in their own right. To be sure, the early explanatory uses of statistical laws and theories, for example in nineteenth century physics, were often propounded in the belief that the micro-phenomena involved in the physical processes under study were all subject to strictly universal laws, and that the use of statistical hypotheses and theories was made necessary only by limitations in our ability individually to measure all those micro-phenomena, and then to perform the vast and complex computations that would be required to account for a given physical phenomenon in full microscopic detail. But this idea has gradually been abandoned: in certain

---

7. A partial explanation may evidently be more or less weak, depending on how much more extensive is the class within which the explanans places the given case (W in our illustration) as compared with the class to which the explanandum-sentence assigns it (F in our case). Furthermore, while some partial explanations are no doubt illuminating and suggest further research that might lead to a fuller explanatory account, there are other arguments that completely lack such merit even though they bear a formal resemblance to our illustration, and might for that reason be qualified as partial explanations. Suppose, for example, that b is F and also G, and that we have a D-N explanation of b being F. Then (save for certain trivial exceptions) the explanans of the latter will automatically afford a basis for a partial explanation of b being G; for it implies that b is F and hence that b is F or G: and the class characterized by 'F or G' contains G as a proper subclass. But I am not concerned here to explore the conditions under which partial explanations may prove fruitful; I simply wish to call attention to the fact that many explanatory accounts offered in the literature of empirical science have the formal characteristics of partial explanations, and that, as a consequence, they overstate the extent to which they explain a given phenomenon.

8. Dray (1963), p. 119.

areas of physics, such as quantum theory, laws of statistical form have come to
be accepted as basic laws of nature. And whatever the future of scientific theorizing may hold in store, this development clearly reflects the realization that
logically, statistical explanation is quite independent of the assumption of strictly
universal laws and thus constitutes a mode of explanation *sui generis*. All this
strongly suggests that under a reasonable extension of the idea of explanatory
completeness, any explanation conforming to our statistical model should
qualify as formally complete, for it assigns to the explanandum event described
by the explanandum statement (or, more properly, to the explanandum statement itself) the logical probability called for by the logical relation between
the explanans and explanandum statements. In this respect, such a statistical
explanation is analogous to one which conforms to the D-N model, and which
thus correctly claims that the explanandum is implied by the explanans (and
hence has the logical probability 1 relative to the latter). In the light of this
analogy, a proposed statistical explanation should be qualified as partial if the
explanans confers the specified probability, not upon the explanandum sentence
actually stated, but upon a weaker one related to it in the manner illustrated by
our example from Freud. The idea may be illustrated very schematically by
reference to that same example. Suppose that the general law we tentatively
formulated as the presumptive basis of Freud's explanation were construed
instead as a statistical law to the effect that in the presence of a strong though
perhaps subconscious wish, the statistical probability is high that if a slip of the
pen is committed it will take a form which expresses and perhaps symbolically
satisfies that wish. Then Freud's account—now construed as claiming that the
explanatory information adduced confers a high logical probability upon the
explanandum statement—would count as a *partial statistical explanation;*
for the explanans confers a high probability, not upon the statement that the
particular slip fell within the class F defined earlier, but upon the weaker statement that the slip belonged to the class W.

4.2.3 *Explanatory Incompleteness vs. Overdetermination.* The considerations just
presented are relevant also to the problem illustrated by the following example:[9]
Suppose that rod r, made of copper $(C\,r)$, is simultaneously subjected to heating
$(H\,r)$ and to longitudinal stress $(S\,r)$, and that, in the process, the rod lengthens
$(L\,r)$. Then it is possible to formulate two different arguments, each of which

9. I am much indebted to my collegue at Princeton, Professor Arthur Mendel, of the
Department of Music, who put to me some searching questions which made me aware of
the problem here considered. In his paper (1962) Mendel takes as his point of departure
a concrete problem in the history of music and by reference to it develops some illuminating
general ideas concerning, among other things, the significance of the covering-law models
for the explanatory objectives of the historian.

constitutes, by the standards we have suggested, a D-N explanation of why the rod lengthened. One of them will be based on the law that copper rods lengthen when heated; the other, on the law that copper rods lengthen when stressed. Schematically:

$$(x) [(C x \cdot H x) \supset L x]$$
$$C r \cdot H r$$
_____
$$L r$$

$$(x) [(C x \cdot S x) \supset L x]$$
$$C r \cdot S r$$
_____
$$L r$$

It might be objected that—even granting the truth of all the premises—both accounts are unacceptable since they are "incomplete": each neglects one of the two factors that contributed to the lengthening. In appraising the force of this objection it is again important to be clear about just what is to be explained. If, as in our example, this is simply the fact that *Lr*, i.e., that *r* lengthened, or that there was *some* increase in the length of *r*, then, I think, either of the two arguments conclusively does *that*, and the charge of incompleteness is groundless. But if we wish to account for the fact that the length of the rod increased by so and so much, then clearly neither of the two arguments will do; for we would have to take into account both the temperature increase and the stress, and we would need quantitative laws governing their joint effect on the length of a copper rod. Such common locutions as 'explaining the increase in the length of a metal rod' have to be handled with care: they are ambiguous in that they refer to at least the two quite different tasks here distinguished.

Adopting a term that is often used in psychoanalytic theorizing, we might say that an event is *overdetermined* if two or more alternative explanations with nonequivalent explanans-sets are available for it. Thus, the occurrence of some lengthening in the copper rod *r* constitutes a case of *explanatory overdetermination* in virtue of the availability of the alternative explanations mentioned above. In this example, the alternative explanations invoke different laws (and consequently some different statements concerning particular facts). In another, perhaps less interesting, kind of situation which under our definition would likewise qualify as explanatory overdetermination, the alternative explanations rest on the same laws, but adduce different particular circumstances[10]. For example, the state of a deterministic physical system at time *t* can be explained, with the help of the relevant laws, by specifying the state of the system at any earlier time; potentially this permits infinitely many alternative explanations no two of which have logcially equivalent explanans-sets.

A problem that bears a certain resemblance to the one just considered has

10. On this point, *cf.* the remarks in Braithwaite (1953), p. 320.

been raised by Scriven, who illustrates it by the following example: In order to explain how a certain bridge came to be destroyed in wartime, "we could appeal to the law 'whenever an atom bomb is released accurately above a bridge and explodes with full force, the bridge is destroyed', plus the appropriate antecedent conditions." But it may also "be the case that whenever 1000 kilograms of dynamite are detonated on the main span of such a bridge it will be destroyed, and that the underground movement has applied just this treatment to this bridge with the attendant destruction occurring between the release and the arrival of the atomic bomb." Scriven holds that this invalidates the bomb explanation, "which cannot account for other features of the event, in this case the time of the destruction." He concludes that in order to rule out such explanations we must impose the requirement of total evidence, even on D-N explanations, in a more specific form which requires "that an explanation be acceptable for a phenomenon only so long as no facts are known about the circumstances surrounding the occurrence of the phenomenon which the explanation cannot accommodate."[11]

But surely the bomb explanation in Scriven's example is unacceptable because its explanans requires the assumption that when the pressure wave of the bomb reached the place in question, there was a bridge there that could be destroyed—an assumption that is false, since at that time the span had already been wrecked by dynamite. Hence, the contemplated bomb explanation is false in the sense specified in section 2, and no additional requirement is needed to disqualify it or other accounts of this kind.

Besides being unnecessary, the specific requirement Scriven suggests in order to rule out the bomb explanation and its likes is, I think, vastly too strong to be tenable. For neither in scientific research nor in our practical pursuits do we require of an acceptable explanation that it accommodate everything we know— or believe we know—about the facts surrounding the explanandum phenomenon. In the case of the bridge, for example, these facts may include a great deal of information about the shape, size, and location of the fragments after the destruction; perhaps the identities of the dynamiters; their objectives; and many other things. Surely we do not require that all of these details must be accounted for by any acceptable explanation of "how the bridge came to be destroyed."

Finally, the condition proposed by Scriven has nothing whatever to do with the requirement of total evidence; in particular, it is not a "more specific" version of it. And Scriven's contention that some such condition must be imposed even on explanations of deductive form because they do not automati-

11. Scriven (1962), pp. 229-30. See also a brief remark, which seems to have the same intent, in Scriven (1963a), pp. 348-49.

cally satisfy the requirement of total evidence[12] overlooks the straightforward proof to the contrary.[13]

4.2.4 *Explanatory Incompleteness and "Concrete Events".* A scientific explanation, we noted earlier, may be regarded as a potential answer to a question of the form 'why is it the case that *p*?', where the place of '*p*' is occupied by an empirical sentence detailing the facts to be explained. Accordingly, both the deductive-nomological and the statistical models of explanation characterize the ex-planandum-phenomenon by means of a *sentence*, the explanandum-sentence. Take, for example, the explanation of individual facts such as that the length of a given copper rod *r* increased during the time interval from 9.00 to 9.01 A.M., or that a particular drawing *d* from a given urn produced a white ball: here the explanandum phenomena are fully described by the sentences 'the length of copper rod *r* increased between 9.00 and 9.01 A.M.' and 'drawing *d* produced a white ball'. And only when understood in this sense, as fully describable by means of sentences, can particular facts or events be amenable to scientific explanation.

But the notion of an individual or particular event is often construed in quite a different manner. An event in this second sense is specified, not by means of a sentence describing it, but by means of a noun phrase such as an individual name or a definite description, as, for example, 'the first solar eclipse of the twentieth century', 'the eruption of Mt. Vesuvius in A.D. 79', 'the assassination of Leon Trotsky', 'the stock market crash of 1929. ' For want of a better terminology, individual events thus understood will be referred to as *concrete events*,[14] and facts and events in the first sense here considered will be called sententially characterizable, or briefly, *sentential facts and events*.

The familiar question of whether individual events permit of a complete explanation is no doubt inspired to a large extent by the conception of an individual event as a concrete event. But what could be meant, in this case, by a complete explanation? Presumably, one that accounts for every aspect of the

---

12. Scriven (1962), p. 230.

13. In a deductively valid argument, the premises constitute conclusive grounds for asserting the conclusion; and whatever part of the total evidence is not included in the premises is ir-relevant to the conclusion in the strict sense that if it were added to the premises, the re-sulting set of sentences would still constitute conclusive grounds for the conclusion. Or, in the terminology of inductive logic: the logical probability which the premises of a D-N argument confer upon the conclusion is 1, and it remains 1 if part or all of the total evidence is added to the premises.

14. I do not wish to suggest that the notion of concrete event here adumbrated is en-tirely clear; in particular, I do not know how to formulate a necessary and sufficient con-dition of identity for concrete events. Gibson's perceptive observations on "What is Explained," in (1960), pp. 188–190, are highly relevant to the issues we are about to examine here.

given event. If that is the idea, then indeed no concrete event can be completely explained. For a concrete event has infinitely many different aspects and thus cannot even be completely described, let alone completely explained. For example, a complete description of the eruption of Mt. Vesuvius in A.D. 79 would have to specify the exact time of its occurrence; the path of the lava stream as well as its physical and chemical characteristics—including temperatures, pressures, densities, at every point—and their changes in the course of time; the most minute details of the destruction wreaked upon Pompeii and Herculaneum; full information about all persons and animals involved in the catastrophe, including the fact that the remains of such and such victims, found at such and such places, are on display at a museum in Naples; and so on *ad infinitum*. It must also mention—for this surely constitutes yet another aspect of that concrete event—all the literature about the subject. Indeed, there seems to be no clear and satisfactory way at all of separating off some class of facts that do not constitute aspects of the concrete event here referred to. Clearly, then, it is quite pointless to ask for a complete explanation of an individual event thus understood.

In sum, a request for an explanation can be significantly made only concerning what we have called sentential facts and events; only with respect to them can we raise a question of the form 'why is it the case that *p*?'. As for concrete events, let us note that what we have called their aspects or characteristics are all of them describable by means of sentences; each of these aspects, then, is a sentential fact or event (e.g., that the eruption of Mt. Vesuvius in A.D. 79 lasted for so many hours; that it killed more than 1000 persons in Pompeii, and so on); with respect to such particular aspects of a concrete event, therefore, the question of an explanation can significantly be raised. And clearly, when we speak of explaining a particular event, such as the abdication of Edward VIII, we normally think only of certain aspects of the event as being under scrutiny; what aspects are thus meant to be singled out for explanatory attention will depend on the context of the inquiry.[15]

Though the issues here touched upon are perhaps discussed most frequently with special reference to historical events in their "individuality and uniqueness," the problems inherent in the notion of a concrete event are by no means limited to the historian's domain. An event such as the solar eclipse of July 20, 1963, also possesses an infinity of physical, chemical, biological, sociological,

15. As Max Weber remarks, with special reference to historical explanation: "When it is said that history seeks to understand the concrete *reality* of an 'event' in its individuality causally, what is obviously not meant by this ... is that it is to ... explain causally the concrete *reality* of an event in the totality of its individual qualities. To do the latter would be not only actually impossible, it would also be a task which is meaningless in principle." (Weber (1949), p. 169. Italics the author's.)

and yet other aspects and thus resists complete description and *a fortiori*, complete explanation. But certain aspects of the eclipse—such as the duration of its totality, and the fact that it was visible in Alaska and subsequently in Maine—may well be capable of explanation.

It would be incorrect, however, to summarize this point by saying that the object of an explanation is always a *kind* of event rather than an individual event. For a kind of event would have to be characterized by means of a predicate-expression, such as 'total solar eclipse' or 'volcanic eruption'; and since this sort of expression is not a sentence, it makes no sense to ask for an explanation of a kind of event. What might in fact be explained is rather the *occurrence of a particular instance of a given kind of event*, such as the occurrence of a total solar eclipse on July 20, 1963. And what is thus explained is definitely an individual event; indeed, it is one that is unique and unrepeatable in view of the temporal location assigned to it. But it is an individual *sentential* event, of course: it can be described by means of the statement that on July 20, 1963, there occurred a total solar eclipse. I agree therefore with Mandelbaum's rejection of Hayek's view that explanation and prediction never refer to an individual event but always to phenomena of a certain kind: "One would think that the prediction of a specific solar eclipse, or the explanation of that eclipse, would count as referring to a particular event even if it does not refer to all aspects of the event, such as the temperature of the sun, or the effect of the eclipse on the temperature of the earth, and the like."[16]

However, given this notion of explaining a particular occurrence of a solar eclipse or of a rainbow, etc., one can speak *derivatively* of a theoretical explanation of solar eclipses or rainbows in general: such an explanation is then one that accounts for any instance of an eclipse or a rainbow. Thus, the notion of explaining particular instances of a given kind of occurrence is the primary one.

4.2.5 *Explanatory Closure: Explanation Sketch.* Perhaps yet another conception of completeness might seem pertinent to the idea of explanation; we shall call it explanatory closure. An explanatory account would be complete in this sense if for every fact or law it invoked, it contained in turn an explanation. In an account with explanatory closure, nothing would be left unexplained. But completeness in this sense obviously calls for an infinite regress in explanation and is therefore unachievable; to seek such completeness is to misunderstand the nature of explanation.

At any stage in the development of empirical science, certain (presumptive) facts will be unexplainable; in particular, those expressed by the most fundamental laws or theoretical principles accepted at the time, those for which no

16. Mandelbaum (1961), p. 233.

explanation by means of a "deeper" theory is at hand. But while unexplained, these ultimate principles need not be unsupported, for, as hypotheses in empirical science, they will have to be susceptible to test, and it may well be that suitable tests have in fact provided strongly supporting evidence for them.

We have by now considered several ways in which a proposed explanation may deviate from the standards incorporated into our analytic models. In some cases, what is intended as an explanatory account will diverge even more strongly from those standards. A proposed explanation, for example, which is not explicit and specific enough to be reasonably qualified as an elliptically formulated explanation or as a partial one, can often be viewed as an *explanation sketch*, i.e., as presenting the general outlines of what might well be developed, by gradual elaboration and supplementation, into a more closely reasoned explanatory argument, based on hypotheses which are stated more fully and which permit of a critical appraisal by reference to empirical evidence.

The decision whether a proposed explanatory account is to be qualified as an elliptically formulated deductive-nomological or statistical explanation, as a partial explanation, as an explanation sketch, or perhaps as none of these is a matter of judicious interpretation. It calls for an appraisal of the intent of the given account and of the background assumptions that may have been left unstated because they are taken to be understood in the given context. Unequivocal criteria of adjudication cannot be formulated for this purpose any more than for deciding whether a given informally stated argument which does not meet reasonably strict standards of deductive validity is to count as nevertheless valid but enthymematically formulated, or as fallacious, or as a sound inductive argument, or perhaps, for lack of clarity, as none of these.

Among the various respects here considered in which a proposed explanation or demonstration may fall short of the logical standards incorporated into some nonpragmatic model of explanation or proof, there are several which can be characterized only by reference to the knowledge, interests, intentions, and so forth of the persons who propose the arguments in question or of those to whom they are addressed; hence, the corresponding concepts are essentially pragmatic. This is true, for example, of the notions of enthymeme, of elliptically formulated explanation, and of explanation sketch.

4.3 CONCLUDING REMARK ON THE COVERING-LAW MODELS. We have found, then, that the explanatory accounts actually formulated in science and in everyday contexts vary greatly in the explicitness, completeness, and precision with which they specify the explanans and the explanandum; accordingly, they diverge more or less markedly from the idealized and schematized covering-law models. But, granting this, I think that all adequate scientific explanations and their everyday counterparts claim or presuppose at least implicitly the deductive or inductive subsumability of whatever is to be explained under general laws or theoretical principles.[17] In the explanation of an individual occurrence, those general nomic principles are required to connect the explanandum event with other particulars, and it is by such nomic connection that the latter acquire the status of explanatory factors. In the explanation of general empirical regularities, the nomic principles invoked express more comprehensive uniformities of which those to be explained are strict or approximate specializations. And the covering-law models represent, as far as I can see, the basic logical structure of the principal modes of such explanatory subsumption.

The construal here broadly summarized is not, of course, susceptible to strict "proof"; its soundness has to be judged by the light it can shed on the rationale and force of explanatory accounts offered in different branches of empirical science. Some of the ways in which this construal of explanation may prove illuminating have already been suggested in the course of developing the covering-law models and characterizing their intended function; other such ways should come into view as we proceed, and particularly when we turn, in later sections, to an analysis of certain peculiar explanatory procedures that seem to be at variance with the covering-law construal of explanation.

5. PRAGMATIC ASPECTS OF EXPLANATION

5.1 INTRODUCTORY REMARKS. Very broadly speaking, to explain something to a person is to make it plain and intelligible to him, to make him understand it. Thus construed, the word 'explanation' and its cognates are *pragmatic* terms: their use requires reference to the persons involved in the process of explaining. In a pragmatic context we might say, for example, that a given account A explains fact X to person P_1. We will then have to bear in mind that the same account may well not constitute an explanation of X for another person P_2, who might not even regard X as requiring an explanation, or who might find the

---

17. This idea needs to be sharply distinguished from another one, which I am not proposing, namely, that any empirical phenomenon can be explained by deductive or inductive subsumption under covering laws. The idea here suggested is that the logic of all scientific explanations is basically of the covering-law variety, but not that all empirical phenomena are scientifically explainable, and even less, of course, that they are all governed by a system of deterministic laws. The question whether all empirical phenomena can be scientifically explained is not nearly as intelligible as it might seem at first glance, and it calls for a great deal of analytic clarification. I am inclined to think that it cannot be given any clear meaning at all; but at any rate, and quite broadly speaking, an opinion as to what laws hold in nature and what phenomena can be explained surely cannot be formed on analytic grounds alone but must be based on the results of empirical research.

account *A* unintelligible or unilluminating, or irrelevant to what puzzles him about *X*. Explanation in this pragmatic sense is thus a relative notion: something can be significantly said to constitute an explanation in this sense only for this or that individual.

Quite similarly, the word 'proof' and its cognates can be used in a pragmatic sense which requires reference to the producers and the recipients of the arguments in question. For example, an argument *Y* that proves a simple geometrical theorem to the complete satisfaction of a tyro may be entirely unacceptable, and thus not a proof at all, for a mathematician; and conversely, what for the mathematician is a sound and illuminating proof may be unintelligible or pointless to the beginner. Generally, whether a given argument *Y* proves (or explains) a certain item *X* to a person *P* will depend not only on *X* and *Y*, but quite importantly also on *P*'s beliefs at the time as well as on his intelligence, his critical standards, his personal idiosyncrasies, and so forth.

The pragmatic aspects of proof form an interesting and important subject for empirical investigation. Piaget, for example, has devoted a great deal of effort to the psychological study of the standards of proof in children of different ages. But for the purposes of mathematics and logic as objective disciplines, we clearly need a concept of proof which is not subjective in the sense of being relative to, and variable with, individuals; a concept in terms of which it makes sense to say that a given argument *Y* is a proof of a given sentence *X* (in a theory) without making any mention of persons who might take cognizance of *Y*. Concepts of proof which have this character can be defined once the mathematical discipline in reference to which the concept is to be used has been suitably formalized.

The case of scientific explanation is similar. For scientific research seeks to account for empirical phenomena by means of laws and theories which are objective in the sense that their empirical implications and their evidential support are independent of what particular individuals happen to test or to apply them; and the explanations, as well as the predictions, based upon such laws and theories are meant to be objective in an analogous sense. This ideal intent suggests the problem of constructing a nonpragmatic concept of scientific explanation—a concept which is abstracted, as it were, from the pragmatic one, and which does not require relativization with respect to questioning individuals any more than does the concept of mathematical proof. It is this nonpragmatic conception of explanation which the covering-law models are meant to explicate.

To propound those models is therefore neither to deny the pragmatic "dimension" of explanation nor to belittle its importance; nor, of course, is it to claim that people will find an explanatory account illuminating or satisfactory only as far as it conforms to one of the covering-law models. To explain a given phenomenon to a person, it will often suffice to call to his attention some particular fact of which he has not properly taken cognizance. This is presumably true of the man mentioned in a newspaper story some years ago who was puzzled to find that it got cold in his house whenever he happened to watch a television program in winter. All he had to be told by way of explanation was that the television set was directly under the thermostat, and thus warmed the latter and shut the heating off. Thus the quest for an explanation is often a quest for the "cause" of the puzzling occurrence, in the loose sense here illustrated. The questioner who accepts a particular causal account as satisfactory will sometimes have background information of a nomological kind—e.g., about the way a thermostat works—which might justify the causal attribution. In other cases, he may lack such information and might still be satisfied by the explanation: the pragmatic conditions for the acceptability of a proposed explanation do not coincide with the logic-systematic ones that the covering-law models are meant to explicate. When the relevant laws are more or less clearly understood and taken for granted by the questioner, it would of course be incorrect to say that his question had the pragmatic function of eliciting covering laws; but it is neither incorrect nor superfluous to make reference to such laws if the logic of the account, and especially the explanatory force of the particular facts mentioned in it, is to be made explicit.

In other contexts—for example, frequently in scientific research—the pragmatic concern prompting the quest for an explanation may be the desire to discover laws or theoretical principles covering a given class of phenomena. And in yet other cases, the questioner may be aware of the requisite particular data and laws but may need to be shown how the explanandum can be derived from this information.[1]

But to call attention to the important pragmatic facets of explanation and to indicate the diverse procedures that may be appropriate in different cases to dispel the perplexity reflected in someone's quest for an explanation is not to show that a nonpragmatic model of scientific explanation must be hopelessly inadequate, just as analogous arguments concerning the notion of proof cannot show that nonpragmatic models of proof must be sterile and unilluminating. As is well known, the contrary is the case.

It is therefore beside the point to complain that the covering-law models

---

1. In an interesting discussion of what are, to a large extent, pragmatic aspects of explanation, Scriven uses the term 'derivation-explanation' for an explanation that consists simply in demonstrating this derivability, and he gives an illustration from the history of science, which shows that the derivation may well present considerable mathematical difficulties and may thus be hard to discover. (Scriven 1959, pp. 461-62).

do not closely match the form in which working scientists actually present their explanations. Those formulations are generally chosen with a particular kind of audience—and thus with particular pragmatic requirements—in mind. This is true also of the way in which mathematicians present their proofs; but the metamathematical theory of proof quite properly abstracts from these pragmatic considerations.[2]

5.2 EXPLAINING HOW-POSSIBLY. An important pragmatic aspect of explanation is reflected in Dray's distinction of "explaining why-necessarily" an event occurred and "explaining how-possibly" an event could have occurred.[3] A D-N explanation might be regarded as adequate for the former purpose; to accomplish the latter is quite a different task, as we will now see.

If a friend tells me that at a party he attended last New Year's Eve his teaspoon promptly melted when he put it into a cup of hot punch, I might ask: how could this possibly have happened—metal does not melt at so low a temperature. Similarly, the news that the *Andrea Doria* had sunk as a result of a collision gave rise to the question how this could possibly have happened, considering that the ship was equipped with the most advanced safety devices and was operated by experienced seamen.

As these examples illustrate, we will normally ask how X could possibly have occurred only if, as Dray puts it, "what we know seems to rule out the possibility of the occurrence which is to be explained,"[4] i.e., if some of the beliefs we hold concerning relevant matters of fact seem to us to make it impossible or at least highly improbable that X should have occurred; herein lies the pragmatic aspect of the question. To give a satisfactory 'how-possibly' explanation, it will be necessary, therefore, to ascertain the empirical assumptions underlying the question and then to show either that some of these are false or else that the questioner was mistaken in thinking that those assumptions warranted his belief that X could not have occurred. In the case of the teaspoon, it might suffice to point out that some metals, such as Wood's alloy, do melt at the temperature of hot punch; and a full covering-law explanation might be achieved by establishing that the teaspoon in question had indeed been one of those made from Wood's alloy for the use of practical jokers.[5]

2. *Cf.* also the comments on this point in section 1 of Bartley's paper (1962), in which Popper's presentation of the deductive model is defended against this charge. For some observations in a similar vein, see Pitt (1959), pp. 585–86.

3. *Cf.* Dray (1957), pp. 158 ff.

4. Dray (1957), p. 161.

5. In a review of Dray's book, Passmore (1958) goes so far as to say that "to answer a 'how possibly' question, unless with a mere guess, is to sketch in a 'why-necessarily' explanation." While this observation seems basically sound, it should, I think, be liberalized so as to call for the sketching either of a 'why-necessarily' or else of a 'why-probably' explanation.

If, as in the case of the *Andrea Doria*, the question 'How could X possibly have occurred?' springs from assumptions that seem to make the occurrence of X highly improbable but not logically to preclude it, then an appropriate answer may consist in pointing out that the questioner is mistaken in some of his factual assumptions or in the belief that his assumptions make the occurrence of X very improbable: these two possibilities are analogous to those considered in the previous illustration. But in addition, we have here a third possibility, suggested also by our earlier discussion of the logic of statistical explanation: all of the questioner's relevant assumptions might be true, and his belief that they make the occurrence of X very improbable may be correct. In that event, the perplexity expressed by the questioner's 'how could it possibly have happened?' may be resolvable by broadening the questioner's total evidence, i.e., by calling to his attention certain further facts whose addition to those previously taken into account will render the occurrence of X less improbable.

Similar observations apply to questions of the form 'why is it not the case that *p*?', which might well be rephrased as 'how-possibly' questions: 'How could it possibly be the case that not-*p*?'. Questions such as 'Why doesn't the Leaning Tower of Pisa topple over?' or 'Why don't the antipodes fall off the earth?', 'If reflection in a plane mirror interchanges right and left, why not also top and bottom?' will normally be raised only if the questioner entertains certain assumptions concerning relevant empirical matters which seem to him to make it certain or, at any rate, highly probable that the specified phenomenon should occur. A pragmatically adequate answer again will have to clear up the empirical or logical misapprehensions underlying this belief.

And, of course, explanation-seeking questions of the standard type 'Why is it the case that *p*?' are often, though by no means invariably, prompted by the belief that *p* would not be the case—a belief which, again, may seem to the questioner to be more or less strongly supported by certain other empirical assumptions which he accepts as being true. And in this event, the questioner may not feel satisfied if he is simply offered, say, a covering-law explanation of

---

Someone who asks how X could possibly have happened will not, as a rule, be satisfied to be told simply that he was mistaken in some of his empirical assumptions, which he thought precluded the occurrence of X; he will also want to be given a set of alternative, and presumably true, assumptions which, in conjunction with the rest of his background beliefs, explain to him why X occurred. The case of the melting spoon illustrates this. But if our questioner should believe that spilling salt is always followed by bad luck within three days, and if he were to ask 'How possibly could I have escaped bad luck though I spilled some salt three days ago?', then the answer could hardly do more than point out that his general hypothesis was false and, perhaps, that in the vast majority of cases, spilling salt is not followed by bad luck; but no 'why-necessarily' explanation for the questioner's avoidance of bad luck will be available.

why p is the case. In order to allay his perplexity he may have to be shown that some of the assumptions underlying his contrary expectation were in error.[6]

5.3 EXPLANATION VS. REDUCTION TO THE FAMILIAR. A predominantly pragmatic conception of explanation as aimed at dispelling the questioner's puzzlement also underlies the widely held view that an explanation must somehow reduce or link the puzzling phenomenon to something with which the questioner is already familiar, and which he accepts as unproblematic. Thus, Bridgman, for example, holds that "the essence of an explanation consists in reducing a situation to elements with which we are so familiar that we accept them as a matter of course, so that our curiosity rests."[7] An examination of this explicitly pragmatic characterization may serve further to clarify and support the case for constructing a nonpragmatic concept of scientific explanation.

Undeniably, many scientific explanations effect, in a sense, a "reduction to the familiar." This might be said, for example, of the wave-theoretical explanation of optical refraction and interference, and of at least some of the explanations achieved by the kinetic theory of heat. In cases of this kind, the concepts and principles invoked in the explanans bear a more or less close resemblance to concepts and principles that have long been used in the description and explanation of some familiar type of phenomenon, such as the propagation of wave motions on the surface of water or the motion of billiard balls.

Concerning the general view of explanation as a reduction to the familiar, let us note first that what is familiar to one person may not be so to another, and that, therefore, this view conceives of explanation as something relative to a questioner. But, as we noted earlier, explanations of the kind empirical science seeks are intended to exhibit objective relationships.

Secondly, the view here under discussion suggests that what is familiar requires no explanation. But this notion does not accord with the fact that scientists have gone to great lengths in an effort to explain "familiar" phenomena, such as the changes of the tides; lightning, thunder, rain, and snow; the blue color of the sky; similarities between parents and their offspring; the fact that the moon appears much larger when it is near the horizon than when it is high in the sky; the fact that certain diseases are "catching," while others are not; and even the familiar fact that it is dark at night. Indeed, the darkness of

6. This aspect of explanation, and various related ones, have been perceptively and lucidly examined by S. Bromberger (1960). For suggestive observations on the pragmatic aspects of explanation, see also Passmore (1962).

7. Bridgman (1927), p. 37. The pragmatic character of this conception is clearly reflected in Bridgman's remark that "an explanation is not an absolute sort of thing, but what is satisfactory for one man will not be for another." *Loc. cit.*, p. 38.

the night sky appears as a phenomenon much in need of explanation, in view of Olbers' paradox. This argument, put forward in 1826 by the German astronomer Heinrich Olbers, rests on a few simple assumptions, roughly to the effect that the distances and the intrinsic luminosities of the stars have about the same frequency distribution throughout the universe in the past as well as at present; that the basic laws for the propagation of light hold true in all spatio-temporal areas of the universe, and that the universe at large is static, i.e., that no large-scale systematic motions take place in it. From these assumptions it follows that the sky, in all directions and at all times, should be of enormous uniform brightness, and that the energy thus streaming in upon the surface of the earth should correspond to a temperature of more than 10,000 degrees Fahrenheit.[8]

Olbers' paradox thus raises a 'how-possibly?' question. An answer to it is suggested by the recent theory that the universe is steadily expanding. This theory implies, first, that Olbers' assumption of a static universe is in error, and it supplies, secondly, a positive explanation of the dark night sky by showing that the energy of the radiation received from very distant stars is enormously reduced by the high velocities of their recession.

This example also illustrates a further point, namely, that instead of reducing the unfamiliar to the familiar, a scientific explanation will often do the opposite: it will explain familiar phenomena with the help of theoretical conceptions which may seem unfamiliar and even counter-intuitive, but which account for a wide variety of facts and are well supported by the results of scientific tests.[9]

These observations are applicable also outside the domain of the natural sciences. Their relevance to sociology, for example, is suggested in the opening passage of a book by Homans: "My subject is a familiar chaos. Nothing is more familiar to men than their ordinary, everyday social behavior . . . every man makes his own generalizations about his own social experience, but uses them *ad hoc* within the range of situations to which each applies, dropping them as soon as their immediate relevance is at an end and never asking how they are related to one another . . . the purpose of this book is to bring out of the familiar chaos some intellectual order."[10] Incidentally, Homans goes on to say that the requisite ordering of a body of empirically established sociological facts, represented by low-level generalizatons, calls for an *explanation* of those facts; and that such explanation is achieved by means of a "set of more general propositions, still of the same form as the empirical ones, from which you can

8. For a fuller presentation of the paradox, and a critical analysis in the light of current cosmological theorizing, see, for example, Bondi (1961), chapter 2, and Sciama (1961), chapter 6.

9. This point is stressed also in Feigl's concise and illuminating article (1949); and it is lucidly illustrated by reference to the theory of relativity in Frank (1957), pp. 133–34.

10. Homans (1961), pp. 1–2.

logically deduce the latter under specified given conditions. To deduce them successfully is to explain them."[11]

To this emphasis on the sociologist's interest in the theoretical explanation of "familiar" generalizations about social behavior, there should be added a reminder that has been stressed by Lazarsfeld, among others; namely, that what are widely regarded as obvious and familiar facts of everyday psychological and sociological experience are sometimes not facts at all but popular stereotypes. This is true—to mention but one of Lazarsfeld's interesting illustrations—of the idea that the intellectual is emotionally less stable than the psychologically more impassive man-in-the-street, and that therefore it was to be expected that among the U.S. soldiers in the Second World War, better educated men showed more psychoneurotic symptoms than those with less education. In fact, the opposite was found to be the case.[12] Thus an explanation of some particular case by reference to the low-level generalization of this sterotype is simply false even though it might be said to effect a reduction to the familiar.

Such reduction, then, as has now been argued at some length, is surely not a necessary condition for an acceptable scientific explanation. But neither is it a sufficient condition; for a request for an explanation is sometimes answered in a way which puts the questioner's curiosity to rest by giving him a sense of familiarity or at-homeness with an initially puzzling phenomenon, without conveying a scientifically acceptable explanation. In this case, one might say, familiarity breeds content, but no insight. For example, as we have just seen, the proffered explanation might be based on a familiar and yet mistaken belief, and will then be false. Or the proposed account might rely on untestable metaphorical or metaphysical ideas rather than on general empirical hypotheses, and then would not afford even a potential scientific explanation. Take for example the "hypothesis of a common subconscious," which has been propounded to explain presumptive telepathic phenomena.[13] It asserts that while in their conscious domains human minds are separate entities, they are connected by a common subconscious, from which the individual consciousnesses emerge like mountainous islands joined by a submarine continent. The suggestive imagery of this account may well evoke a sense of intuitive understanding of telepathic phenomena; the latter seem to have been explained by reduction to ideas with which we are quite familiar. Yet we have been given a simile rather than a scientific explanation. The account offers us no grounds

---

11. Homans (1961), pp. 9–10, italics the author's.

12. See Lazarsfeld (1949), pp. 379–80.

13. See the critical reference in Price (1945) and cf. Carington's use of the idea as "a simile" (1949, pp. 223ff.), as well as his more specific account of the conception of a common subconscious, loc. cit., pp. 208ff.

on which it would be reasonable to expect the occurrence of telepathic phenomena, nor does it give us any clues as to the conditions under which such phenomena are likely to occur. Indeed, in the form here outlined the notion of a common subconscious has no clear implications concerning empirical phenomena and is not amenable, therefore, to objective test or to significant explanatory or predictive use.

A similar critique applies to neovitalistic explanations of certain biological phenomena in terms of entelechies or vital forces. Such accounts do not specify under what conditions a vital force will exert its influence and what specific form its manifestations will take, nor, in the case of external interference with an organism, to what extent an entelechy will compensate for the resulting disturbance. By contrast, an explanation of planetary motions in terms of the Newtonian theory of gravitation specifies what gravitational forces will be exerted upon a given planet by the sun and by other planets, given their masses and distances, and it specifies further what changes in motion are to be expected as a result of those forces. Both accounts invoke certain "forces" that cannot be directly observed—one of them, vital forces, the other, gravitational ones; yet the latter account has explanatory status while the former does not. This is a consequence of the fact that the Newtonian theory offers specific laws governing gravitational forces, whereas neovitalism specifies no laws governing vital forces and is, in effect, only metaphorical. Thus, it is covering laws or theoretical principles that are crucial to a scientific explanation, rather than the sense of familiarity that its wording may impart.

The laws invoked in a proposed scientific explanation are of course capable of test; and adverse test results may lead to their rejection. No such fate threatens explanations in terms of similes or metaphors: since they do not specify what to expect under any empirical conditions, no empirical test can possibly discredit them. But absolute immunity to disconfirmation is not an asset but a fatal defect when we are concerned, as is scientific research, to arrive at an objectively testable and empirically well-supported body of empirical knowledge. An account that has no implications concerning empirical phenomena cannot serve this purpose, however strong its intuitive appeal: from the point of view of science, it is a *pseudo-explanation*, an explanation in appearance only.

In sum then, it is neither necessary nor sufficient for the scientific adequacy of an explanation that it should reduce the explanandum to ideas with which we are already familiar.

6. MODELS AND ANALOGIES IN SCIENTIFIC EXPLANATION

Explanatory accounts offered in empirical science are sometimes formulated in terms of a "model" of the phenomena to be explained, or in terms of analogies between those phenomena and others that have been previously explored. In the present section I propose to examine some forms of this procedure and to appraise their explanatory significance.

Let us consider first the use—quite widespread in the nineteenth and early twentieth centuries—of more or less complex mechanical systems as models of electric, magnetic, and optical phenomena, of the luminiferous ether, and so forth. The importance that some eminent scientists attributed to such representations is reflected in the famous pronouncement of Sir William Thomson (later Lord Kelvin):

> I never satisfy myself until I can make a mechanical model of a thing. If I can make a mechanical model I can understand it. As long as I cannot make a mechanical model all the way through I cannot understand. . . .[1]

> My object is to show how to make a mechanical model which shall fulfill the conditions required in the physical phenomena that we are considering, whatever they may be. At the time when we are considering the phenomenon of elasticity in solids, I want to show a model of that. At another time, when we have vibrations of light to consider, I want to show a model of the action exhibited in that phenomenon. . . . It seems to me that the test of "Do we or not understand a particular subject in physics?" is, "Can we make a mechanical model of it?"[2]

Sir Oliver Lodge, whose book on electricity presents a multitude of mechanical models, says in a similar vein:

> Think of electrical phenomena as produced by an all-permeating liquid embedded in a jelly; think of conductors as holes and pipes in this jelly, of an electrical machine as a pump, of charge as excess or defect, of attraction as due to strain, of discharge as bursting. . . . By thus thinking you will get a more real grasp of the subject and insight into the actual processes occurring in Nature—unknown though these may still strictly be—than if you employed the old ideas of action at a distance, or contented yourselves with no theory at all on which to link the facts. . . . I am also convinced that it is unwise to drift along among a host of complicated phenomena without guide other than that afforded by hard and rigid mathematical equations.[3]

These pronouncements reflect variants of the idea that explanation in science must involve a reduction to the familiar. What this variant demands is not simply that an explanation somehow render a phenomenon plausible or familiar, but more specifically that it provide a model governed by the laws of mechanics, which in this context are accorded the status of familiar principles.

But just what does the construction of a mechanical model accomplish? It is not intended, of course, to identify the modeled phenomenon with the

1. Thomson (1884), pp. 270-71.
2. Thomson (1884), pp. 131-32.
3. Lodge (1889), pp. 60-61.

model. An electric current maintained in a wire by means of a battery is not claimed to be the same thing as the flow of a liquid through pipes, maintained by means of a pump, nor the same thing as an inextensible loop of cord kept circulating over pulleys by means of a sinking weight.[4] The claim is merely that there obtains an analogy between the model and the phenomenon it represents. And the relevant analogy lies in a formal similarity between certain laws governing the mechanical system and corresponding laws for the modeled phenomenon.

Consider, for example, the often cited analogy between the flow of an electric current in a wire and the flow of a fluid in a pipe. If the fluid flows with moderate speed through a fairly narrow pipe with circular inner cross section then according to Poiseulle's law the volume V of fluid flowing through a fixed cross-section per second is proportional to the difference in pressure between the ends of the pipe:

(6.1a) $V = c \cdot (p_1 - p_2)$

This law has the same form as Ohm's law for the flow of electricity in a metallic conductor:

(6.1b) $I = k \cdot (v_1 - v_2)$

Here the strength of the current, I, may be said to represent the amount of electric charge flowing through a fixed cross-section of the wire per second; $v_1 - v_2$ is the potential difference maintained between the ends of the wire; and k is the reciprocal of its resistance.

The analogy goes further. The factor c in (6.1a) is inversely proportional to the length l_1 of the pipe:

(6.2a) $c = \dfrac{c'}{l_1}$

and similarly, the factor k in (6.1b) is inversely proportional to the length, l_2, of the wire:

(6.2b) $k = \dfrac{k'}{l_2}$

Thus, the analogy in virtue of which the flow of a fluid here constitutes a model of the flow of a current may be characterized as follows: A certain set of laws governing the former phenomenon has the same syntactical structure as a corresponding set of laws for the latter phenomenon; or, more explicitly,

4. A profusion of such models can be found in Lodge (1889) and in Thomson (1884). A hydrodynamic model that represents in quite a similar manner certain aspects of the behavior of nervous systems is described in S. B. Russell (1913).

the empirical terms (i.e., those which are not logical or mathematical)[5] occurring in the first set of laws can be matched, one by one, with those of the second set in such a way that if in one of the laws of the first set each term is replaced by its counterpart, a law of the second set is obtained; and vice versa. Two sets of laws of this kind will be said to be syntactically isomorphic. Briefly, then, the relevant similarity or "analogy" between a model of the kind here considered and the modeled type of a phenomenon consists in a *nomic isomorphism*, i.e., a *syntactic isomorphism between two corresponding sets of laws*. The notion of model thus obtained is not limited to mechanical systems, of course; we can speak, in the same sense, also of electrical, chemical, and still other kinds of "analogical models."

But in our illustration, as in other cases of analogical modeling, the isomorphism has its limits: some laws for the flow of a fluid in pipes do not carry over to electric currents in wires. For example, if the length of the pipe and the pressure difference between its ends are fixed, V is proportional to the fourth power of the radius of the cross sections, whereas under corresponding circumstances, the current is proportional to the square of the wire's cross section:

$$(6.3a) \quad V = \frac{\pi r_1^4}{8 l_1 s} \ (p_1 - p_2)$$

$$(6.3b) \quad I = \frac{\pi r_2^2}{l_2 q} \ (v_1 - v_2)$$

Here, s is the viscosity of the fluid and q the specific resistance of the metal of which the wire is made; r_1 is the radius of the inner cross section of the pipe; and r_2 is the radius of the wire.

Thus, the statement that a system S_1 is an analogical model of a system S_2 is elliptical. A complete sentence expressing the relationship would have to take the form: 'S_1 is an analogical model of S_2 with respect to the sets of laws L_1, L_2'. This sentence is true if the laws in L_1 apply to S_1 snd those in L_2 to S_2, and if L_1 and L_2 are syntactically isomorphic.[6]

The concept of analogy as a nomic isomorphism plays an important role in Maxwell's essay on Faraday's lines of force. Maxwell here says: "By a physical analogy I mean that partial similarity between the laws of one science

---

5. Physical constants such as 's' and 'q' in (6.3a) and (6.3b) count here as empirical terms.

6. This characterization of analogical models accords with Maxwell's and Duhem's conceptions of analogy in physics, about which more will be said presently. It is also supported by the way in which Boltzmann (1891) uses mechanical models to represent the Carnot cycle in the theory of heat (1891, chapter 2) and various electric phenomena. Heinrich Hertz's general concept of a "dynamic model" reflects the same basic idea; *cf.* Hertz (1894), p. 197.

and those of another which makes each of them illustrate the other." He notes, concerning the analogy between light and the vibrations of an elastic medium, that "though its importance and fruitfulness cannot be overestimated, we must recollect that it is founded only on a resemblance *in form* between the laws of light and those of vibrations."[7] Maxwell continues: "It is by the use of analogies of this kind that I have attempted to bring before the mind, in a convenient and manageable form, those mathematical ideas which are necessary to the study of the phenomena of electricity. . . . I am not attempting to establish any physical theory . . . , and . . . the limit of my design is to shew how, by a strict application of the ideas and methods of Faraday, the connexion of the very different orders of phenomena which he has discovered may be clearly placed before the mathematical mind."[8] The analogy Maxwell then develops in detail rests on a representation of Faraday's lines of force by tubes through which an incompressible liquid flows. It is of interest to note that while Maxwell is able to give an analogical representation of a great many electric and magnetic phenomena, he finds himself unable to extend the analogy when he comes to the discussion of what Faraday had called the electro-tonic state; here, he resorts to the formulation of a theory in purely mathematical form.[9]

The views of men like Kelvin and Lodge concerning the importance of analogical models for explanation in physics were severely criticized by Duhem. Duhem sees the aim of physics in the construction of theories couched in precise mathematical terms, from which empirically established laws can be deduced, and he argues that mechanical models contribute nothing to that objective. In reference to Lodge's book Duhem comments: "Here is a book meant to expound the modern theories of electricity . . .; it talks only of cords that move over pulleys, that wind themselves up on drums, that traverse beads, that carry weights; of tubes that pump water and of others that expand and contract; of cog wheels that mesh with each other and drive toothed racks; we thought we were entering the peaceful and carefully ordered abode of reason, and we find ourselves in a factory."[10] Duhem goes on to complain that far from facilitating the understanding of a theory "for a French reader," the use of such mechanical models requires of him a serious effort just to understand the working of the complicated apparatus and to recognize analogies between the properties of the model and the theory that is being illustrated.

Although Duhem rejects the explanatory use of mechanical models, he

7. Maxwell (1864), p. 28, italics the author's.
8. Maxwell (1864), p. 29.
9. Maxwell (1864), pp. 51ff. For a fuller discussion of Maxwell's views on the importance of analogies for physical theorizing, see Turner's studies (1955), (1956).
10. Translated from Duhem (1906), p. 111.

stresses that, by contrast, analogies may prove very fruitful in physical research. The analogies he has in mind are those based on what we have called nomic isomorphisms. He mentions, for example, Ohm's transfer of the laws of heat conduction to electric conduction, and he stresses the importance of those cases in which extensive theories for two distinct and dissimilar categories of phenomena have the same algebraic form.[11]

However, if our characterization is correct, then the mechanical models scorned by Duhem exhibit nomic isomorphisms of basically the same kind as those scientific analogies in Duhem's sense which are not specifically formulated in the parlance of models. Duhem's distinction between models and analogies, for which he states no precise criteria, then reflects not a difference in logical status, but rather a difference in the precision and the scope of the isomorphic sets of laws. Among the laws governing a mechanical model, those which carry over isomorphically to the modeled phenomenon are usually few in number and limited in scope, so that sometimes several different models are used to represent different aspects of one kind of physical entity or phenomenon. For example, Kelvin offers quite different mechanical models of molecules to represent elasticity in crystals, the dispersion of light, and the rotation of the plane of polarization of a light beam;[12] and Lodge designs entirely different mechanical systems, of the sort referred to by Duhem in the passage quoted earlier, to represent various electrostatic, electrodynamic, and electromagnetic phenomena. In the case of fruitful analogies of the kind envisaged by Duhem, on the other hand, the isomorphic laws or theoretical principles are stated in precise mathematical terms and are strong enough to permit the deduction of a great variety of consequences which themselves constitute important laws. This is illustrated by the extensive nomic isomorphisms that permit the application of the mathematical theory of wave motions to certain parts of mechanics, optics, and quantum mechanics.[13]

In order to appraise the explanatory significance of analogical models, and more generally of analogies based on nomic isomorphisms, let us suppose that some "new" field of inquiry is being explored, and that we try to explain the phenomena encountered in it by analogical reference to some "old," previously explored domain of inquiry. This calls for the establishment of an isomorphism

---

11. Duhem (1906), pp. 152-54. Boltzmann characterizes physical analogies in a similar manner: "... Nature seemed, as it were, to have built the most diverse things exactly according to the same plan, or, as the analytic mathematician says dryly, the same differential equations hold for the most diverse phenomena." Translated from Boltzmann (1905), p. 7.

12. *Cf.* Thomson (1884).

13. Further examples of analogies based on nomic isomorphisms in physics will be found in Seeliger's article (1948); for an illuminating discussion, well illustrated by examples, of the significance of nomic isomorphisms in physics, see also Watkins (1938), chapter 3.

between a set of laws, say L_1, pertaining to the old field and a corresponding set, say L_2, in the new. To that end, we obviously must first discover a suitable set L_2 of laws in the new field. But once this has been done, those laws can be used directly for the explanation of the "new" phenomena, without any reference to their structural isomorphism with the set L_1. For the systematic purposes of scientific explanation, reliance on analogies is thus inessential and can always be dispensed with.

This observation applies equally to analogical models of a nonmechanical sort, such as the physico-chemical systems which have been used to imitate phenomena that are often considered as specifically biological. Leduc, for example,[14] was able to produce by purely chemical means a large variety of osmotic growths whose highly diversified forms strikingly resemble those of familiar plants and animals, and which, in their development, exhibit remarkable analogies to organic growths. The analogical models thus obtained are based on an isomorphism of non-quantitative laws:

> An osmotic growth has an evolutionary existence; it is nourished by osmosis and intussusception; it exercises a selective choice on the substances offered to it; it changes the chemical constitution of its nutriment before assimilating it. Like a living thing it ejects into its environment the waste products of its function. Moreover, it grows and develops structures like those of living organisms, and it is sensitive to many exterior changes, which influence its form and development. But these very phenomena—nutrition, assimilation, sensibility, growth, and organization— are generally asserted to be the sole characteristics of life.[15]

These analogies, and various others, between organisms and physico-chemical systems have often been used to answer the vitalistic claim that growth, metabolism, regeneration, and the like are phenomena that cannot be exhibited by a "machine" or by a system governed exclusively by physico-chemical laws.[16] But, while the models can refute that contention, they do not provide a positive theoretical explanation of the biological phenomena in question. In fact, Leduc does not even state any physico-chemical laws that would explain the striking plantlike shapes exhibited by some of the osmotic growths he produces by chemical means; even less, therefore, does he establish that the

---

14. See Leduc's profusely illustrated books (1911), (1912).

15. Leduc (1911), p. 159.

16. *Cf.*, for example, the crystal analogy, which is discussed in Bertalanffy (1933), pp. 100-102; and see also the instructive discussion of physico-chemical models of biological phenomena in Bonhoeffer (1948), where the motivating consideration here referred to is explicitly suggested. In this context, we might mention also some more recent physical models of certain aspects of learning, whose construction, again, is prompted at least in part by the desire to counter vitalistic and similar claims: such models are presented in Baernstein and Hull (1931) and Krueger and Hull (1931).

same laws also account for the shapes of the "natural" plants modeled by those artificial growths. Similar comments apply to "metabolism," "regeneration," and so forth in osmotic and in organic growths.

Besides, the isomorphisms exhibited by Leduc's and similar models concern only regularities of a vague qualitative kind illustrated by the passage quoted above: organisms grow and decay, and so do their osmotic counterparts; there is an exchange of materials between organism and environment, and an exchange of materials between each of the models and its environment; there is some measure of repair of injuries in organisms and in their physico-chemical models, and so on. Because of their lack of specificity, generalizations of this kind do not have much explanatory force. In this respect, the analogies here exhibited are vastly inferior to those between water waves and electromagnetic waves, for example, which rest on a syntactical isomorphism of two extensive theories formulated in mathematical terms.

As we noted, all references to analogies or analogical models can be dispensed with in the systematic statement of scientific explanations. But the discovery of an isomorphism between different sets of laws or theoretical principles may prove useful in other respects.

First, it may make for "intellectual economy":[17] If certain laws governing a "new" class of phenomena are isomorphic with those for another class, which have already been studied in detail, then all the logical consequences of the latter can be transferred to the new domain by simply replacing all extra-logical terms by their counterparts. An important study by Gauss[18] takes as its point of departure the observation that the forces of gravitational attraction and of electric and magnetic attraction and repulsion between any two "elements" are all inversely proportional to the square of their distance and directly proportional to the product of their masses or electric charges, or magnetic strengths, respectively. On the basis of this nomic isomorphism, Gauss develops a general mathematical theory for all forces governed by a law of the specified form, and especially for the corresponding potentials, without distinguishing between the different subject matters to which the resulting theory can be applied.[19] This aspect of nomic isomorphisms has recently found important practical applications in the construction of analogue computers and similar devices. For example, the isomorphism underlying the analogy between the flow of a

17. Duhem (1906), p. 154.
18. Gauss (1840).
19. The discovery and utilization of nomic isomorphisms between different fields of inquiry is one of the objectives of "general system theory" as conceived by Bertalanffy; see his brief statements (1951) and (1956), where many further references will be found. Some comments on the program of exploring isomorphisms in the manner envisaged by Bertalanffy are included in Hempel (1951a).

liquid through a pipe and the flow of an electric current through a wire enables the designer of a large and costly water-pumping system to determine the optimal characteristics of the pumps and the network of pipes by means of small and inexpensive electric analogues.

Analogies and models based on nomic isomorphisms may also facilitate one's grasp of a set of explanatory laws or theoretical principles for a new domain of inquiry by exhibiting a parallel with explanatory principles for a more familiar domain: in this manner, they can contribute to the pragmatic effectiveness of an explanation.

More important, well-chosen analogies or models may prove useful "in the context of discovery," i.e., they may provide effective heuristic guidance in the search for new explanatory principles. Thus, while an analogical model itself explains nothing, it may suggest extensions of the analogy on which it was originally based. Norbert Wiener mentions a case of this kind. An analogy he and Bigelow had envisaged between certain types of voluntary human behavior and the behavior of a machine governed by a negative feedback system suggested to them that there might exist, for purposive behavior, an analogue to the conditions, which are theoretically well understood, in which a feedback system breaks down through a series of wild oscillations. Such an analogue was indeed found in the pathological condition of purpose tremor, in which a patient trying to pick up an object overshoots the mark and then goes into uncontrollable oscillations.[20] To give another example: Maxwell appears to have arrived at his equations for the electromagnetic field by judicious use of mechanical analogies of electromagnetic phenomena. This led Boltzmann to say that the high praise Heinrich Hertz had bestowed on Maxwell's theoretical accomplishment was earned primarily by Maxwell's ingenuity in devising fruitful mechanical analogies rather than by his mathematical analysis.[21]

Analogies may prove useful in devising, and in expanding, microstructure theories such as the kinetic theory of heat or the theory accounting for the coding and transmission of genetic information in terms of specific hypotheses about the molecular structure of the genes. It should be noted, however, that such theories are intended to explain observable macrophysical uniformities by suitable assumptions about the underlying microphysical structures and processes and that the latter are not, as a rule, presented as analogical models only. When Lord Kelvin sought to account for uniformities in the absorption

20. See Wiener (1948), pp. 13-15 and chapter 4.
21. Boltzmann (1905), p. 8; also (1891), p. iii. For various other illustrations and an illuminating general discussion of the role of analogies in physical theorizing, see Nagel (1961), pp. 107-17.

and dispersion of light by construing each of the material molecules involved in these processes on the model of a set of nested rigid metal spheres separated from each other by springs, he did not, of course, claim to describe the actual microstructure of matter, and it would have been beside the point to request evidence in support of the assumption that molecules consist of nested metal spheres and springs. However, the kinetic theory of heat does assert, among other things, that a gas consists of molecules in rapid motion; it specifies the numbers and masses of the particles involved, the distribution of their velocities and its dependence on the temperature, the mean free paths of the molecules and the mean time interval between successive collisions, and so forth; and in regard to these and many other specific implications, supporting evidence can be significantly asked for and can indeed be supplied.

Similarly, theories about the elementary particles constituting the atomic nuclei of various elements, or about the molecular structure of the genes, are presented as accounts of the actual structure of the systems in question, and not just as analogical models. Like any other theory in empirical science, such microstructure theories are put forward "until further notice," i.e., with the understanding that they may have to be modified or completely withdrawn in the light of subsequently discovered unfavorable evidence; and often they are offered only as approximations. Nevertheless, they differ in the respect just indicated from accounts formulated in terms of analogical models.

In some microstructure theories, the basic constituents of the macrophenomena under study are assumed to be governed by laws that are identical or syntactically isomorphic with a set of laws governing an already well-explored field of inquiry. A characteristic example is the assumption that the motions and collisions of gas molecules conform to the laws for the motions and collisions of elastic billiard balls. Indeed, some writers have insisted that the basic assumptions or equations of any good scientific theory must exhibit that kind of analogy. One eloquent proponent of this view is the physicist N. R. Campbell.

Campbell considers it the principal function of theories to provide deductive explanations of laws, i.e., of "propositions which assert uniformities discovered by experiment or observation."[22] He characterizes a theory as consisting of two sets of propositions, which he calls the hypothesis and the dictionary. The hypothesis is formulated in terms of "ideas which are characteristic of the theory," or in terms of theoretical concepts, as we might say. The dictionary provides a physical interpretation of the hypothesis by translating some but not necessarily all of its propositions into others which involve no theoretical

22. Campbell (1920), p. 71.

concepts and which can be verified or falsified, without any reference to the theory, by suitable experiments or observations.[23]

Campbell demands of a scientific theory that it be capable of explaining empirically established laws: such explanation consists in deducing the laws from the hypothesis in conjunction with the dictionary. "But," he insists, "in order that a theory may be valuable it must have a second characteristic; it must display an analogy. The propositions of the hypothesis must be analogous to some known laws." He adds: "analogies are not 'aids' to the establishment of theories; they are an utterly essential part of theories, without which theories would be completely valueless and unworthy of the name."[24] In support of this contention, Campbell constructs a small quasi-theoretical system which does deductively imply an empirical law, but which clearly is not an acceptable scientific theory; and this, in Campbell's opinion, because its hypothesis lacks the requisite analogy to known laws. Let us briefly consider that system, which I will call S.[25]

The hypothesis of S is expressed in terms of four quantitative theoretical concepts a, b, c, d, which are functions of certain "independent variables" u, v, w,.... The hypothesis states that a and b are constant functions, and that c is identical with d.

The dictionary of S consists of the following two specifications: the statement that $(c^2 + d^2) a = R$, where R is a positive rational number, implies that the resistance of some particular piece of pure metal is R; and the statement that $cd/b = T$ implies that the temperature of the same piece of metal is T.

Now, the hypothesis of S deductively implies that

$$(c^2 + d^2) a \left/ \frac{cd}{b} \right. = 2\,ab = \text{constant}$$

Interpreting the quotient on the left by means of the dictionary we obtain, according to Campbell, the following law: "The ratio of the resistance of a piece of pure metal to its absolute temperature is constant." (Actually, this

23. Campbell (1920), pp. 122, states: "The dictionary relates some of these propositions of which the truth or falsity is known to certain propositions involving the hypothetical ideas by stating that if the first set of propositions is true then the second set is true and *vice versa*; this relation may be expressed by the statement that the first set *implies* the second." (Italics supplied.) This is clearly a nonstandard use of the word 'implies'; in the following discussion, I will therefore use the phrase 'deductively implies' to refer to the nonsymmetrical logical relation, in contradistinction to the symmetrical relation which Campbell has in mind, and which I suggested by saying that according to Campbell the dictionary *translates* certain theoretical propositions into empirical ones.

24. Campbell (1920), p. 129.

25. See Campbell (1920), pp. 123-24.

proposition follows only for the particular piece of metal referred to in the dictionary; but let us waive this point as inessential for the idea under consideration).

This law, then, is logically deducible from the system S and is in this sense explained by S. But Campbell argues: "If nothing but this were required we should never lack theories to explain our laws; a schoolboy in a day's work could solve the problems at which generations have laboured in vain by the most trivial process of trial and error. What is wrong with the theory . . . , what makes it absurd and unworthy of a single moment's consideration, is that it does not display any analogy."[26]

Campbell is certainly right in rejecting the "theory" S, but his diagnosis of its shortcomings seems to me incorrect. What is wrong with the theory, so it seems to me, is that it has no empirically testable consequences other than the law in question (and whatever is logically implied by it alone); whereas a worthwhile scientific theory explains an empirical law by exhibiting it as one aspect of more comprehensive underlying regularities, which have a variety of other testable aspects as well, i.e., which also imply various other empirical laws. Such a theory thus provides a systematically unified account of many different empirical laws. Besides, as was noted in section 2, a theory will normally imply refinements and modifications of previously established empirical laws rather than deductively imply the laws as originally formulated.

The diagnosis that it is this defect rather than the absence of analogy which disqualifies S can be further supported by the observation that systems can readily be constructed which do display some analogy to known laws and which are nevertheless worthless for science because they suffer from the same defect as S. For example, let the hypothesis of a system S' assert of four theoretical quantities a, b, c, d that for any object u,

$$c(u) = \frac{k_1 a(u)}{b(u)}; \quad d(u) = \frac{k_2 b(u)}{a(u)}$$

where k_1 and k_2 are numerical constants; and let the dictionary of S' specify that for any piece u of pure metal, $c(u)$ is its resistance and $d(u)$ the reciprocal of its absolute temperature. Then S', too, deductively implies the law cited above, and, in addition, each of the two propositions in the hypothesis displays an analogy to a known law; for example, to Ohm's law. Yet, S' does

---

26. Campbell (1920), pp. 129–30. Campbell allows, however, that there is a type of theory, illustrated by Fourier's theory of heat conduction, for which analogy may play a less important role (pp. 140–44). For the purposes of the present discussion, those theories clearly need not be considered.

not qualify as a scientific theory any more than does S, and clearly for the same reason.

While thus, in my judgment, Campell fails to establish that analogy plays an essential logic-systematic role in scientific theorizing and theoretical explaining, some of his pronouncements squarely place his requirement of analogy within the domain of the pragmatic-psychological aspects of explanation. This is illustrated by his statement that "an analogy is a function of the contemplating mind; when we say that one set of propositions is analogous to another we are saying something about its effect on our minds; whether or no it produces that effect on the minds of others, it will still have that effect on our own."[27] Surely, analogy thus subjectively conceived cannot be an indispensible aspect of objective scientific theories.

Considering the great heuristic value of structural analogies, it is natural that a scientist attempting to frame a new theory should let himself be guided by concepts and laws that have proved fruitful in previously explored areas. But if these should fail, he will have to resort to ideas that depart more and more from the familiar ones. In Bohr's early theory of the atom, for example, the assumption of electrons orbiting around the nucleus without radiating energy violates the principles of classical electrodynamics; and in the subsequent development of quantum theory, the analogy of the basic theoretical principles to "known laws" has been reduced considerably further in return for increased scope and greater explanatory and predictive power.

What remains as the principal requirement for scientific explanation is thus the inferential subsumption of the explanandum under comprehensive general principles, irrespective of the analogies these may display to previously established laws.

There is yet another kind of model, often referred to as theoretical or mathematical model, which is widely used for explanatory purposes, for example in psychology, sociology, and economics. It is exemplified by the numerous mathematical models of learning, by theoretical models of attitude change and of conflict behavior, and by a great variety of models for social, political, and economic phenomena.[28]

---

27. Campbell (1920), p. 144. For further light on these issues see Hesse (1963); chapter 2 of this book has the form of a dialogue between a "Campbellian" and a "Duhemian", in which various arguments concerning the significance of models and analogies for scientific theorizing are surveyed and suggestively appraised.

28. The relevant literature is vast, and only a very few specific references can be given here. A particularly lucid general discussion of theoretical models in psychology, together with a specific model of conflict behavior, is presented in Miller (1951). On models for learning, see for example Bush and Mosteller (1955); the introduction of this book lucidly formulates the methodology of the authors' procedure. The collective volume Lazarsfeld (1954)

(continued overleaf)

Broadly speaking, and disregarding many differences in detail, a theoretical model of this kind has the character of a theory with a more or less limited scope of application. Its basic assumptions concern interdependencies of different characteristics of the subject matter in question. Those characteristics are often, but not always, represented by quantitative parameters or "variables"; these may be more or less directly observable or measurable, or they may have the status of theoretical concepts with at least a partial empirical interpretation, effected, perhaps, by "operational definition." This is true, for example, of those parameters which represent statistical probabilities for certain kinds of behavior. The basic hypotheses of the model often construe some of the parameters as mathematical functions of others, but they do not always have this quantitative character.[29] From the basic hypotheses, in conjunction with the interpretation, specific consequences can be inferred concerning the empirical phenomena to which the model pertains: thus, it becomes possible to test the model and to put it to explanatory and predictive use. The resulting explanations and predictions may be deductive-nomological or inductive-statistical, depending on the form of the hypotheses included in the model.

The use of the term 'theoretical model' rather than 'theory' is perhaps meant to indicate that the systems in question have distinct limitations, especially when compared with advanced physical theories. To begin with, their basic assumptions are often known to be idealizations or oversimplifications. For example, they may disregard certain factors that are known to be of some relevance to the given subject matter; this would be true, e.g., of a theoretical model for economic behavior based on the assumption of strict economic rationality of the agents concerned. Next, the formulation of the interrelations between different factors may be deliberately oversimplified, perhaps in order to make the application of the model to particular cases mathematically manageable. In addition, the class of phenomena with which the model is concerned may be quite limited; for example, a theoretical model of decision making under risk might be restricted to decisions which are made under rather arti-

---

29. This is true, for example, of Miller's theoretical model of conflict behavior, which is formulated in terms of comparative hypotheses such as "The tendency to approach a goal is stronger the nearer the subject is to it." Miller (1951), p. 90.

---

includes presentations of mathematical models for various aspects of social behavior as well as essays devoted to the analysis of particular models or to general problems concerning the methodology of model construction. An excellent general account of the role of mathematical models in the social sciences is given in Arrow (1951), and the symposia Society for Experimental Biology (1960) and International Union of History and Philosophy of Sciences (1961) contain some interesting papers on the role of models in empirical science. The essay Brodbeck (1959) includes illuminating observations on the character and the function of theoretical models.

ficial experimentally controlled conditions, and which are limited to a small number of rather trivial options.

But such peculiarities can also be found in the field of physical theorizing, and they do not bar the systems in question from the status of potentially explanatory theories. However, a limited scope and only approximate validity within that scope may severely restrict the actual explanatory and predictive value of a theoretical model.

7. GENETIC EXPLANATION AND COVERING LAWS

The covering-law models have often been criticized on the ground that while they may correctly represent the structure and the import of some of the explanations put forward by empirical science, they fail to do justice to many others. In the present section and in those that follow I propose to examine some important modes and aspects of scientific explanation that have been cited in support of this contention, and I will attempt to indicate what light the covering-law conception can shed upon their logic and their force.

One explanatory procedure, which is widely used in history, though not in history alone, is that of genetic explanation; it presents the phenomenon under study as the final stage of a developmental sequence, and accordingly accounts for the phenomenon by describing the successive stages of that sequence.

Consider, for example, the practice of selling indulgences, in the form it had taken when Luther was a young man. The ecclesiastic historian H. Boehmer tells us that until the beginning of the twentieth century, "the indulgence was in fact still a great unknown quantity, at sight of which the scholar would ask himself with a sigh: 'Where did it come from?'" An answer was suggested by Adolf Gottlob, who tackled the problem by asking himself what led the popes and bishops to offer indulgences. As a result, ". . . origin and development of the unknown quantity appeared clearly in the light, and doubts as to its original meaning came to an end. It revealed itself as a true descendant of the time of the great struggle between Christianity and Islam, and at the same time a highly characteristic product of Germanic Christianity."[1]

According to this conception,[2] the origins of the indulgence date back to the ninth century, when the popes were strongly concerned with the fight against Islam. The Mohammedan fighter was assured by the teachings of his

1. Boehmer (1930), p. 91. Gottlob's study, *Kreuzablass und Almosenablass*, was published in 1906; *cf.* the references to the work of Gottlob and other investigators in Schwiebert (1950), notes to chapter 10.

2. I am here following the accounts in Boehmer (1930), chapter 3 and in Schwiebert (1950), chapter 10.

religion that if he were to be killed in battle his soul would immediately go to heaven, but the Christian had to fear that he might still be lost if he had not done the regular penance for his sins. To allay these doubts, John VII, in 877, promised absolution for their sins to crusaders who should be killed in battle. "Once the crusade was so highly thought of, it was an easy transition to regard participation in a crusade as equivalent to the performance of atonement . . . and to promise remission of . . . penances in return for expeditions against the Church's enemies."[3] Thus, there was introduced the indulgence of the Cross, which granted complete remission of the penitential punishment to all those who participated in a religious war. "If it is remembered what inconveniences, what ecclesiastical and civil disadvantages the ecclesiastical penances entailed, it is easy to understand that penitents flocked to obtain this indulgence."[4] A further strong incentive came from the belief that whoever obtained an indulgence secured liberation not only from the ecclesiastical penances, but also from the corresponding suffering in purgatory after death. The benefits of these indulgences were next extended to those who, being physically unfit to participate in a religious war, contributed the funds required to send a soldier on a crusade. In 1199, Pope Innocent III recognized the payment of money as adequate qualification for the benefits of a crusading indulgence.

When the crusades were on the decline, new ways were explored of raising funds through indulgences. Thus, there was instituted a "jubilee indulgence," to be celebrated every hundred years, for the benefit of pilgrims coming to Rome on that occasion. The first of these indulgences, in 1300, brought in huge sums of money, and the interval between successive jubilee indulgences was therefore reduced to 50, 33, and even 25 years. And from 1393 on, the jubilee indulgence was made available, not only in Rome, but everywhere in Europe, through special agents who were empowered to absolve penitent sinners upon receiving appropriate payment. The development went still further: in 1477, a dogmatic declaration by Sixtus IV attributed to the indulgence the power of delivering even the dead from purgatory.

Undeniably, a genetic account of this kind can enhance our understanding of a historical phenomenon. But its explanatory role seems to me basically nomological in character. For the successive stages singled out for consideration surely must be qualified for their function by more than the fact that they form a temporal sequence and that they all precede the final stage, which is to be explained: the mere enumeration in a yearbook of "the year's important events" in the order of their occurrence clearly is not a genetic explanation of the final event or of anything else. In a genetic explanation each stage must be

---

3. Boehmer (1930), p. 92.
4. Boehmer (1930), p. 93.

shown to "lead to" the next, and thus to be linked to its successor by virtue of some general principles which make the occurrence of the latter at least reasonably probable, given the former. But in this sense, even successive stages in a physical phenomenon such as the free fall of a stone may be regarded as forming a genetic sequence whose different stages—characterized, let us say, by the position and the velocity of the stone at different times—are interconnected by strictly universal laws; and the successive stages in the movement of a steel ball bouncing its zigzaggy way down a Galton Board[5] may be regarded as forming a genetic sequence with probabilistic connections.

The genetic accounts given by historians are not, of course, of the purely nomological kind suggested by these examples from physics. Rather, they combine a certain measure of nomological interconnecting with more or less large amounts of straight description. For consider an intermediate stage mentioned in a genetic account. Some aspects of it will be presented as having evolved from the preceding stages (in virtue of connecting laws, which often will be no more than hinted at); other aspects, which are not accounted for by information about the preceding development, will be descriptively added because they are relevant to an understanding of subsequent stages in the genetic sequence. Thus, schematically speaking, a genetic explanation will begin with a pure description of an initial stage; thence, it will proceed to an account of a second stage, part of which is nomologically linked to, and explained by, the characteristic features of the initial stage, while the balance is simply added descriptively because of its relevance for the explanation of some parts of the third stage, and so forth.[6]

The following diagram schematically represents the way nomological explanation is combined with straightforward description in a genetic account of this kind:

$$S_1 \nearrow \left.\begin{matrix} S'_2 \\ \\ +D_2 \end{matrix}\right\} S_2 \nearrow \left.\begin{matrix} S'_3 \\ \\ +D_3 \end{matrix}\right\} S_3 \nearrow \ldots \nearrow \left.\begin{matrix} S'_{n-1} \\ \\ +D_{n-1} \end{matrix}\right\} S_{n-1} \rightarrow S_n$$

Each arrow indicates a presumptive nomic connection between two successive stages; it presupposes uniformities which as a rule are not stated fully

---

5. For a description of the device and a probabilistic analysis of its workings, see, for example, Mises (1939), pp. 237–40.

6. This conception of the structure of genetic explanation in history is in basic accord with that set forth by Nagel (1961), pp. 564–68, in the context of a very substantial and comprehensive discussion of problems in the logic of historical inquiry. The presupposition of connecting generalizations in historic-genetaic explanations is emphasized also in Frankel (1959), p. 412 and in Goldstein (1958), pp. 475–79. On the role of "coherent narrative" *vs.* covering-law explanation in natural history, see also Goudge (1958).

and explicitly, and which may be of the strictly universal kind or—more likely—of a statistical kind. $S_1, S_2, \ldots, S_n$ are sets of sentences expressing all the information that the genetic account gives about the first, second, .., nth stage. For each of these stages except the first and the last, the information thus provided falls into two parts: one—represented by $S'_2, S'_3, \ldots, S'_{n-1}$— describes those facts about the given stage which are explained by reference to the preceding stage; the other—represented by $D_2, D_3, \ldots, D_{n-1}$—constitutes information about further facts which are adduced without explanation, because of their explanatory significance for the next stage. It will hardly be necessary to re-emphasize that this characterization of genetic explanation is highly schematic; it is intended to exhibit the affinities which this procedure has to nomological explanation on one hand and to description on the other. In practice, these two components will often be hard to separate; instead of neatly presenting a set of interconnecting but distinct stages in temporal succession, a genetic account is likely to give descriptions of, and suggest connections between, a great variety of facts and events that are spread over a certain temporal range and are not easily grouped into clusters constituting successive stages.

In our illustration the assumption of some connecting laws or lawlike principles is indicated by the references to motivating factors; for example, the explanatory claims made for the popes' desire to secure a fighting force or to amass even larger funds clearly presupposes psychological assumptions about the manner in which an intelligent individual will tend to act, in the light of his factual beliefs, when he seeks to attain a given objective. Psychological uniformities are implicit also in the reference to the fear of purgatory as explaining the eagerness with which indulgences were bought. Again, when one historian observes that the huge financial success of the first jubilee indulgence "only whetted the insatiable appetite of the popes. The period of time was variously reduced from 100 to 50, to 33, to 25 years,"[7] the explanation thus suggested rests on a psychological assumption akin to the idea of reinforcement by rewards. But, of course, even if some formulation of this idea were explicitly adduced, the resulting account would provide at the very most a partial explanation; it could not show, for example, why the intervening intervals should have had the particular lengths here mentioned.

Those factors which, in our illustration, are simply described or tacitly presupposed as "brute facts," to use Nagel's phrase,[8] include, for example, the relevant doctrines, the organization, and the power of the Church; the occurrence of the crusades and the eventual decline of this movement; and a great

7. Schwiebert (1950), p. 304.
8. Nagel (1961), p. 566.

many additional factors which are not explicitly mentioned, but which have to be understood as background conditions if the genetic account is to serve its explanatory purpose.

Let us consider briefly another example of genetic explanation, taken from Toynbee. In 1839 the principal maternity hospital in the city of Alexandria was located on the grounds of the navy arsenal. "This sounds odd," Toynbee notes, "but we shall see that it was inevitable as soon as we retrace the sequence of events that led to this at first surprising result."[9] Toynbee's genetic account is, briefly, as follows. By 1839 Mehmed 'Ali Pasha, the Ottoman governor of Egypt, had been at work for more than thirty years to equip himself with effective armaments, and particularly with a fleet of warships in the Western style. He realized that his naval establishment would not be self-sufficient unless he was in a position to have his warships built in Egypt by native workers, and that a competent group of Egyptian naval technicians could be trained only by Western naval specialists, who would have to be hired for this purpose. The governor therefore advertised for Western experts, offering them very attractive salaries. But the specialists who applied for the positions were unwilling to come without their families, and they wanted to be sure of medical care that was adequate by Western standards. The governor therefore also hired Western physicians to attend the naval experts and their families. The doctors found, however, that they had time to do additional work; and, "being the energetic and public-spirited medical practitioners that they were, they resolved to do something for the local Egyptian population as well. . . . Maternity work was obviously the first call. So a maternity hospital arose within the precincts of the naval arsenal by a train of events which, as you will now recognize, was inevitable."[10]

Toynbee thus seeks to explain the initially odd fact in question by showing how it came about "inevitably," as the final stage of a sequence of interconnected events; and he refers to the case as an example of the "process of one thing leading to another"[11] in intercultural relations. But wherein lies the inevitability with which one thing leads to the next? At several points in Toynbee's account, the presumptive connection is suggested by the explanatory reference to the motivating reasons of the agents; but these provide explanatory grounds for the resulting actions only on the assumption that people motivated by such and such reasons will *generally* act, or will *tend* to act, in certain characteristic ways. Thus, the conception of one thing inevitably leading to another here presupposes a connection by lawlike principles that hold for certain kinds of

9. Toynbee (1953), p. 75.
10. *Ibid.*, p. 77.
11. *Ibid.*, p. 75.

human action. The character of such principles and the logic of the explanations based on them will be examined more closely in sections 9 and 10 of this essay.

I will now briefly consider some controversial issues concerning genetic explanation in history on which the preceding considerations might shed some light.

Dray has argued that genetic explanation in history has logical peculiarities which can be thrown into relief by a comparison with what he calls "the model of the continuous series."[12] He illustrates the model by an account that explains the stalling of an automobile engine by tracing it back to a leak in the oil reservoir: as a result of the leak, the oil drained out, which deprived the cylinders and pistons of lubrication, thus leading to frictional heating and expansion of the pistons and cylinder walls, so that the metals locked tightly and the engine stopped. Dray puts much emphasis on the claim that by revealing the mechanism of the failure, this stepwise account provides an understanding that would not be conveyed by citing a covering law linking the failure directly to the leak: "*Of course* the engine seized up—and I say this because I can now envisage a *continuous series of happenings* between the leak and the engine seizure which themselves are quite understandable—as the original sequence 'leak-to-seizure' was not."[13]

If I understand it correctly, Dray's defense of this claim rests to a considerable extent on undeniable pragmatic differences between the two accounts: the sequential account affords an insight that is not provided when the final stage is immediately linked to the initial one. But this pragmatic difference is associated, I think, with a non-pragmatic one which justifies the claim that the two accounts differ in explanatory power. To see this, let us, for the sake of the argument, grant nomological status to the statement, L, that whenever the oil reservoir of a properly built car develops a leak, its engine will fail. This law could then be invoked for a low-level explanation of certain particular cases of engine failure. The sequential account, on the other hand, traces the process through a sequence of stages and presents each of these as governed by certain "sub-laws", as Dray calls them, such as those connecting the friction between pistons and cylinder walls with heating and expansion of the metals. But an adequate set of such laws will enable us not only to account for particular cases of engine failure, but also to explain why the law L holds, i.e., why it is that an oil leak in a properly built car *generally* leads to engine failure.

In the case of genetic explanation in history, there is an additional reason for

12. Dray (1957), pp. 66 ff.
13. *Ibid.*, p. 68, italics the author's. For observations in a similar vein and further illustrations, see Danto (1956), pp. 23–25.

regarding an account by stages as essential for the achievement of understanding: here we have no overall law which, in analogy to the law *L* of the preceding example, links the final stage of the process immediately to the initial one. As our schematic characterization indicates, the particular data about the initial stage do not by themselves suffice to account for all specified aspects of the final stage. To explain the latter, we need further data, and these are provided in installments by the information about additional "brute facts" in the descriptions of the intervening stages.

Our construal of genetic explanation also does justice to the complaint that the laws we might actually be able to adduce in the context of historical explanation, including psychological and other laws of common experience, prove trivial and inadequate when we try to account for the rich and distinctive peculiarities which supposedly make historical events unique, and which are therefore of special interest to the historian. Considering, for example, the subtlety and complexity of some of the psychological explanations that have been proposed for the actions of historical figures, this charge may be somewhat overstated; but undeniably it has a good deal of merit. And the model just outlined makes allowance for the difficulty by providing for the introduction into a genetic account of a more or less extensive mass of details which are simply described, without being explained by reference to other particular facts and connecting uniformities.

8. EXPLANATION-BY-CONCEPT

Another mode of explanation which presumably presents difficulties for the covering-law conception has been pointed out by Dray, who considers its role in historical inquiry. Dray calls it "explaining what" or "explanation-by-concept," on the ground that a request for an account of this kind typically takes the form 'what was it that happened in this case?', and that the historian "deals with it by offering an explanation of the form 'it was a so-and-so'."[1] Dray illustrates the idea by a passage from Ramsey Muir's *Short History of the British Commonwealth*. It describes certain changes that took place in late eighteenth century England—such as the enclosure of agricultural lands, the beginnings of industrial production, and the improvement of communication—and then continues: "It was not merely an economic change that was thus beginning; it was a social revolution." Dray argues that though the historian does not attempt to tell us here why or how the events under investigation came about, his "assertion, 'it was a social revolution', is an explanation never-

---

1. Dray (1959), p. 403, italics the author's.

theless. It explains what happened *as* a social revolution."[2] Dray characterizes this kind of account as "explanation by means of a general concept rather than a general law. For the explanation is given by finding a satisfactory *classification* of what seems to require explanation."[3] Dray adds that if any generalization is essential to this kind of explanation, then it does not take the form of a general law; for "what is to be explained is a collection of happenings or conditions, *x*, *y* and *z*; and the relevant generalization would be of the form: '*x*, *y* and *z* amount to a Q'. Such an explanatory generalization is summative; it allows us to refer to *x*, *y* and *z* collectively as 'a so-and-so'. And historians find it intellectually satisfying to be able to represent the events and conditions they study as related in this way."[4]

But surely not every such representation can be regarded as explanatory: the particular occurrences referred to by Muir, for example, might be truthfully but unilluminatingly classified also as changes involving more than 1000 persons and affecting an area of over 100 square miles. If there is explanatory significance to characterizing *x*, *y*, and *z* collectively as a Q, it is because the characterization implies that the particular cases fit into, or conform to, some general pattern that is characteristic of Q.

I will illustrate this first by some examples which show, at the same time, that the procedure in question is also used outside the domain of historiography.

Torricelli's explanation of why a simple suction pump can raise water by no more than 34 feet has been said to rest on the "conceptual scheme" of a "sea of air" surrounding the earth.[5] But clearly that scheme has explanatory force only because it assumes a nomic analogy between the sea of air and a sea of water, namely, that "there would be an air pressure on all objects submerged in this sea of air exactly as there is water pressure below the surface of the ocean,"[6] and that the pressure is determined by the weight of the column of air above the object in question: this is indeed how Torricelli reasoned. Thus the explanation by means of his conceptual scheme effects a subsumption of the explanandum phenomenon under general hypotheses.

Next, as an example that shows a clear similarity to that cited by Dray, consider the statement: 'Otto's running nose and inflamed eyes, and the red spots surrounded by white areas that have just appeared on the mucous linings of his cheeks are not just isolated occurrences: they are, all of them, symptoms marking the onset of a full-blown case of the measles'. This diagnostic classifi-

---

2. *Ibid.*, italics the author's.
3. Dray (1959), p. 404, italics the author's.
4. *Ibid.*, p. 406.
5. Conant (1951), p. 69.
6. *Ibid.*

cation accounts for the particular complaints cited by pointing out that they jointly conform to the clinical pattern of the measles; i.e., that they are of certain characteristic kinds and occur in a characteristic temporal order, that they will be followed by further specific symptoms, and that the illness will tend to take a certain characteristic course. To interpret a set of complaints as manifestations of the measles is surely to claim that they fit into a certain pattern of regularities (which will be of statistical rather than of strictly universal form); and such an account accords with the covering-law conception of explanation.

Or consider the "classification" of a particular sequence of lightning and thunder as a case of a powerful electric discharge generating a violent disturbance of the air. This does indeed have explanatory import, but clearly by virtue of pointing out that the particular set of events showed the characteristics generally exhibited by powerful discharges and by the disturbances they create in the air; or, more precisely, that they conform to the laws characteristic of the sort of phenomenon as an instance of which the particular case is classified or interpreted.

In Dray's quotation from Muir, the pronouncement "it was a social revolution" similarly carries the suggestion that an explanatory diagnosis is being offered—a suggestion that is reinforced by the following amplificatory passage, which directly follows the sentence quoted by Dray: "The old, settled, stable order which we described as existing in Britain in the middle of the eighteenth century was being wholly transformed. . . . But the full significance of this change was as yet quite unrealized. Securely enthroned, the old governing classes were wholly blind to the forces that were at work beneath their feet, undermining the very foundations of their power, and making it inevitable that sooner or later the political system should be readjusted to accord with the change in the social order."[7] We have here the suggestion of a diagnosis or interpretation to the effect that the particular changes in agriculture, industrial production, and communications that Muir had described before were early manifestations of a larger process whose different phases are not associated coincidentally, but with some inevitability. Thus again—if only very vaguely and sketchily—the particular cases are assigned a place in a comprehensive pattern of connections. Whatever explanatory significance Muir's statement may have—and to me, it seems rather slight—surely lies in the suggestion of a diagnosis of the sort that is more plainly illustrated by our preceding two illustrations, which conform, in broad outline, to the covering-law conception.

7. Muir (1922), p. 123.

Other examples of what Dray calls explanation-by-concept are provided by the various interpretations of the American Civil War as the result of a conspiracy by some Northern—or Southern—groups of "wicked men"; as a quarrel between two rival regions; as a contest over types of government; as an outgrowth of the "irrepressible conflict" between freedom and slavery; as a basically economic contest; and so forth.[8] Each of these explanations of the Civil War "as a so-and-so" attributes special or overriding causal significance to factors of some special type and accordingly presupposes suitable nomic connections in support of those assumptions.[9]

Dray explicitly acknowledges that "explanation-by-concept may sometimes *in fact* subsume the explicandum under law,"[10] but holds that this is not generally the case. Specifically, he takes issue with an earlier statement of mine that "what is sometimes, misleadingly, called an explanation by means of a certain *concept* is, in empirical science, actually an explanation in terms of *universal hypotheses* containing that concept."[11] Against this view, Dray argues as follows: "Presumably the law which lurks in the background when something is explained 'as a revolution' is one which would contain the concept in its apodosis. . . . But to explain, say, what happened in France in 1789 'as a revolution' would surely not be equivalent to bringing it under any law of the form, 'Whenever C_1, C_2, . . . , C_n then a revolution'."[12] But my earlier remark does not limit an explanation-by-concept to one general hypothesis, nor does it limit the explanatory hypotheses to the type envisaged by Dray. It applies as well, for example, to the explanation of certain complaints "as symptoms of the measles," which rests on general hypotheses to the effect that if a person suffers from the measles, then he will exhibit symptoms of such a kind; here, the explanatory concept is referred to in the protasis rather than in the apodosis.

Or consider what might loosely be called "explaining the glow of a falling meteorite as a case of intense heat generated by friction." Here several laws are involved, among them two to the effect that a body moving through air

8. On these different interpretations see, for example, Beale (1946).

9. The problem of weighting causal factors according to their relative importance in a historical explanation is lucidly dealt with in Nagel (1961), pp. 582-88.

10. Dray (1959), p. 405, italics the author's.

11. Hempel (1942), footnote 3, italics in the original. Homans has recently stressed the same point in reference to sociology. He holds that much of modern sociological theory fails to explain anything, partly because "much of it consists of systems of categories, or pigeonholes, into which the theorist fits different aspects of social behavior. . . . but this in itself is not enough to give it explanatory power. . . . The science also needs a set of general propositions about the relations between the categories, for without such propositions explanation is impossible." Homans (1961), p. 10.

12. Dray (1959), p. 404.

encounters friction and that friction generates heat; so that the explanatory concepts might be said to figure partly in the protasis, partly in the apodosis of the corresponding general laws.

Dray's own example is stated so sketchily that it is difficult to appraise the explanation supposedly achieved. A statement characterizing what happened in France in 1789 as a revolution would seem to provide a very vague description rather than any explanation of those events. Some explanatory import might be claimed if the concept of revolution were understood in a restricted technical sense implying perhaps a sequence of characteristic stages in the process, or certain characteristic changes in the structure of political power, or the like; then some of the particular events of 1789 might be shown to conform to the patterns implied by the given concept of revolution and might thus be regarded as partly explained by it. But in this case, the explanation would evidently be achieved by reference to the implied uniformities.

In sum, then, an explanatory use of concepts must always rely on corresponding general hypotheses.

9. DISPOSITIONAL EXPLANATION

Another kind of explanation that has been held to defy a covering-law analysis invokes in a characteristic manner certain dispositional properties of the objects or agents whose "behavior" is to be accounted for; I will refer to this procedure as dispositional explanation.

The familiar method of explaining human decisions and actions in terms of purposes, beliefs, character traits, and the like is basically of this kind; for to ascribe to an agent such motivating factors is to assign to him certain more or less complex dispositional characteristics: this has been argued in detail by Ryle[1], whose ideas have had great influence on the discussion of the subject. Explanations by motivating reasons will be examined in some detail in section 10. In the present section we will consider the logical structure of some dispositional explanations in physics and compare it with that of explanations by covering laws.

Consider first an example discussed by Ryle. When a window pane shatters upon being struck by a stone, the breaking of the glass can be causally explained, according to Ryle, by pointing out that a stone hit it; but we often seek an explanation in a different sense: "We ask why the glass shivered when struck by the stone and we get the answer that it was because the glass was brittle."[2]

---

1. See especially Ryle (1949).
2. Ryle (1949), p. 88.

Here the explanation is achieved, not by specifying an independent event "which stood to the fracture of the glass as cause to effect",[3] but by attributing to the glass a certain dispositional property, brittleness. To ascribe this property to a particular window pane is, at least by implication, to assert a *general* hypothesis, roughly to the effect that if at any time the pane is sharply struck by any physical body, or is sharply twisted by any agent, it will fly into fragments. But while thus being general in character, a dispositional statement nevertheless also mentions a particular individual, such as the window pane. In this respect, dispositional statements differ from general laws, which Ryle construes as making no mention of individuals at all. To indicate their resemblance to general laws and also their difference from them, Ryle calls dispositional statements "law-like."[4]

It should be noted, however, that neither of the two kinds of explanation here distinguished by Ryle is sufficient by itself to account for the given event. The report that the pane was struck by a stone explains its being broken only in conjunction with the additional information that the pane was brittle: it is in virtue of the general hypothesis implied by this dispositional attribution that being hit by the stone becomes a cause rather than an accidental antecedent in regard to the breaking of the pane. Similarly, the dispositional statement can explain the breaking of the glass only when taken in conjunction with the report that the glass was sharply struck; and indeed, as we saw, Ryle himself describes the dispositional statement as explaining "why the glass shivered when struck by the stone," and not simply why the glass shivered. Thus either of the two explanations here distinguished is incomplete and requires complementa-

---

3. *Ibid.*

4. For details, see Ryle (1949), pp. 43-44, 89, 120-25. Strictly speaking, the intended distinction between law-like sentences and general laws cannot be satisfactorily explicated in terms of whether or not the sentences in question "mention particular things or persons," as Ryle (*loc. cit.*, p. 123) puts it; for explicit mention of an individual can be circumvented by rephrasing. For example, the general sentence 'All places on the surface of the earth within 100 miles of the North Pole are cold' would count as law-like because it mentions the North Pole. Yet it can be rephrased as 'All polar places are cold', where 'polar' is used as synonymous with 'lying on the surface of the earth within 100 miles of the North Pole'; and under the contemplated criterion, the rephrasal would have to be counted as a general law because it does not mention (i.e., it does not contain a designation of) any particular person, place, or thing. For a fuller discussion of the issue *cf.* Hempel and Oppenheim (1948), section 6 and Goodman (1955), expecially chapters 1 and 3. Note, incidentally, that Goodman uses the term 'lawlike' in the sense quite different from Ryle's, namely, to refer to sentences having all the characteristics of a law, except for possibly being false (*loc. cit.*, p. 27). To avoid a lengthy digression, we will here forego an attempt to offer a more adequate explication of the important distinction made by Ryle, and will consider the idea as intuitively sufficiently clear for our present purposes.

tion by the other. Jointly, they provide an adequate account, which might be schematically formulated as follows:

(C_1) The pane was sharply struck by a stone at time t_1

(L_1) For any time t it is the case that if the pane is sharply struck at t,

(9.1)   then it breaks at t

(E_1) The pane broke at t_1

This àccount is a deductive-nomological explanation except for invoking a law-like statement instead of a completely general law. In this latter respect, the argument is in good company: Galileo's and Kepler's laws, for example, surely are used for explanatory purposes; and yet the former, when fully stated, specifies that its formula applies to free fall near the surface of the earth, and it thus mentions an individual object; while Kepler's laws, as originally conceived, refer to the motions of the planets of one particular object, the Sun. To be sure, these laws have since been subsumed under the Newtonian laws of motion and of gravitation, which are of completely general form. A similar step is possible in the example of the broken window, where the statement 'the pane was brittle' may be replaced in the explanatory argument by a completely general hypothesis, 'All glass is brittle (under standard conditions)', and the singular statement 'The pane was made of glass (and was under standard conditions)'.

However, currently available theories do not enable us to perform this sort of subsumption under strictly general laws or theoretical principles for all law-like statements, and especially for all statements ascribing psychological dispositions to individuals. But one other step can always be taken even in these cases: instead of putting the explanatory dispositional statement into the form of a generalization mentioning a particular individual in the manner of L_1 in (9.1), we can express it by two separate statements: a singular one, asserting that the given individual has the dispositional property in question, say, D; and a completely general one characterizing the disposition D. In the case of (9.1), this would amount to replacing the sentence L_1 by the following two:

(C_2) The pane was brittle at time t_1.

(L_2) Any brittle object, if sharply struck at any time, breaks at that time.

It might be objected that the only general statement which occurs in the resulting modification of (9.1), namely L_2, does not have the character of an *empirical law* about brittle objects, but rather that of a *definition* of brittleness; and that accordingly, the explanatory force of the argument continues to reside in the attribution of brittleness to a particular pane, and thus in the law-like statement L_1 rather than in a general law about all brittle objects.

This objection carries some weight when a dispositional characteristic represents just one kind of law-like behavior, such perhaps as breaking under specified impact. But a dispositional characteristic, say M, of the kind invoked for explanatory purposes can usually manifest itself in a variety of symptomatic ways, depending on the circumstances.[5] For example, magnetization of an iron bar can manifest itself by the fact that iron filings will cling to its ends; but also by the fact that one of its ends will attract the north pole, the other one the south pole of a compass needle; and no less by the fact that if the bar is broken in two, each of the parts will display the two kinds of disposition just described for the whole bar. Many of the "symptom statements" thus characterizing some peculiar way in which M may manifest itself might be regarded as expressing either a necessary or a sufficient condition for the presence of M, and M itself might be referred to as a broadly dispositional characteristic. To such characteristics the objection at hand does not apply, as I will now try to show.

Symptom sentences expressing necessary conditions for M might take the following form:

(9.2a) If an object or individual x has the property M, then under test conditions, or stimulus conditions, of kind S_1, x will regularly respond in manner R_1; under conditions S_2, in manner R_2; and so on.

Symptom sentences expressing sufficient conditions for M might correspondingly take the form:

(9.2b) If x is in conditions of kind S^1, then if x responds in manner R^1, x has the property M; if x is in S^2, then if x responds in manner R^2, x has the property M; and so on.[6]

Each symptom sentence of either type may be regarded as expressing a partial criterion of application for the term 'M'.

The construal of symptom statements as expressing strictly necessary or strictly sufficient conditions for M is an oversimplification in many cases. For example, in medical symptom statements and in the formulation of partial criteria for character traits, beliefs, desires, etc., the connection between

---

5. That the attribution of a disposition usually implies many hypothetical propositions has been stressed by Ryle (1949), pp. 43-44. Earlier, a much fuller formal study of the logic of such broadly dispositional concepts had been carried out by Carnap in his essay "Testability and Meaning" (1936-37), esp. Part 2, which specifically provided for the possibility of introducing a scientific term by means of a set of reduction sentences, each of which is a symptom sentence in our sense. For a more recent discussion, which sheds further light on the issues here considered, see also Carnap (1956).

6. The two types of symptom sentences, or partial criteria of application, here considered correspond to the two basic types of "reduction sentences" in Carnap's study (1936-37); see especially section 8, "Reduction Sentences."

M and its symptomatic manifestations will often have to be conceived as probabilistic in character. In this case, the symptom sentences might take the following statistical forms, which are counterparts to (9.2a) and (9.2b) above:

(9.3a) For objects or individuals that have the property M and are under test conditions of kind S_1 (S_2, . . .), the statistical probability of responding in manner R_1 (R_2, . . .) is r_1 (r_2, . . .).

(9.3b) For objects or individuals that are under test conditions of kind S^1 (S^2, . . .) and respond in manner R^1 (R^2, . . .), the statistical probability of possessing the property M is r' (r'', . . .).

For the sake of full concentration on the basic issues presently under discussion, however, we will limit our attention, for the time being, to broadly dispositional traits M characterized by non-probabilistic symptom sentences of the forms (9.2a) and (9.2b).

Let U be the set of all symptom sentences for M. This set evidently implies a sentence, expressible in terms of 'R_1','S_1','R_2','S_2', . . . , 'R^1','S^1','R^2','S^2', . . . to the effect that any x satisfying some one of the sufficient conditions for M as specified in U also satisfies any one of the necessary conditions for M as specified in U.[7] As will be shown presently, this statement normally has the character of a general empirical law: and if the symptom statements for M thus jointly have empirical implications, they clearly cannot all be claimed to hold true simply by definitional fiat.[8]

To illustrate by reference to an earlier example: one of the necessary conditions for an iron bar being magnetic might be:

(9.4a) If an iron bar x is magnetic then if iron filings are placed close to x (condition S_1), the filings will cling to its ends (response R_1).

And one of the sufficient conditions might be:

(9.4b) If an iron bar x is in the vicinity of a compass needle (condition S^1) then if one of its ends attracts the north pole of the needle and repels the south pole, whereas the other end shows the opposite behavior (response R^1), then x is magnetic (has property M).

But jointly, these two symptom sentences imply the general statement that any iron bar which satisfies the compass needle condition also satisfies the iron filings condition: and this surely is not a definitional truth, but a statement that has the character of an empirical law.

Thus, as a rule, the set U of symptom statements for a broadly dispositional

---

7. This statement is equivalent to what Carnap calls the "representative sentence" of the set U of reduction sentences for M; for it "represents, so to speak, the factual content" of U. See Carnap (1936–37), pp. 451.

8. This point is lucidly argued and illustrated, by reference to the broadly dispositional concept of a person *wanting* a certain state of affairs, in Brandt and Kim (1963), pp. 428–29.

term has empirical consequences. But then it would be quite arbitrary to construe some of those symptom statements as analytic–definitional and to assign to others the status of empirical laws.[9] For this would amount to decreeing that the former were not liable to modification if empirical evidence should be found to conflict with the laws implied by the set U; but in empirical science no statements other than logical and mathematical truths can be regarded as enjoying such unqualified immunity. Accordingly, the total set of symptom statements is more appropriately regarded as part of the system of general laws governing the concept in question.

Suppose, now, that in order to explain why a given particular object or individual i behaved in a certain manner, say R_3, it is pointed out that i was in a situation of kind S_3, and that i has a broadly dispositional property M whose presence is characterized by the disposition to respond to S_1 in manner R_1, to S_2 in manner R_2, to S_3 in manner R_3, and so on. This explanatory argument may then be schematized as follows:

(C_1) i was in a situation of kind S_3
(C_2) i has the property M
(9.5) (L) Any x with the property M will, in a situation of kind S_3, behave in manner R_3

(E) i behaved in manner R_3

This account is clearly of deductive-nomological form; for the general statement L, as we have just noted, has to be accorded the status of an empirical law rather than that of a "mere definition."

But the preceding account of "dispositional explanation" calls for some further qualification. What has been said so far might suggest, for example, that to ascribe to an iron bar the "broadly dispositional property" of being magnetic is tantamount to attributing to it a set of simple dispositions, each of them characterized, in the sense reflected by our symptom statements, by the association of some specific kind of manifest "response" with certain manifest "stimulus conditions." This would be too simple a conception, however. For the general physical statements pertaining to the property of being magnetic include, besides such symptom statements, also certain general laws which represent no dispositional tendencies, and which are no less characteristic of the concept of being magnetic than are the pertinent symptom statements. Among them is the law that a moving magnetic field will produce an electric field, which implies that in a closed wire loop near a moving magnet an electric current will be induced, which in turn implies a general statement concerning

9. On this point, see also pp. 113-115 in this volume.

the response made by an ammeter which is put into a closed wire loop near a moving magnet. This last statement may be regarded as a further symptom statement for the property of being magnetic, but it should be noted that the symptom here specified is associated with the property of being magnetic by virtue of theoretical principles connecting the given characteristic with other theoretical concepts, such as that of electric and magnetic fields and their interrelations. Thus, when a concept like that of a magnet functions in a theory, then, in applying it to some particular object, we are not simply attributing to this object a set, however extensive, of dispositions to display certain kinds of observable response under given, observable stimulus conditions: the assignment also has various theoretical implications, including the attribution of other "broadly dispositional" characteristics.

These observations concerning the theoretical aspects of broadly dispositional concepts also will be found relevant to an analysis of the explanatory role of motivating reasons, which forms the subject of the next section.

10. THE CONCEPT OF RATIONALITY AND THE LOGIC OF EXPLANATION BY REASONS

10.1 Two Aspects of the Concept of Rationality. In the present section, I propose to examine the logic of the familiar method of accounting for human decisions and actions in terms of motivating reasons—a method widely held to be entirely different from the explanatory procedures of the natural sciences and to defy analysis by means of the covering-law models.

In an explanation by motivating reasons the idea of rationality usually plays an important role; and I will therefore begin with some remarks on this concept. To qualify a given action as rational is to put forward an *empirical hypothesis* and a *critical appraisal*. The hypothesis is to the effect that the action was done for certain reasons, that it can be *explained* as having been motivated by them. The reasons will include the ends that the agent presumably sought to attain, and the beliefs he presumably entertained concerning the availability, propriety, and probable effectiveness of alternative means of attaining those ends. The critical appraisal implied by the attribution of rationality is to the effect that, judged in the light of the agent's beliefs, the action he decided upon constituted a *reasonable* or *appropriate* choice of means for achieving his end. These two aspects of the concept of rational action will now be examined in turn.

10.2 Rationality as a Normative–Critical Concept. The clarification of the critical, or normative, idea of rational action calls for the statement of clear criteria of rationality which might provide us with standards for appraising the rationality of particular actions, and which might thus also guide us in making rational decisions.

Rationality in this sense is obviously a relative concept. Whether a given action—or the decision to perform it—is rational will depend on the objectives the action is meant to achieve and on the relevant empirical information available at the time of the decision. Broadly speaking, an action will qualify if, on the given information, it offers optimal prospects of achieving its objectives. Let us now consider more closely the key concepts invoked in this characterization: the concepts of the information basis and of the objectives of an action, and finally that of rationality relative to a given basis and given objectives.

If we are to choose a rational course of action in pursuit of given ends, we will have to take into account all available information concerning such matters as the particular circumstances in which the action is to be taken; the different means by which, in these circumstances, the given ends might be attained; and the side-effects and aftereffects that may be expected from the use of different available means.

The total empirical information available for a given decision may be thought of as represented by a set of sentences, which I will call the *information-basis* of the decision or of the corresponding action. This construal of the empirical basis for a decision takes account of an obvious but important point: to judge the rationality of a decision, we have to consider, not what empirical facts—particular facts as well as general laws—are actually relevant to the success or failure of the action decided upon, but what information concerning such facts is available to the decision-maker. Indeed, a decision may clearly qualify as rational even though it is based on incomplete or false empirical assumptions. For example, the historian, precisely in order to present an action by a historical figure as rational, will often have to assume—and may well be able to show on independent grounds—that the agent was incompletely informed, or that he entertained false beliefs concerning relevant empirical matters.

But while the information basis of a rational action thus need not be true, should there not at least be good reasons for believing it true? Should not the basis satisfy a requirement of adequate evidential support? Some writers do consider this a necessary condition of rational action, and this view is indeed quite plausible. For example, as one of its recent advocates, Quentin Gibson, points out: "If someone were, carefully and deliberately, to walk round a ladder because he believed, without evidence, that walking under it would bring him bad luck, we would not hesitate to say that he acted irrationally."[1]

---

1. Gibson (1960), p. 43. Chapters 4 and 14 of Gibson's work include many illuminating observations on the questions examined in this section.

No doubt we often understand rationality in this restricted sense. But if we wish to construct a concept of rational action that might later prove useful in explaining certain types of human behavior, then it seems preferable not to impose on it a requirement of evidential support; for in order to explain an action in terms of the agent's reasons, we need to know what the agent believed, but not necessarily on what grounds. For example, an explanation of the behavior of Gibson's ladder-shunner in terms of motivating reasons would have to invoke the man's superstitious beliefs, but not necessarily the grounds on which he holds them; and the man may well be said to be acting quite reasonably, given his beliefs.

From the information basis of a decision I now turn to its objectives. In very simple cases, an action might be construed as intended to bring about a particular state of affairs, which I will call the end state. But even in such simple cases, some of the courses of action which, according to the information basis, are available and are likely to bring about the end state, may nevertheless be ruled out because they violate certain general constraining principles, such as moral or legal norms, contractual commitments, social conventions, the rules of the game being played, or the like. Accordingly, the contemplated action will be aimed at achieving the end state without such violation. What I will call its *total objective* may then be characterized by a set E of sentences describing the intended end state, in conjunction with a set N of constraining norms.

Again, as in the case of the empirical basis, I will not impose the requirement that there must be "good reasons" for adopting the given ends and norms: rationality of an action will be understood in a strictly relative sense, as its suitability, judged by the given information, for achieving the specified objective.

How can such suitability be defined? For decision situations of the simple kind just contemplated, a characterization can readily be given: if the information basis contains general laws by virtue of which certain of the available actions would be bound to achieve the total objective, then, clearly, any one of those actions will count as rational in the given context. If the information basis does not single out any available action as a sufficient means for attaining the objective, it may yet assign a numerical probability of success to each of the different available actions; in this case, any action will count as rational whose probability of success is not exceeded by that of any available alternative.

For many problems of rational decision, however, the available information, the objectives, and the criteria of rationality cannot be construed in this simple manner. Our construal becomes inapplicable, in particular, when the objective of a proposed action does not consist in attaining a specified end state. This is quite frequently the case, as we will now see.

To begin with, even when a particular end state is aimed at, the available information will often indicate that there are several alternative ways of definitely or probably attaining it, each attended by a different set of side-effects and aftereffects which are not part of it. Some of these anticipated incidental consequences will be regarded as more or less desirable, others as undesirable. In a theoretical model of such decision situations the total goal must accordingly be indicated, not simply by describing the desired end state, but by specifying the relative desirability of the different total outcomes that may result from the available courses of action.

In the mathematical theory of decision-making, various models of rational choice have been constructed in which those desirabilities are assumed to be specified in numerical terms, as the so-called utilities of the different total outcomes.

The case in which the given information basis also specifies the 'probabilities[2] of the different outcomes is called *decision under risk*. For this case, one criterion of rationality has gained wide acceptance, namely that of *maximizing expected utility*. The expected utility which, on the given information, is associated with a contemplated course of action is determined by multiplying, for each possible outcome of the action, its probability with its utility, and adding the products. An action, or the decision to perform it, then qualifies as rational if its expected utility is maximal in the sense of not being exceeded by the expected utility of any alternative action.

Another decision problem which has been the subject of mathematical study, and which is of considerable philosophic interest, is that of *decision under uncertainty*. Here it is assumed that the given information basis indicates the different available courses of action and specifies for each a set of mutually exclusive and jointly exhaustive possible outcomes, without, however, assigning probabilities to them;[3] finally, each of the possible outcomes is assumed to have

2. The probabilities and utilities here referred to are subject to certain mathematical requirements which cannot be discussed in the context of the present paper. The classical statement is given in von Neumann and Morgenstern (1947); lucid presentations of the requirements, and of the reasons underlying them, will be found in Luce and Raiffa (1957), chaps. 1–4 and in Baumol (1961), chaps. 17 and 18. Among the questions passed over here is the very important one of how the concept of the probability of outcomes should be understood in the context of decision theory. For a large class of problems the familiar statistical construal of probability as a long-run relative frequency will be practically sufficient, and the current mathematical theory of games and decisions does rely on it to a large extent. Alternative conceptions have been proposed, however. Among them are Carnap's concept of inductive or logical probability (*cf.* Carnap (1950), (1962) and the concept of personal probability (*cf.* Savage (1954), especially chaps. 3 and 4).

3. Strictly speaking, this situation cannot arise on a theory of inductive logic, such as Carnap's, according to which the given empirical information, whatever it may be, always assigns a definite logical probability to each of the statements describing one of the possible outcomes.

been assigned a utility. By way of illustration, suppose that you are offered as a present the metal ball that you will obtain by one single drawing made, at your option, from one of two urns. You are given the information that the metal balls are of the same size; that the first urn contains platinum balls and lead balls in an unspecified proportion; and the second urn, gold and silver balls in an unspecified proportion. Suppose that the utilities you assign to platinum, gold, silver, and lead are in the ratio of 1000:100:10:1. From which urn is it rational to draw? Several quite different criteria of rational choice under uncertainty have been set forth in recent decision theory. Perhaps the best-known of them is the *maximin rule*; it directs us to maximize the minimum utility, i.e., to choose an action whose worst possible outcome is at least as good as the worst possible outcome of any alternative. In our example, this calls for a drawing from the second urn; for at worst, it will give you a silver ball, whereas the worst outcome of a drawing from the first urn would give you a lead ball. This rule clearly represents a policy of extreme caution, reflecting the pessimistic maxim: act on the assumption that the worst possible outcome will result from your action.

An alternative policy, expressed by the so-called *maximax rule*, reflects the optimistic expectation that our action will lead to the best possible outcome; it directs us to choose a course of action whose best possible outcome is at least as good as the best possible outcome of any alternative action open to us. In our example, the proper decision under this rule would be to draw from the first urn; for at best this will give us a platinum ball, whereas a drawing from the second urn can at best yield a gold ball.

Various interesting alternative rules have been proposed for the case of decision under uncertainty, but for our purposes it is not necessary to consider them here.[4]

The mathematical models here briefly characterized do not offer us much help for a rational solution of the grave and complex decision problems that confront us in our daily affairs. For in these cases, we are usually far from having the data required by our models: we often have no clear idea of the available courses of action, nor can we specify the possible outcomes, let alone their probabilities and utilities. In contexts, however, where such information is available, mathematical decision theory has been applied quite successfully even to rather complicated problems, for example, in industrial quality control and some phases of strategic planning.

But whatever their practical promise, these models contribute, I think, to the analytic clarification of the concept of rational action. In particular, they

4. Accounts of those rules can be found, for example, in Luce and Raiffa (1957), chap. 13 and in Baumol, chap. 19.

throw into relief the complex, multiply relative, character of this concept; and they show that some of the characterizations of rational action which have been put forward in the philosophical literature are of a deceptive neatness and simplicity. For example, Gibson, in his careful and illuminating study, remarks: "there may be various alternative ways of achieving an end. To act rationally. . . is to select what on the evidence is *the best* way of achieving it";[5] and he refers to "an elementary logical point—namely, that, given certain evidence, there can only be one correct solution to the problem as to the best way of achieving a given end."[6] Gibson offers no criterion for what constitutes the best solution; but surely, what he asserts here is not an elementary logical point, and indeed it is not true. For, first, even when the decision situation is of a kind for which one definite criterion of rational choice may be assumed to be available and agreed upon—for example, the principle of maximizing expected utilities—then that criterion may qualify several different courses of action as equally rational. Secondly, and more importantly, there are various kinds of decision, such as decision under uncertainty, for which there is not even agreement on a criterion of rationality, where maximin opposes maximax and both are opposed by various alternative rules.

It is important to bear in mind that the different competing criteria of rationality do not reflect differences in the evaluation of the various ends which, on the given information, are attainable: all the competing rules here referred to presuppose that the utilities of those ends have been antecedently fixed. Rather, the different decision rules or criteria of rationality reflect different inductive attitudes, and in some cases, as we saw, different degrees of optimism or pessimism as to what to expect of the world, and correspondingly different degrees of boldness or caution in the choice of a course of action.

The diversity of conflicting rules proposed for decision under uncertainty suggests the question whether it might not be possible to specify some unique sense of rationality which is independent of such differences of outlook, and which can be shown to be more adequate than the conceptions of rationality reflected by the competing criteria we have mentioned. The prospects of specifying such a sense are dim indeed, and this again is indicated by some results of mathematical decision theory. Specifically, it is possible to formulate a set of general desiderata, or conditions of adequacy, for any proposed decision rule, and to show that though each of the desiderata appears perfectly reasonable and, so to speak, "essential" to rational choice, nevertheless (i) every decision rule that has been proposed in the literature violates one or more of the desiderata, and, indeed (ii) despite their intuitive plausibility, the desiderata are

5. Gibson (1960), p. 160, italics the author's.
6. Gibson (1960), p. 162.

logically incompatible.[7] This result certainly must serve as a warning against the assumption that the idea of rationality, or of the best way to act in a given situation, is reasonably clear, and that the formulation of criteria which make the notion explicit is a basically trivial, though perhaps tedious, explicatory task.

The considerations here outlined concerning the critical or normative notion of rationality have important implications for the explanatory use of the idea of rational action, as we will now see.

10.3 RATIONALITY AS AN EXPLANATORY CONCEPT. Human actions are often explained in terms of motivating reasons. The preceding considerations suggest that a full statement of those reasons will have to indicate the agent's objectives as well as his beliefs about the means available to him and their probable consequences. And the explanation will aim at showing that the action was to be expected in view of those objectives and beliefs. Such explanatory accounts rest therefore, as Peters has put it, on the "concealed assumption" that "*men are rational* in that they will take means which lead to ends if they have the information and want the ends."[8] Here, then, the concept of rationality is used in an explanatory hypothesis. Let us now examine the logic of such explanations.

10.3.1 *Dray's Concept of Rational Explanation.* As our point of departure let us choose Dray's stimulating and suggestive study of such explanations and particularly of their role in historical inquiry[9]—a study which led him to conclude that "the explanation of individual human behavior as it is usually given in history has features which make the covering law model peculiarly inept."[10] Dray refers to the kind of explanation here referred to, namely, explanation by motivating reasons, as *rational explanation* because, as he says, it "displays the *rationale* of what was done" by offering "a reconstruction of the agent's *calculation* of means to be adopted toward his chosen end in the light of the circumstances in which he found himself. To explain the action we need to know what considerations convinced him that he should act as he did."[11] But Dray attributes to rational explanation a further characteristic, which clearly assigns an essential role to the evaluative or critical concept of rationality. According to him, the "goal of such explanation is to show that what was done was the thing to have done for the reasons given, rather than merely the thing

---

7. For details see Luce and Raiffa (1957), chap. 13, especially sections 3 and 4.

8. Peters (1958), p. 4, italics supplied. For another statement concerning the explanatory and predictive use of the assumption of rationality, *cf.* Gibson (1960), p. 164.

9. See especially Dray (1957), chap. 5 and Dray (1963).

10. Dray (1957), p. 118.

11. Dray (1957), pp. 124 and 122, italics the author's.

that is done on such occasions, perhaps in accordance with certain laws."[12] Hence, "Reported reasons, if they are to be explanatory in the rational way, must be *good* reasons at least in the sense that *if* the situation had been as the agent envisaged it. . . then what was done would have been the thing to have done."[13] To show that the agent had good reasons for his action, a rational explanation must therefore invoke, not a general empirical law, but a "*principle of action,*" which expresses "a judgment of the form: 'When in a situation of type $C_1 . . . C_n$ the thing to do is x'."[14] Thus, such explanations contain "an element of *appraisal* of what was done."[15] And it is precisely in this reliance on a principle of action expressing a standard of appropriateness or rationality that Dray sees the essential difference between rational explanations and those accounts which explain a phenomenon by subsuming it under covering general laws that describe certain uniformities but do not appraise.

Dray does not further specify the character of the "situations" referred to in his principles of action; but in order to do justice to his intent, those situations must surely be taken to include such items as (i) the end the agent sought to attain, (ii) the agent's beliefs concerning the empirical circumstances in which he had to act and concerning the means available to him for the attainment of his objective, (iii) moral, religious, or other norms to which the agent was committed. For only when these items are specified does it make sense to raise the question of the appropriateness of what the agent did in the given situation.

It seems fair, then, to say that according to Dray's conception, a rational explanation answers a question of the form 'why did agent A do X?' by offering an explanans of the following type (instead of Dray's '$C_1 . . . C_n$', we write 'C' for short, bearing in mind that the situation thus referred to may be very complex):

> A was in a situation of type C
> In a situation of type C the appropriate thing to do is X

But this construal of rational explanation presupposes a criterion of rationality which, for the given kind of situation, singles out one particular course of action as *the* thing to do: and as we saw earlier this presupposition is highly questionable.

More importantly however, even if such a criterion were available, an account of the form here considered cannot possibly explain why A did X. For according to the requirement of adequacy set forth in section 2.4 of this essay, any adequate answer to the question why a given event occurred will

---

12. Dray (1957), p. 124.
13. Dray (1957), p. 126, italics the author's.
14. Dray (1957), p. 132, italics the author's.
15. Dray (1957), p. 124, italics the author's.

have to provide information which, if accepted as true, would afford good grounds for believing that the event did occur. Now, the information that agent *A* was in a situation of kind *C* and that in such a situation the rational thing to do is *x*, affords grounds for believing that *it would have been rational for A to do x*, but no grounds for believing that *A* did in fact do *x*.[16] To justify this latter belief, we clearly need a further explanatory assumption, namely that—at least at the time in question—*A* was a *rational agent* and thus was *disposed* to do whatever was rational under the circumstances.

But when this assumption is added, the answer to the question 'Why did *A* do *x*?' takes on the following form:

(Schema R)

A was in a situation of type C
A was a rational agent
In a situation of type C, any rational agent will do x

Therefore, A did x

This schema of rational explanation differs in two respects from what I take to be Dray's construal: first, the assumption that *A* was a rational agent is explicitly added; and second, the evaluative or appraising principle of action, which specifies the thing to do in situation *C*, is replaced by an empirical generalization stating how rational agents will act in situations of that kind. Thus, Dray's construal fails just at the point where it purports to exhibit a logical difference between explanations by reference to underlying reasons and explanations by subsumption under general laws, for in order to ensure the explanatory efficacy of a rational explanation, we found it necessary to replace Dray's normative principle of action by a statement that has the character of a general law. But this restores the covering-law form to the explanatory account.

That the appraising function which Dray considers essential for rational explanation has no explanatory import is shown also by this consideration: Doubts concerning a given explanation in terms of a specified rationale could not significantly be expressed in the form 'Was *X* actually the thing to do under the circumstances?', but they might well take the form 'Was *A* actually inclined to regard *X* as the thing to do?'. Accordingly, it would be irrelevant to argue, in defense of a proposed explanation, that *X* was indeed (by some theoretical standard of rationality) "the thing to do," whereas it would be distinctly relevant to show that *A* was generally disposed to do *X* under circumstances of the specified kind. And the explanatory import of this

---

16. The same objection has been raised, in effect, by Passmore, in the following comment on Dray's conception: ". . . explanation by reference to a 'principle of action' or a 'good reason' is not, by itself, explanation at all. . . . For a reason may be a 'good reason'—in the sense of being a principle to which one *could* appeal in justification of one's action—without having in fact the slightest influence on us." Passmore (1958), p. 275, italics the author's.

latter information would be completely independent of whether the contemplated action did or did not conform to the explainer's—or the questioner's—standards of rationality.

In thus disagreeing with Dray's analysis of rational explanation, I do not wish to deny that an explanatory account in terms of motivating reasons may well have evaluative overtones: what I maintain is only that whether a critical appraisal is included in, or suggested by, a given account, is irrelevant to its explanatory force; and that an appraisal alone, by means of what Dray calls a principle of action, cannot explain at all why A did in fact do x.

10.3.2 *Explanation by Reasons as Broadly Dispositional.* The notion of rational agent invoked in Schema R above must of course be conceived as a descriptive-psychological concept governed by objective criteria of application; any normative or evaluative connotations it may carry with it are inessential for its explanatory use. To be sure, normative preconceptions as to how a truly rational person ought to behave may well influence the choice of descriptive criteria for a rational agent—just as the construction of tests, and thus the selection of objective criteria, for intelligence, verbal aptitude, mathematical aptitude, and the like will be influenced by pre-systematic conceptions and norms. But the descriptive-psychological use of the term 'rational agent' (just like that of the terms 'IQ', 'verbal aptitude', 'mathematical aptitude', and the like) must then be governed by the objective empirical rules of application that have been adopted, irrespective of whether this or that person (e.g., the proponent of a rational explanation or the person to whom it is addressed) happens to regard those objective rules as conformable to his own normative standards of rationality.

By whatever specific empirical criteria it may be characterized, rationality in the descriptive-psychological sense is a *broadly dispositional trait;* to say of someone that he is a rational agent is to attribute to him, by implication, a complex bundle of dispositions. Each of these may be thought of as a tendency to behave—uniformly or with a certain probability—in a characteristic way under conditions of a given kind, whose full specifications may have to include information about the agent's objectives and beliefs, about other aspects of the psychological and biological state he is in, and about his environment. To explain an action in terms of the agent's reasons and his rationality is thus to present the action as conforming to those general tendencies, or as being a manifestation of them.[17] According as the sentences expressing the tendencies

17. This construal is in basic agreement, of course, with the general conception set forth in Ryle (1949). For a lucid characterization, in accordance with Ryle's ideas, of the force of explanations referring to an agent's wants, intentions, and plans, see Gardiner (1952), Part IV, section 3; and *cf.* also the expository and critical discussion in Dray (1957), pp. 144 and *passim.*

in question are of strictly universal form or of a statistical form such as (9.3a), or (9.3b), the resulting dispositional explanation will be deductive or inductive-probabilistic in character. But in any event it will subsume the given particular case under a general uniformity. However, this brief general characterization must now be amplified and must also be qualified in certain points of detail.

To begin with, the dispositions implied by the psychological concept of rational agent are not simply dispositions to respond to specifiable external stimuli with certain characteristic modes of overt behavior. They differ in this respect from at least some of the dispositions implied when we say of a person that he is allergic to ragweed pollen; for to say this is to imply, among other things, that he will exhibit the symptoms of a head cold when exposed to the pollen. When we call someone a rational agent, we assert by implication that he will behave in characteristic ways if he finds himself in certain kinds of situation; but such situations cannot be described simply in terms of environmental conditions and external stimuli; for characteristically they include the agent's objectives and his relevant beliefs. To mark this difference, we might say that the dispositions implied by attributing rationality to a person are *higher-order-dispositions*; for the beliefs and ends-in-view in reponse to which, as it were, a rational agent acts in a characteristic way are not manifest external stimuli but rather, in turn, broadly dispositional features of the agent. Indeed, to attribute to someone a particular belief or end-in-view is to imply that in certain circumstances he will tend to behave in certain ways which are indicative or symptomatic of his belief or his end-in-view.

There is yet another reason why we must avoid an overly narrow dispositional construal of an agent's beliefs, objectives, and rationality; and the qualified phrase 'broadly dispositional' is meant to serve as a reminder of this point as well: a statement attributing to a person certain objectives or beliefs or the property of being a rational agent, implies, *but is not equivalent to*, a set of other statements attributing to the person certain clusters of dispositions.

To elucidate and support this view, I will first adduce an analogous case from physics. To say of a body that it is electrically charged or that it is magnetic is to attribute to it, *by implication*, bundles of dispositions to respond in characteristic or symptomatic ways to various testing procedures. But this does not exhaust what is being asserted; for the concepts of electric charge, magnetization, and so on are governed by a network of theoretical principles interconnecting a large number of physical concepts. Conjointly, these theoretical principles determine an indefinitely large set of empirically testable consequences, among them various dispositional statements which provide operational criteria for ascertaining whether a given body is electrically charged, magnetic, and the like. Thus, the underlying theoretical assumptions contribute essentially to what is being asserted by the attribution of those physical properties. Indeed, it is only in conjunction with such theoretical background assumptions that a statement attributing an electric charge to a given body implies a set of dispositional statements; whereas the whole set of dispositional statements does not imply the statement about the charge, let alone the theoretical background principles.

Now, to be sure, the psychological concepts that serve to indicate a person's beliefs, objectives, moral standards, rationality, and so forth, do not function in a theoretical network comparable in scope or explicitness to that of electromagnetic theory. Nevertheless, we use those psychological concepts in a manner that clearly presupposes certain similar connections—we might call them *quasi-theoretical connections*.[18] For example, we assume that the overt behavior shown by a person pursuing a certain objective will depend on his beliefs; and conversely. Thus the attribution to Henry of the belief that the streets are slushy will be taken to imply that he will put on galoshes only on suitable assumptions about his objectives and indeed about his further beliefs,[19] such as that he wants to go out, wants to keep his feet dry, believes that his galoshes will serve the purpose, is not in too much of a hurry to put them on, and so on. This plainly reflects the assumptions of many complex interdependencies among the psychological concepts in question. And it is these assumptions which determine our expectations as to what behavioral manifestations, including overt action, a psychological trait will have in a particular case.

To reject the construal of those characteristics as simply bundles of behavioral dispositions is not to conjure up again the ghost in the machine, so deftly and subtly exorcised by Ryle and earlier—more summarily, but on basically similar grounds—by the logical behaviorism of Carnap.[20] The point is rather that in order to characterize the psychological features in question, we have to consider not only their dispositional implications, which provide operational criteria for attributing certain beliefs, objectives, and the like; we must also take account of the quasi-theoretical assumptions connecting them. For these, too, govern the use of those concepts, and they are not logically implied by the sets of dispositional statements associated with them.

18. Some plausible quasi-theoretical principles for the concept of an agent having a certain objective, or "wanting" a certain state of affairs, are set forth by Brandt and Kim (1963), p. 427, who suggest that the concept "wants" might helpfully be viewed as a theoretical construct. Tolman (1951) presents, in somewhat schematic and programmatic outline, a psychological model theory of action which includes among its "intervening variables" the "Belief-Value Matrix" as well as the "Need System" of the agent, but which also, quite rightly, considers the external conditions in which the action takes place.

19. On this point, *cf.* Chisholm (1962), pp. 513 ff. and especially p. 517.

20. See Ryle (1949); Carnap (1938) and, for a more technical account, Carnap (1936–37).

10.3.3 *Epistemic Interdependence of Belief Attributions and Goal Attributions.* The quasi-theoretical connections just referred to give rise to a problem that requires at least brief consideration. For our purposes it will suffice to examine one form of it, which is of fundamental importance to the idea of rational explanation. What sorts of dispositions do we attribute to a person by implication when we assert that he has certain specified objectives or beliefs? The statement that Henry *wants* a drink of water implies, among other things, that Henry is disposed to drink a liquid offered him—provided that he *believes* it to be potable water (and provided that he has no overriding reasons for refusing it). Thus, ascription of an objective here has implications concerning characteristic overt behavior only when taken in conjunction with ascriptions of appropriate beliefs. Similarly, in our earlier example, the hypothesis that Henry *believes* the streets to be slushy implies the occurrence of characteristic overt behavior only when taken in conjunction with suitable hypotheses about Henry's *objectives*.

Indeed, it seems that a hypothesis about an agent's objectives generally can be taken to imply the occurrence of specific overt action only when conjoined with appropriate hypotheses about his beliefs, and *vice versa*. Hence, strictly speaking, an examination of an agent's behavior can serve to test assumptions about his beliefs or about his objectives, not separately, but only in suitable pairs. That is, belief attributions and goal attributions are *epistemically interdependent*.

This fact does not make it impossible, however, to ascertain a person's beliefs or his objectives. For often we have good antecedent information about one of the interpendent items, and then a hypothesis about the other may be tested by ascertaining how the person acts in certain situations. For example, if we have good grounds for the assumption that our man is subjectively honest, that he endeavors to "tell the truth", then his answers to our questions may afford a reliable indication of his beliefs. Conversely, we are often able to test a hypothesis about a person's objectives by examining his behavior in certain critical situations because we have good reason to assume that he has certain relevant beliefs.

But the epistemic interdependence here referred to does raise the question whether an explanation by motivating reasons ever requires the explanatory assumption that the acting person was, at least at the time in question, a rational agent. How this question arises can be seen by taking a closer look at the test criteria for belief attributions and for goal attributions.

Suppose we know an agent's beliefs and wish to test the hypothesis that he wants to attain goal G. Just what sort of action is implied by this hypothesis? The criterion used in such cases seems to be roughly this: if A actually wants to attain G then he will follow a course of action which, in the light of his beliefs, offers him the best chance of success. In the parlance of our earlier discussion, therefore, the test of our goal attribution appears to presuppose the assumption that A will choose an action that is rational relative to his objectives and beliefs. This would mean that the way in which we use a person's actions as evidence in ascertaining his goals has the assumption of rationality built right into it. An analogous comment applies to the way in which we normally use the actions of a person whose objectives we know as evidence in ascertaining his beliefs.[21] But this seems to discredit the construal of rational explanation as involving, in the manner suggested in Schema R, an explanatory hypothesis to the effect that the person in question was a rational agent. For the considerations just outlined suggest that this hypothesis is always made true by a tacit convention implicit in our test criteria for the attribution of motivating objectives and beliefs to the agent. If this is generally the case, then the assumption of rationality could not possibly be violated; any apparent violation would be taken to show only that our conjectures about the agent's beliefs, or those about his objectives, or both, were mistaken. And, undeniably, such will in fact often be our verdict.

But will it always be so? I think there are various kinds of circumstances in which we might well retain our assumptions about the agent's beliefs and objectives and abandon instead the assumption of rationality. First of all, in deciding upon his action, a person may well overlook certain relevant items of information which he clearly believes to be true and which, if properly taken into account, would have called for a different course of action. Second, the agent may overlook certain aspects of the total goal he is seeking to attain, and may thus decide upon an action that is not rational as judged by his objectives and beliefs. Third, even if the agent were to take into account all aspects of his total goal as well as all the relevant information at his disposal, and even if he should go through a deliberate "calculation of means to be adopted toward his chosen end" (to repeat an earlier quotation from Dray), the result may still fail to be a rational decision because of some logical flaw in his calculation. Clearly there could be strong evidence, in certain cases, that an agent had fallen short of rationality in one of the ways here suggested; and indeed, if his decision had been made under pressure of time or under emotional strain, fatigue, or other disturbing influences, such deviations from rationality would be regarded as quite likely. (This reflects another one of the quasi-theoretical connections among the various psychological concepts that play a role in explanations by reasons or by motives.)

21. Cf., for example, the discussion in Churchman (1961), pp. 288-91, which illustrates this point.

In sum then, rationality of human actions is not guaranteed by conventions implicit in the criteria governing the attribution of goals and beliefs to human agents; there may be good grounds for ascribing to an agent certain goals and beliefs and yet acknowledging that his action was not rationally called for by those goals and beliefs.

10.3.4 *Rational Action as an Explanatory Model Concept.* For further clarification of the role that the assumption of rationality plays in explanations by motivating reasons, it may be illuminating to ask whether the concept of rational agent might not be viewed as an idealized explanatory model comparable to the explanatory concept of an ideal gas, that is, a gas conforming exactly to Boyle's and Charles's laws. No actual gas strictly satisfies those laws; but there is a wide range of conditions within which many gases conform very closely to the account the model gives of the interrelations between temperature, pressure, and volume. Moreover, there are more general, but less simple laws—such as van der Waals', Clausius', and others—which explain to a large extent the deviations from the ideal model that are exhibited by actual gases.

Perhaps the concept of a rational agent can be similarly regarded as an explanatory model characterized by an "ideal law," to the effect that the agent's actions are strictly rational (in the sense of some specific criterion) relative to his objectives and beliefs. How could this programmatic conception be implemented? How could an explanatory model of rational action be precisely characterized, and how could it be applied and tested?

As noted earlier, the concept of rationality is by no means as clear and unequivocal as is sometimes implied in the literature on rational explanation. But let us assume that the proposed explanatory use of the concept is limited, to begin with, to cases of a relatively simple type for which some precise criterion of rationality can be formulated and incorporated into our model.

Then there is still the question of how to apply the model to particular instances, how to test whether a given action does in fact conform to the criterion of rationality the model incorporates. And this raises a perplexing problem. The problem is not just the practical one of how to *ascertain* an agent's beliefs and actions in a given case, but the conceptual one of what is to be *understood* by the beliefs and objectives of an agent at a given time, and by what logical means they might be properly characterized. Let me amplify this briefly.

A person must surely be taken to hold many beliefs of which he is not conscious at the time, but which could be elicited by various means. Indeed, a person may be held to believe many things he has never thought of and perhaps never will think of as long as he lives. If he believes that seven and five are twelve we would surely take him to believe also that seven speckled hens and five more make twelve speckled hens, although he may never consciously entertain this particular belief. Generally, a man will be taken to believe certain things that are consequences of other things he believes; but surely he cannot be taken to believe *all* those consequences since, to mention but one reason, his logical perspicacity is limited.

Hence, while in a theoretical model of the normative or critical concept of rational decision the information basis may be construed as a set of statements that is closed under an appropriate relation of logical derivability, this assumption cannot be transferred to an explanatory model of rational decision. In particular, a person may well give his believing assent to *one* of a pair of logically equivalent statements but withhold it from the other—although both express the same proposition. It seems clear, therefore, that the objects of a person's beliefs cannot be construed to be propositions each of which may be represented by any one of an infinite set of equivalent statements: in specifying an agent's beliefs, the mode of its formulation is essential. (This peculiarity seems closely akin to what Quine has called the referential opacity of belief sentences.)[22]

Presumably, then, in an explanatory model conception of rational action, the agent's beliefs should be represented by some set of sentences that is not closed under logical derivability. But what set? For example, should a person's belief-set be taken to include all sentences to which he could be induced to assent by pertinent questions and arguments, no matter how numerous or complex? Clearly such construal is unwarranted if we are interested in specifying a set of beliefs that can be regarded as motivating factors in explaining an action done by the agent. Where the boundary line of the belief-set is to be drawn—conceptually, not just practically—is a puzzling and obscure question.

Similar observations apply to the problem of how to characterize an agent's total objectives in a given decision situation.

Consequently, though in a normative-critical model of decision, rationality is always judged by reference to the total information basis and the total objective specified, it would be self-defeating to incorporate into an explanatory model of rational action the principle that a rational agent acts optimally, as judged by specified criteria, on the basis of his total set of objectives and beliefs: this notion is simply too obscure.

10.3.5 *The Model of a Consciously Rational Agent.* A way out seems to be suggested by the observation that many explanations present an action as determined

---

22. *Cf.* Quine (1960), section 30; and see also sections 35, 44, 45, which deal further with the problems of a logically adequate construal of belief-attributions. Several of these problems, and similar ones concerning the construal of goal-attributions, are searchingly examined in Scheffler (1963), Part I, section 8.

by reasons which presumably the agent took consciously into account in making his decision. Let us say that a person is a *consciously rational agent* (at a certain time) if (at that time) his actions are rational (in the sense of some clearly specified criterion) relative to those of his objectives and beliefs which he consciously takes into account in arriving at his decision.

By way of exploring the potential applicability of this model of a consciously rational agent, let us consider Bismarck's editing of the so-called Ems telegram, which played a crucial role in touching off the war between France and Prussia in 1870. Political relations between the two nations had been strained by France's strong opposition to the prospect, which for some time seemed likely, of a Hohenzollern prince accepting the throne of Spain. Bismarck had hoped that this issue might provide Prussia with a *casus belli* against France; but the prince resigned his candidacy, and the prospect of a military conflict with France seemed to vanish. At this juncture a French emissary approached King William of Prussia, who was staying at the spa of Ems, with the request that the king rule out resumption of the candidacy for all future times. The king declined this and informed Bismarck of the incident in a telegram in which he indicated no ruffled feelings but simply sought to convey his reasons for refusing the request. The king explicitly left it to Bismarck to decide whether to publish the content of the telegram. Bismarck seized the opportunity to edit the text for publication in a manner calculated to induce France to go to war. The reasons behind this action have been discussed by many writers, including Bismarck himself.

In his memoirs,[23] Bismarck states, first of all, his reasons for seeking war against France. Among these are his concern to preserve Prussia's national honor; his belief that otherwise the resulting loss of prestige would gravely interfere with the development of a German Reich under Prussian leadership; the expectation that a national war against France would serve to bridge the differences between many of the German nations Bismarck sought to unite; and the information, provided by the chief of the General Staff, that in view of Prussia's state of military preparedness no advantage was to be expected from deferring the outbreak of war. Bismarck concludes this part of his account with the words: "All these considerations, conscious and unconscious, strengthened my opinion that war could be avoided only at the cost of the honour of Prussia and of the national confidence in it. Under this conviction I made use of the royal authorization . . . to publish the contents of the telegram; and . . . I reduced the telegram by striking out words, but without adding or altering."[24]

23. Bismarck (1899), pp. 97 ff. The text of the King's telegram is quoted on p. 97, that of the edited version on pp. 100-101.
24. Bismarck (1899), p. 100.

The edited version of the Ems telegram created the impression that the king had treated the French emissary in an insulting manner. In his memoirs, Bismarck candidly states his reasons for this choice of means toward his end: he expected that the edited text would "have the effect of a red rag upon the Gallic bull. Fight we must. . . . Success, however, essentially depends upon the impression which the origination of the war makes upon us and others; it is important that we should be the party attacked, and this Gallic overweening and touchiness will make us if we announce in the face of Europe . . . that we fearlessly meet the public threats of France."[25] The publication of the edited text had the effect Bismarck had expected: in Paris it was taken as a national insult, and the French Cabinet decreed mobilization.

As for the explanatory force of Bismarck's own account or of those given by various historians, let us note first that no matter how illuminating a statement of motivating reasons may be, it cannot, and does not purport to, shed light on one very important aspect of Bismarck's action, namely, why the thought of editing the text occurred to him in the first place. In the context of our explanation by reasons, the statement that it did occur to him is simply offered as an explanatory datum, as part of the requisite specification of what courses of action the agent believed were open to him. Thus the explanatory account we have surveyed can claim at most to answer the question: given that the possibility occurred to Bismarck, why did he choose that course of action?

Let us consider now to what extent the explanation here outlined conforms to the model of a consciously rational action. First of all, it does represent Bismarck as having arrived at his decision as a result of a careful deliberation concerning the best available means toward his end of provoking France into going to war. The account indicates further that in the given situation, Bismarck believed several courses of action open to him: publication of an edited version of the telegram; publication of the original text; and no publication at all. In his estimate the first alternative, and it alone, was likely to have the desired effect. Hence if the list of motivating considerations is factually correct and complete in the sense of omitting none of the possibilities actually contemplated by Bismarck, then the account shows that his action was that of a consciously rational agent, and that relative to his beliefs and objectives it was rational in the sense of one of the simplest criteria mentioned in section 10.2.

Actually, however, the account is not likely to be strictly complete. For example, Bismarck must have considered, however briefly, some alternative courses of action—among them, different ways of editing the text—which are

25. Bismarck (1899), p. 101.

not mentioned in his own statement nor in the accounts given by various other writers who have dealt with the matter. The available studies suggest that Bismarck may have fleetingly entertained the possibility of releasing the relevant information to all Prussian embassies but not to the press for publication. Thus, there are good reasons to doubt that the available accounts are actually as complete as would be necessary to exhibit Bismarck's action as consciously rational. In defense of the presumptive omissions, it might be argued that greater completeness would have been pedantic and gratuitous, for does not the very fact that Bismarck chose to publish an edited version suffice to show that even if he should have entertained alternatives other than those explicitly mentioned, he dismissed them as less promising? This is indeed quite a plausible way of defending the claim that among all the possible actions he considered, Bismarck chose what in his estimate was the optimal one; but as far as this argument is relied on, the rationality of Bismarck's decision is safeguarded by tacitly building it into our construal of Bismarck's expectations: he could not have expected much of the alternatives or else he would have acted differently.

Thus, though in the case of the Ems telegram an unusually large amount of apparently reliable information on the motivating reasons is available, and though Bismarck's decision seems to have been arrived at by cool and careful deliberation, the rigorous requirements of the model of consciously rational action are not completely satisfied.

There are other cases which perhaps come even closer to the "ideal" of the model. Consider, for example, a competent engineer who seeks an optimal solution to a problem of design for which the range of permissible solutions is clearly delimited, the relevant probabilities and utilities are precisely specified, and even the criterion of rationality to be employed (e.g., maximization of expected utilities) is explicitly stated. In this case, the objectives and beliefs that determine the engineer's decision may be taken to be fully indicated by the specification of the problem; and by applying to the engineer the explanatory model of a consciously rational agent (whose standard of rationality is that specified in the given problem) we can explain—or predict—his arriving at a solution, or set of solutions, which is identical with the theoretically optimal one.

The broadly dispositional property of conscious rationality need not, and indeed cannot, be conceived as an enduring trait. A man may be disposed to act with conscious rationality at some times, when psychological and environmental conditions are favourable, yet fail to do so at other times, when disturbing external circumstances or such factors as fatigue, pain, or preoccupation with other matters prevent strictly rational deliberation. But similarly, a given body of gas may behave "ideally" at certain times, when it is at high temperature and under low pressure, yet nonideally at other times, when the circumstances are reversed.

However, while for a given body of gas the conditions of near-ideal behavior can be stated with considerable precision in terms of just a few quantitative parameters, the conditions under which a given individual will come very close to acting with conscious rationality can be indicated only vaguely and by means of a long, and open-ended, list of items which includes environmental as well as physiological and psychological factors. Very broadly speaking, the explanatory model concept of consciously rational action will be applicable in those cases where the decision problem the agent seeks to solve is clearly structured and permits of a relatively simple solution, where the agent is sufficiently intelligent to find the solution, and where circumstances permit careful deliberation free from disturbing influences.[26]

The idea of a consciously rational agent, with its very limited scope of application, does not offer the only way in which a model concept of rational decision might be put to explanatory and predictive use. One interesting alternative has been put forward in a study by Davidson, Suppes, and Siegel.[27] These investigators present an empirical theory of human choice which is modeled on the mathematical model of decision under risk and incorporates the hypothesis that the choices made by human subjects will be rational in the precise sense of maximizing expected utilities.

As might be anticipated, the rigorously quantitative character of the theory has the price of limiting its applicability to decisions of a rather simple type, which permit of strict experimental control. In the authors' test of the theory, the subjects had to make a series of decisions each of which called for a choice between two options. Each option offered the prospect of either gaining a specified small amount of money or losing some other specified small amount, depending on the outcome of a certain random experiment, such as rolling a regular die with peculiar markings on its faces. The random experiments, their possible outcomes, and the corresponding gains or losses were carefully described to the subject, who then made his choice.

The results of this experiment conformed quite well to the hypothesis that the subjects would choose the option with the greater *expected utility*, where the expected utility of an option is computed on the basis of theoretically postulated *subjective* probabilities and utilities which the different outcomes have for the choosing individual. The theory proposed by the authors provides an objective, if indirect, method for the simultaneous and independent measurement of such subjective probabilities and utilities for a given agent. Experimental

26. *Cf.* also the observations in Gibson (1960), pp. 165–68, which bear on this point.
27. Davidson, Suppes, and Siegel (1957).

study shows that the subjective probability which a specified outcome possesses for a given subject is not, in general, equal to its objective probability, even though the subject may know the latter; nor are the subjective utilities proportional to the corresponding monetary gains or losses. Indeed, a person normally will be entirely unaware of the subjective probabilities and utilities which, on the theory under consideration, the possible outcomes possess for him.

Thus, as far as the theory is correct, it gives a quite peculiar twist to the idea of rational action: though the subjects make their choices in clearly structured decision situations, with full opportunity for antecedent deliberation and even calculation, they act rationally (in a precisely defined quantitative sense) relative to subjective probabilities and utilities which they do not know, and which, therefore, they cannot take into account in their deliberations. They act rationally in the sense of acting *as if* they were trying to maximize expected utilities. Here, then, we seem to have a type of conscious decision which is *nonconsciously rational* with quantitative precision.

10.3.6 *The "Rationality" of Nondeliberative Actions. Explanation by Unconscious Motives.* Many purposive actions are taken without prior conscious deliberation, without any calculation of means to be chosen toward the attainment of an envisaged end; and yet such actions are often accounted for in terms of motivating reasons. Dray, who specifically includes such accounts in the scope of his analysis, argues that his conception of rational explanation is applicable to any purposive action, on the ground that "in so far as we say an action is purposive at all, no matter at what level of conscious deliberation, there is a calculation which could be constructed for it: the one the agent would have gone through if he had had time, if he had not seen what to do in a flash, if he had been called upon to account for what he did after the event, etc. And it is by eliciting some such calculation that we explain the action".[28]

But the explanatory significance of reasons or calculations constructed in this manner is certainly puzzling. If an agent arrives at his decision "in a flash" rather than by deliberation then it seems false to say that the decision can be accounted for by some argument which the agent might have gone through under more propitious circumstances, or which he might produce later if called upon to account for his action; for, by hypothesis, no such argument was in fact gone through by the agent at the crucial time; considerations of appropriateness or rationality played no part in shaping his decision, and an explanation in terms of such deliberations or calculations is simply fictitious.

Nevertheless I think Dray has a point in viewing some nondeliberative

28. Dray (1957), p. 123.

actions as akin to those which are decided upon by careful deliberation. For "rational explanations" of such actions may be viewed as broadly dispositional accounts invoking certain behavior patterns which the agent acquired by a learning process whose initial phases did involve conscious reflection and deliberation. Consider, for example, the complex set of maneuvers required in driving a car through heavy traffic, in using a sewing machine, or in performing a surgical operation: all these are learned by training processes which initially involve more or less complex deliberation, but which eventually come to be performed automatically, with little or no conscious reflection, yet often in a manner that the agent would have chosen if he had given the matter adequate thought. Accordingly, a particular action of this kind might be explained, not by a constructed calculation which in fact the agent did not carry out, but by exhibiting it as a manifestation of a general behavioral disposition which the agent has learned in the manner just suggested.[29]

The attempt to explain a given action by means of motivating reasons faces another well-known difficulty: it will frequently result in a rationalization rather than an explanation, especially when it relies on the reasons adduced by the agent himself. As G. Watson remarks, "Motivation, as presented in the perspective of history, is often too simple and straightforward, reflecting the psychology of the Age of Reason. . . . Psychology has come . . . to recognize the enormous weight of irrational and intimately personal impulses in conduct. In history, biography, and in autobiography, especially of public characters, the tendency is strong to present 'good' reasons instead of 'real' reasons."[30] Accordingly, as Watson goes on to point out, it is important, in examining the motivation of historical figures, to take into account the significance of such psychological mechanisms as reaction formation, "the dialectic dynamic by which stinginess cloaks itself in generosity, or rabid pacifism arises from the attempt to repress strong aggressive impulses."[31]

Increasing awareness that actions may be prompted to a considerable extent by motivating factors of which the agent is not conscious has prompted some historians to place strong emphasis on a more systematic use of the ideas of psychoanalysis or related depth-psychological theories in the context of his-

29. Scheffler (1963), pp. 115-16, has suggested in a similar fashion that an interpretation in terms of learning may illuminate some types of teleological statements about human behavior. On this point, see also the highly relevant article Suppes (1961); and *cf.* Gibson (1960), pp. 157-58, where a dispositional construal of nondeliberately rational acts is presented.

30. Watson (1940), p. 36.

31. *Ibid.* For some suggestive observations from a psychoanalytic point of view on the notion of "rationalization" in specifying the motives for an action, *cf.* F. Alexander (1940).

torical explanation. W. L. Langer's presidential address before the American Historical Association in 1957,[32] is a forceful statement of and plea for, this program.

Similar considerations have led some philosophical writers on motivation to distinguish, in explanations of a person's action, between "his reasons" for doing what he did and "the reasons" or "the real reasons" for his action.[33] In his illuminating study of historical explanation, Gardiner makes this observation on the latter notion: "In general, it appears safe to say that by a man's 'real reasons' we mean those reasons he would be prepared to give under circumstances where his confession would not entail adverse consequences to himself. An exception to this is the psycho-analyst's usage of the expression where different criteria are adopted."[34] But if Gardiner is right in his characterization of what is ordinarily understood by a man's real reasons for acting the way he did, then surely the historian in search of reasons that will correctly explain human actions will have to forego reliance on "real reasons" in the ordinary sense if psychological and other investigations show that they do not yield as adequate an understanding of human actions as does an interpretation in terms of less familiar conceptions, including perhaps a theory of subconscious motivation. That such a reorientation is in fact needed has been strongly urged by Langer: "Viewed in the light of modern depth psychology, the homespun, commonsense psychological interpretations of past historians, even some of the greatest, seem woefully inadequate, not to say naive. Clearly the time has come for us to reckon with a doctrine that strikes so close to the heart of our own discipline."[35]

As for the notion of the "real reasons" for a given action, I would say then, first, that psychological or historical explanation cannot be bound by the use of that notion in everyday discourse. But secondly, I doubt that the characterization which Gardiner suggests in an expressly tentative fashion does full justice even to what we mean in ordinary language when we speak of the real reasons that prompted a given action. For the idea of subconscious motives is quite familiar in our time, and we are therefore prepared to say in ordinary discourse that the reasons given by an agent may not be the "real reasons" behind his action, even if his statement is subjectively honest and he has no grounds to expect adverse consequences. And no matter whether an expla-

32. Langer (1958). For observations in a similar vein, see chap. 3 of Hughes (1964) and Mazlish's Introduction to the anthology, Mazlish (1963), which includes a number of specific examples of psychoanalytically inspired interpretations of historical materials.

33. See, for example, Peters (1958), pp. 3-9 and *passim.*

34. Gardiner (1952), p. 136.

35. Langer (1958), p. 90. Peters (1958), p. 63, explicitly notes that an unconscious wish might constitute "the reason" for a man's action.

nation of human actions is attempted in ordinary language or in the technical terms of some theory, the overriding criterion for what—if anything—should count as a "real," and thus explanatory, reason for a given action is surely not to be found by examining the way in which the term 'real reason' has thus far been used, but by investigating what conception of real reasons would yield the most satisfactory explanation of human conduct. Ordinary usage gradually changes accordingly.

The logical structure of explanations in terms of subconscious motives and processes is again broadly dispositional in the sense we considered earlier: the ascription of such motives amounts to attributing to the agent certain broadly dispositional characteristics, and the reference to subconscious mechanisms or to psychodynamic processes reflects the assumption of laws or theoretical principles involving those characteristics. To say this is not, however, to imply that all psychoanalytic interpretations that have actually been offered meet the basic requirements for scientifically adequate dispositional explanations. In fact, the empirical or operational criteria of application for psychoanalytic concepts, and the theoretical principles in which these concepts function, are often not nearly as clear as is desirable in the interest of objective applicability and testability.[36] But it should not be forgotten that in this respect common-sense motivational explanations, too, often leave much to be desired, and furthermore, that efforts are being made to put psychoanalytic and similar conceptions into a methodologically more satisfactory form.

10.3.7 *A Note on Causal Aspects of Dispositional Explanations.* It is often held that explanations in terms of motivating reasons, learned skills, personality traits, and the like, being dispositional in character, are for this reason noncausal. But this thesis seems to me misleading. For, first of all, as is shown by schemata (9.1) and (9.5), a dispositional explanation invokes, in addition to the appropriate dispositional property M, also the presence of circumstances, say S, in which the property M will manifest itself by the symptom—say, behavior of the kind R—whose occurrence is to be explained. For example, the attribution of venality to an agent will explain his having committed treason only in conjunction with suitable further assumptions, such as that he was offered a large bribe, which in virtue of his venal propensity led to the act in question. Here the offer of a bribe, in analogy to the impact of the stone in (9.1), may be said, in everyday parlance, to have caused the explanandum event. Dispositional explanations of this kind, therefore, cannot be said to be noncausal.

36. On this point, see, for example, the critique presented in Nagel (1959); and *cf.* also the critique and the defense of psychoanalytic conceptions in various other essays included in Hook (1959).

To be sure, possession of the dispositional property *M* would not ordinarily count as a cause: but then, the possession of *M* alone does not explain the given event.

Thus when Gardiner remarks that an explanation of the form '*x* did *y* because he wanted *z*' does not refer to a causal relation between two events,[37] he is right in the sense that the statement '*x* wanted *z*' does not describe an event, but ascribes to *x* a broadly dispositional property. But a because-sentence of the specified form surely affords an explanation only on the further assumption that *x* was in circumstances in which, at least by his lights, doing *y* could be expected to lead to *z*; and when supplemented by this further statement, the account takes on the form (9.5), which cannot be said to be noncausal. Gardiner's insistence that "motivational explanations ... are not causal at all"[38] may serve a good purpose in cautioning—as it is intended to do—against the conception of motives as ghostly causes of overt behavior, and against the notion that "in history we have to do with a world of 'mental agencies', mysteriously lying behind the world of physical bodies and actions, separate from it and yet controlling it";[39] but it runs the risk of obscuring the close similarities here noted between motivational explanations and certain other accounts generally considered as causal.[40]

11. CONCLUDING REMARKS

At the beginning of this essay we contrasted reason-seeking and explanation-seeking why-questions. The former solicit grounds that will make empirical

37. Gardiner (1952), p. 124.

38. Gardiner (1952), pp. 133-34. *Cf.* also Ryle's view that "to explain an action as done from a specified motive or inclination is not to describe the action as the effect of a specified cause. Motives are not happenings and are not therefore of the right type to be causes." (1949, p. 113).

39. Gardiner (1952), p. 51.

40. In this context, see also the suggestive discussion of dispositions, reasons, and causes in Dray (1957), pp. 150-55. In contrast to the view that "only events and processes can be causes" (p. 151), Dray holds that a dispositional characteristic "is a type of 'standing condition'; and standing conditions, as well as precipitating ones, can be causes." (p. 152). The thesis that explanation by reasons is "a species of ordinary causal explanation" is interestingly argued, on rather different grounds than those here presented, in Davidson (1963), where also a number of further objections are examined. It should also be borne in mind that the everyday conception of causal explanation is rather narrow and vague and that at least in physics it has been replaced by the more general and precise conception of an explanation by means of a deterministic theory. It is illustrated by the case, considered in section 2, of the Newtonian theory of motion and of gravitation: given the "state" of a closed system of point masses at some time, the theory determines the state of the system at any other time and thus permits the explanation of a particular state of the system by reference to an earlier one. The terms of the causal relation consist here, not in events, but in momentary *states* of the system, as represented by the masses, positions, and velocities of the constituent particles at the moment in question.

statements *credible*; the latter solicit information that will explain empirical facts and thus render them *intelligible*. Our main concern has been to examine the ways in which science answers why-questions of the latter type and to characterize the kind of understanding it thereby affords.

We noted that scientific explanation is not aimed at creating a sense of familiarity with the explanandum; "reduction to the familiar" is at best an incidental aspect of it. The understanding it conveys lies rather in the insight that the explanandum fits into, or can be subsumed under, a system of uniformities represented by empirical laws or theoretical principles. Depending on the logical character of the uniformities, such subsumption will be deductive or inductive in a sense which our two basic models are intended to make explicit.

I would like to stress here once more that there are profound logical differences between those two modes of explanation. Not that in a statistical account the explanandum sentence is qualified by a modal clause such as 'probably' or 'almost certainly'; the explanandum is a nonmodal sentence in probabilistic no less than in deductive-nomological explanation and prediction. But in inductive-statistical explanation in contrast to its deductive counterpart, the explanans makes the explanandum only more or less probable and does not imply it with deductive certainty. Another difference, which so far does not seem to have received attention, lies in what I called the epistemic relativity of probabilistic explanation, i.e., the fact that we can significantly speak of a probabilistic explanation, even a potential one, only relative to some class K of statements representing a particular knowledge situation. The concept of deductive-nomological explanation requires no such relativization.

The explanatory role of presumptive laws and theoretical principles was illustrated and made explicit by an analysis of various kinds of explanation offered in different fields of empirical science. That survey does not claim completeness; it could have been expanded by examining the explanatory use of typological concepts and theories, of functional analysis, of psychoanalytic ideas, and so forth.[1]

The central theme of this essay has been, briefly, that all scientific explanation involves, explicitly or by implication, a subsumption of its subject matter under general regularities; that it seeks to provide a systematic understanding of empirical phenomena by showing that they fit into a nomic nexus. This construal, which has been set forth in detail in the preceding sections, does

---

1. The first two of these further topics are dealt with in two other essays in this volume: "Typological Methods in the Natural and the Social Sciences" and "The Logic of Functional Analysis." An interesting and useful collection of explanatory accounts from physics, biology, psychology, and history is offered in Kahl (1963).

not claim simply to be descriptive of the explanations actually offered in empirical science; for—to mention but one reason—there is no sufficiently clear generally accepted understanding as to what counts as a scientific explanation. The construal here set forth is, rather, in the nature of an *explication*, which is intended to replace a familiar but vague and ambiguous notion by a more precisely characterized and systematically fruitful and illuminating one. Actually, our explicatory analysis has not even led to a full definition of a precise "explicatum"-concept of scientific explanation; it purports only to make explicit some especially important aspects of such a concept.[2]

Like any other explication, the construal here put forward has to be justified by appropriate arguments. In our case, these have to show that the proposed construal does justice to such accounts as are generally agreed to be instances of scientific explanation, and that it affords a basis for a systematically fruitful logical and methodological analysis of the explanatory procedures used in empirical science. It is hoped that the arguments presented in this essay have achieved that objective.

BIBLIOGRAPHY

Alexander, F. "Psychology and the Interpretation of Historical Events." In Ware (1940), pp. 48-57.

Alexander, H. G. "General Statements as Rules of Inference?" In Feigl, Scriven, and Maxwell (1958), pp. 309-29.

Arrow, K. J. "Mathematical Models in the Social Sciences." In Lerner, D. and H. D. Laswell (eds.) *The Policy Sciences*. Stanford: Stanford University Press, 1951, pp. 129-54.

Baernstein, H. D. and Hull, C. L. "A Mechanical Model of the Conditioned Reflex." *The Journal of General Psychology* 5:99-106 (1931).

Barker, S. F. *Induction and Hypothesis*. Ithaca, N.Y.: Cornell University Press, 1957.

Barker, S. F. "The Role of Simplicity in Explanation." In Feigl and Maxwell (1961), pp. 265-74.

Bartley, W. W. "Achilles, the Tortoise, and Explanation in Science and History." *The British Journal for the Philosophy of Science* 13:15-33 (1962).

Baumol, William J. *Economic Theory and Operations Analysis*. Englewood Cliffs, N. J.: Prentice-Hall, 1961.

Baumrin, B. (ed.) *Philosophy of Science. The Delaware Seminar*. Volume I, 1961-62. New York: John Wiley & Sons, 1963.

2. That a fuller characterization of this concept, and *a fortiori* a complete explicative definition, poses further problems is made clear in section 6 of the essay "Studies in the Logic of Explanation" and in the Postscript to it. Another question that arises here is mentioned in footnote 33 of that essay as reprinted in the present volume.

Beale, H. K. "What Historians Have said About the Causes of the Civil War." In *Theory and Practice in Historical Study: A Report of the Committee on Historiography*, Social Science Research Council, Bulletin 54; New York: 1946, pp. 53-92.

Bertalanffy, L. von. *Modern Theories of Development*. London: Oxford University Press, 1933.

Bertalanffy, L. von. "Problems of General System Theory." *Human Biology* 23:302-12 (1951).

Bertalanffy, L. von. "General System Theory." In Bertalanffy, L. von, and A. Rapoport, (eds.) *General Systems. Yearbook of the Society for the Advancement of General Systems Theory*. Volume I, 1956.

Bismarck, Otto von. *Bismarck. The Man and the Statesman: Being the Reflections and Reminiscences of Otto, Prince von Bismarck*. Translated from the German under the supervision of A. J. Butler. Volume II. New York: Harper and Row, 1899.

Boehmer, H. *Luther and the Reformation in the Light of Modern Research*. Translated by E. S. G. Potter. New York: The Dial Press, 1930.

Boltzmann, L. *Vorlesungen über Maxwells Theorie der Elektrizität und des Lichtes*. I. Theil. Leipzig: Barth, 1891.

Boltzmann, L. *Populäre Schriften*. Leipzig: Barth, 1905.

Bonhoeffer, K. F. "Über physikalisch-chemische Modelle von Lebensvorgängen." *Studium Generale* 1:137-43 (1948).

Bondi, H. *The Universe at Large*. London: Heinemann, 1961.

Braithwaite, R. B. *Scientific Explanation*. Cambridge, England: Cambridge University Press, 1953.

Brandt, R. and J. Kim. "Wants as Explanations of Actions." *The Journal of Philosophy* 60:425-35 (1963).

Bridgman, P. W. *The Logic of Modern Physics*. New York: Macmillan, 1927.

Brodbeck, May. "Models, Meaning, and Theories." In Gross (1959), pp. 373-403.

Brodbeck, May. "Explanations, Predictions, and 'Imperfect' Knowledge." In Feigl and Maxwell (1962), pp. 231-72.

Bromberger, S. "The Concept of Explanation." Ph.D. thesis, Harvard University, 1960.

Bromberger, S. "An Approach to Explanation." In Butler, R. (ed.) *Studies in Analytical Philosophy*. Oxford: Blackwell, forthcoming.

Bush, R. R. and F. Mosteller. *Stochastic Models for Learning*. New York: John Wiley & Sons, 1955.

Campbell, N. R. *Physics: The Elements*. Cambridge, England: Cambridge University Press, 1920.

Campbell, N. R. *What is Science?* New York: Dover, 1952. (First published in 1921.)

Carington, W. *Matter, Mind and Meaning*. London: Methuen, 1949.

Carnap, R. "Testability and Meaning." *Philosophy of Science* 3, 1936 and 4, 1937. Reprinted in part in Feigl and Brodbeck (1953).

Carnap, R. *The Logical Syntax of Language*. New York: Harcourt, Brace and World, 1937.

Carnap, R. "Logical Foundations of the Unity of Science." In *International Encyclopedia of Unified Science*, Volume I, Number 1. Chicago: University of Chicago Press, 1938. Reprinted in Feigl and Sellars (1949), pp. 408-23.

Carnap, R. "On Inductive Logic." *Philosophy of Science* 12:72-97 (1945).

Carnap, R. *Logical Foundations of Probability*. Chicago: University of Chicago Press 1950; second, revised, edition 1962. Cited in this essay as Carnap (1950).

Carnap, R. "Inductive Logic and Science." *Proceedings of the American Academy of Arts and Sciences*, volume 80:187-97 (1951-54).

Carnap, R. *The Continuum of Inductive Methods*. Chicago: University of Chicago Press, 1952.

Carnap, R. "The Methodological Character of Theoretical Terms." In Feigl and Scriven (1956), 38-76.

Carnap, R. "The Aim of Inductive Logic." In Nagel, Suppes, and Tarski (1962), pp. 303-18.

Chisholm, R. "Sentences about Believing." In Feigl, Scriven, and Maxwell (1958), pp. 510-20.

Churchman, C. W. *Prediction and Optimal Decision*. Englewood Cliffs, N. J.: Prentice-Hall, 1961.

Cohen, M. R. and E. Nagel. *An Introduction to Logic and Scientific Method*. New York: Harcourt, Brace & World, 1934.

Conant, James B. *Science and Common Sense*. New Haven: Yale University Press, 1951.

Craig, W. "Replacement of Auxiliary Expressions." *Philosophical Review* 65:38-55 (1956).

Cramér, H. *Mathematical Methods of Statistics*. Princeton: Princeton University Press, 1946.

Danto, A. C. "On Explanations in History." *Philosophy of Science* 23:15-30 (1956).

Davidson, D. "Actions, Reasons, and Causes." *The Journal of Philosophy* 60:685-700 (1963).

Davidson, D., P. Suppes, and S. Siegel. *Decision Making: An Experimental Approach*. Stanford: Stanford University Press, 1957.

Dewey, John. *How We Think*. Boston: D. C. Heath & Co., 1910.

Donagan, A. "Explanation in History." *Mind* 66:145-64 (1957). Reprinted in Gardiner (1959), pp. 428-43.

Dray, W. "Explanatory Narrative in History." *Philosophical Quarterly* 4:15-27 (1954).

Dray, W. *Laws and Explanation in History*. Oxford: Oxford University Press, 1957.

Dray, W. "'Explaining What' in History." In Gardiner (1959), pp. 403-08.

Dray, W. "The Historical Explanation of Actions Reconsidered." In Hook (1963), pp. 105-35.

Duhem, P. *La Théorie Physique. Son Objet et Sa Structure*. Paris: Chevalier et Rivière, 1906. (Also translated by P. P. Wiener, under the title *The Aim and Structure of Physical Theory*. Princeton: Princeton University Press, 1954).

Feigl, H. "Some Remarks on the Meaning of Scientific Explanation." In Feigl and Sellars (1949), pp. 510-14.

Feigl, H. "Notes on Causality." In Feigl and Brodbeck (1953), pp. 408-18.

Feigl, H. and M. Brodbeck (eds.) *Readings in the Philosophy of Science*. New York: Appleton-Century-Crofts, 1953.

Feigl, H. and G. Maxwell (eds.) *Current Issues in the Philosophy of Science*. New York: Holt, Rinehart & Winston, 1961.

Feigl, H. and G. Maxwell (eds.) *Minnesota Studies in the Philosophy of Science*, Volume III. Minneapolis: University of Minnesota Press, 1962.

Feigl, H. and M. Scriven (eds.) *Minnesota Studies in the Philosophy of Science*, Volume I. Minneapolis: University of Minnesota Press, 1956.

Feigl, H., M. Scriven, and G. Maxwell (eds.) *Minnesota Studies in the Philosophy of Science*, Volume II. Minneapolis: University of Minnesota Press, 1958.

Feigl, H. and W. Sellars (eds.) *Readings in Philosophical Analysis*. New York: Appleton-Century-Crofts, 1949.

Feyerabend, P. K. "Explanation, Reduction, and Empiricism." In Feigl and Maxwell (1962), pp. 28–97.

Feyerabend, P. K. Review of Hanson (1963) in *Philosophical Review* 73:264–66 (1964).

Frank, P. *Philosophy of Science*. Englewood Cliffs, N.J.: Prentice-Hall, 1957.

Frankel, C. "Explanation and Interpretation in History." In Gardiner (1959), pp. 408–27. Reprinted from *Philosophy of Science* 24:137–55 (1957).

French, T. M. *The Integration of Behavior*. Volume I. *Basic Postulates*. Chicago: University of Chicago Press, 1952.

Freud, S. *Psychopathology of Everyday Life*. Translated by A. A. Brill. New York: The New American Library (Mentor Book Series), 1951.

Galilei, Galileo. *Dialogues Concerning Two New Sciences*. Translated by H. Crew and A. de Salvio. Evanston: Northwestern University, 1946.

Gallie, W. B. "Explanation in History and the Genetic Sciences." *Mind* 64:1955. Reprinted in Gardiner (1959), pp. 386–402.

Gardiner, P. *The Nature of Historical Explanation*. Oxford: Oxford University Press, 1952.

Gardiner, P. (ed.). *Theories of History*. New York: The Free Press, 1959.

Gasking, D. "Causation and Recipes." *Mind* 64:479–87 (1955).

Gauss, C. F. "Allgemeine Lehrsaetze in Beziehung auf die im verkehrten Verhaeltnisse des Quadrats der Entfernung wirkenden Anziehungs- und Abstossungs-Kraefte." (Published 1840) Reprinted in *Ostwalds Klassiker der exacten Wissenschaften*, No. 2, Leipzig: Wilhelm Engelmann, 1889.

Gibson, Q. *The Logic of Social Enquiry*. London: Routledge and Kegan Paul; New York: Humanities Press, 1960.

Goldstein, L. J. "A Note on the Status of Historical Reconstructions." *The Journal of Philosophy* 55:473–79 (1958).

Goodman, Nelson. "The Problem of Counterfactual Conditionals." *The Journal of Philosophy* 44:113–28 (1947). Reprinted, with minor changes, as the first chapter of Goodman (1955).

Goodman, Nelson. *Fact, Fiction, and Forecast*. Cambridge, Mass.: Harvard University Press, 1955.

Goudge, T. A. "Causal Explanation in Natural History." *The British Journal for the Philosophy of Science* 9:194–202 (1958).

Gross, L. (ed.) *Symposium on Sociological Theory*. New York: Harper & Row, 1959.

Grünbaum, A. "Temporally Asymmetric Principles, Parity between Explanation and Prediction, and Mechanism vs. Teleology." In Baumrin (1963), pp. 57–96.

Grünbaum, A. *Philosophical Problems of Space and Time*. New York: Knopf, 1963a.

Hanson, N. "On the Symmetry between Explanation and Prediction." *The Philosophical Review* 68:349–58 (1959).

Hanson, N. R. *The Concept of the Positron. A Philosophical Analysis*. Cambridge, England: Cambridge University Press, 1963.

Helmer, O. and P. Oppenheim. "A Syntactical Definition of Probability and of Degree of Confirmation." *The Journal of Symbolic Logic* 10:25–60 (1945).

Helmer, O. and N. Rescher. "On the Epistemology of the Inexact Sciences." *Management Science* 6:1959.

Hempel, C. G. "The Function of General Laws in History." *The Journal of Philosophy* 39:35-48, 1942. Reprinted in this volume.

Hempel, C. G. "Studies in the Logic of Confirmation." *Mind* 54:1-26 and 97-121 (1945). Reprinted in this volume.

Hempel, C. G. "A Note on the Paradoxes of Confirmation." *Mind* 55:79-82 (1946).

Hempel, C. G. "Problems and Changes in the Empiricist Criterion of Meaning." *Revue Internationale de Philosophie*, No. 11:41-63 (1950).

Hempel, C. G. "The Concept of Cognitive Significance: A Reconsideration." *Proceedings of the American Academy of Arts and Sciences*, Vol. 80, No. 1:61-77 (1951).

Hempel, C. G. "General System Theory and the Unity of Science." *Human Biology* 23:313-27 (1951a).

Hempel, C. G. "The Theoretician's Dilemma." In Feigl, Scriven, and Maxwell (1958), pp. 37-98. Reprinted in this volume.

Hempel, C. G. "Empirical Statements and Falsifiability." *Philosophy* 33:342-48 (1958a).

Hempel, C. G. "The Logic of Functional Analysis." In Gross (1959), pp. 271-307. Reprinted in this volume.

Hempel, C. G. "Inductive Inconsistencies." *Synthese* 12: 439-69 (1960). Reprinted in this volume.

Hempel, C. G. "Deductive-Nomological *vs*. Statistical Explanation." In Feigl and Maxwell (1962), pp. 98-169.

Hempel, C. G. and P. Oppenheim. "A Definition of 'Degree of Confirmation'." *Philosophy of Science* 12: 98-115 (1945).

Hempel, C. G., and P. Oppenheim. "Studies in the Logic of Explanation." *Philosophy of Science* 15:135-75 (1948). Reprinted in this volume.

Henson, R. B. "Mr. Hanson on the Symmetry of Explanation and Prediction." *Philosophy of Science* 30:60-61 (1963).

Hertz, H. *Die Prinzipien der Mechanik*. Leipzig: Johann Ambrosius Barth, 1894.

Hesse, Mary, B. *Models and Analogies in Science*. London and New York: Sheed and Ward, 1963.

Homans, George C. *Social Behavior. Its Elementary Forms*. New York: Harcourt, Brace & World, 1961.

Hook, S. (ed.). *Psychoanalysis, Scientific Method, and Philosophy*. New York: New York University Press, 1959.

Hook, S. (ed.). *Philosophy and History*. New York: New York University Press, 1963.

Hughes, H. S. *History as Art and Science*. New York: Harper & Row, 1964.

International Union of History and Philosophy of Sciences. *The Concept and the Role of the Model in Mathematics and Natural and Social Sciences*. Dordrecht, Holland: D. Reidel, 1961.

Kahl, R. (ed.). *Studies in Explanation. A Reader in the Philosophy of Science*. Englewood Cliffs, N. J.: Prentice-Hall, 1963.

Kemeny, J. G. and P. Oppenheim. "Degree of Factual Support." *Philosophy of Science* 19:307-24 (1952).

Kemeny, J. G., and P. Oppenheim. "On Reduction." *Philosophical Studies* 7:6-19 (1956).

Keynes, J. M. *A Treatise on Probability*. London: Macmillan, 1921.

Kim, J. "Explanation, Prediction, and Retrodiction: Some Logical and Pragmatic Considerations." Ph.D. thesis, Princeton University, 1962.

Körner, S. (ed.). *Observation and Interpretation: Proceedings of the Ninth Symposium of the Colston Research Society.* New York: Academic Press, and London: Butterworths Scientific Publications, 1957.

Kolmogoroff, A. *Grundbegriffe der Wahrscheinlichkeitsrechnung.* Berlin: Springer, 1933.

Krueger, R. G. and Hull, C. L. "An Electro-Chemical Parallel to the Conditioned Reflex." *The Journal of General Psychology* 5:262-69 (1931).

Langer, W. L. "The Next Assignment." *The American Historical Review* 63: 283-304 (1958). Reprinted in Mazlish (1963), pp. 87-107. Page references are to reprinted text.

Lazarsfeld, P. F. "The American Soldier—An Expository Review." *Public Opinion Quarterly* 13:377-404 (1949).

Lazarsfeld, P. F. *Mathematical Thinking in the Social Sciences.* New York: The Free Press, 1954.

Leduc, S. *The Mechanism of Life.* Translated by W. D. Butcher, New York: Rebman Co., 1911.

Leduc, S. *La Biologie Synthétique.* Paris, 1912.

Lewis, C. I. *An Analysis of Knowledge and Valuation.* La Salle, Ill.: Open Court Publishing Co., 1946.

Lodge, Sir O. *Modern Views of Electricity.* London: Macmillan, 1889.

Luce, R. D. and H. Raiffa. *Games and Decisions.* New York: John Wiley, 1957.

Mandelbaum, M. "Historical Explanation: The Problem of 'Covering Laws'." *History and Theory* 1:229-42 (1961).

Mandler, G. and W. Kessen. *The Language of Psychology.* New York: John Wiley & Sons, 1959.

Margenau, H. *The Nature of Physical Reality.* New York: McGraw-Hill, 1950.

Mazlish, B. (ed.). *Psychoanalysis and History.* Englewood Cliffs, N.J.: Prentice-Hall, 1963.

Maxwell, J. C. "On Faraday's Lines of Force." *Transactions of the Cambridge Philosophical Society,* 10:27-83 (1864).

Mendel, A. "Evidence and Explanation." In *Report of the Eighth Congress of the International Musicological Society, New York, 1961.* La Rue, Jan (ed.). Kassel: Bärenreiter-Verlag, 1962. Volume II, pp. 3-18.

Miller, N. E. "Comments on Theoretical Models. Illustrated by the Development of a Theory of Conflict Behavior." *Journal of Personality* 20:82-190 (1951).

Mises, R. von. *Wahrscheinlichkeitsrechnung und ihre Anwendungen in der Statistik und theoretischen Physik.* Wien, 1931. Republished New York: M. S. Rosenberg, 1945.

Mises, R. von. *Probability, Statistics and Truth.* London: William Hodge & Co., 1939.

Mises, R. von. *Positivism. A Study in Human Understanding.* Cambridge, Mass.: Harvard University Press, 1951.

Moulton, F. R. and J. R. Schifferes. *The Autobiography of Science.* Garden City, N.Y.: Doubleday & Co., 1945.

Muir, R. *A Short History of the British Commonwealth.* Volume II. London: George Philip and Son, 1922.

Nagel, E. *Principles of the Theory of Probability.* Chicago: University of Chicago Press, 1939.

Nagel, E. *Logic without Metaphysics.* New York: The Free Press, 1956.

Nagel, E. "Methodological Issues in Psychoanalytic Theory." In Hook (1959), pp. 38-56.

Nagel, E. *The Structure of Science: Problems in the Logic of Scientific Explanation.* New York: Harcourt, Brace & World, Inc., 1961.

Nagel, E., P. Suppes, and A. Tarski (eds.). *Logic, Methodology, and Philosophy of Science: Proceedings of the 1960 International Congress*. Stanford: Stanford University Press, 1962.

Neumann, J. von and O. Morgenstern. *Theory of Games and Economic Behavior*. Princeton: Princeton University Press, 2d. ed., 1947.

Passmore, J. "Law and Explanation in History." *The Australian Journal of Politics and History* 4-269:76 (1958).

Passmore, J. "Explanation in Everyday Life, in Science, and in History." *History and Theory* 2-105:23 (1962).

Peters, R. S. *The Concept of Motivation*. London: Routledge and Kegan Paul; New York: Humanities Press, 1958.

Pitt, J. "Generalizations in Historical Explanation." *The Journal of Philosophy* 56:578-86 (1959).

Popper, K. R. *Logik der Forschung*. Vienna: Springer, 1935.

Popper, K. R. "The Propensity Interpretation of the Calculus of Probability, and the Quantum Theory." In Körner (1957), pp. 65-70.

Popper, K. R. "The Aim of Science." *Ratio* 1:24-35 (1957a).

Popper, K. R. *The Logic of Scientific Discovery*. London: Hutchinson, 1959.

Popper, K. R. *Conjectures and Refutations*. New York: Basic Books (1962).

Price, H. H. "The Theory of Telepathy." *Horizon* 12: 45-63 (1945).

Quine, W. V. O. *Word and Object*. Published jointly by Technology Press of the Massachusetts Institute of Technology and John Wiley and Sons, New York. 1960.

Ramsey, F. P. *The Foundations of Mathematics and Other Logical Essays*. London: Routledge and Kegan Paul; New York: Harcourt, Brace & World, 1931.

Reichenbach, H. *The Theory of Probability*. Berkeley and Los Angeles: The University of California Press, 1949.

Rescher, N. "A Theory of Evidence." *Philosophy of Science* 25:83-94 (1958).

Rescher, N. "Discrete State Systems, Markov Chains, and Problems in the Theory of Scientific Explanation and Prediction." *Philosophy of Science* 30:325-45 (1963).

Russell, S. B. "A Practical Device to Simulate the Working of Nervous Discharges." *The Journal of Animal Behavior* 3:15-35 (1913.)

Ryle, G. *The Concept of Mind*. London: Hutchinson, 1949.

Ryle, G. "'If', 'So', and 'Because'." In Black, M. (ed.). *Philosophical Analysis*. Ithaca, N.Y.: Cornell University Press, 1950.

Savage, L. J. *The Foundations of Statistics*. New York: John Wiley & Sons, 1954.

Scheffler, I. "Explanation, Prediction, and Abstraction." *The British Journal for the Philosophy of Science* 7:293-309 (1957).

Scheffler, I. *The Anatomy of Inquiry: Philosophical Studies in the Theory of Science*. New York: Alfred A. Knopf, 1963.

Schlick, M. "Die Kausalität in der gegenwärtigen Physik." *Die Naturwissenschaften* 19 (1931). Translated by D. Rynin, "Causality in Contemporary Physics." *The British Journal for the Philosophy of Science* 12:177-93 and 281-98 (1962).

Schwiebert, E. G. *Luther and His Times*. St. Louis: Concordia Publishing House, 1950.

Sciama, D. W. *The Unity of the Universe*. Garden City, N.Y.: Doubleday and Co. (Anchor Books), 1961.

Scriven, M. "Definitions, Explanations, and Theories." In Feigl, Scriven, and Maxwell (1958), pp. 99-195.

Scriven, M. "Truisms as the Grounds for Historical Explanations." In Gardiner (1959), pp. 443-75.

Scriven, M. "Explanation and Prediction in Evolutionary Theory." *Science* 130:477-82 (1959a).

Scriven, M. "Explanations, Predictions, and Laws." In Feigl and Maxwell (1962), pp. 170-230.

Scriven, M. "The Temporal Asymmetry between Explanations and Predictions." In Baumrin (1963), pp. 97-105.

Scriven, M. "New Issues in the Logic of Explanation." In Hook (1963a), pp. 339-61.

Seeliger, R. "Analogien und Modelle in der Physik." *Studium Generale* 1:125-37 (1948).

Sellars, W. "Inference and Meaning." *Mind* 62:313-38 (1953).

Sellars, W. "Counterfactuals, Dispositions, and the Causal Modalities." In Feigl, Scriven, and Maxwell (1958), pp. 225-308.

Society for Experimental Biology. *Models and Analogues in Biology: Symposia of the Society for Experimental Biology, Number XIV*. Cambridge, England: Cambridge University Press, 1960.

Suppes, P. "The Philosophical Relevance of Decision Theory." *The Journal of Philosophy* 58:605-14 (1961).

Svedberg, T. *Die Existenz der Moleküle*. Leipzig: Akademische Verlagsgesellschaft, 1912.

Thomson, Sir William. *Notes of Lectures on Molecular Dynamics and the Wave Theory of Light*. Baltimore: The Johns Hopkins University, 1884.

Tolman, E. C. "A Psychological Model." In Parsons, T. and E. A. Shils (eds.) *Toward a General Theory of Action*. Cambridge, Mass.: Harvard University Press, 1951; pp. 277-361.

Toulmin, S. *The Philosophy of Science*. London: Hutchinson, 1953.

Toulmin, S. *The Uses of Argument*. Cambridge, England: Cambridge University Press, 1958.

Toulmin, S. *Foresight and Understanding*. London: Hutchinson, 1961; New York: Harper & Row (Torchbook), 1963.

Toynbee, A. *The World and the West*. London: Oxford University Press, 1953.

Turner, J. "Maxwell on the Method of Physical Analogy." *The British Journal for the Philosophy of Science* 6:226-38 (1955).

Turner, J. "Maxwell on the Logic of Dynamical Explanation." *Philosophy of Science* 23:36-47 (1956).

Ware, C. F. (ed.). *The Cultural Approach to History*. New York: Columbia University Press, 1940.

Watkins, W. H. *On Understanding Physics*. Cambridge, England: Cambridge University Press, 1938.

Watson, G. "Clio and Psyche: Some Interrelations of Psychology and History." In Ware (1940), pp. 34-47.

Weber, Max. *On the Methodology of the Social Sciences*. Translated and edited by Shils, E. A. and H. A. Finch. New York: The Free Press, 1949.

Weingartner, R. H. "The Quarrel about Historical Explanation." *The Journal of Philosophy* 58:29-45 (1961).

Wiener, N. *Cybernetics*. New York: John Wiley & Sons, 1948.

Williams, D. C. *The Ground of Induction*. Cambridge, Mass.: Harvard University Press, 1947.

INDEX OF NAMES

INDEX OF SUBJECTS